# Year 2

# Biology

## The complete course for AQA

Let's face it, Biology is a tough subject. You'll need to get to grips with a lot of difficult concepts, and have plenty of practical skills up your lab-coat sleeve.

But don't worry — this brilliant CGP book covers everything you'll need for the new AQA course. It's packed with clear explanations, exam practice, advice on maths skills and practical investigations... and much more!

It even includes a free Online Edition to read on your PC, Mac or tablet.

**How to get your free Online Edition**

Go to **cgpbooks.co.uk/extras** and enter this code...

2989 4059 7045 8781

This code will only work once. If someone has used this book before you, they may have already claimed the Online Edition.

# Contents

## Introduction



## Practical and Maths Skills



## Topics

### Topic 5 — A: Photosynthesis and Respiration



### Topic 5 — B: Energy Transfer and Nutrient Cycles



### Topic 6 — A: Stimuli and Responses



### Topic 6 — B: Nervous Coordination



### Topic 6 — C: Homeostasis



### Topic 7 — A: Genetics

## Topic 7 — B: Populations and Evolution



## Topic 7 — C: Populations in Ecosystems



## Topic 8 — A: Mutations and Gene Expression



## Topic 8 — B: Genome Projects and Gene Technologies



## Exam Help

EXAM HELP



## Reference

# How to use this book

## Learning Objectives

- These tell you exactly what you need to learn, or be able to do, for the exams.
- There's a specification reference at the bottom that links to the AQA specification.

## Practice Questions — Application

- Annoyingly, the examiners expect you to be able to apply your knowledge to new situations — these questions are here to give you plenty of practice at doing this.
- All the answers are in the back of the book (including any calculation workings).

## Practice Questions — Fact Recall

- There are a lot of facts you need to learn — these questions are here to test whether you know them.
- All the answers are in the back of the book.

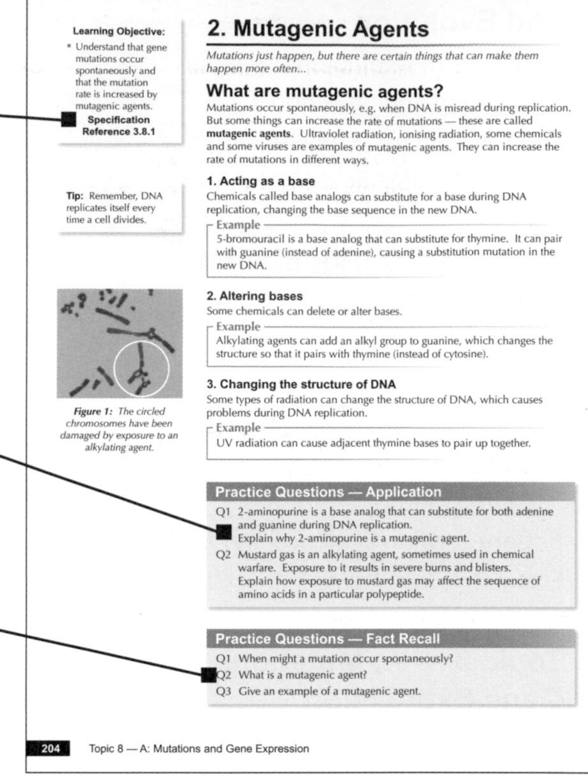

**Learning Objective:**
- Understand that gene mutations occur spontaneously and that the mutation rate is increased by mutagenic agents.

**Specification Reference 3.8.1**

## 2. Mutagenic Agents

*Mutations just happen, but there are certain things that can make them happen more often...*

### What are mutagenic agents?

Mutations occur spontaneously, e.g. when DNA is misread during replication. But some things can increase the rate of mutations — these are called **mutagenic agents**. Ultraviolet radiation, ionising radiation, some chemicals and some viruses are examples of mutagenic agents. They can increase the rate of mutations in different ways.

**Tip:** Remember, DNA replicates itself every time a cell divides.

**1. Acting as a base**

Chemicals called base analogs can substitute for a base during DNA replication, changing the base sequence in the new DNA.

Example

5-bromouracil is a base analog that can substitute for thymine. It can pair with guanine (instead of adenine), causing a substitution mutation in the new DNA.

**2. Altering bases**

Some chemicals can delete or alter bases.

Example

Alkylating agents can add an alkyl group to guanine, which changes the structure so that it pairs with thymine (instead of cytosine).

*Figure 1: The circled chromosomes have been damaged by exposure to an alkylating agent.*

**3. Changing the structure of DNA**

Some types of radiation can change the structure of DNA, which causes problems during DNA replication.

Example

UV radiation can cause adjacent thymine bases to pair up together.

**Practice Questions — Application**

Q1 2-aminopurine is a base analog that can substitute for both adenine and guanine during DNA replication. Explain why 2-aminopurine is a mutagenic agent.

Q2 Mustard gas is an alkylating agent, sometimes used in chemical warfare. Exposure to it results in severe burns and blisters. Explain how exposure to mustard gas may affect the sequence of amino acids in a particular polypeptide.

**Practice Questions — Fact Recall**

Q1 When might a mutation occur spontaneously?

Q2 What is a mutagenic agent?

Q3 Give an example of a mutagenic agent.

204 Topic 8 — A: Mutations and Gene Expression

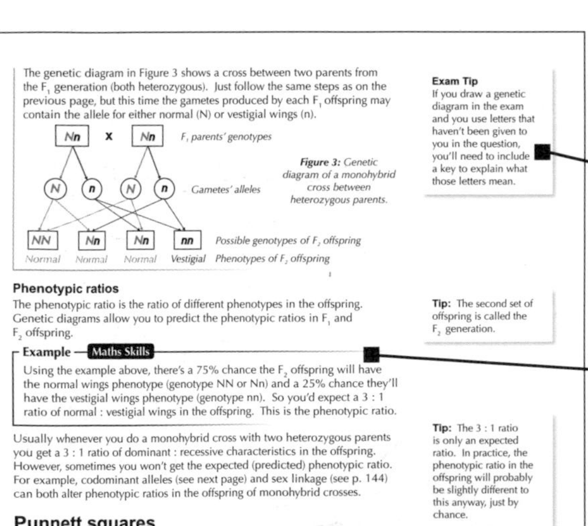

The genetic diagram in Figure 3 shows a cross between two parents from the $F_1$ generation (both heterozygous). Just follow the same steps as on the previous page, but this time the gametes produced by each $F_1$ offspring may contain the allele for either normal (N) or vestigial wings (n).



*Figure 3: Genetic diagram of a monohybrid cross between heterozygous parents.*

**Exam Tip**
If you draw a genetic diagram in the exam and you use letters that haven't been given to you in the question, you'll need to include a key to explain what those letters mean.

**Phenotypic ratios**

The phenotypic ratio is the ratio of different phenotypes in the offspring. Genetic diagrams allow you to predict the phenotypic ratios in $F_1$ and $F_2$ offspring.

**Tip:** The second set of offspring is called the $F_2$ generation.

**Example — Maths Skills**

Using the example above, there's a 75% chance the $F_2$ offspring will have the normal wings phenotype (genotype NN or Nn) and a 25% chance they'll have the vestigial wings phenotype (genotype nn). So you'd expect a 3 : 1 ratio of normal : vestigial wings in the offspring. This is the phenotypic ratio.

Usually whenever you do a monohybrid cross with two heterozygous parents you get a 3 : 1 ratio of dominant : recessive characteristics in the offspring. However, sometimes you won't get the expected (predicted) phenotypic ratio. For example, codominant alleles (see next page) and sex linkage (see p. 144) can both alter phenotypic ratios in the offspring of monohybrid crosses.

**Tip:** The 3 : 1 ratio is only an expected ratio. In practice, the phenotypic ratio in the offspring will probably be slightly different to this anyway, just by chance.

**Punnett squares**

A Punnett square is just another way of showing a genetic diagram. The Punnett squares below show the same crosses as p. 138 and above.

Example

**Step 1:** Work out the alleles the gametes would have.



| Gametes' alleles | N | N |
|---|---|---|
| n | Nn | Nn |
| n | Nn | Nn |

Possible genotypes of $F_1$ offspring

**Step 2:** Cross the parents' gametes to show the possible genotypes of the $F_1$ generation — all heterozygous, Nn.

| Gametes' alleles | N | n |
|---|---|---|
| N | NN | Nn |
| n | Nn | nn |

Possible genotypes of $F_2$ offspring

Normal : vestigial
3 : 1
Ratio of phenotypes in $F_2$ offspring

**Step 3:** Cross the gametes of the $F_1$ generation to show the possible genotypes of the $F_2$ generation. The Punnett square shows a 75% chance that offspring will have normal wings and a 25% chance that they'll have vestigial wings, i.e. a 3 : 1 ratio.

**Exam Tip**
It's up to you whether you draw a diagram or a Punnett square in the exam, whichever you find easier. You must make sure you label your diagram though, so it's clear what you're trying to show.

Topic 7 — A: Genetics 139

## Exam Tips

There are tips throughout the book to help with all sorts of things to do with answering exam questions.

## Maths Skills Examples

There's a range of maths skills that you could be expected to apply in your exams. Examples that show these maths skills in action are marked up like this. There's also a Practical and Maths Skills section at the front of the book.

## Examples

These are here to help you understand the theory.

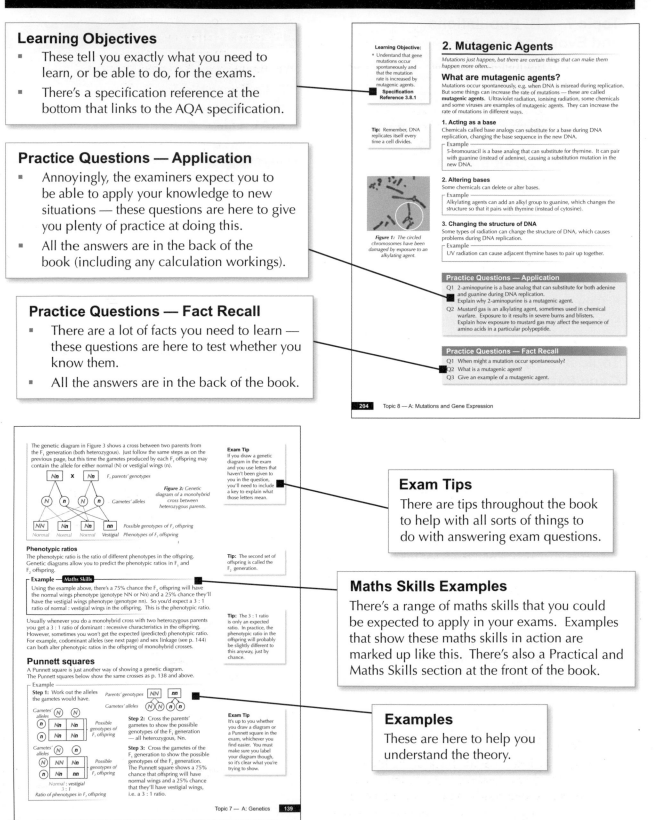

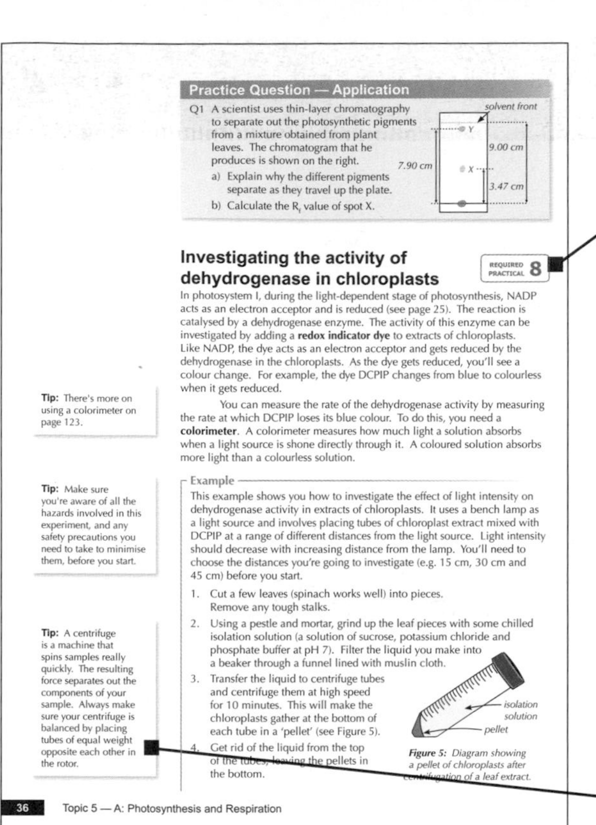

Practice Question — Application

Q1 A scientist uses thin-layer chromatography to separate out the photosynthetic pigments from a mixture obtained from plant leaves. The chromatogram that he produces is shown on the right.

a) Explain why the different pigments separate as they travel up the plate.

b) Calculate the $R_f$ value of spot X.



**Investigating the activity of dehydrogenase in chloroplasts** REQUIRED PRACTICAL 8

In photosystem I, during the light-dependent stage of photosynthesis, NADP acts as an electron acceptor and is reduced (see page 25). The reaction is catalysed by a dehydrogenase enzyme. The activity of this enzyme can be investigated by adding a **redox indicator dye** to extracts of chloroplasts. Like NADP, the dye acts as an electron acceptor and gets reduced by the dehydrogenase in the chloroplasts. As the dye gets reduced, you'll see a colour change. For example, the dye DCPIP changes from blue to colourless when it gets reduced.

You can measure the rate of the dehydrogenase activity by measuring the rate at which DCPIP loses its blue colour. To do this, you need a **colorimeter**. A colorimeter measures how much light a solution absorbs when a light source is shone directly through it. A coloured solution absorbs more light than a colourless solution.

**Tip:** There's more on using a colorimeter on page 123.

**Tip:** Make sure you're aware of all the hazards involved in this experiment, and any safety precautions you need to take to minimise them, before you start.

**Tip:** A centrifuge is a machine that spins samples really quickly. The resulting force separates out the components of your sample. Always make sure your centrifuge is balanced by placing tubes of equal weight opposite each other in the rotor.

Example

This example shows you how to investigate the effect of light intensity on dehydrogenase activity in extracts of chloroplasts. It uses a bench lamp as a light source and involves placing tubes of chloroplast extract mixed with DCPIP at a range of different distances from the light source. Light intensity should decrease with increasing distance from the lamp. You'll need to choose the distances you're going to investigate (e.g. 15 cm, 30 cm and 45 cm) before you start.

1. Cut a few leaves (spinach works well) into pieces. Remove any tough stalks.
2. Using a pestle and mortar, grind up the leaf pieces with some chilled isolation solution (a solution of sucrose, potassium chloride and phosphate buffer at pH 7). Filter the liquid you make into a beaker through a funnel lined with muslin cloth.
3. Transfer the liquid to centrifuge tubes and centrifuge them at high speed for 10 minutes. This will make the chloroplasts gather at the bottom of each tube in a 'pellet' (see Figure 5).
4. Get rid of the liquid from the top of the tubes, leaving the pellets in the bottom.



*Figure 5: Diagram showing a pellet of chloroplasts after centrifugation of a leaf extract.*

36 Topic 5 — A: Photosynthesis and Respiration

## Required Practicals

There are some key practicals that you'll be expected to do throughout your course. You'll need to know all about them for the exams. Information about these practicals is marked up with a Required Practical stamp.

## Practical Skills

There are some key practical skills that you'll not only need to use in your Required Practicals, but that you could be tested on in the exams too. These skills are covered in the Practical and Maths Skills section at the front of the book.

## Tips

These are here to help you understand the theory.

## Exam-style Questions

- Practising exam-style questions is really important — you'll find some at the end of each section.
- They're the same style as the ones you'll get in the real exams — some will test your knowledge and understanding and some will test that you can apply your knowledge.
- All the answers are in the back of the book, along with a mark scheme to show you how you get the marks.

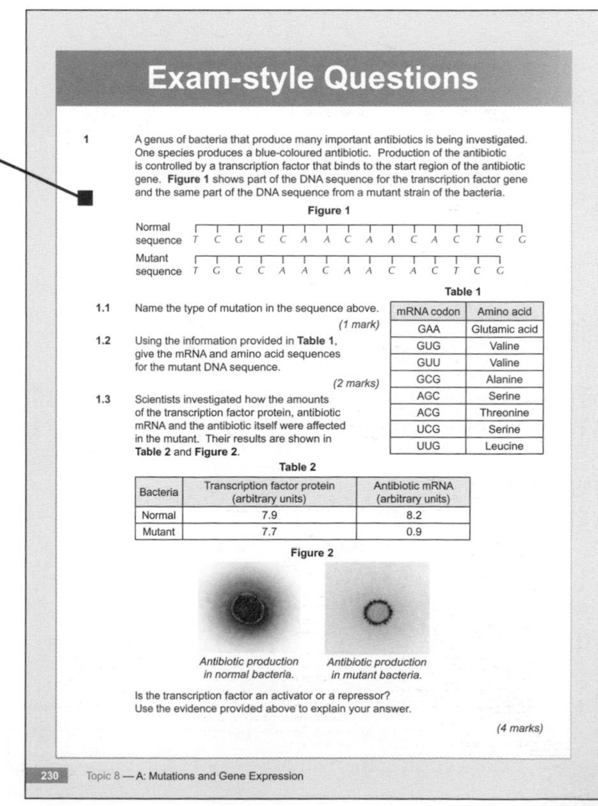

Exam-style Questions

1 A genus of bacteria that produce many important antibiotics is being investigated. One species produces a blue-coloured antibiotic. Production of the antibiotic is controlled by a transcription factor that binds to the start region of the antibiotic gene. **Figure 1** shows part of the DNA sequence for the transcription factor gene and the same part of the DNA sequence from a mutant strain of the bacteria.

**Figure 1**

Normal sequence T C G C C A A C A A C A C T C G

Mutant sequence T G C C A A C A A C A C T C G

1.1 Name the type of mutation in the sequence above. *(1 mark)*

1.2 Using the information provided in **Table 1**, give the mRNA and amino acid sequences for the mutant DNA sequence. *(2 marks)*

1.3 Scientists investigated how the amounts of the transcription factor protein, antibiotic mRNA and the antibiotic itself were affected in the mutant. Their results are shown in **Table 2** and **Figure 2**.

**Table 1**

| mRNA codon | Amino acid |
|---|---|
| GAA | Glutamic acid |
| GUG | Valine |
| GUU | Valine |
| GCG | Alanine |
| AGC | Serine |
| ACG | Threonine |
| UCG | Serine |
| UUG | Leucine |

**Table 2**

| Bacteria | Transcription factor protein (arbitrary units) | Antibiotic mRNA (arbitrary units) |
|---|---|---|
| Normal | 7.9 | 8.2 |
| Mutant | 7.7 | 0.9 |

**Figure 2**

*Antibiotic production in normal bacteria.* *Antibiotic production in mutant bacteria.*

Is the transcription factor an activator or a repressor? Use the evidence provided above to explain your answer.

*(4 marks)*

230 Topic 8 — A: Mutations and Gene Expression

## Exam Help

There's a section at the back of the book stuffed full of things to help with your exams.

## Glossary

There's a glossary at the back of the book full of all the definitions you need to know for the exams, plus loads of other useful words.

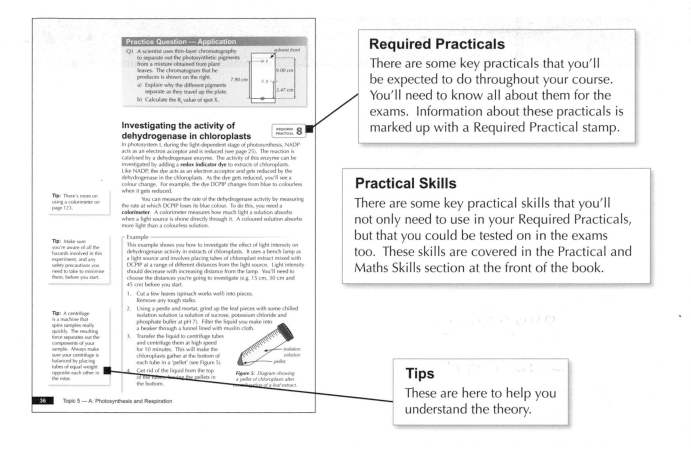

Published by CGP

Editors:
Charlotte Burrows, Katherine Faudemer, Rachel Kordan, Christopher Lindle, Rachael Marshall, Christopher McGarry, Sarah Pattison, Claire Plowman, Rachael Rogers, Camilla Simson and Hayley Thompson.

Contributors:
Sophie Anderson, Gloria Barnett, Jessica Egan, Derek Harvey.

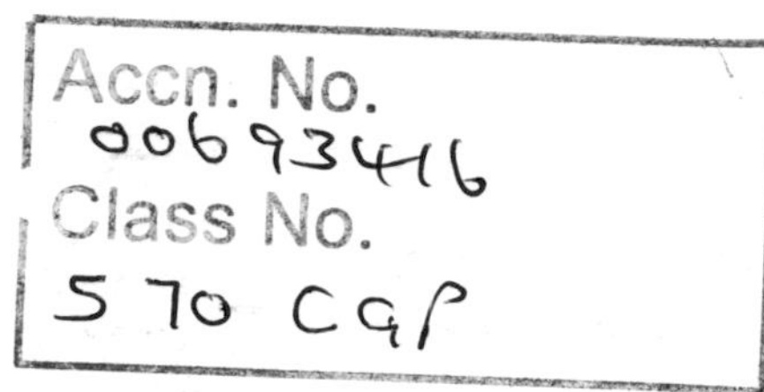


ISBN: 978 1 78294 324 2

With thanks to Janet Cruse-Sawyer, Megan Pollard, Ellen Shores and Karen Wells for the proofreading.
With thanks to Laura Jakubowski for the copyright research.

Printed by Elanders Ltd, Newcastle upon Tyne.
Clipart from Corel®

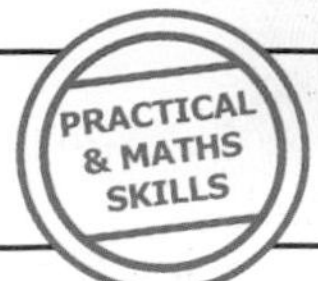




# 1. Planning an Experiment

*You have to do practical work in class as part of your course. You'll be asked about it in exams too, so you need to know how to plan the perfect experiment.*

**Exam Tip**
At least 15% of your A-level Biology marks will come from assessment of Practical Skills in the exams — so you really do need to know this stuff.

## Testing a theory

Before you start planning an experiment, you need to be clear about what you're trying to find out. Like all scientists, you should start off by making a **prediction** or **hypothesis** — a specific testable statement, based on theory, about what will happen in the experiment. You then need to plan a good experiment that will provide evidence to support the prediction — or help disprove it.

**Example**

**Theory** — photosynthesis requires light. The rate of photosynthesis is affected by light intensity.

**Prediction** — rate of photosynthesis will increase as light intensity increases.

**Experiment** — measure the rate of photosynthesis at various light intensities.

**Tip:** The results of your experiment can't be used to prove that your theory is right, but can be used as evidence for or against it. There's more about what results mean on pages 13-14.

## Getting good results

A good experiment is one that will give results that are:

- **Precise** — Precise results don't vary much from the mean. Precision is reduced by **random error** (the unpredictable way in which all measurements vary).
- **Repeatable and reproducible** — Repeatable means that if the same person repeats the experiment using the same methods and equipment, they will get the same results. Reproducible means that if someone different does the experiment, using a slightly different method or piece of equipment, the results will still be the same.
- **Valid** — Valid results answer the original question. To get valid results you need to control all the variables (see below) to make sure you're only testing the thing you want to.
- **Accurate** — Accurate results are really close to the true answer. **Human interpretation** of a measurement (e.g. determining a colour change) can **reduce** the accuracy of results.

**Tip:** Precise results are sometimes referred to as reliable results.

Here are some things you need to consider when designing a good experiment:

### 1. Variables

**Variables** are quantities that have the potential to change, e.g. temperature, pH. In an experiment you usually change one variable and measure its effect on another variable.

- The variable that you change is called the **independent variable**.
- The variable that you measure is called the **dependent variable**.

All the other variables should be controlled — when you're investigating a variable you need to keep everything else that could affect it constant. This means you can be sure that only your independent variable is affecting the thing you're measuring (the dependent variable).

**Exam Tip**
Examiners love getting you to comment on experimental design or suggest improvements to methods — e.g. how a method could be improved to make the results more precise.

**Example**

For an investigation into how light intensity affects rate of photosynthesis:

- Light intensity is the independent variable.
- Rate of photosynthesis is the dependent variable.
- pH, temperature and the time the experiment is left for should all stay the same (and the quantities should be recorded to allow someone else to reproduce the experiment).

**Exam Tip**
If you get an exam question asking why a control is important in a particular experiment, make sure your answer is specific to that experiment (not just about why controls are good in general).

## 2. Controls

**Negative controls** are used to check that only the independent variable is affecting the dependent variable. Negative controls aren't expected to have any effect on the experiment.

**Example**

When investigating how light intensity affects the rate of photosynthesis, you should set up a negative control in which the experiment is carried out in the dark. No photosynthesis should happen with this control.

**Positive controls** can also be used. They should show what a positive result of the experiment should look like, to check that it is possible.

**Example**

If you're testing for the presence of glucose in a solution, you could carry out a Benedict's test. Before you start the experiment, you could test a solution that you know contains glucose to show what a positive glucose test result looks like. This is your positive control.

**Tip:** In a study with human participants, you should try to keep the variables of all the participants the same, e.g. they should all be the same age, sex, etc.

In studies, **control groups** are used. The subjects in the study are split into two groups — the experimental group and the control group. The control group is treated in exactly the same way as the experimental group, except for the factor you're investigating.

**Example**

If you were investigating the effect of eating a low sodium (salt) diet on blood pressure, you'd have two groups. One group would be the experimental group and be given a diet low in sodium. The other group would be a control group, who would be given a diet in which sodium wasn't reduced. This is done so that you can tell that any decrease in blood pressure is due to the low sodium diet and nothing else.

**Tip:** When testing a new drug to see if it works, the control group is given a placebo instead of the drug. A placebo is a dummy pill or injection that looks exactly like the real drug, but doesn't contain the drug. It's used to make sure that people don't improve just because they think they're being treated.

## 3. Repeats

Taking several repeat measurements and calculating the mean can reduce the effect of random error on your experiment, making your results more precise. Doing repeats and getting similar results each time also shows that your data is repeatable. This makes it more likely that the same results could be reproduced by another scientist in an independent experiment.

**Example**

For an investigation into how light intensity affects rate of photosynthesis, the experiment should be repeated at least three times for each light intensity used. A mean result should be calculated for each light intensity (see page 5).

Repeating measurements also reduces the likelihood that the results are due to chance — see next page.

### 4. Sample Size

Sample size is the number of samples in the investigation, e.g. the number of people in a drug trial. As with carrying out repeats, having a large sample size reduces the likelihood that the results are due to chance (e.g. if you get the same result twice it might be because of chance, but if you get it 100 times it's much more likely that it's not due to chance).

**Tip:** Scientists can use statistical tests to figure out if a result is likely to be due to chance or not. See page 9 for more.

## Taking accurate measurements

When you're planning an experiment you need to decide what it is you're going to measure and how often you're going to take measurements.

> **Example**
> If you're investigating the rate of photosynthesis, you could measure the volume of oxygen produced over time or the volume of carbon dioxide used over time. E.g. you could take measurements at 30 or 60 second intervals.



Then you need to choose the most appropriate apparatus, equipment and techniques for the experiment.

The measuring apparatus you use has to be sensitive enough to measure the changes you're looking for. For example, if you need to measure small changes in pH, a pH meter (which can measure pH to several decimal places) would be more sensitive than indicator paper.

The technique you use has to be the most appropriate one for your experiment. E.g. if you want to measure the concentration of glucose in an unknown solution, using a colorimeter in conjunction with quantitative Benedict's reagent will help you to get more accurate results than simply comparing the colour differences of the solutions by eye (see pages 122-124).

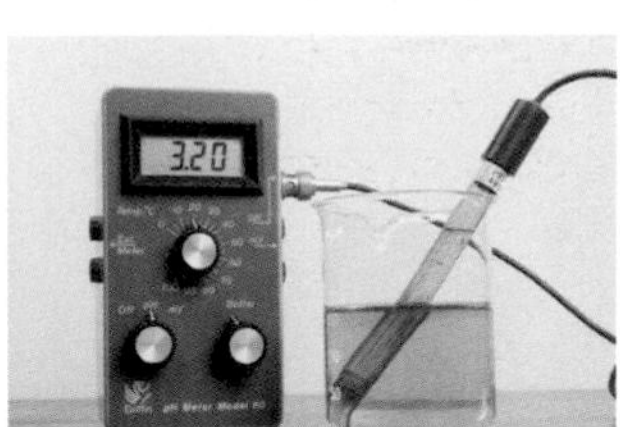


***Figure 1:*** *pH meters can be used to measure small changes in pH.*

## Risk assessments

In order to work safely, you need to carry out a risk assessment for your experiment. To do this, you need to identify:

**All the dangers in the experiment.**
For example, any hazardous chemicals, microorganisms or naked flames.

**Who is at risk from these dangers.**
This could be you and your lab partner, but it could also be anyone who is in the same room or building.

**What can be done to reduce the risk.**
You should wear a lab coat and safety goggles as a standard precaution, but you may need to take other safety precautions, such as:

- Wearing gloves, if your experiment involves substances that are likely to irritate the skin.
- Carrying out your experiment in a fume cupboard if it involves volatile chemicals (see page 35), and keeping flammable chemicals away from naked flames (e.g. Bunsen burner flames).
- Using aseptic techniques if you are culturing microorganisms.

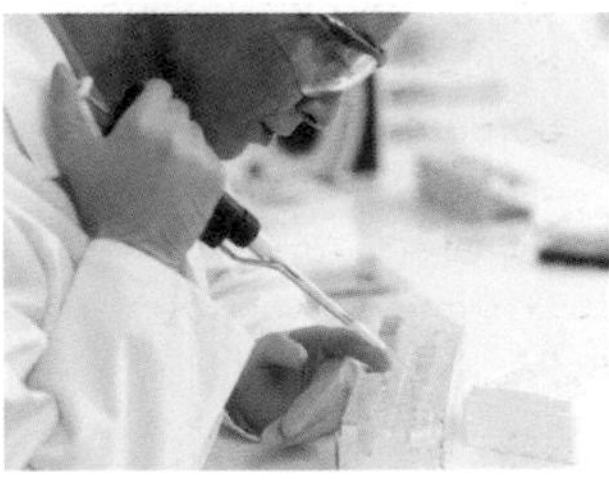

***Figure 2:*** *A scientist wearing eye protection, gloves and a lab coat to protect her while she works.*

**Tip:** You should remember aseptic techniques from Year 1 of your course — they're used when working with microorganisms to prevent contamination of cultures (and people) with unwanted microbes and pathogens.

## Ethical issues

You also need to consider any ethical issues in your experiment.

> **Example**
> If you're using living animals (e.g. insects) you must treat them with respect. This means handling them carefully and keeping them away from harmful chemicals, extreme heat sources and other things that might cause them physical discomfort.

# 2. Carrying Out an Experiment

*As part of your A-level in Biology, you're expected to carry out Required Practicals and be familiar with the techniques and apparatus involved in each one (see page 17). You could be asked about the skills you've learnt in your exams.*

## Using the correct apparatus and techniques

Examiners could ask you about a whole range of different apparatus and techniques. Make sure you know how to use all the instruments and equipment you've come across in class and can carry out all the techniques too. Here are some examples of equipment you should be able to use:

**Examples**

**Measuring cylinders and graduated pipettes**

These have a scale so you can measure specific volumes. Whichever one you use, make sure you read the volume from the bottom of the meniscus (the curved upper surface of the liquid) when it's at eye level — see Figure 1.

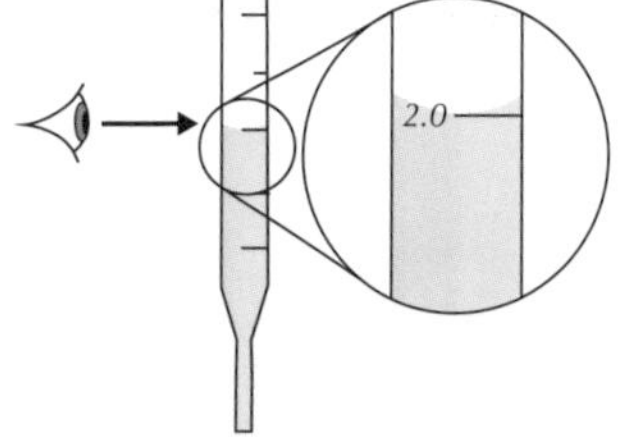


***Figure 1:*** *Measuring volume using the bottom of the meniscus.*

**Water baths**

Make sure you allow time for water baths to heat up before starting your experiment. Don't forget that your solutions will need time to get to the same temperature as the water before you start the experiment too. Also, remember to check the temperature of the water bath with a thermometer during the investigation to make sure it doesn't change.

**Data loggers**

Decide what you are measuring and what type of data logger you will need, e.g. temperature, pH. Connect an external sensor to the data logger if you need to. Decide how often you want the data logger to take readings depending on the length of the process that you are measuring.

**Tip:** A data logger (or data recorder) is an electronic device that can record data over time using a sensor. They can sometimes be connected to a computer.

You should also make sure you know how to do all the Required Practicals described in this book. You should be able to apply the techniques described in them to different contexts. For example, pages 36-37 describe how to use a colorimeter and a redox indicator dye to investigate the rate of dehydrogenase activity in chloroplasts. You could use a similar technique (i.e. a colorimeter and a redox indicator dye) to investigate the rate of respiration in yeast.

## Recording data

As you get your results, you need to record them. It's a good idea to draw a **table** to record the results of your experiment in. When you draw a table, make sure you include enough rows and columns to record all of the data you need to. You might also need to include a column for processing your data (e.g. working out the mean — see next page). Make sure each column has a heading so you know what's going to be recorded where. The units should be in the column heading only, not the table itself — see Figure 2. The independent variable should be recorded in the left-hand column and the dependent variable in the right.

**Tip:** If you're recording your data as decimals, make sure you do it to a consistent number of decimal places, e.g. when you're analysing your results, it makes sense to compare values that have been rounded to the same level of accuracy.

***Figure 2:*** *Table showing the rate of a reaction at three different concentrations of substrate.*

*heading* · *column* · *units* · *data* · *row*

| Concentration of substrate / mol $dm^{-3}$ | Rate of reaction / $cm^3$ $min^{-1}$ |
|---|---|
| 0.2 | 10 |
| 0.4 | 13 |
| 0.6 | 17 |

## Anomalous results

When you look at all the data in your table, you may notice that you have a result that doesn't seem to fit in with the rest at all. These results are called **anomalous results**. You should investigate anomalous results — if you can work out what happened (e.g. you measured something totally wrong) you can ignore them when processing your results. However, you can't just exclude a value just because you don't like the look of it.

**Tip:** Doing repeats makes it easier to spot anomalous results.

# 3. Processing Data

*Processing data means taking raw data and doing some calculations with it, to make it more useful. This is where your maths skills really come in.*

**Exam Tip**
At least 10% of your A-level Biology marks will come from assessment of maths skills in the exams.

## Summarising your data

Once you've collected all your data, it's useful to summarise it using a few handy-to-use figures — like the mean and the range.

### Mean and range

When you've done repeats of an experiment you should always calculate a **mean** (a type of average). To do this add together all the data values and divide by the total number of values in the sample.

You might also need to calculate the **range** (how spread out the data is). To do this find the largest data value and subtract the smallest data value from it. You shouldn't include anomalous results when calculating the mean or the range.

**Tip:** When people talk about an average, they are usually referring to the mean value.

**Example** — Maths Skills

**Compare the mean absorbance and range of absorbance for test tubes A and B in the table on the right.**

| *Test tube* | *Absorbance of solution / absorbance units (AU)* | | |
|---|---|---|---|
| | *Repeat 1* | *Repeat 2* | *Repeat 3* |
| *A* | *0.31* | *0.50* | *0.52* |
| *B* | *1.2* | *0.84* | *1.5* |

To calculate the means:

- Add up the three data values for A, then divide by three.
  *A: (0.31 + 0.50 + 0.52) ÷ 3 = 1.33 ÷ 3 =* ***0.44 AU*** *(2 s.f.)*
- Do the same for B.
  *B: (1.2 + 0.84 + 1.5) ÷ 3 = 3.54 ÷ 3 =* ***1.2 AU*** *(2 s.f.)*

**B has the higher mean.**

To find the range of results for each test tube, subtract the smallest result from the largest result.

*A: 0.52 – 0.31 =* ***0.21 AU*** *B: 1.5 – 0.84 =* ***0.66 AU***

**A has the smaller range.**

**Tip:** Averages and range values have the same units as the data used in the calculation.

**Tip:** S.f. stands for 'significant figures'. You can find out how many significant figures to use when rounding answers on page 7.

### Standard deviation

Standard deviation can be more useful than the range because it tells you how values are spread about the mean rather than just the total spread of data. A small standard deviation means the repeated results are all similar and close to the mean, i.e. they are precise.

**Tip:** The mean (and other averages, see next page), range and standard deviation are all examples of descriptive statistics. Descriptive statistics simply describe any patterns in the data.

### Median and mode

Like the mean, the median and mode are both types of average.

To calculate the median, put all your data in numerical order. The median is the middle value in this list. If you have an even number of values, the median is halfway between the middle two values.

To calculate the mode, count how many times each value comes up. The mode is the number that appears most often. A set of data might not have a mode — or it might have more than one.

**Tip:** If all the values in your data are different, there won't be a mode at all.

**Example** — Maths Skills

**The heights of bean plants (in millimetres) were measured six weeks after planting. The results were as follows:**

**112 102 106 120 98 106 80 105 106 110 95 98**

**Calculate the median and mode of these results.**

1. Put the data in numerical order:

   *80 95 98 98 102 105 106 106 106 110 112 120*

2. Find the middle value (the median):

   *There are 12 values, so the median is between the 6th and 7th numbers. The 6th number is 105 and the 7th is 106, so the median is **105.5 mm**.*

3. Count how many times each value comes up to find the mode:

   *106 comes up three times. None of the other numbers come up more than twice. So the mode is **106 mm**.*

**Tip:** To find the value halfway between two numbers, add the two numbers together and then divide by two. E.g. 105 + 106 = 211, 211 ÷ 2 = 105.5.

## Calculating percentages

Calculating **percentages** helps you to compare amounts from samples of different sizes. To give the amount X as a percentage of sample Y, you need to divide X by Y, then multiply by 100.

**Example** — Maths Skills

**In a DNA molecule containing 3000 bases, 900 of the bases are cytosine. What percentage of the bases are cytosine?**

1. Divide 900 by 3000: 900 ÷ 3000 = 0.30
2. Multiply by 100: 0.30 × 100 = **30%**

### Calculating percentage change

Calculating **percentage change** helps to quantify how much something has changed, e.g. the percentage change in the growth rate of pea plants when a fertiliser is added. To calculate it you use this equation:

$$\text{Percentage change} = \frac{\text{final value} - \text{original value}}{\text{original value}} \times 100$$

A positive value indicates an increase and a negative value indicates a decrease.

**Exam Tip**
The examiners just love getting you to calculate percentage changes, including percentage increases and decreases, so make sure you learn this formula.

**Example** — Maths Skills

**A person's blood glucose concentration before a meal was 4.2 mmol $dm^{-3}$. Two hours after a meal it was 6.5 mmol $dm^{-3}$. Calculate the percentage change.**

$$\text{Percentage change} = \frac{6.5 - 4.2}{4.2} \times 100 = \mathbf{55\%} \text{ (2 s.f.)}$$

**Tip:** This means that the person's blood glucose concentration was 55% higher after the meal.

Percentage change can be either positive or negative, depending on whether the value has gone up or down. However, percentage increase and percentage decrease are both written as positive numbers because the direction of the change has already been taken into account.

## Using ratios

**Ratios** can be used to compare lots of different types of quantities. For example, an organism with a surface area to volume ratio of 2 : 1 would theoretically have a surface area twice as large as its volume.

Ratios are usually most useful in their simplest (smallest) form. To simplify a ratio, divide each side by the same number. It's in its simplest form when there's nothing left you can divide by. To get a ratio of X : Y in the form X : 1, divide both sides by Y.

**Examples — Maths Skills**

- To simplify the ratio 28 : 36, divide both sides by 4. You get **7 : 9**.
- To write the ratio 28 : 36 in the form of X : 1, just divide both sides by 36:

  $28 \div 36 = 0.78 \qquad 36 \div 36 = 1$

  So the ratio is **0.78 : 1**.

**Tip:** If you're not sure what number to divide by to simplify a ratio, start by trying to divide both sides by a small number, e.g. 2 or 3, then check to see if you can simplify your answer further. E.g. you could simplify 28 : 36 by dividing each side by 2 to get 14 : 18. But you could simplify it further by dividing by 2 again to get 7 : 9. You can't simplify the ratio any further, so it's in its simplest form.

## Rounding to significant figures

The first **significant figure** of a number is the first digit that isn't a zero. The second, third and fourth significant figures follow on immediately after the first (even if they're zeros). When you're processing your data you may well want to round any really long numbers to a certain number of significant figures.

**Example**

0.6874976 rounds to **0.69** to **2 s.f.** and to **0.687** to **3 s.f.**

**Tip:** You may also want to round measurements to a certain number of significant figures when you're recording your data, e.g. if you're using a data logger that records data to several decimal places.

When you're doing calculations using measurements given to a certain number of significant figures, you should give your answer to the lowest number of significant figures that was used in the calculation.

**Example — Maths Skills**

For the calculation: $1.2 \div 1.85 = 0.648648648...$

1.2 is given to 2 significant figures. 1.85 is given to 3 significant figures. So the answer should be given to 2 significant figures.

Round the final significant figure (0.6$\underline{4}$8) up to 5: $1.2 \div 1.85 = \mathbf{0.65}$ **(2 s.f.)**

**Tip:** When rounding a number, if the next digit after the last significant figure you're using is less than 5 you should round it down, and if it's 5 or more you should round it up.

The lowest number of significant figures in the calculation is used because the fewer digits a measurement has, the less accurate it is. Your answer can only be as accurate as the least accurate measurement in the calculation.

## Writing numbers in standard form

When you're processing data you might also want to change very big or very small numbers that have lots of zeros into something more manageable — this is called standard form.

**Examples**

1 000 000 can be written $1 \times 10^6$. 0.017 can be written $1.7 \times 10^{-2}$.

To do this you just need to move the decimal point left or right. The number of places the decimal point moves is then represented by a power of 10 — this is positive for big numbers, and negative for numbers smaller than one.

**Tip:** When you're writing a measurement in standard form, make sure you keep the same number of significant figures. E.g. 0.00400 $cm^3$ = $4.00 \times 10^{-3}$ $cm^3$. This'll make sure that you don't lose any accuracy.

**Tip:** Double check you've got it right by doing the multiplication — you should end up with the number you started with. So for this example, you'd check $1.65 \times 10^4$ = 16 500.

**Example — Maths Skills**

**To write 16 500 in standard form:**

1. Move the decimal point to give the smallest number you can between 1 and 10.

   *16 500* ⟶ *1.6500*

2. Count the number of places the decimal point has moved.

   *The decimal point has moved four places to the left.*

3. Write that number as the power of ten. If the decimal point has moved to the left, the power is positive. If the decimal point has moved to the right, the power is negative.

   *16 500 =* $\mathbf{1.65 \times 10^4}$

## Converting between units

When processing your data, you need to have all the data in the correct units. Make sure you can convert between common units of time, length and volume.

**Examples**

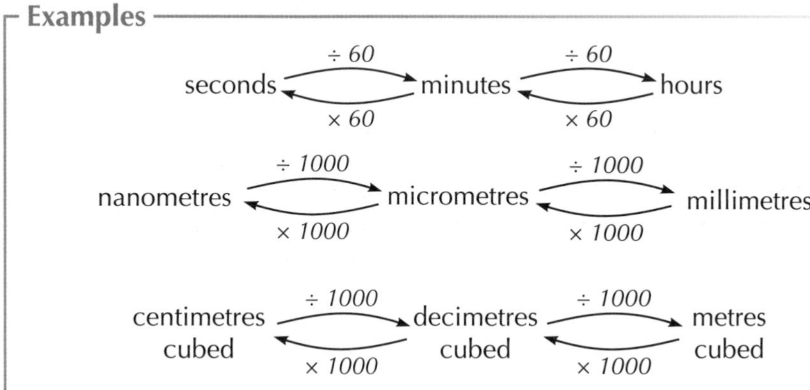


**Tip:** One decimetre cubed (1 $dm^3$) is the same as one litre (1 L).

**Examples — Maths Skills**

1. **10 $cm^3$ of glucose solution is needed to create a dilution series. What is the volume of glucose solution needed in $dm^3$?**

   There are 1000 $cm^3$ in one $dm^3$, so you need to divide by 1000:
   10 $cm^3$ ÷ 1000 = **0.01 $dm^3$**

2. **The volume of carbon dioxide produced over time was measured in an experiment into aerobic respiration in yeast. The rate of $CO_2$ production was found to be 3.7 $cm^3 min^{-1}$. What is this rate in $cm^3 s^{-1}$?**

   3.7 $cm^3 min^{-1}$ means 3.7 $cm^3$ carbon dioxide was produced per minute. You want to find out the volume produced per second. There are 60 seconds in one minute, so you need to divide the volume by 60:
   3.7 $cm^3 min^{-1}$ ÷ 60 = **0.06 $cm^3 s^{-1}$**

**Tip:** Statistical tests are inferential statistics. This means they allow you to 'infer' things (draw conclusions) from the data.

## Statistical tests

Statistical tests are used to analyse data mathematically. You can be more confident in your **conclusions** (see page 13), if they're based on results that have been analysed using a statistical test.

If you're planning on analysing your data using a statistical test, you first need to come up with a **null hypothesis** — this is a special type of hypothesis that states there is no significant difference (or correlation) between the things you're investigating. You then collect data to try to disprove the null hypothesis before analysing it statistically. There's more on null hypotheses on page 151.

### Student's t-test

You can use the Student's t-test when you have two sets of data that you want to compare. It tests whether there is a significant difference in the means of the two data sets. The value obtained is compared to a critical value, which helps you decide how likely it is that the results or 'differences in the means' were due to chance. If the value obtained from the t-test is greater than the critical value at a probability (**P value**) of 5% or less (≤ 0.05), then you can be 95% confident that the difference is significant and not due to chance. This is called a **95% confidence limit** — which is good enough for most biologists to reject the null hypothesis.

### Chi-squared test

You can use the chi-squared test when you have categorical (grouped) data and you want to know whether your observed results are statistically different from your expected results. You compare your result to a critical value — if it's larger than the critical value at P = 0.05, you can be 95% certain the difference is significant. There's more on chi-squared on pages 151-153.

### Correlation coefficient

A correlation coefficient, e.g. the Spearman's rank correlation coefficient, allows you to work out the degree to which two sets of data are correlated (see p.13 for more on correlation). It is given as a value between 1 and –1. A value of 1 indicates a strong positive correlation, 0 means there is no correlation and –1 is a strong negative correlation. You can then compare your result to a critical value to see whether or not the correlation is significant.

**Exam Tip**
In the exams, you could be asked which statistical test you'd use to analyse some data and to explain why you'd use it, as well as to interpret the test result.

**Exam Tip**
When you're talking about the results of a statistical test and using the 95% confidence limit, make sure you refer to the probability as less than 0.05 or 5%, <u>not</u> 0.05%.

**Tip:** If the result of your statistical test is greater than (>) the critical value at a P value of less than 2% (< 0.02), or even 1%, you can be even more confident that the difference is significant.

# 4. Presenting Data

*Presenting your data can make it easier for you to understand your results and spot any trends. You need to choose the best way to present your data.*

**Tip:** Make sure you're familiar with the symbols > (greater than), >> (much greater than), < (less than) and << (much less than).

## Qualitative and discrete data

**Qualitative** data is non-numerical data, e.g. blood group, hair colour. **Discrete** data is numerical data that can only take certain values in a range, e.g. shoe size, number of patients. You can use **bar charts** or **pie charts** to present these types of data.

**Example**

The bar chart below shows the number of bacterial colonies present on a series of agar plates (labelled A-D).

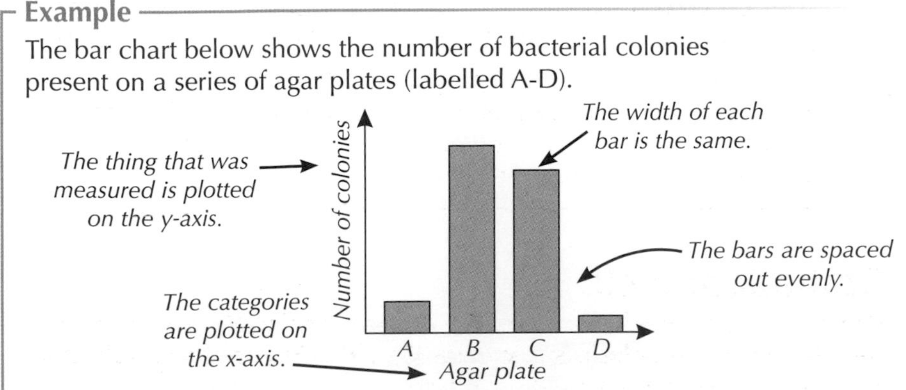
The thing that was measured is plotted on the y-axis.
Number of colonies
The width of each bar is the same.
The bars are spaced out evenly.
The categories are plotted on the x-axis.
A
B
C
D
Agar plate

**Tip:** Qualitative data can also be called categorical data — all the data can be sorted into categories and values between categories don't exist.

# Continuous data

**Continuous** data is data that can take any value in a range, e.g. height or weight. You can use **line graphs** or **histograms** to present this type of data.

**Exam Tip**
If you are asked to draw a graph or chart in your exam, don't forget to label the axes (including the quantity and units), choose a sensible scale and make sure that it covers at least half the graph paper.

## Line graphs

Line graphs often show how a variable changes over time. The data on both axes is continuous.

**Tip:** The graph on the right is a line graph. Line graphs look a bit like scattergrams (see below), but the points on line graphs are joined together.

Example

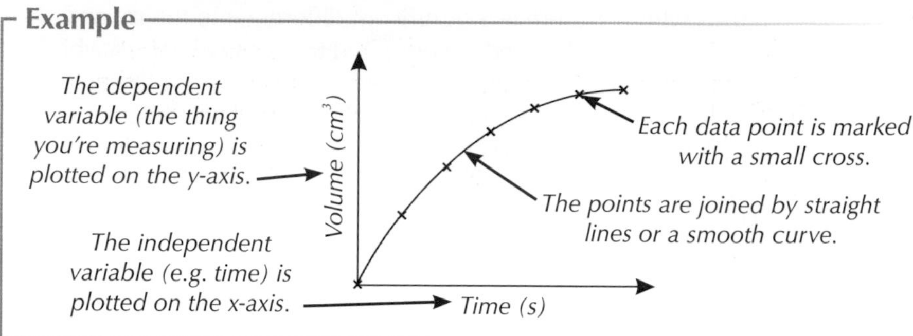
The dependent variable (the thing you're measuring) is plotted on the y-axis.
Volume ($cm^3$)
The independent variable (e.g. time) is plotted on the x-axis.
Time (s)
Each data point is marked with a small cross.
The points are joined by straight lines or a smooth curve.

## Histograms

Histograms are a useful way of displaying frequency data when the independent variable is continuous. They may look like bar charts, but it's the area of the bars that represents the frequency (rather than the height). The height of each bar is called the **frequency density**. The data for a histogram is split into groups called classes, rather than categories.

**Tip:** Don't be fooled by the height of the bars in a histogram — the tallest bar doesn't always belong to the class with the greatest frequency.

**Tip:** The class width is the range of the class. The width of the whole histogram shows the range of all the results.

Example

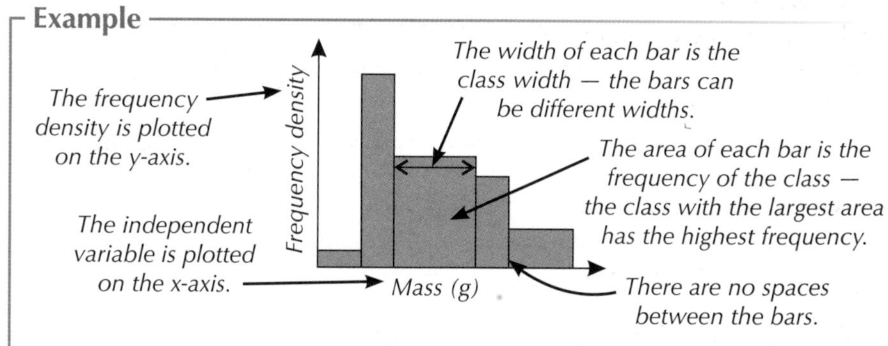
The frequency density is plotted on the y-axis.
Frequency density
The independent variable is plotted on the x-axis.
Mass (g)
The width of each bar is the class width — the bars can be different widths.
The area of each bar is the frequency of the class — the class with the largest area has the highest frequency.
There are no spaces between the bars.

You calculate the frequency density using this formula:

frequency density = frequency ÷ class width

# Scattergrams

When you want to show how two variables are related (correlated) you can use a **scattergram**. Both variables must be numbers.

**Tip:** Scattergrams can also be called scatter graphs, or scatter diagrams.

**Tip:** Data that's made up of numbers is called quantitative data.

Example

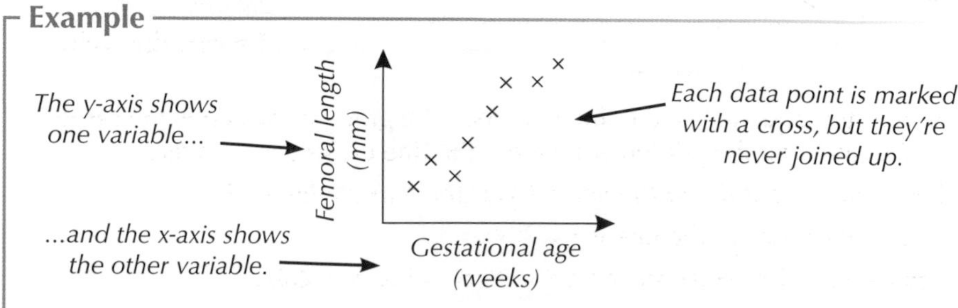
The y-axis shows one variable...
Femoral length (mm)
...and the x-axis shows the other variable.
Gestational age (weeks)
Each data point is marked with a cross, but they're never joined up.

You can draw a **line** (or curve) **of best fit** on a scattergram to help show the trend in your results. To do so, draw the line through or as near to as many points as possible, ignoring any anomalous results.

> **Tip:** You should never join the points together on a scattergram.
>
> 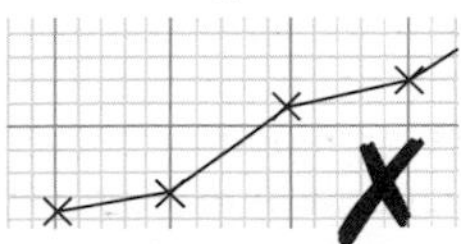
>
> A line of best fit shows a trend rather than changes between data points.

**Example**

The number of organisms of one species on a rocky beach was recorded at different distances from the shore. The graph below shows the results, including a line of best fit.

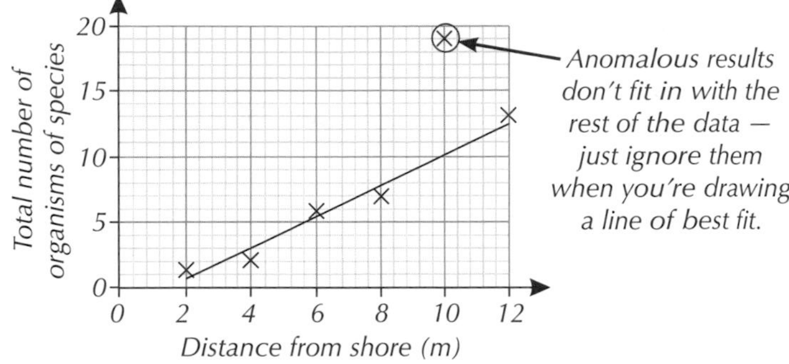


> **Tip:** A trend shown by a scattergram is called a correlation. There's more about correlation and what it means on page 13.

## Finding the rate from a graph

Rate is a measure of how much something is changing over time. Calculating a rate can be useful when analysing your data, e.g. you might want to the find the rate of a reaction. You can find the rate from a graph that shows a variable changing over time by finding the **gradient** (how steep it is):

### Linear graphs

For a linear graph you can calculate the rate by finding the gradient of the line, using the equation:

$$\text{Gradient} = \frac{\text{Change in } y}{\text{Change in } x}$$

**Change in *y*** is the change in value on the *y*-axis and **change in *x*** is the change in value on the *x*-axis. The equation of a straight line can always be written in the form $y = mx + c$, where $m$ is the gradient and $c$ is the $y$-intercept (this is the value of $y$ when the line crosses the $y$-axis).

> **Tip:** Linear graphs are graphs with a straight line.

> **Tip:** When using this equation to find a rate, $x$ should always be the time.

**Example** — Maths Skills

**Find the rate at which the sodium ion concentration changes on the graph below and use it to find the equation of the line.**

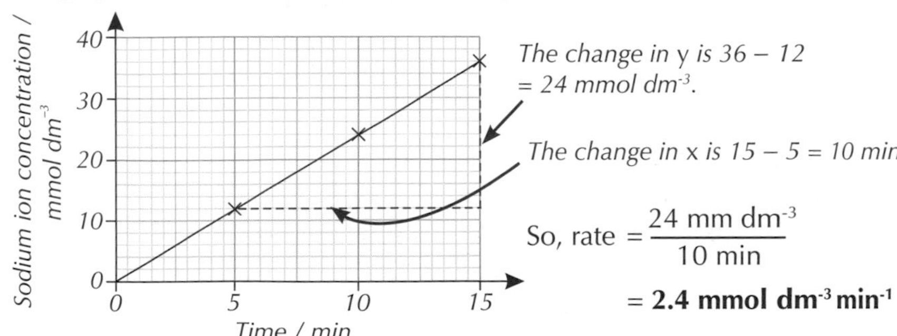


So, rate $= \frac{24 \text{ mm dm}^{-3}}{10 \text{ min}}$

$= \mathbf{2.4 \text{ mmol dm}^{-3} \text{ min}^{-1}}$

To find the equation of the line you need the gradient (which is the same as the rate) and the $y$-intercept (where the line crosses the $y$-axis).

*The gradient is 2.4 and the line crosses the y-axis where y is 0.*

So the equation for the line is $y = 2.4x + 0$.

Since $c = 0$, the equation can be written as just $\mathbf{y = 2.4x}$.

> **Tip:** When drawing a triangle to calculate a gradient like this, the hypotenuse of the triangle should be at least half as long as the line of the graph itself.

> **Tip:** The units for the gradient are the units for $y$ divided by the units for $x$. Here the units are mmol $\text{dm}^{-3}$ $\text{min}^{-1}$ or millimoles per decimetre cubed per minute.

Knowing the equation of the line allows you to estimate results not plotted on the graph:

**Example — Maths Skills**

**Estimate the concentration of sodium ions after 20 minutes.**

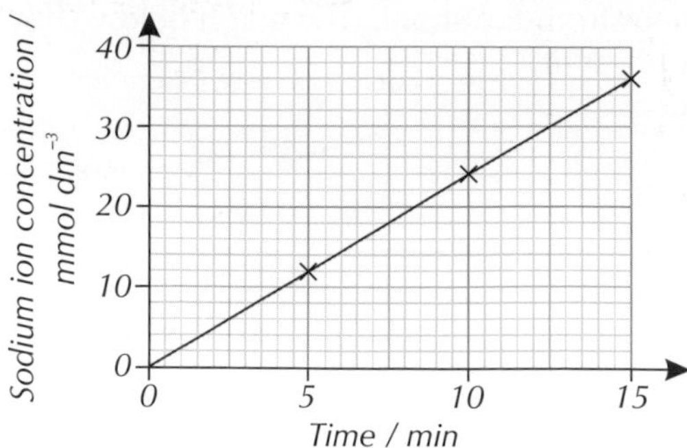


The equation for the line is $y = 2.4x$ (see previous example), where $y$ is the concentration of sodium ions (in mmol dm$^{-3}$) and $x$ is the time (in minutes).

To find the value of $y$ when $x$ is 20 minutes, just replace $x$ with 20 in the equation. $y = 2.4 \times 20 =$ **48 mmol dm$^{-3}$**

**Tip:** The graph on the right is a linear graph in which one variable increases in proportion with the other. The symbol for 'proportional to' is '$\propto$'. Here, you can say that concentration of sodium ions $\propto$ time.

**Tip:** 48 mmol dm$^{-3}$ is an estimate because you are assuming that the relationship between the two variables doesn't change after 15 minutes (so as time increases, the concentration of sodium ions keeps increasing at the same rate).

## Curved graphs

For a curved (non-linear) graph you can find the rate by drawing a **tangent**. A tangent is a straight line that touches a single point on the curve. You can then calculate the gradient of the tangent to find the rate.

**Find the rate of reaction when time = 30 s on the graph below.**

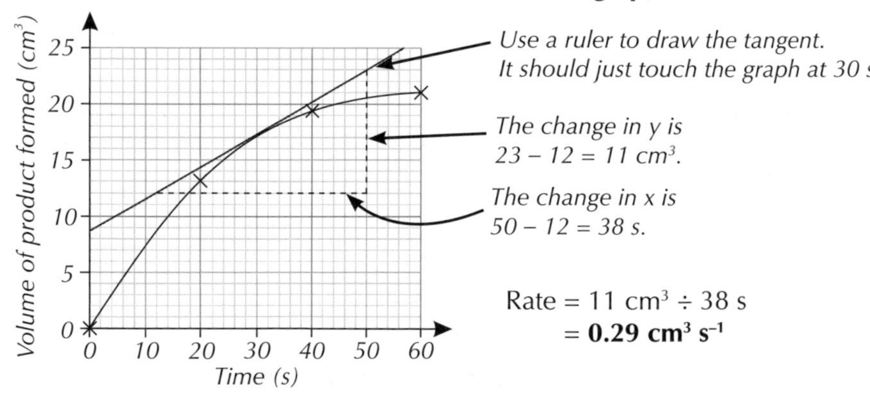


Rate = 11 cm$^3$ ÷ 38 s
= **0.29 cm$^3$ s$^{-1}$**

**Tip:** Extend the tangent right across the graph — it'll make calculating the gradient easier as you'll have more points to choose from.

**Tip:** Remember, the gradient of a tangent only tells you the rate at that particular point on the graph.

In the exam, you might be asked to give the ratio of the rates at different times in a reaction. Don't panic — just use the method above to find the rate at each time and give your answer as a ratio (see example on the next page).

You might also be asked to find the average (or mean) rate over a particular period of time — if so, you can just draw a straight line between the first and last point in that time period and calculate the gradient of the line to find the rate. This is also shown in the example on the next page.

**Example** — **Maths Skills**

**Find the ratio of the average rate of reaction over the first 30 seconds to the average rate of reaction during the final 30 seconds on the graph below. Give your answer in the form X : 1.**

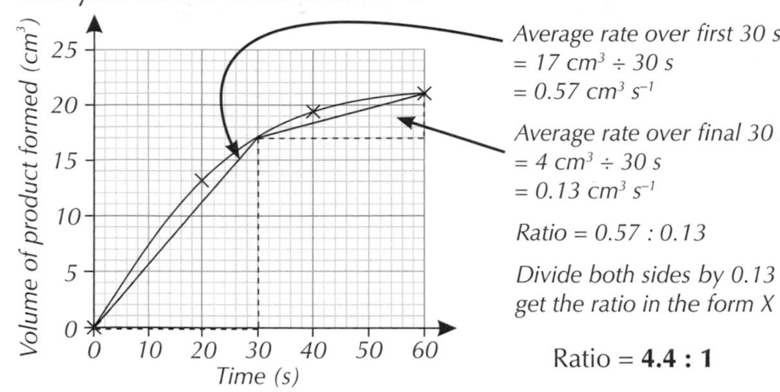

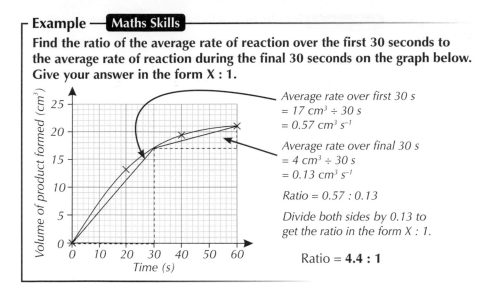

*Average rate over first 30 s*
*= 17 $cm^3$ ÷ 30 s*
*= 0.57 $cm^3$ $s^{-1}$*

*Average rate over final 30 s*
*= 4 $cm^3$ ÷ 30 s*
*= 0.13 $cm^3$ $s^{-1}$*

*Ratio = 0.57 : 0.13*

*Divide both sides by 0.13 to get the ratio in the form X : 1.*

Ratio = **4.4 : 1**

**Tip:** There's more on ratios and converting them into the form X : 1 on page 7.

# 5. Concluding and Evaluating

*You need to be able to draw conclusions from your results and evaluate them. You also need to be able to draw conclusions from other people's data and evaluate them — which is what you're likely to be asked to do in your exams.*

## Drawing conclusions from data

Conclusions need to be **valid**. A conclusion can only be considered as valid if it uses valid data (see page 1).

### Correlations and causal relationships

You can often draw conclusions by looking at the relationship (**correlation**) between two variables:

| *Positive* | *Negative* | *No correlation* |
|---|---|---|
| *As one variable increases the other increases.* | *As one variable increases the other decreases.* | *There is no relationship between the variables.* |

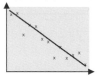

**Tip:** The closer the points are to the line of best fit, the stronger the correlation. You can calculate a correlation coefficient (see p. 9) to get a numerical value for how strong the correlation is.

You have to be very careful when drawing conclusions from data like this because a correlation between two variables doesn't always mean that a change in one variable causes a change in the other (the correlation could be due to chance or there could be a third variable having an effect).

If there's a relationship between two variables and a change in one variable does cause a change in the other it's called a **causal relationship**. It can be concluded that a correlation is a causal relationship if every other variable that could possibly affect the result is controlled.

**Tip:** In reality, concluding that a correlation is a causal relationship is very hard to do — correlations are generally accepted to be causal relationships if lots of studies have found the same thing, and scientists have figured out exactly how one factor causes the other.

### Drawing specific conclusions

When you're making a conclusion you can't make broad generalisations from data — you have to be very specific. You can only conclude what the results show and no more.

**Exam Tip**
Being able to recognise correlations and causal relationships comes up a lot in Biology. It's really important that you learn how to do this and understand the difference between the two.

**Example — Maths Skills**

**Figure 1** shows the results from an investigation into the effect of concentration of a plant growth factor X on the height of Plant Species A.

**What you can conclude from these results:**
The only conclusion you can draw is that as the concentration of growth factor X increases, the height of Plant Species A increases.

**What you can't conclude from these results:**
You can't conclude that this is true for any other plant growth factor or any other plant species — the results could be completely different. Without more information about what other variables were controlled, you can't conclude that the increasing concentration of growth factor X has caused the increase in height of Plant Species A either.

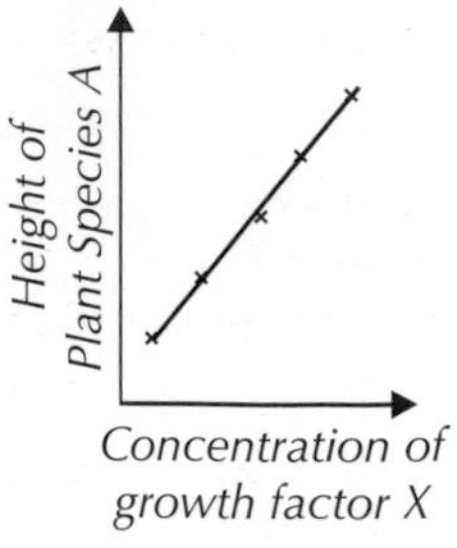


*Figure 1: The relationship between concentration of growth factor X and height of Plant Species A.*

**Tip:** A reading is when you make a judgement about one value, e.g. when you read a value off a mass balance. A measurement is when you judge two values and find the difference, e.g. when you measure length with a ruler.

## Uncertainty in data

When you draw a conclusion, it's often a good idea to talk about the uncertainty in your data — in other words, the amount of error there might be. The results you get from an experiment won't be completely perfect — there'll always be a degree of uncertainty in your readings or measurements due to limits in the sensitivity of the apparatus you're using.

A ± sign tells you the range in which the true value lies (usually to within a 95% confidence level). The range is called the **margin of error**.

**Example**

A 10 $cm^3$ pipette has graduations to mark every 0.1 $cm^3$. If you measure a volume with it, you are measuring to the nearest 0.1 $cm^3$ — the real volume could be up to 0.05 $cm^3$ less or 0.05 $cm^3$ more. The uncertainty value of the pipette is ± 0.05 $cm^3$, and so its margin of error is 0.1 $cm^3$ (see Figure 2).

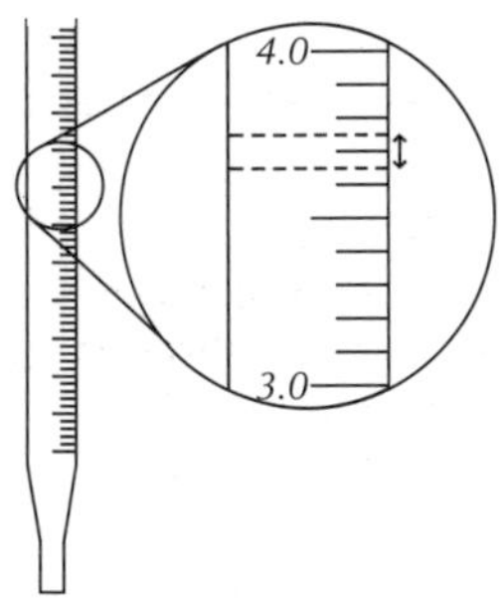


*Figure 2: The margin of error for a reading of 3.7 $cm^3$ using a 10 $cm^3$ pipette.*

If you're combining readings or measurements, you'll need to combine their uncertainties:

**Example — Maths Skills**

In a serial dilution, 5.0 $cm^3$ of glucose solution is transferred using a pipette that measures to the nearest 0.5 $cm^3$. It is added to 10.0 $cm^3$ water that was measured in a graduated cylinder with graduations to mark every 1.0 $cm^3$.

The uncertainty in the pipette is ± 0.25 $cm^3$, or 0.3 $cm^3$ to 1 d.p.
The uncertainty in the graduated cylinder is ± 0.5 $cm^3$.

So the total uncertainty will be 0.3 $cm^3$ + 0.5 $cm^3$ = **± 0.8 $cm^3$**.

**Tip:** You usually quote an uncertainty to the same number of decimal places as the value — so we've rounded 0.25 up to 0.3 here.

### Calculating percentage error

If you know the uncertainty value of your measurements, you can calculate the percentage error using:

$$\text{percentage error} = \frac{\text{uncertainty}}{\text{reading}} \times 100$$

**Example — Maths Skills**

50 $cm^3$ of HCl is measured with an uncertainty value of ± 0.05 $cm^3$.

The percentage error = $\frac{0.05}{50} \times 100$ = **0.1%**

## Minimising errors in data

One obvious way to reduce errors in your measurements is to buy the most sensitive equipment available. In real life there's not much you can do about this one — you're stuck with whatever your school or college has got. But there are other ways to lower the uncertainty in experiments.

**Example — Measuring a greater amount of something**

Using a 500 $cm^3$ cylinder with an uncertainty value of ± 2.5 $cm^3$ to measure 100 $cm^3$ of liquid will give you a percentage error of: $\frac{2.5}{100} \times 100 = \mathbf{2.5\%}$

But if you measure 200 $cm^3$ in the same cylinder, the percentage error is: $\frac{2.5}{200} \times 100 = \mathbf{1.25\%}$

Hey presto — you've just halved the uncertainty.

**Tip:** You can also minimise errors by using a larger sample size, as this reduces the chance of getting a freak result — see page 3.

## Evaluating results

When you evaluate your results, you need to think about whether they were repeatable and reproducible and whether they were valid.

**Repeatability**

- Did you take enough repeat readings or measurements?
- Would you do more repeats if you were to do the experiment again?
- Did you get similar data each time you carried out a repeat measurement?

If you didn't do any repeats, or enough repeats, you can't be sure your data is repeatable. Your repeated results need to be similar too. If you repeated a measurement three times and got a completely different result each time, your results aren't repeatable (or precise).

**Reproducibility**

Have you compared your results with other people's results and if so, were they similar? If not, you can't be sure your data is reproducible.

**Validity**

- Does your data answer the question you set out to investigate?
- Were all the variables controlled?

If you didn't control all the variables, you haven't answered the original question and your data isn't valid.

**Example**

You could only conclude from your results that the rate of photosyntheses increases with light intensity (see page 1) if you controlled all the other variables that could have affected rate of photosynthesis in your experiment, e.g. pH, temperature, etc.

**Exam Tip**
If you're given data or a method to evaluate in the exam, you should be asking similar questions, e.g. were all the variables controlled? And if not, how should they have been controlled?

**Tip:** Think about whether other scientists could gain data showing the same relationships that are shown in your data.

## Evaluating methods

When you evaluate your method, you need to think about how you could improve your experiment if you did it again. Here are some things to consider:

- Is there anything you could have done to make your results more precise or accurate?
- Were there any limitations in your method, e.g. should you have taken measurements more frequently?
- Was your sample size large enough?
- Were there any sources of error in your experiment?
- Could you have used more sensitive apparatus or equipment?

**Tip:** This is where you take the uncertainty of your measurements (see previous page) into account. Think about the size of the margin for error, and whether you could have reduced the uncertainty.

**Exam Tip**

Data questions are fairly common in the exams. You might be given a conclusion for the data and asked to evaluate it — this just means you have to give reasons why it is (or isn't) a valid conclusion. You could also be asked how far data supports a conclusion — it requires a similar type of answer.

# Having confidence in your conclusion

Once you've evaluated your results and method, you can decide how much confidence you have in your conclusion. For example, if your results are repeatable, reproducible and valid and they back up your conclusion then you can have a high degree of confidence in your conclusion.

You can also consider these points if you're asked to evaluate a conclusion in the exam.

**Example**

A study examined the effect of soil pH on marram grass. A 40 m transect was set up, running from the shoreline and heading inland. The percentage cover of marram grass was measured by placing a 1 $m^2$ quadrat (divided into 100 squares) at 5 m intervals along the transect and counting the number of squares containing marram grass. At each sample point, the pH of the soil was measured using a pH probe. The results are shown in Figure 3:

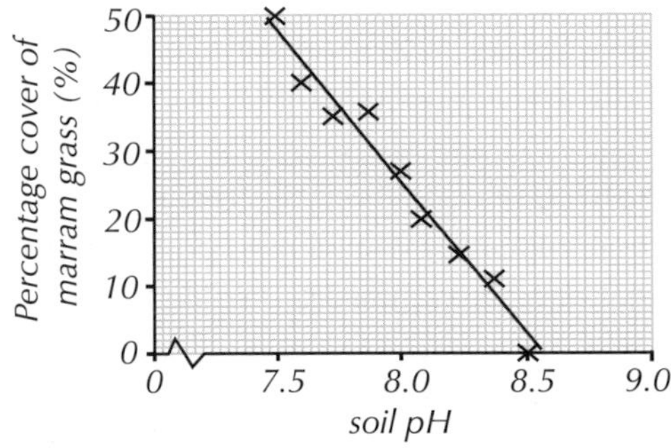


***Figure 3:*** *Scattergram to show relationship between soil pH and percentage cover of marram grass.*

**A student who read this study concluded that in seashore habitats a higher soil pH causes the percentage cover of marram grass to decrease. Does the data support this conclusion? Explain your answer.**

**Yes** — The data in the graph supports the conclusion as it shows that as the soil pH increases, the percentage cover of marram grass decreases — soil pH has a negative correlation with the percentage cover of marram grass.

**No** — You can't conclude that increasing soil pH causes the percentage cover of marram grass to decrease. Other factors may have been involved — for example, the soil moisture content or salinity may have changed over the course of the transect, or there may have been more competition from other species. This means you don't know how valid the study is — you can't be sure that the factor being investigated (soil pH) is the only one affecting the thing being measured (percentage cover of marram grass).

Also, the study is quite small — only one 40 metre transect was used. The trend shown by the data may not appear if more than one transect was studied, or if a longer transect was used.

The results are also limited by the method of sampling. We don't know how the transect line was chosen. It could have been chosen in an area which had a higher percentage cover of marram grass than other places along the shoreline.

**Overall** — The limits of the study mean that the student's conclusion isn't well supported.

# 6. The Practical Endorsement

*Alongside your A-level exams, you have to do a separate 'Practical Endorsement'. This assesses practical skills that can't be tested in a written exam.*

## What is the Practical Endorsement?

The Practical Endorsement is assessed slightly differently to the rest of your course. Unlike the exams, you don't get a mark for the Practical Endorsement — you just have to get a pass grade.

In order to pass the Practical Endorsement, you have to carry out at least twelve practical experiments and demonstrate that you can:

- use a range of specified apparatus, e.g. you must be able to use a colorimeter (see page 123),
- carry out a range of specified practical techniques, e.g. you must be able to use sampling techniques in fieldwork (see pages 181-183).

The twelve practicals that you do are most likely to be the twelve Required Practicals that form part of the AQA A-level Biology course — these cover all the techniques you need to be able to demonstrate for your Practical Endorsement. You may carry out other practicals as well, or instead, which may also count towards your Practical Endorsement. You'll do the practicals in class, and your teacher will assess you as you're doing them.

You'll need to keep a record of all your assessed practical activities. Required Practicals 1 to 6 are all part of the Year 1 material (Topics 1 to 4) so you may have already done some experiments that count towards the Practical Endorsement in Year 1 of the course. This book contains information about Required Practicals 7 to 12 (which are all part of the Year 2 material).

**Exam Tip**
You could also get asked questions about the Required Practicals in your written exams.

**Tip:** Throughout this book, examples of methods you could use for the Required Practicals are marked up with a big stamp, like this one:

REQUIRED PRACTICAL 

## Assessment of the Practical Endorsement

When assessing your practical work, your teacher will be checking that you're able to do five things:

### 1. Follow written methods and instructions

Make sure you read any instructions you are given fully before you start work and that you understand what you're about to do. This will help you to avoid missing out any important steps or using the wrong piece of apparatus.

### 2. Use apparatus and investigative methods correctly

You need to be able to demonstrate that you can use apparatus and carry out practical techniques correctly (see above), and that you can do so without too many reminders from your teacher. This means being able to carry out a procedure in the right order, as well as being able to fix problems when you come across them.

You'll also need to show that you can identify which variables need to be controlled in an experiment and how to control them (see page 1). If you can't easily control all the variables, you'll need to show that you can find a way around this, e.g. by using a negative control (see page 2). Finally, you'll need to demonstrate that you can decide which apparatus to use and what measurements you'll take with it to get the most accurate results (see page 3 for more).

**Tip:** You won't necessarily need to demonstrate each of these things every time you carry out a practical.

**Tip:** You'll be given the opportunity to build up to some of the more difficult skills.

Tip: The CLEAPSS® website has a database with details of the potential harm that hazardous substances you're likely to come across could cause. It also has student safety sheets, and your school or college may have CLEAPSS® Hazcards® you can use. These are all good sources of information if you're writing a risk assessment.

Tip: Reporting your results may involve presenting them in a graph or chart. See pages 9-11 for more.

Tip: Your teacher might ask you to keep a lab book — a notebook in which you write up all your practical activities and record all the results.

Tip: If you're unsure whether the information on a website is true or not, try and find the same piece of information in a different place. The more sources you can find for the information, the more likely it is to be correct.

Tip: There are lots of slightly different ways of referencing sources, but the important thing is that it's clear where you found the information.

### 3. Use apparatus and materials safely

This means being able to carry out a risk assessment (see page 3) to identify the dangers in your experiment and what you can do to reduce the risks associated with those dangers. You'll also have to show that you can work safely both in the lab and in the field, using appropriate safety equipment to reduce the risks you've identified, and that you can adjust your method as you go along to make it safer if necessary.

### 4. Make observations and record results

You need to show that you can make accurate observations that are relevant to your experiment and that you can collect data that's valid, accurate and precise. When you record the data, e.g. in a table, you need to make sure you do so to an appropriate level of accuracy and you include things like the units. Make sure you follow the rules on drawing tables from page 5.

### 5. Carry out supporting research and write reports using appropriate references

You need to show that you can write up an investigation properly. As well as reporting your results and analysing them, you'll need to draw conclusions about your findings, describe the method and apparatus you used, and write down any safety precautions you took.

You'll also need to show that you can use computer software to process your data. This might mean drawing a graph of your results using the computer, or using a computer programme to carry out a statistical test.

You'll need to write up any research you've done too (e.g. to help you with planning a method or to draw your conclusions) and properly cite the sources that you've used.

## Research, references and citations

You can use books or the Internet to carry out research, but there a few things you'll need to bear in mind:

- Not all the information you find on the Internet will be true. It's hard to know where information comes from on forums, blogs and websites that can be edited by the general public, so you should avoid using these. Websites of organisations such as the Nuffield Foundation and the National Health Service (NHS) provide lots of information that comes from reliable scientific sources. Scientific papers and textbooks are also good sources of reliable information.
- It may sound obvious, but when you're using the information that you've found during your research, you can't just copy it down word for word. Any data you're looking up should be copied accurately, but you should rewrite everything else in your own words.
- When you've used information from a source, you need to cite the reference properly. Citations allow someone else to go back and find the source of your information. This means they can check your information and see you're not making things up out of thin air. Citations also mean you've properly credited other people's data that you've used in your work. A citation for a particular piece of information may include the title of the book, paper or website where you found the information, the author and/or the publisher of the document and the date the document was published.

Topic 5 | A: Photosynthesis and Respiration

# 1. Photosynthesis, Respiration and Energy

*The ability to store, transfer and release energy is really important for plants and animals. That's where photosynthesis and respiration come in.*

## Why is energy important?

Plant and animal cells need energy for biological processes to occur.

**Examples**

- Plants need energy for things like photosynthesis, active transport (e.g. to take in minerals via their roots), DNA replication, cell division and protein synthesis.
- Animals need energy for things like muscle contraction, maintenance of body temperature, active transport, DNA replication, cell division and protein synthesis.

**Tip:** Without energy, the biological processes described would stop and the plant or animal would die.

## Photosynthesis and energy

Photosynthesis is the process where energy from light is used to make glucose from water ($H_2O$) and carbon dioxide ($CO_2$). The light energy is converted to chemical energy in the form of glucose — $C_6H_{12}O_6$. The overall equation is:

$$6CO_2 + 6H_2O + \text{Energy} \longrightarrow C_6H_{12}O_6 + 6O_2$$

Energy is stored in the glucose until the plants (or other photosynthesising organisms, e.g. algae) release it by respiration. Animals obtain glucose by eating plants (or by eating other animals, which have eaten plants), then respire the glucose to release energy.

Photosynthesis is an example of a **metabolic pathway** — the process occurs in a series of small reactions controlled by enzymes.

**Tip:** Any organism that carries out photosynthesis is known as a 'photoautotroph' (an organism that can make its own food using light energy). The process of photosynthesis is the same in all photoautotrophs, suggesting that they all evolved from a common ancestor.

## Respiration and energy

Plant and animal cells release energy from glucose — this process is called respiration. This energy is used to power all the biological processes in a cell. There are two types of respiration:

- **Aerobic respiration** — respiration using oxygen.
- **Anaerobic respiration** — respiration without oxygen.

Aerobic respiration produces carbon dioxide and water, and releases energy. The overall equation is:

$$C_6H_{12}O_6 + 6O_2 \longrightarrow 6CO_2 + 6H_2O + \text{Energy}$$

Anaerobic respiration in plants and yeast produces ethanol and carbon dioxide and releases energy. In humans, anaerobic respiration produces lactate and releases energy. Aerobic and anaerobic respiration are both examples of metabolic pathways.

**Tip:** Energy is never created or destroyed. It's always converted from one form to another. For example, in photosynthesis light energy is converted to chemical energy (glucose). This energy is then used to fuel biological processes.

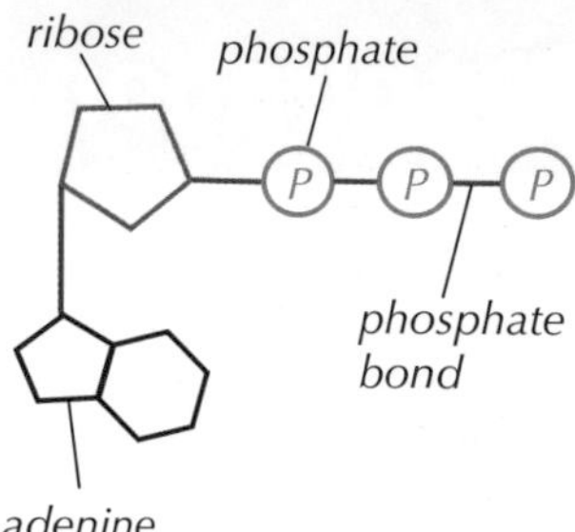


***Figure 1:*** *The structure of adenosine triphosphate (ATP). It consists of adenine, ribose and three phosphate groups.*

**Tip:** Adenosine <u>di</u>phosphate has <u>two</u> phosphate groups. Adenosine <u>tri</u>phosphate has <u>three</u> phosphate groups.

**Tip:** In a cell there's a constant cycle between ADP and $P_i$, and ATP. This allows energy to be stored and released as it's needed.

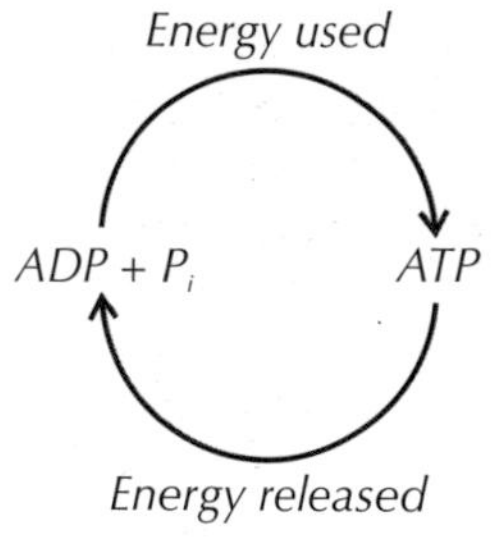


**Tip:** It's important to remember that ATP isn't energy — it's a store of energy. Energy is used to make ATP, then it's released when ATP is hydrolysed to ADP and $P_i$.

# ATP

As you learnt in Topic 1, ATP (adenosine triphosphate) is the immediate source of energy in a cell.

A cell can't get its energy directly from glucose. So, in respiration, the energy released from glucose is used to make ATP. ATP is made from the nucleotide base adenine, combined with a ribose sugar and three phosphate groups (see Figure 1). It carries energy around the cell to where it's needed.

ATP is synthesised via a condensation reaction between ADP (adenosine diphosphate) and inorganic phosphate ($P_i$) using energy from an energy-releasing reaction, e.g. the breakdown of glucose in respiration. The energy is stored as chemical energy in the phosphate bond (see Figure 2). The enzyme **ATP synthase** catalyses this reaction.

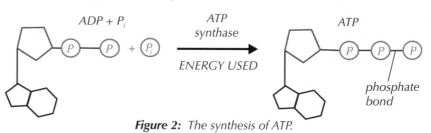

ADP + $P_i$
ATP synthase
ENERGY USED
ATP
phosphate bond

***Figure 2:*** *The synthesis of ATP.*

This process is known as **phosphorylation** — adding phosphate to a molecule. ADP is phosphorylated to ATP.

ATP then diffuses to the part of the cell that needs energy. Here, it's broken down back into ADP and inorganic phosphate ($P_i$). Chemical energy is released from the phosphate bond and used by the cell. **ATP hydrolase** catalyses this reaction.

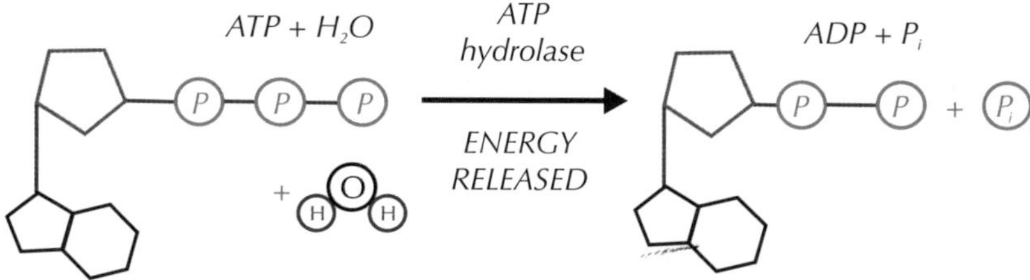


***Figure 3:*** *The breakdown of ATP.*

This process is known as **hydrolysis**. It's the splitting (lysis) of a molecule using water (hydro). The ADP and inorganic phosphate are recycled and the process starts again.

# ATP's properties

ATP has specific properties that make it a good energy source.

- ATP stores or releases only a small, manageable amount of energy at a time, so no energy is wasted as heat.
- It's a small, soluble molecule so it can be easily transported around the cell.
- It's easily broken down, so energy can be easily released instantaneously.
- It can be quickly remade.
- It can make other molecules more reactive by transferring one of its phosphate groups to them (phosphorylation).
- ATP can't pass out of the cell, so the cell always has an immediate supply of energy.

## The compensation point

Plants carry out both photosynthesis and respiration. Both processes can occur at the same time and at different rates. The rate at which photosynthesis takes place is partly dependent on the light intensity of the environment that the plant is in (see page 30).

There's a particular level of light intensity at which the rate of photosynthesis exactly matches the rate of respiration. This is called the **compensation point** for light intensity.

One way to work out the compensation point for a plant is to measure the rate at which oxygen is produced and used by a plant at different light intensities. Because photosynthesis produces oxygen and respiration uses it, in this case, the compensation point is the light intensity at which oxygen is being used as quickly as it is produced (see the example below). The rate of $CO_2$ production and use could also be measured — photosynthesis uses $CO_2$ and respiration produces it.

**Tip:** The products of photosynthesis (e.g. $O_2$) can be used as reactants in respiration and vice versa. Reactants can also come from elsewhere (e.g. $O_2$ can come from air).

**Tip:** The compensation point is different for different species of plants.

**Example — Maths Skills**

The graph below shows the net oxygen generation by a plant grown in a controlled environment under different light intensities. When the rate of oxygen production equals the rate of oxygen usage, oxygen generation is zero. This is the compensation point.

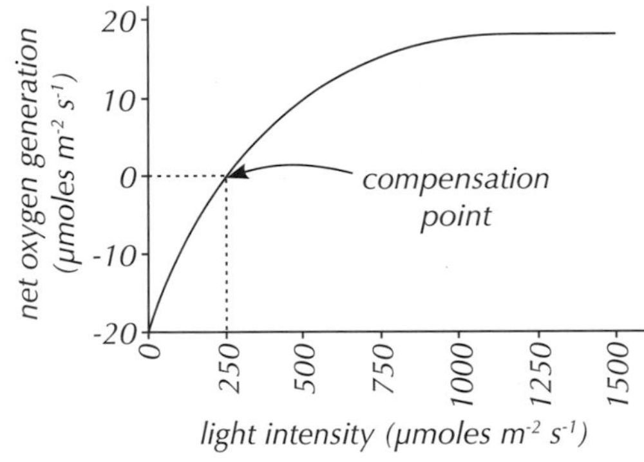


In this example, the compensation point occurs at a light intensity of **250 μmoles $m^{-2}$ $s^{-1}$**.

**Exam Tip**
μmoles $m^{-2}$ $s^{-1}$ (micromoles per metre squared per second) is a unit that can be used when measuring light intensity. Don't panic if you see unfamiliar units like this in the exam — just focus on what the axis is showing you, e.g. here it's light intensity.

**Exam Tip**
Graphs showing the compensation point won't always show oxygen generation. If you haven't seen the factors used on the scales of the graph in the exam before, don't panic. Just remember that the compensation point is the point at which photosynthesis and respiration are occurring at the same rate and apply your knowledge to work it out from the graph you've been given.

### Practice Question — Application

Q1 The graph on the right shows the $CO_2$ uptake of a plant over the course of a day in early spring.

a) Give the times when compensation points occur.

b) Suggest and explain why the compensation points occur at these particular times.

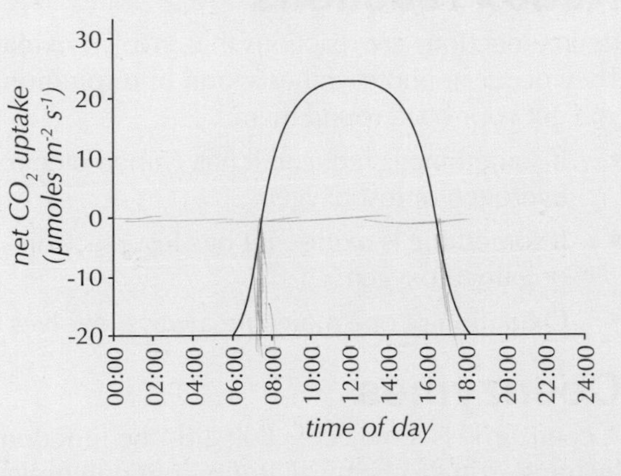

# 2. Photosynthesis and the Light-dependent Reaction

**Learning Objective:**

- Know the light-dependent reaction in such detail as to show that:
  - chlorophyll absorbs light, leading to photoionisation of chlorophyll,
  - some of the energy from electrons released during photoionisation is conserved in the production of ATP and reduced NADP,
  - the production of ATP involves electron transfer associated with the transfer of electrons down the electron transfer chain and passage of protons across chloroplast membranes, and is catalysed by ATP synthase embedded in these membranes (chemiosmotic theory),
  - photolysis of water produces protons, electrons and oxygen.

**Specification Reference 3.5.1**

*In photosynthesis, light energy is used to make glucose. It involves a series of reactions, but before we get stuck into it you need to know a bit of background information...*

## Chloroplasts

Photosynthesis takes place in the chloroplasts of plant cells. Chloroplasts are small, flattened organelles surrounded by a double membrane (see Figure 1). **Thylakoids** (fluid-filled sacs) are stacked up in the chloroplast into structures called **grana** (singular = granum). The grana are linked together by bits of thylakoid membrane called **lamellae** (singular = lamella).

Chloroplasts contain **photosynthetic pigments** (e.g. chlorophyll a, chlorophyll b and carotene). These are coloured substances that absorb the light energy needed for photosynthesis. The pigments are found in the thylakoid membranes — they're attached to proteins. The protein and pigment is called a **photosystem**. There are two photosystems used by plants to capture light energy. Photosystem I (or PSI) absorbs light best at a wavelength of 700 nm and photosystem II (PSII) absorbs light best at 680 nm.

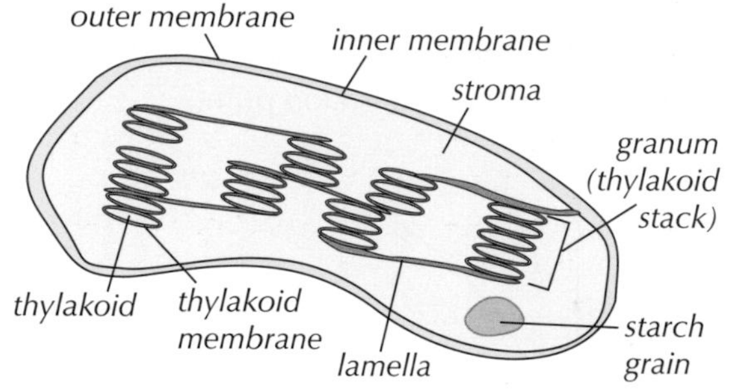


**Figure 1:** *The structure of a chloroplast.*

Contained within the inner membrane of the chloroplast and surrounding the thylakoids is a gel-like substance called the **stroma** — see Figure 1. It contains enzymes, sugars and organic acids. Carbohydrates produced by photosynthesis and not used straight away are stored as starch grains in the stroma.

## Redox reactions

Redox reactions are reactions that involve **oxidation** and **reduction**. They occur in photosynthesis (and in respiration) so it's really important that you get your head round them:

- If something is reduced it has gained electrons ($e^-$), and may have gained hydrogen or lost oxygen.
- If something is oxidised it has lost electrons, and may have lost hydrogen or gained oxygen.
- Oxidation of one molecule always involves reduction of another molecule.

**Tip:** One way to remember electron and hydrogen movement is OILRIG. **O**xidation **I**s **L**oss, **R**eduction **I**s **G**ain.

## Coenzymes

A coenzyme is a molecule that aids the function of an enzyme. They work by transferring a chemical group from one molecule to another. A coenzyme used in photosynthesis is **NADP**. NADP transfers hydrogen from one molecule to another — this means it can reduce (give hydrogen to) or oxidise (take hydrogen from) a molecule.

**Tip:** When hydrogen is transferred between molecules, electrons are transferred too.

# The stages of photosynthesis

There are actually two stages that make up photosynthesis — the light-dependent reaction and the light-independent reaction. The next few pages are all about the light-dependent reaction, but before we get into all that you need to know how the two stages link together.

### 1. The light-dependent reaction

As the name suggests, this reaction needs light energy — see Figure 3. It takes place in the thylakoid membranes of the chloroplasts. Here, light energy is absorbed by chlorophyll (and other photosynthetic pigments) in the photosystems. The light energy excites the electrons in the chlorophyll, giving them more energy, which eventually causes them to be released from the chlorophyll molecule. This process is called **photoionisation**. The chlorophyll molecule is now a positively charged ion.

Some of the energy from the released electrons is used to add a phosphate group to ADP to form ATP, and some is used to reduce NADP to form reduced NADP. ATP transfers energy and reduced NADP transfers hydrogen to the light-independent reaction. During the process, $H_2O$ is oxidised to $O_2$.

### 2. The light-independent reaction (the Calvin cycle)

As the name suggests, this reaction doesn't use light energy directly. (But it does rely on the products of the light-dependent reaction.) It takes place in the stroma of the chloroplast — see Figure 3. Here, the ATP and reduced NADP from the light-dependent reaction supply the energy and hydrogen to make glucose from $CO_2$.

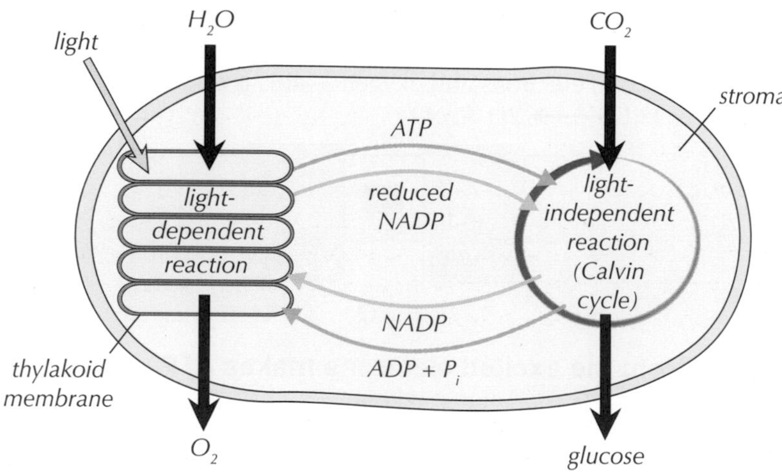


*Figure 3: How the light-dependent and light-independent reactions link together in a chloroplast.*

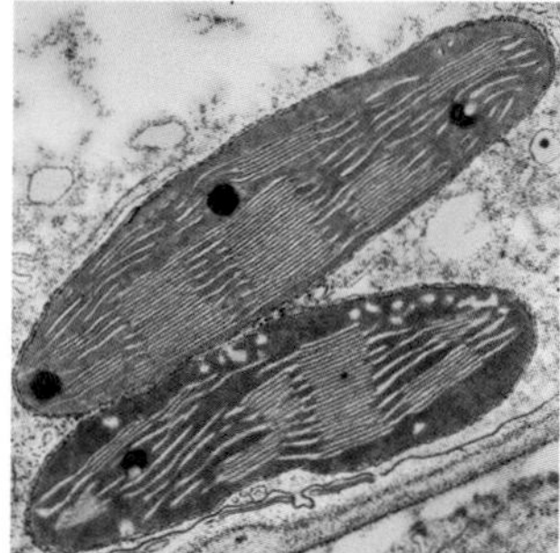

*Figure 2: A cross-sectional image of two chloroplasts.*

**Tip:** Reduced NADP is also written as NADPH — it's NADP that's gained a hydrogen. Remember OILRIG (see previous page) — reduction is gain.

**Tip:** See pages 27-29 for loads more information on the Calvin cycle.

**Tip:** The light-independent reaction can take place in the dark. However, it needs the products of the light-dependent reaction, (ATP and reduced NADP) so in reality it only continues for a little while after it gets dark.

# The light-dependent reaction

In the light-dependent reaction, the energy resulting from the photoionisation of chlorophyll is used for three things:

1. Making ATP from ADP and inorganic phosphate. This is called **photophosphorylation** — it's the process of adding phosphate to a molecule using light.
2. Making reduced NADP from NADP.
3. Splitting water into protons ($H^+$ ions), electrons and oxygen. This is called **photolysis** — it's the splitting (lysis) of a molecule using light (photo) energy.

The light-dependent reaction actually includes two types of photophosphorylation — non-cyclic and cyclic. Each of these processes has different products and is explained on the next couple of pages.

**Tip:** To remind yourself what photosystems are, take a look back at page 22.

**Tip:** Not all of the electron carriers are shown in these diagrams.

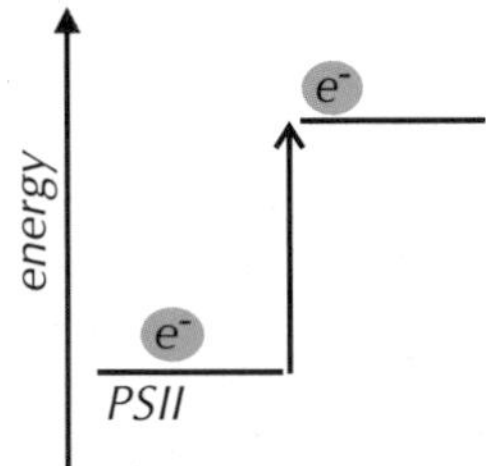


***Figure 4:*** *Light energy excites electrons in PSII, moving them to a higher energy level.*

**Tip:** So the $O_2$ in photosynthesis comes from water and is made in the light-dependent reaction. It diffuses out of the chloroplast and eventually into the atmosphere for us to breathe. Good old plants.

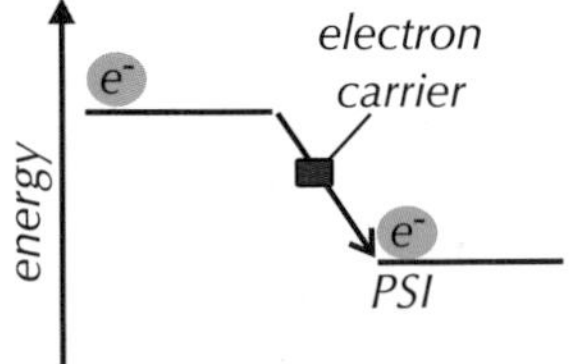


***Figure 5:*** *The excited electrons lose energy as they pass down the electron transport chain.*

## Non-cyclic photophosphorylation

Non-cyclic photophosphorylation produces ATP, reduced NADP and oxygen ($O_2$). To understand the process you need to know that the photosystems (in the thylakoid membranes) are linked by **electron carriers**. Electron carriers are proteins that transfer electrons. The photosystems and electron carriers form an **electron transport chain** — a chain of proteins through which excited electrons flow. There are several processes going on all at once in non-cyclic photophosphorylation — they're shown separately in the diagrams below.

### 1. Light energy excites electrons in chlorophyll

Light energy is absorbed by PSII. The light energy excites electrons in chlorophyll. The electrons move to a higher energy level (i.e. they have more energy — see Figure 4). These high-energy electrons are released from the chlorophyll and move down the electron transport chain to PSI.

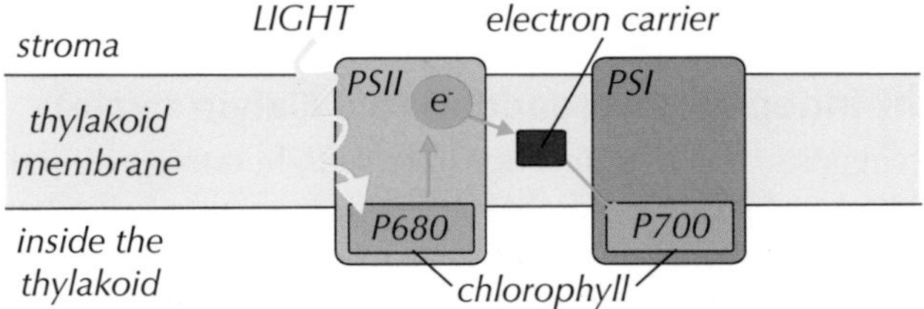


### 2. Photolysis of water produces protons, electrons and oxygen

As the excited electrons from chlorophyll leave PSII to move down the electron transport chain, they must be replaced. Light energy splits water into protons ($H^+$ ions), electrons and oxygen — this is photolysis.
The reaction is: $H_2O \longrightarrow 2H^+ + \frac{1}{2}O_2$

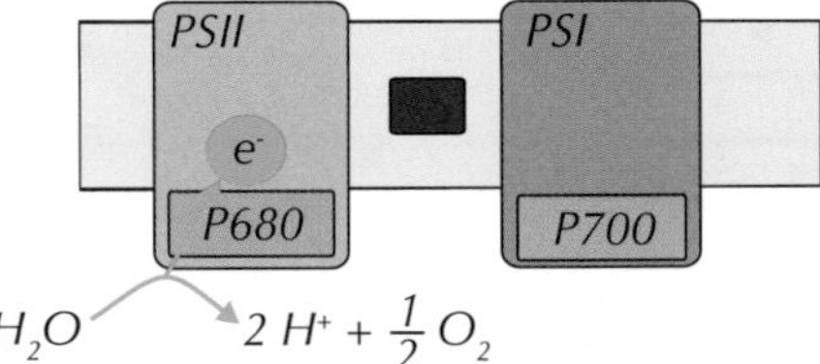


### 3. Energy from the excited electrons makes ATP

The excited electrons lose energy as they move down the electron transport chain (see Figure 5). This energy is used to transport protons ($H^+$ ions) into the thylakoid so that the thylakoid has a higher concentration of protons than the stroma. This forms a proton gradient across the thylakoid membrane. Protons move down their concentration gradient, into the stroma, via the enzyme ATP synthase, which is embedded in the thylakoid membrane. The energy from this movement combines ADP and inorganic phosphate ($P_i$) to form ATP.

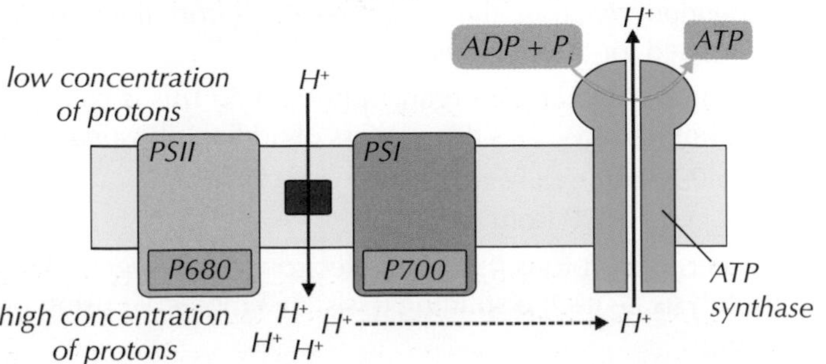

**4. Energy from the excited electrons generates reduced NADP**

Light energy is absorbed by PSI, which excites the electrons again to an even higher energy level. Finally, the electrons are transferred to NADP, along with a proton ($H^+$ ion) from the stroma, to form reduced NADP.

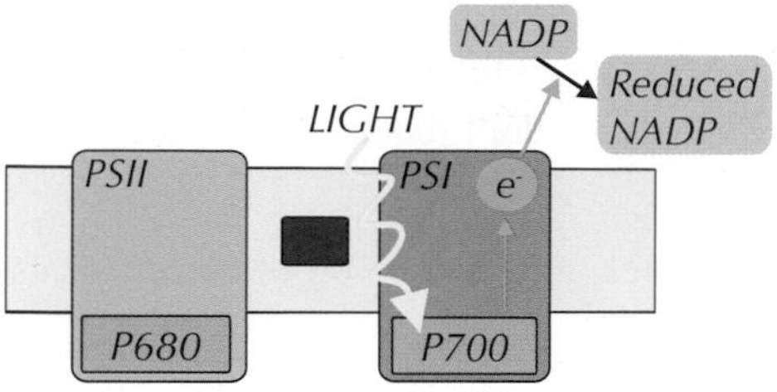


Tip: Remember a 'proton' is just another word for a hydrogen ion ($H^+$).

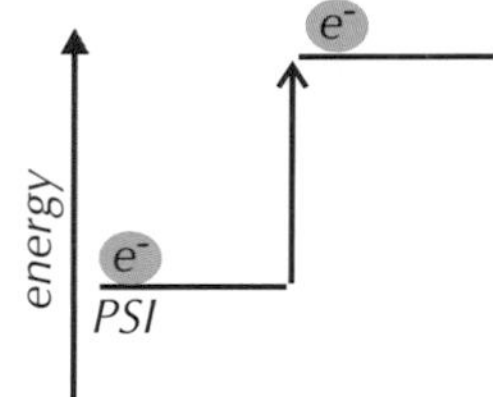


***Figure 6:*** *Light energy excites electrons in PSI to an even higher energy level.*

## Chemiosmotic theory

The process of electrons flowing down the electron transport chain and creating a proton gradient across the membrane to drive ATP synthesis is called chemiosmosis. It's described by the chemiosmotic theory.

**Tip:** The ATP and reduced NADP made here in the light-dependent reaction are really important for use later on in the light-independent reaction (see page 27).

## Cyclic photophosphorylation

Cyclic photophosphorylation produces ATP and only uses PSI. It's called 'cyclic' because the electrons from the chlorophyll molecule aren't passed onto NADP, but are passed back to PSI via electron carriers. This means the electrons are recycled and can repeatedly flow through PSI. This process doesn't produce any reduced NADP or oxygen — it only produces small amounts of ATP.

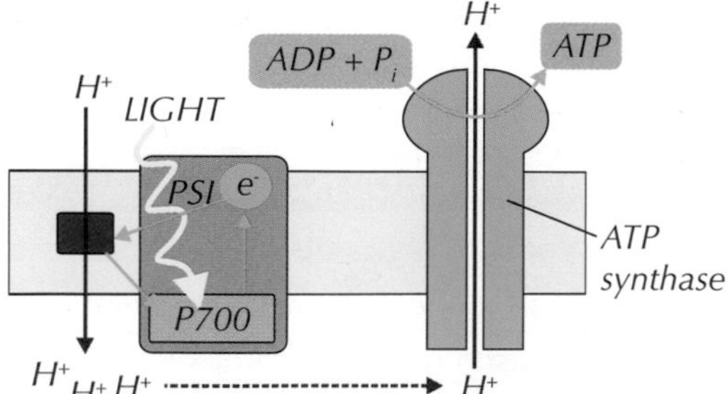


**Tip:** ATP is formed in the same way in cyclic photophosphorylation as in non-cyclic photophosphorylation — by the movement of protons across the thylakoid membrane.

## Practice Questions — Application

Q1 This diagram on the right shows a process in the light-dependent reaction.

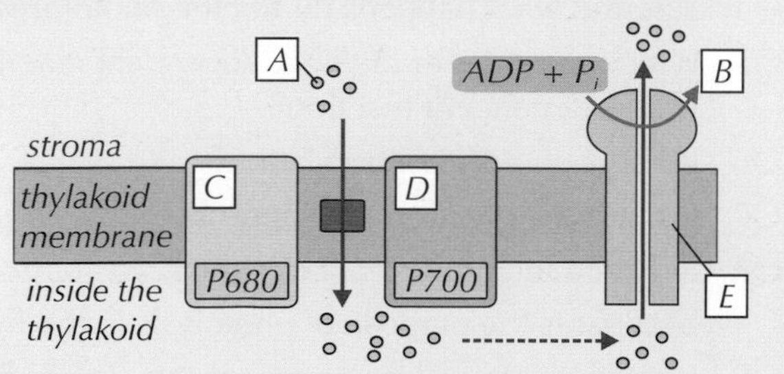


a) The object labelled A in the diagram is transported across the thylakoid membrane, so that its concentration is higher in the thylakoid than in the stroma.

i) What is the name of object A?

ii) Explain why it is important that the concentration of object A is higher inside the thylakoid than in the stroma.

**Tip:** Tempting as it is, you need to be able to answer this question without looking back at the last couple of pages.

**Tip:** Q1 continues on the next page.

b) What is the name of structure C?

c) Which structure, C or D, is involved in cyclic photophosphorylation?

d) What does cyclic photophosphorylation produce?

Q2 The diagram below shows the energy levels of electrons at different stages of the light-dependent reaction of photosynthesis.

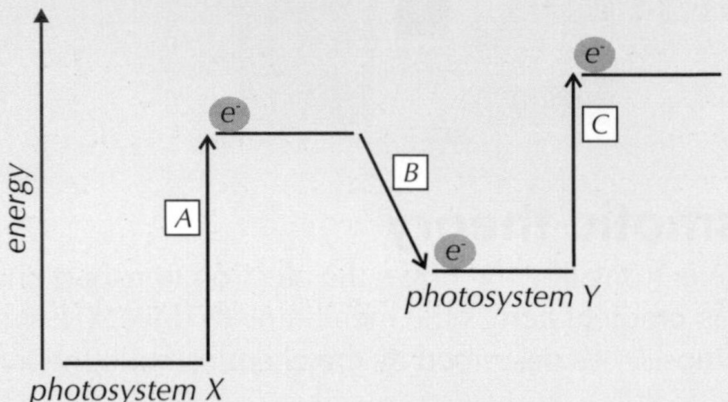


a) What are the correct names of photosystems X and Y?

b) Explain what is happening at stage A on the diagram.

c) Electrons lose energy at stage B in the diagram. What is this energy used for?

d) At point C in the diagram, electrons reach their highest energy level. What happens to the electrons after this point in non-cyclic photophosphorylation?

## Practice Questions — Fact Recall

Q1 a) What are photosynthetic pigments?

b) Give one example of a photosynthetic pigment.

Q2 NADP is a coenzyme used in photosynthesis. What chemical group does it transfer between molecules?

Q3 Where in the chloroplast does the light-dependent reaction take place?

Q4 Describe what happens during the photoionisation of chlorophyll.

Q5 Which products of the light-dependent reaction are needed in the light-independent reaction?

Q6 What is photophosphorylation?

Q7 What is the electron transport chain?

Q8 a) Name the products of the photolysis of water.

b) What is the purpose of photolysis in the light-dependent reaction?

Q9 Excited electrons lose energy as they move down the electron transport chain. Explain how this leads to ATP synthesis.

Q10 Name the products of:

a) non-cyclic photophosphorylation,

b) cyclic photophosphorylation.

**Tip:** Make sure you get your head round what happens in cyclic and non-cyclic phosphorylation (see pages 24-25) — don't get them mixed up.

# 3. Photosynthesis and the Light-independent Reaction

*The light-independent reaction is the second (and final, phew) stage of photosynthesis. It uses the products of the light-dependent reaction (ATP and reduced NADP) to make organic substances for the plant.*

## The Calvin cycle

The light-independent reaction is also called the Calvin cycle. It takes place in the stroma of the chloroplasts. It makes a molecule called **triose phosphate** from carbon dioxide ($CO_2$) and **ribulose bisphosphate** (a 5-carbon compound). Triose phosphate can be used to make glucose and other useful organic substances. There are a few steps in the cycle, and it needs ATP and $H^+$ ions to keep it going. The reactions are linked in a cycle (see Figure 1), which means the starting compound, ribulose bisphosphate, is regenerated.

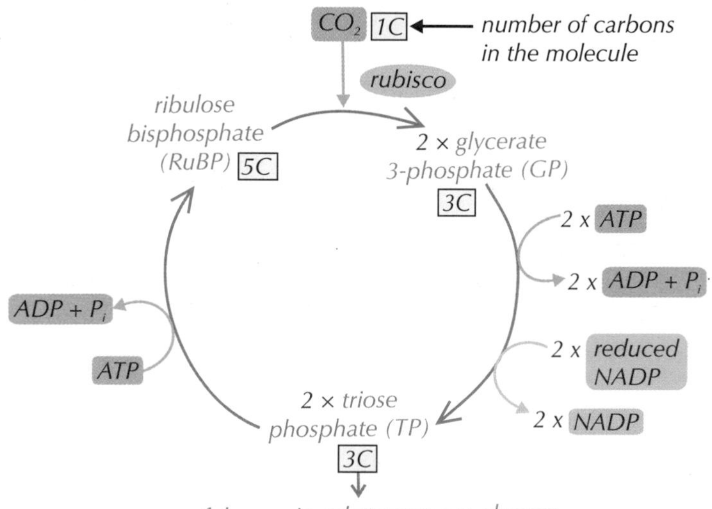


***Figure 1:** One turn of the Calvin cycle.*

Here's what happens at each stage in the cycle:

### 1. Formation of glycerate 3-phosphate

$CO_2$ enters the leaf through the stomata and diffuses into the stroma of the chloroplast. Here, it's combined with ribulose bisphosphate (RuBP). This reaction is catalysed by the enzyme **rubisco**. This gives an unstable 6-carbon compound, which quickly breaks down into two molecules of a 3-carbon compound called **glycerate 3-phosphate** (GP).

### 2. Formation of triose phosphate

The hydrolysis of ATP (from the light-dependent reaction) provides energy to **reduce** the 3-carbon compound, GP, to a different 3-carbon compound called triose phosphate (TP). This reaction also requires $H^+$ ions, which come from reduced NADP (also from the light-dependent reaction). Reduced NADP is recycled to NADP. This is shown in the diagram at the top of the next page. Some triose phosphate is then converted into useful organic compounds (e.g. glucose) and some continues in the Calvin cycle to regenerate RuBP.

**Learning Objectives:**

- Know that the light-independent reaction uses reduced NADP from the light-dependent reaction to form a simple sugar, and that the hydrolysis of ATP, also from the light-dependent reaction, provides the additional energy for this reaction.
- Know the light-independent reaction in such detail to show that:
  - carbon dioxide reacts with ribulose bisphosphate (RuBP) to form two molecules of glycerate 3-phosphate (GP) and that this reaction is catalysed by the enzyme rubisco,
  - ATP and reduced NADP from the light-dependent reaction are used to reduce GP to triose phosphate,
  - some of the triose phosphate is used to regenerate RuBP in the Calvin cycle,
  - some of the triose phosphate is converted to useful organic substances.

**Specification Reference 3.5.1**

**Exam Tip**

Don't panic if you get a diagram of the Calvin cycle in the exam that doesn't look exactly the same as the one above — as long as you remember the key points shown here then you'll be fine.

2 × ATP 2 × ADP + Pi 2 × reduced NADP 2 × NADP

2 × GP (3C) → 2 × TP (3C)

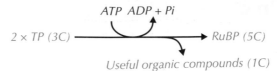

### 3. Regeneration of ribulose bisphosphate

Five out of every six molecules of TP produced in the cycle aren't used to make useful organic compounds, but to regenerate RuBP. Regenerating RuBP uses the rest of the ATP produced by the light-dependent reaction.

ATP ADP + Pi

2 × TP (3C) → RuBP (5C)

Useful organic compounds (1C)

**Tip:** Useful organic compounds have more than one carbon atom, e.g. glucose has six carbon atoms. This means the cycle has to turn more than once to make them — see below.

## Hexose sugars

Hexose sugars are simple 6-carbon sugars, e.g. glucose (see Figure 2). One hexose sugar is made by joining two molecules of triose phosphate (TP) together. Hexose sugars can be used to make larger carbohydrates (see next page).

The Calvin cycle needs to turn six times to make one hexose sugar. The reason for this is that three turns of the cycle produces six molecules of triose phosphate (because two molecules of TP are made for every one $CO_2$ molecule used). Five out of six of these TP molecules are used to regenerate ribulose bisphosphate (RuBP). This means that for three turns of the cycle, only one TP is produced that's used to make a hexose sugar.

A hexose sugar has six carbons though, so two TP molecules are needed to form one hexose sugar. This means the cycle must turn six times to produce two molecules of TP that can be used to make one hexose sugar — see Figure 3. Six turns of the cycle need 18 ATP and 12 reduced NADP from the light-dependent reaction.

This might seem a bit inefficient, but it keeps the cycle going and makes sure there's always enough RuBP ready to combine with $CO_2$ taken in from the atmosphere.

**Tip:** It's really important that RuBP is regenerated. If it wasn't then glycerate 3-phosphate wouldn't be formed, the Calvin cycle would stop and photosynthesis would be unable to continue.

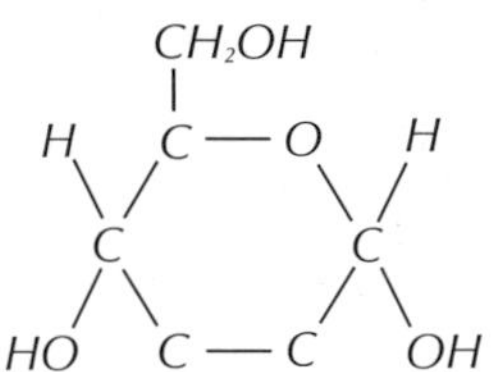


**Figure 2:** *The structure of glucose, a hexose sugar.*

**Exam Tip**
If you're asked in the exam to work out how many turns of the Calvin cycle are needed to produce a certain number of hexose sugars you need to remember that five out of every six TP molecules are used to regenerate RuBP.

6 × $CO_2$
1 × 6 = 6C in total
rubisco
12 × glycerate 3-phosphate (GP)
12 × 3 = 36C in total
12 x ATP
12 x ADP + $P_i$
12 x reduced NADP
12 x NADP
12 × triose phosphate (TP)
12 × 3 = 36C in total
2 × TP 2 × 3 = 6C in total
1 × hexose sugar, e.g. glucose
1 × 6 = 6C in total
10 × TP
10 × 3 = 30C in total
6 × ATP
6 × ADP + $P_i$
6 × ribulose bisphosphate(RuBP)
6 × 5 = 30C in total

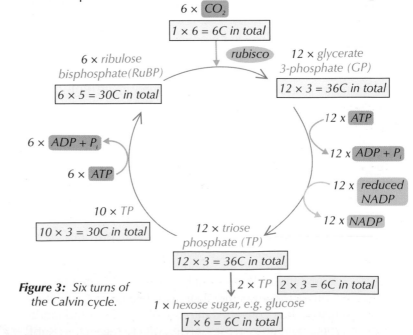

**Figure 3:** *Six turns of the Calvin cycle.*

**Tip:** Six turns of the Calvin cycle produce 12 GP molecules because one turn produces 2 GP, so 6 × 2 = 12 GP.

## Carbohydrates, lipids and proteins

The Calvin cycle is the starting point for making all the organic substances a plant needs. Triose phosphate (TP) and glycerate 3-phosphate (GP) molecules are used to make carbohydrates, lipids and amino acids:

- **Carbohydrates** — hexose sugars are made from two triose phosphate molecules (see the previous page) and larger carbohydrates (e.g. sucrose, starch, cellulose — see Figure 4) are made by joining hexose sugars together in different ways.
- **Lipids** — these are made using glycerol, which is synthesised from triose phosphate, and fatty acids, which are synthesised from glycerate 3-phosphate.
- **Amino acids** — some amino acids are made from glycerate 3-phosphate.

**Tip:** The Calvin cycle is also called carbon fixation, because carbon from $CO_2$ is 'fixed' into an organic molecule.

***Figure 4:*** *Cellulose strands in a plant cell wall made from hexose sugars.*

### Practice Questions — Application

Q1 Rubisco is an enzyme that catalyses the first reaction in the Calvin cycle. Some scientists are trying to genetically modify rubisco to try to increase the speed at which it works. They believe if they can make rubisco work faster then plants will be able to produce organic substances, such as glucose, more quickly. Use your knowledge of photosynthesis to explain how increasing the speed of rubisco could increase the speed of glucose production.

Q2 Phosphoribulokinase is an enzyme involved in the regeneration of ribulose bisphosphate. If this enzyme stopped working properly, suggest what effect it would have on the light-independent reaction of photosynthesis in a plant. Explain your answer.

**Tip:** Rubisco is one of the slowest-working enzymes in the natural world.

**Tip:** The Calvin cycle can be summarised as follows:

*Inputs*
*$CO_2$*
*ATP*
*Reduced NADP*
↓
*Outputs*
*Organic substances*
*RuBP*

### Practice Questions — Fact Recall

Q1 a) What is the name of the 5-carbon compound that combines with carbon dioxide to form an unstable 6-carbon compound in the first reaction of the Calvin cycle?

b) The 6-carbon compound produced only exists fleetingly before it breaks down into two molecules of a 3-carbon compound. What is the name of this 3-carbon compound?

Q2 a) Write out a word equation to show the formation of two molecules of triose phosphate.

b) Is this reaction an oxidation or reduction reaction?

Q3 Describe the role of ATP in the Calvin cycle.

Q4 If six molecules of triose phosphate (TP) are produced by the Calvin cycle, how many of these will be used to regenerate ribulose bisphosphate?

Q5 To make one hexose sugar:

a) How many turns of the Calvin cycle are needed?

b) How many molecules of ATP are needed?

c) How many molecules of reduced NADP are needed?

Q6 Describe how the products of the Calvin cycle are used to make:

a) large carbohydrates b) lipids

# 4. Limiting Factors in Photosynthesis

*Plants have optimum conditions for photosynthesis. If you're a budding gardener then these pages are for you...*

**Learning Objectives:**
- Be able to identify environmental factors that limit the rate of photosynthesis.
- Be able to evaluate data relating to common agricultural practices used to overcome the effect of these limiting factors.

**Specification Reference 3.5.1**

## Optimum conditions for photosynthesis

The ideal conditions for photosynthesis vary from one plant species to another, but the conditions below would be ideal for most plant species in temperate climates like the UK.

### 1. High light intensity of a certain wavelength

Light is needed to provide the energy for the light-dependent reaction — the higher the intensity of the light, the more energy it provides. Only certain wavelengths of light are used for photosynthesis. The photosynthetic pigments chlorophyll a, chlorophyll b and carotene only absorb the red and blue light in sunlight (see Figure 1).

**Tip:** Green light is reflected, which is why plants look green.

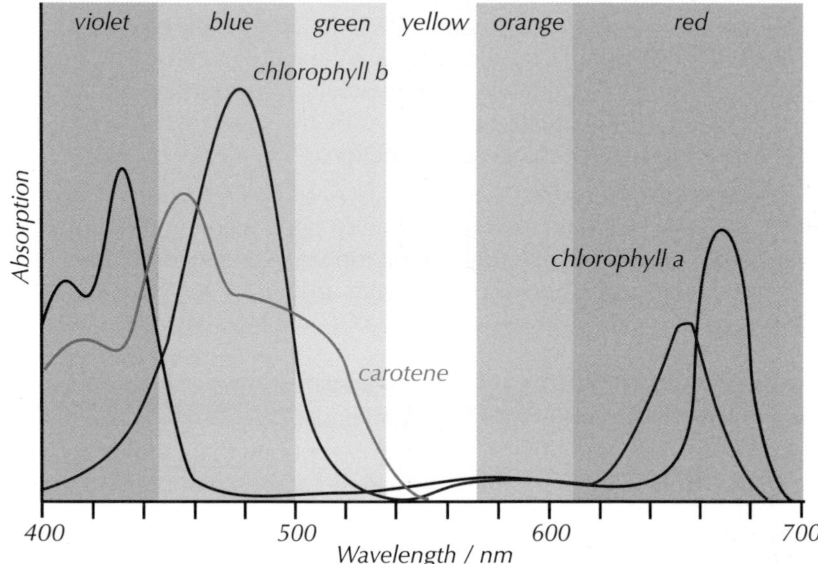


***Figure 1:*** *The wavelengths of light absorbed by chlorophylls a and b, and carotene.*

### 2. Temperature around 25 °C

Photosynthesis involves enzymes (e.g. ATP synthase, rubisco). If the temperature falls below 10 °C the enzymes become inactive, but if the temperature is more than 45 °C they may start to **denature**. Also, at high temperatures stomata close to avoid losing too much water. This causes photosynthesis to slow down because less carbon dioxide enters the leaf when the stomata are closed.

**Tip:** When an enzyme becomes denatured, the bonds holding its tertiary structure together break. It loses its 3D shape so the active site won't fit the substrate. The enzyme can no longer function as a catalyst.

**Tip:** Remember: stomata are pores in the epidermis of a plant that allow gas exchange.

### 3. Carbon dioxide at 0.4%

Carbon dioxide makes up 0.04% of the gases in the atmosphere. Increasing this to 0.4% gives a higher rate of photosynthesis, but any higher and the stomata start to close.

### 4. Water

Plants also need a constant supply of water — too little and photosynthesis has to stop but too much and the soil becomes waterlogged (reducing the uptake of minerals such as magnesium, which is needed to make chlorophyll a).

**Tip:** There's less oxygen in waterlogged soil, so roots are unable to respire aerobically. This means there's less ATP available for the active transport of minerals into roots.

# Limiting factors of photosynthesis

Light, temperature and carbon dioxide can all limit photosynthesis. All three of these things need to be at the right level to allow a plant to photosynthesise as quickly as possible. If any one of these factors is too low or too high, it will limit photosynthesis (slow it down). Even if the other two factors are at the perfect level, it won't make any difference to the speed of photosynthesis as long as that factor is at the wrong level.

**Tip:** A limiting factor is a variable that can slow down the rate of a reaction.

**Examples**

- On a warm, sunny, windless day, it's usually carbon dioxide that's the limiting factor.
- At night it's the light intensity that's the limiting factor.

***Figure 2:*** *As night falls, light intensity begins to limit the rate of photosynthesis.*

However, any of these factors could become the limiting factor, depending on the environmental conditions. The graphs below show the effect of each limiting factor on the rate of photosynthesis:

**Examples**

### Light intensity

Between points A and B, the rate of photosynthesis is limited by the light intensity. So as the light intensity increases, so can the rate of photosynthesis. Point B is the **saturation point** — increasing light intensity after this point makes no difference, because something else has become the limiting factor. The graph now levels off.

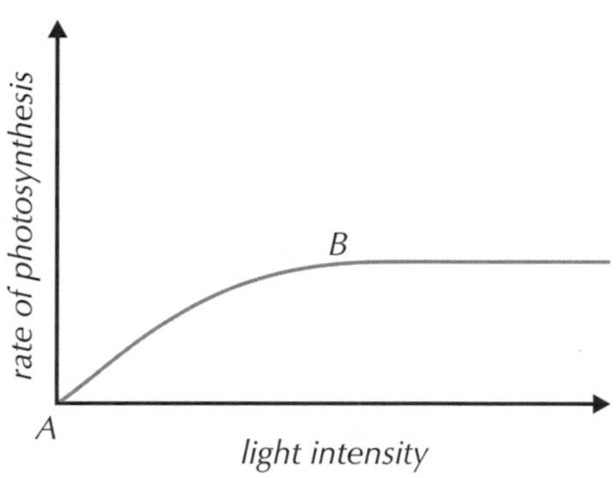


**Tip:** The saturation point is where a factor is no longer limiting the reaction — something else has become the limiting factor.

### Temperature

Both these graphs level off when light intensity is no longer the limiting factor. The graph at 25 °C levels off at a higher point than the one at 15 °C, showing that temperature must have been a limiting factor at 15 °C.

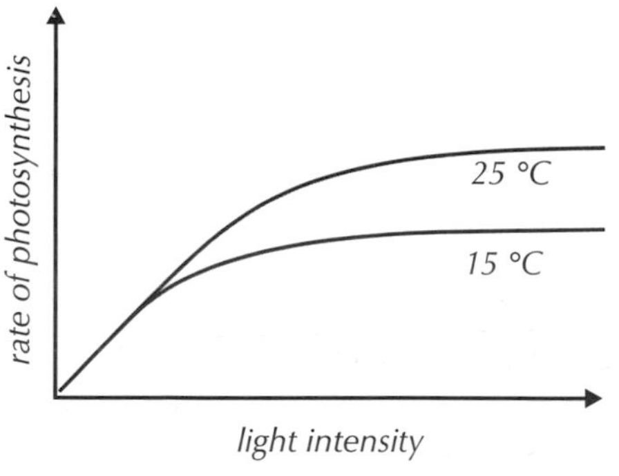


**Tip:** As each of the graphs level off, it doesn't mean that photosynthesis has stopped — it means that the rate of photosynthesis is not increasing anymore.

### Carbon dioxide concentration

Both these graphs level off when light intensity is no longer the limiting factor. The graph at 0.4% carbon dioxide ($CO_2$) levels off at a higher point than the one at 0.04%, so carbon dioxide concentration must have been a limiting factor at 0.04% carbon dioxide. The limiting factor here isn't temperature because it's the same for both graphs (25 °C).

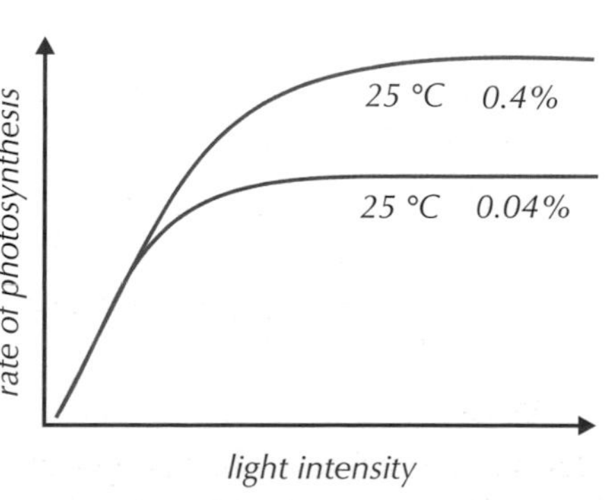

# Increasing plant growth

Agricultural growers (e.g. farmers) know the factors that limit photosynthesis and therefore limit plant growth. This means they try to create an environment where plants get the right amount of everything that they need, which increases growth and so increases yield. Growers create optimum conditions in **glasshouses**, in the following ways:

**Tip:** A greenhouse is the same thing as a glasshouse.

| Limiting Factor | Management in Glasshouse |
|---|---|
| Carbon dioxide concentration | Carbon dioxide is added to the air, e.g. by burning a small amount of propane in a carbon dioxide generator. |
| Light | Light can get in through the glass. Lamps provide light at night time. |
| Temperature | Glasshouses trap heat energy from sunlight, which warms the air. Heaters and cooling systems can also be used to keep a constant optimum temperature, and air circulation systems make sure the temperature is even throughout the glasshouse. |

**Tip:** Similar techniques can also be used in polytunnels (tunnels made of polythene, under which plants can be grown).

***Figure 3:*** *Lamps in greenhouses provide light at night.*

# Interpreting data on limiting factors

You need to be able to interpret data on limiting factors.
Here are some examples of the kind of data you might get in the exam:

**Tip:** Remember the wavelength of light is also important. Agricultural growers will often use red or blue lights to maximise photosynthesis. If they used green light it would be reflected by the plants — see page 30.

**Examples**

### Carbon dioxide

The graph below shows the effect on plant growth of adding carbon dioxide to a greenhouse.

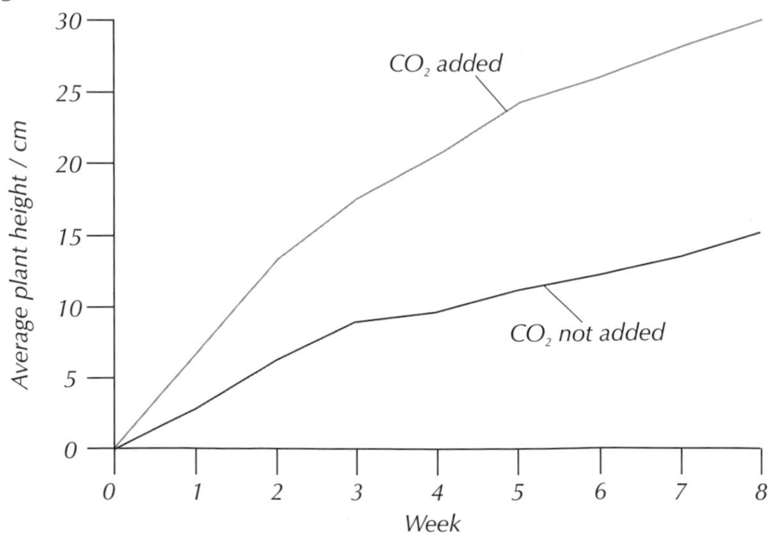


In the greenhouse with added carbon dioxide plant growth was faster (the line is steeper) and on average the plants were larger after 8 weeks than they were in the control greenhouse (30 cm compared to only 15 cm in the greenhouse where no carbon dioxide was added).

This is because the plants use carbon dioxide to produce glucose by photosynthesis. The more carbon dioxide they have, the more glucose they can produce, meaning they can respire more and so have more ATP for DNA replication, cell division and protein synthesis, i.e. growth.

**Tip:** In this study, the negative control was growing plants in a greenhouse where $CO_2$ wasn't added. Using this control would have made sure that no other factors, apart from the level of $CO_2$, were affecting the results. For more information on controls see page 2.

## Light intensity

The graph below shows the effect of light intensity on plant growth, and the effect of two different types of heater:

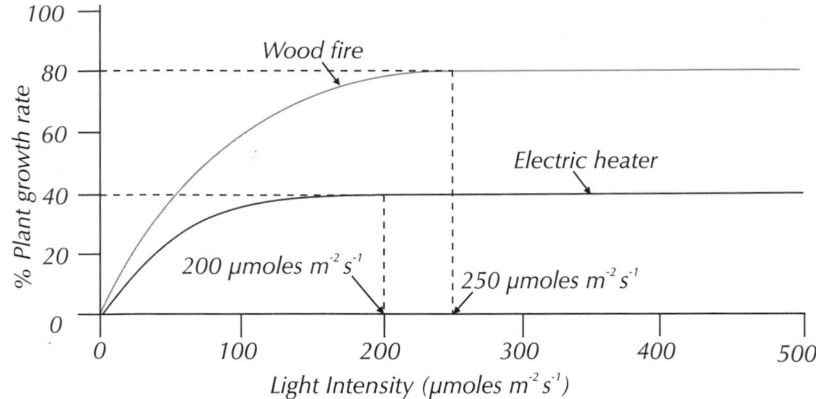


- At the start of the graph, the greater the light intensity the greater the plant growth.
- At 200 μmoles $m^{-2}$ $s^{-1}$ of light the bottom graph flattens out, showing that carbon dioxide concentration or temperature is limiting growth in these plants.
- At 250 μmoles $m^{-2}$ $s^{-1}$ of light the top graph flattens out. The difference between the two graphs could be because the wood fire increases the temperature more than the electric heater or because it's increasing the concentration of carbon dioxide in the air (an electric heater doesn't release carbon dioxide).

**Tip:** If you were conducting this experiment you would have to measure the temperature and the carbon dioxide concentration in each situation to be able to decide which was actually the factor limiting photosynthesis.

## Practice Question — Application

Q1 An agricultural scientist is investigating the effect of irradiance (the amount of light energy hitting a surface) and increasing atmospheric $CO_2$ concentration on the rate of $CO_2$ uptake by a tomato crop. The results are shown in the graph below. The plants were grown in laboratory conditions, in which temperature was kept constant.

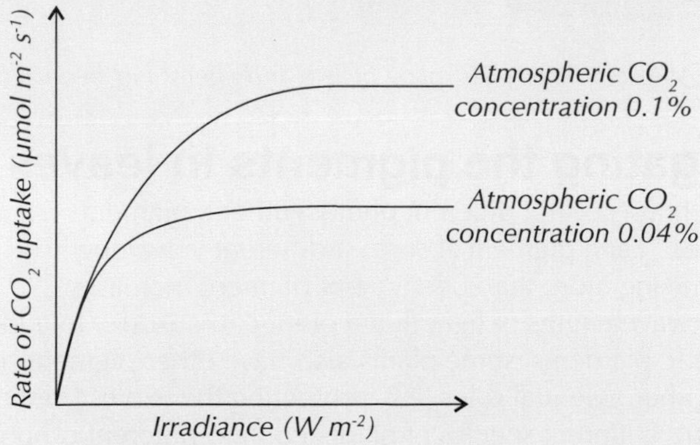


a) Explain why the rate of $CO_2$ uptake initially increases with increasing irradiance.

b) Explain why both lines on the graph eventually level off.

c) The scientist concluded that using a paraffin heater to increase the $CO_2$ in a glasshouse would improve the tomato yield. Evaluate how far the data supports this conclusion.

# 5. Photosynthesis Experiments

*You need to know how to carry out two types of experiment related to different aspects of photosynthesis for your exams.*

**Learning Objectives:**

- Be able to use chromatography to investigate the pigments isolated from leaves of different plants, e.g. leaves from shade-tolerant and shade-intolerant plants or leaves of different colours (Required Practical 7).
- Be able to carry out an investigation into the effect of a named factor on the rate of dehydrogenase activity in extracts of chloroplasts (Required Practical 8).

**Specification Reference 3.5.1**

## Chromatography

Chromatography is used to separate stuff in a mixture — once it's separated out, you can often identify the components. **Paper chromatography** and **thin-layer chromatography** are two types of chromatography.

### How does chromatography work?

All types of chromatography have the same basic set up:

- A **mobile phase** — where the molecules can move. In both paper and thin-layer chromatography, the mobile phase is a liquid solvent.
- A **stationary phase** — where the molecules can't move. In paper chromatography, the stationary phase is a piece of chromatography paper. In thin-layer chromatography, the stationary phase is a thin (0.1-0.3 mm) layer of solid, e.g. silica gel, on a glass or plastic plate (called a TLC plate).

All types of chromatography work using the same basic principle:

- The mobile phase moves through or over the stationary phase.
- The components in the mixture spend different amounts of time in the mobile phase and the stationary phase.
- The components that spend longer in the mobile phase travel faster or further. The time spent in the different phases is what separates out the components of the mixture (see Figure 1).

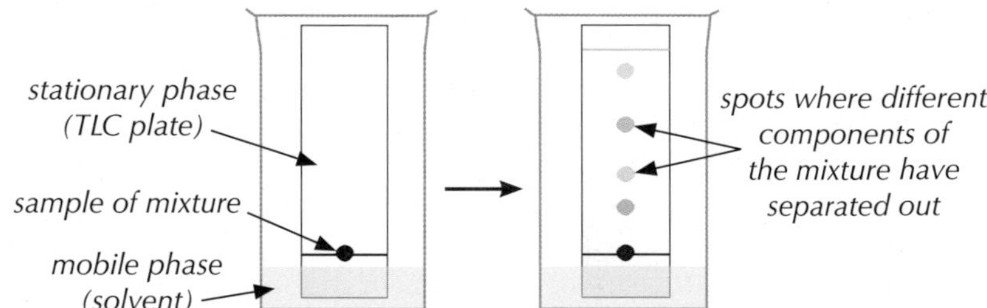


***Figure 1:*** *An example of a TLC plate before and after it has been allowed to run.*

**Tip:** The pattern of spots you end up with is called a chromatogram.

## Investigating the pigments in leaves

REQUIRED PRACTICAL 7

All plants contain several different photosynthetic pigments in their leaves. Each pigment absorbs a different wavelength of light, so having more than one type of pigment increases the range of wavelengths of light that a plant can absorb. In addition to photosynthetic pigments, some plants also have other pigments in their leaves, which play other essential roles, e.g. protecting the leaves from excessive UV radiation. Different species of plants contain different proportions and mixtures of pigments.

A sample of pigments can be extracted from the leaves of a plant and separated using paper or thin-layer chromatography. You can then identify the pigments present in the sample by calculating their **$R_f$ values**. An $R_f$ value is the distance a substance has moved through the stationary phase in relation to the solvent. Each pigment has a specific $R_f$ value, under specific conditions, which can be looked up in a database.

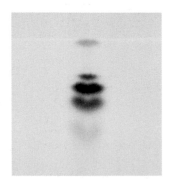

***Figure 2:*** *Plant pigments that have been separated by thin-layer chromatography.*

**Example**

This example shows you how to use TLC to compare the pigments present in shade-tolerant plants (e.g. hostas) and shade-intolerant plants (e.g. chrysanthemums). Make sure you're wearing a lab coat, eye protection and gloves before you start.

1. Grind up several leaves from the shade-tolerant plant you're investigating with some anhydrous sodium sulfate, then add a few drops of propanone.
2. Transfer the liquid to a test tube, add some petroleum ether and gently shake the tube. Two distinct layers will form in the liquid — the top layer is the pigments mixed in with the petroleum ether.
3. Transfer some of the liquid from the top layer into a second test tube with some anhydrous sodium sulfate.
4. Draw a horizontal pencil line near the bottom of a TLC plate. Build up a concentrated spot of the liquid from step 3 on the line by applying several drops, ensuring each one is dry before the next is added. This is the point of origin.
5. Once the plate is completely dry, put the plate into a small glass container with some prepared solvent (e.g. a mixture of propanone, cyclohexane and petroleum ether) — just enough so that the point of origin is a little bit above the solvent. Put a lid on the container and leave the plate to develop. As the solvent spreads up the plate, the different pigments move with it, but at different rates — so they separate.
6. When the solvent has nearly reached the top, take the plate out and mark the solvent front (the furthest point the solvent has reached) with a pencil and leave the plate to dry in a well-ventilated place.
7. There should be several new coloured spots on the chromatography plate between the point of origin and the solvent front. These are the separated pigments. You can calculate their $R_f$ values and look them up in a database to identify what the pigments are. You can calculate the $R_f$ value using this formula:

$$R_f \text{ value} = \frac{B}{A} = \frac{\text{distance travelled by spot}}{\text{distance travelled by solvent}}$$

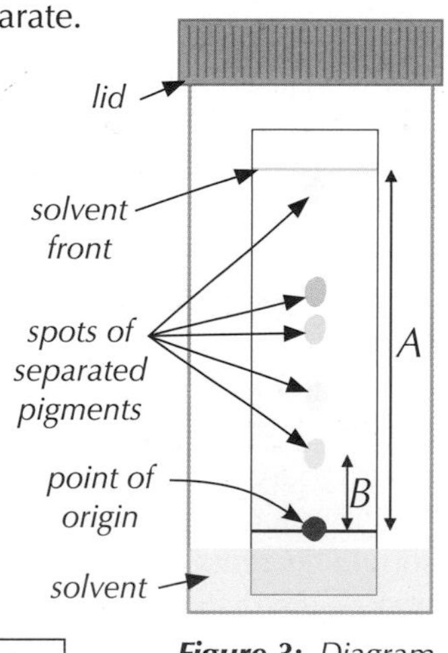

***Figure 3:*** *Diagram showing plant pigments separated by thin layer chromatography.*

8. Repeat the process for the shade-intolerant plant you're investigating and compare the pigments present in their leaves.

You may find that the mixture of pigments in the leaves of the shade-tolerant plant is quite different compared to the shade-intolerant plant. One way that shade-tolerant plants can adapt to the light conditions in their environment is by possessing a different proportion of photosynthetic pigments, which allows the plant to make the best use of the light available to it. The mixture of non-photosynthetic pigments is also likely to be different. For example, the chloroplasts of shade-tolerant plants are adapted for photosynthesis in low light conditions, but really sensitive to higher levels of light. These plants sometimes produce dark red and purple pigments called anthocyanins, which are thought to protect their chloroplasts from brief exposure to higher light levels.

**Tip:** Make sure you carry out a risk assessment before you do this experiment. Be especially aware of the hazards involved with using propanone, petroleum ether and the chromatography solvent, which are toxic and highly flammable.

**Tip:** It's best to do steps 2 and 5 in a fume cupboard as the chemicals used are volatile (evaporate easily) and the vapours are hazardous.

**Tip:** Some plants (including chrysanthemums) can cause allergies in some people. Handle them carefully.

**Tip:** You could use the same technique to investigate the pigments in different coloured leaves. Follow the protocol described here, but change the leaves you use.

**Tip:** $R_f$ values are always between 0 and 1.

**Tip:** The stationary phase and solvent that you use will affect the $R_f$ value. If you're looking up $R_f$ values, you need to check that they were recorded under the same conditions as your experiment.

## Practice Question — Application

Q1 A scientist uses thin-layer chromatography to separate out the photosynthetic pigments from a mixture obtained from plant leaves. The chromatogram that he produces is shown on the right.

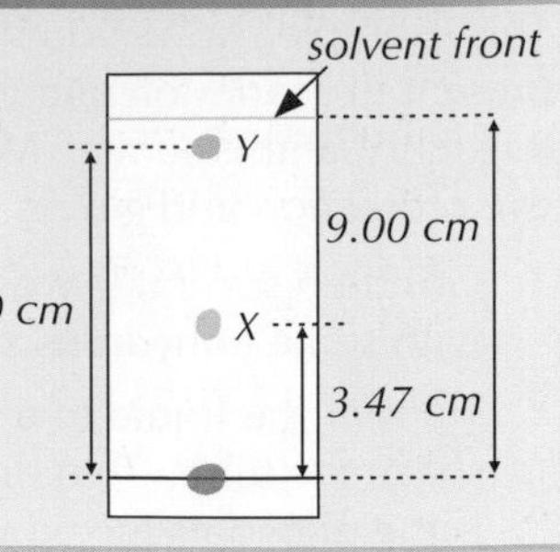


a) Explain why the different pigments separate as they travel up the plate.

b) Calculate the $R_f$ value of spot X.

## Investigating the activity of dehydrogenase in chloroplasts

REQUIRED PRACTICAL 8

In photosystem I, during the light-dependent stage of photosynthesis, NADP acts as an electron acceptor and is reduced (see page 25). The reaction is catalysed by a dehydrogenase enzyme. The activity of this enzyme can be investigated by adding a **redox indicator dye** to extracts of chloroplasts. Like NADP, the dye acts as an electron acceptor and gets reduced by the dehydrogenase in the chloroplasts. As the dye gets reduced, you'll see a colour change. For example, the dye DCPIP changes from blue to colourless when it gets reduced.

You can measure the rate of the dehydrogenase activity by measuring the rate at which DCPIP loses its blue colour. To do this, you need a **colorimeter**. A colorimeter measures how much light a solution absorbs when a light source is shone directly through it. A coloured solution absorbs more light than a colourless solution.

**Tip:** There's more on using a colorimeter on page 123.

### Example

This example shows you how to investigate the effect of light intensity on dehydrogenase activity in extracts of chloroplasts. It uses a bench lamp as a light source and involves placing tubes of chloroplast extract mixed with DCPIP at a range of different distances from the light source. Light intensity should decrease with increasing distance from the lamp. You'll need to choose the distances you're going to investigate (e.g. 15 cm, 30 cm and 45 cm) before you start.

1. Cut a few leaves (spinach works well) into pieces. Remove any tough stalks.
2. Using a pestle and mortar, grind up the leaf pieces with some chilled isolation solution (a solution of sucrose, potassium chloride and phosphate buffer at pH 7). Filter the liquid you make into a beaker through a funnel lined with muslin cloth.
3. Transfer the liquid to centrifuge tubes and centrifuge them at high speed for 10 minutes. This will make the chloroplasts gather at the bottom of each tube in a 'pellet' (see Figure 5).
4. Get rid of the liquid from the top of the tubes, leaving the pellets in the bottom.

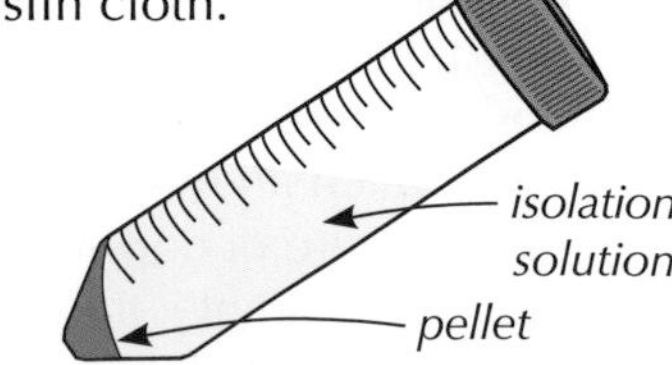


*Figure 5: Diagram showing a pellet of chloroplasts after centrifugation of a leaf extract.*

**Tip:** Make sure you're aware of all the hazards involved in this experiment, and any safety precautions you need to take to minimise them, before you start.

**Tip:** A centrifuge is a machine that spins samples really quickly. The resulting force separates out the components of your sample. Always make sure your centrifuge is balanced by placing tubes of equal weight opposite each other in the rotor.

5. Re-suspend the pellets in fresh, chilled isolation solution. This is your chloroplast extract. Store it on ice for the rest of the experiment.
6. Set up a colorimeter with a red filter and zero it using a cuvette (a cuboid-shaped vessel used in colorimeters) containing the chloroplast extract and distilled water.
7. Set up a test tube rack at a set distance from a bench lamp. Switch the lamp on.
8. Put a test tube in the rack, add a set volume of chloroplast extract to the tube and a set volume of DCPIP. Mix the contents of the tube together.
9. Immediately take a sample of the mixture from the tube and add it to a clean cuvette. Then place the cuvette in your colorimeter and record the absorbance. Do this every 2 minutes for the next ten minutes.
10. Repeat steps 7 to 9 for each distance under investigation.
11. You should also check whether the absorbance changes at each distance in two negative control tubes. The first should contain only DCPIP and chilled isolation solution (no chloroplast extract). The second should contain both DCPIP and chloroplast extract, but it should be wrapped in tin foil (so no light reaches the contents of the tube). No change in absorbance should be seen for these two controls.

If dehydrogenase activity is taking place, the absorbance will decrease as the DCPIP gets reduced and loses its blue colour. The faster the absorbance decreases, the faster the rate of dehydrogenase activity.

You can plot a graph of absorbance against time for each distance from the light source. Then compare your results to determine how light intensity affects the rate of the dehydrogenase enzyme.

**Tip:** You can use a similar method to investigate the effects of other factors on dehydrogenase activity in chloroplasts, e.g. temperature and photosynthetic inhibitors.

**Tip:** The first negative control tube should show that the chloroplast extract is needed to make DCPIP change colour. The second negative control tube should show that light is needed to make DCPIP change colour.

**Tip:** Ideally, you'd repeat the experiment at each distance at least three times and plot the mean absorbance at each 2 minute interval. Alternatively, if your classmates are doing exactly the same experiment as you, you might be able to pool your results to obtain repeat readings.

## Practice Questions — Fact Recall

Q1 Explain how chromatography can be used to separate the components in a mixture.

Q2 Explain how DCPIP acts as a redox indicator dye.

Q3 Describe how you could prepare an extract of chloroplasts from spinach leaves in order to investigate dehydrogenase activity.

**Learning Objectives:**

- Know that respiration produces ATP.
- Know that respiratory substrates other than glucose include the breakdown products of lipids and amino acids, which enter the Krebs cycle.
- Know that glycolysis is the first stage of anaerobic and aerobic respiration. It occurs in the cytoplasm and is an anaerobic process. It involves the following stages:
  - phosphorylation of glucose to glucose phosphate, using ATP,
  - production of triose phosphate,
  - oxidation of triose phosphate to pyruvate with a net gain of ATP and reduced NAD.
- Know that if respiration is aerobic, pyruvate from glycolysis enters the mitochondrial matrix by active transport.
- Know that if respiration is only anaerobic, pyruvate can be converted to ethanol or lactate using reduced NAD. The oxidised NAD produced in this way can be used in further glycolysis.

**Specification Reference 3.5.2**

# 6. Aerobic and Anaerobic Respiration

*Respiration is the process that allows cells to produce ATP from glucose.*

## Aerobic vs anaerobic respiration

Respiration can be done aerobically (with oxygen) or anaerobically (without oxygen). Both types of respiration produce ATP, but anaerobic respiration produces less. Both also start with the process of **glycolysis**. The stages after glycolysis differ.

## Mitochondria

The reactions in aerobic respiration take place in the mitochondria. You covered mitochondrial structure in Topic 2, but you might want to refresh your memory of it before you start this section — see Figure 1. The folds (cristae) in the inner membrane of the mitochondrion provide a large surface area to maximise respiration.

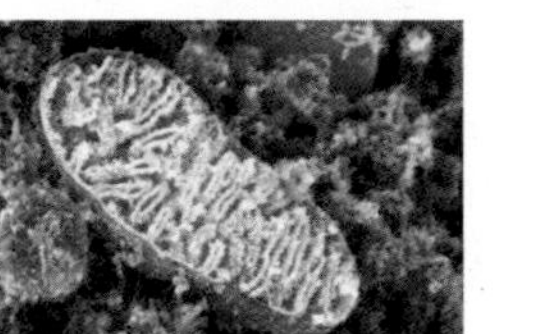

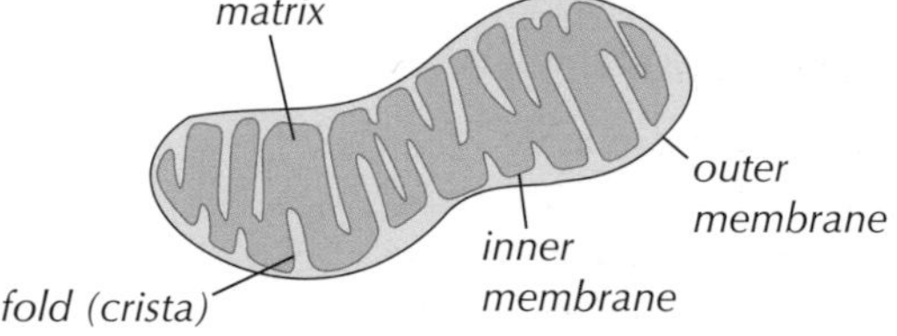


***Figure 1:*** *A mitochondrion in a nerve cell (left) and mitochondrial structure (right).*

## Coenzymes

As you saw in photosynthesis, a coenzyme is a molecule that aids the function of an enzyme by transferring a chemical group from one molecule to another. Coenzymes used in respiration include **NAD**, **coenzyme A** and **FAD**. NAD and FAD transfer hydrogen from one molecule to another. This means they can reduce (give hydrogen to) or oxidise (take hydrogen from) a molecule. Coenzyme A transfers acetate between molecules (see page 41).

## Aerobic respiration

There are four stages in aerobic respiration:

1. Glycolysis.
2. The link reaction.
3. The Krebs cycle.
4. Oxidative phosphorylation.

The first three stages are a series of reactions. The products from these reactions are used in the final stage to produce loads of ATP. The first stage happens in the cytoplasm of cells and the other three stages take place in the mitochondria. There's more about the final three stages of aerobic respiration on pages 41-43.

Glucose can be used as a respiratory substrate in both aerobic and anaerobic respiration. However, glucose isn't the only respiratory substrate that can be used in aerobic respiration. Some products resulting from the breakdown of other molecules, such as fatty acids from lipids and amino acids from proteins, can be converted into molecules that are able to enter the Krebs cycle (usually acetyl CoA — see page 41).

**Anaerobic respiration** doesn't involve the link reaction, the Krebs cycle or oxidative phosphorylation. The products of glycolysis are converted to ethanol or lactate instead (see next page).

## Glycolysis

Glycolysis makes **pyruvate** from glucose. Glycolysis involves splitting one molecule of glucose (with 6 carbons — 6C) into two smaller molecules of pyruvate (3C). The process happens in the cytoplasm of cells. Glycolysis is the first stage of both aerobic and anaerobic respiration and doesn't need oxygen to take place — so it's an anaerobic process.

## Stages in glycolysis

There are two stages in glycolysis — phosphorylation and oxidation. First, ATP is used to phosphorylate glucose to triose phosphate. Phosphorylation is the process of adding phosphate to a molecule. Then triose phosphate is oxidised, releasing ATP. Overall there's a net gain of 2 ATP and 2 reduced NAD.

### 1. Phosphorylation

Glucose is phosphorylated using a phosphate from a molecule of ATP. This creates 1 molecule of **glucose phosphate** and 1 molecule of ADP.

ATP is then used to add another phosphate, forming hexose bisphosphate.

Hexose bisphosphate is then split into 2 molecules of **triose phosphate**.

### 2. Oxidation

Triose phosphate is oxidised (loses hydrogen), forming 2 molecules of **pyruvate**. NAD collects the hydrogen ions, forming 2 **reduced NAD**. 4 ATP are produced, but 2 were used up in stage one, so there's a net gain of 2 ATP.

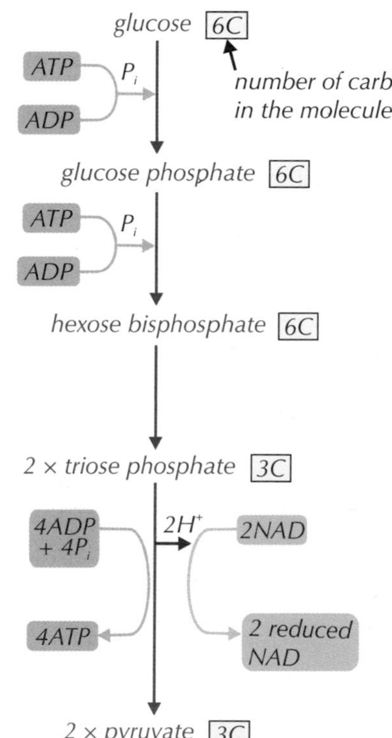


**Exam Tip**
The important thing to remember here for your exams is that 1 molecule of glucose gets phosphorylated using 1 molecule of ATP to produce 1 molecule of glucose phosphate.

**Tip:** Remember the first part of OILRIG, (page 22) — oxidation is loss, so when triose phosphate is oxidised it loses hydrogen.

## The products of glycolysis — aerobic respiration

Here's what happens to all the products of glycolysis in aerobic respiration.

| Products from glycolysis | Where it goes |
|---|---|
| 2 reduced NAD | To oxidative phosphorylation |
| 2 pyruvate | Actively transported into the mitochondrial matrix for use in the link reaction |
| 2 ATP (net gain) | Used for energy |

**Tip:** Glycolysis takes place in the cytoplasm of cells because glucose can't cross the outer mitochondrial membrane. Pyruvate can cross this membrane, so the rest of the reactions in aerobic respiration occur within the mitochondria.

## The products of glycolysis — anaerobic respiration

In anaerobic respiration, the pyruvate produced in glycolysis is converted into ethanol (alcoholic fermentation) or lactate (lactate fermentation) using reduced NAD.

**Tip:** Glycolysis only produces 2 ATP, so anaerobic respiration only produces 2 ATP. Aerobic respiration has further stages (see pages 41-43), so produces more ATP.

### Alcoholic fermentation

This occurs in plants and yeast.

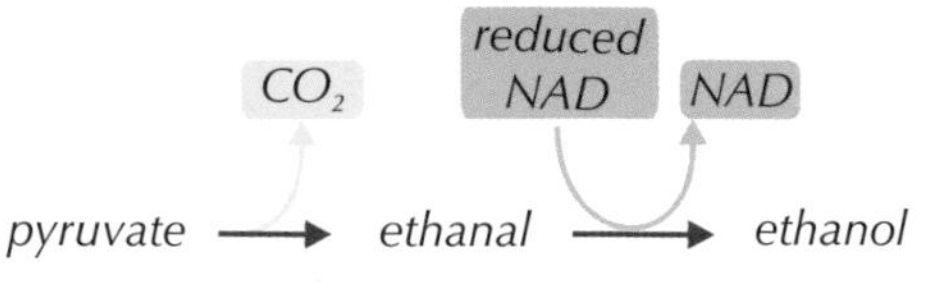


### Lactate fermentation

This occurs in animal cells and some bacteria.

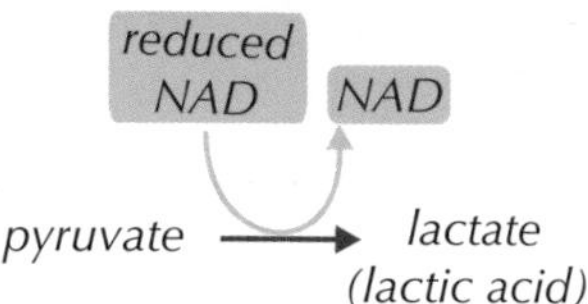


The production of lactate or ethanol regenerates oxidised NAD. This means glycolysis can continue even when there isn't much oxygen around, so a small amount of ATP can still be produced to keep some biological process going... clever.

### Practice Questions — Application

Q1 Hexokinase is an enzyme that catalyses the production of glucose phosphate.

a) Suggest and explain how hexokinase is involved in glycolysis.

b) Suggest a benefit of hexokinase being inhibited by the product of this reaction.

Q2 The diagram below shows two possible fates of glucose in anaerobic conditions.

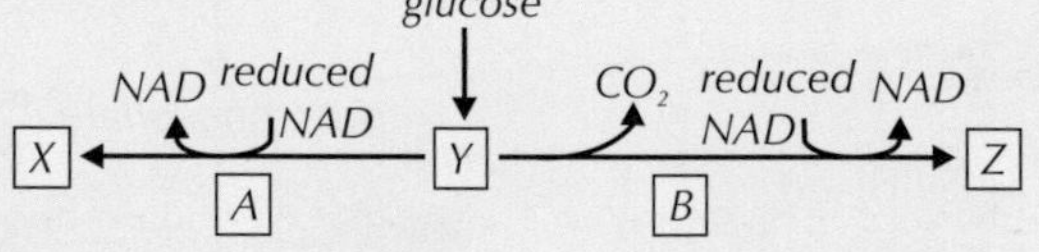


a) What is the name of substance:

i) X? ii) Y? iii) Z?

b) Which process, A or B:

i) is lactate fermentation? ii) happens in plant cells?

iii) can happen in bacterial cells?

### Practice Questions — Fact Recall

Q1 What is ATP used for in glycolysis?

Q2 What role does the coenzyme NAD play in glycolysis?

Q3 If five molecules of glucose enter the process of glycolysis, how many molecules of pyruvate will be produced?

Q4 During fermentation, reduced NAD is oxidised to NAD. What happens to this oxidised NAD?

Q5 What is the final product of anaerobic respiration by animal cells?

# 7. Aerobic Respiration — The Mitochondrial Reactions

*Aerobic respiration starts in the cytoplasm with glycolysis. The rest of aerobic respiration, starting with the link reaction, takes place in the mitochondria.*

## The link reaction

The link reaction converts the pyruvate produced in glycolysis (see page 39) to acetyl coenzyme A. Pyruvate is **decarboxylated**, so one carbon atom is removed from pyruvate in the form of carbon dioxide. At the same time, pyruvate is **oxidised** to form acetate and NAD is reduced to form reduced NAD. Acetate is then combined with coenzyme A (CoA) to form acetyl coenzyme A (acetyl CoA). No ATP is produced in this reaction.

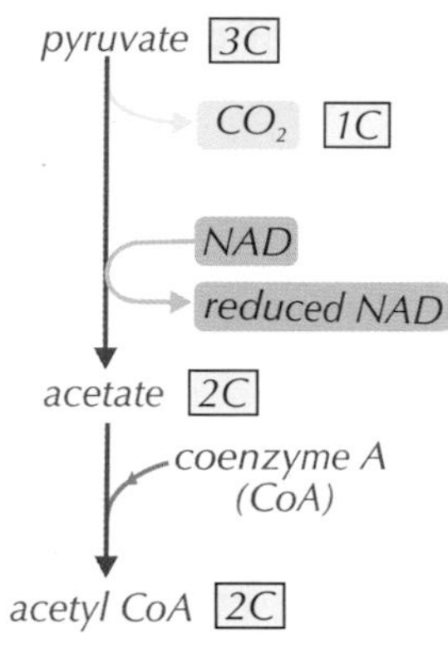


### How many times does the link reaction occur per glucose molecule?

Two pyruvate molecules are made for every glucose molecule that enters glycolysis. This means the link reaction and the third stage (the Krebs cycle) happen twice for every glucose molecule.

### The products of the link reaction

Here's what happens to the products of two link reactions (i.e. for one glucose molecule):

| Products from two link reactions | Where it goes |
|---|---|
| 2 acetyl coenzyme A | To the Krebs cycle |
| 2 carbon dioxide | Released as a waste product |
| 2 reduced NAD | To oxidative phosphorylation |

## The Krebs cycle

The Krebs cycle produces reduced coenzymes and ATP. It involves a series of oxidation-reduction reactions, which take place in the matrix of the mitochondria. The cycle happens once for every pyruvate molecule.

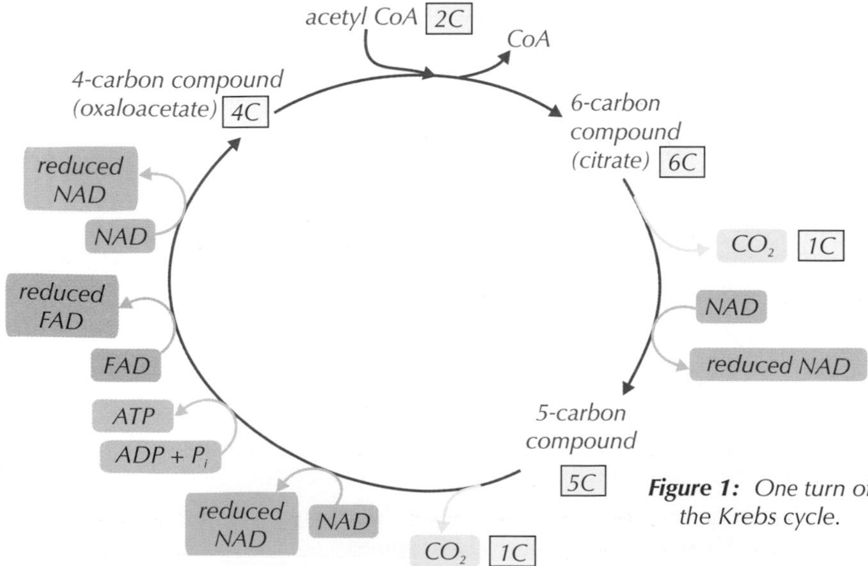


**Figure 1:** *One turn of the Krebs cycle.*

**Learning Objectives:**

- Understand aerobic respiration in such detail as to show that:
  - pyruvate is oxidised to acetate, producing reduced NAD in the process,
  - acetate combines with coenzyme A in the link reaction to produce acetylcoenzyme A,
  - acetylcoenzyme A reacts with a four-carbon molecule, releasing coenzyme A and producing a six-carbon molecule that enters the Krebs cycle,
  - in a series of oxidation-reduction reactions, the Krebs cycle generates reduced coenzymes and ATP by substrate-level phosphorylation, and carbon dioxide is lost,
  - synthesis of ATP by oxidative phosphorylation is associated with the transfer of electrons down the electron transfer chain and passage of protons across inner mitochondrial membranes and is catalysed by ATP synthase embedded in these membranes (chemiosmotic theory).

**Specification Reference 3.5.2**

**Tip:** In respiration carbon dioxide is produced in the link reaction and the Krebs cycle.

Here's what happens at each stage in the Krebs cycle:

### 1. Formation of a 6-carbon compound

Acetyl CoA from the link reaction combines with a four-carbon molecule (oxaloacetate) to form a six-carbon molecule (citrate). Coenzyme A goes back to the link reaction to be used again.

**Tip:** Coenzyme A transfers acetate between molecules (see page 38 for a reminder on coenzymes in respiration).

### 2. Formation of a 5-carbon compound

The six-carbon citrate molecule is converted to a five-carbon molecule. **Decarboxylation** occurs, where carbon dioxide is removed. **Dehydrogenation** also occurs. The hydrogen is used to produce reduced NAD from NAD.

citrate (6C) → ($CO_2$; NAD → reduced NAD) → 5-carbon compound

**Tip:** Dehydrogenation is the removal of hydrogen from a molecule.

### 3. Regeneration of oxaloacetate

The five-carbon molecule is then converted to a four-carbon molecule. (There are some intermediate compounds formed during this conversion, but you don't need to know about them.) Decarboxylation and dehydrogenation occur, producing one molecule of reduced FAD and two of reduced NAD. ATP is produced by the direct transfer of a phosphate group from an intermediate compound to ADP. When a phosphate group is directly transferred from one molecule to another it's called **substrate-level phosphorylation**. Citrate has now been converted into oxaloacetate.

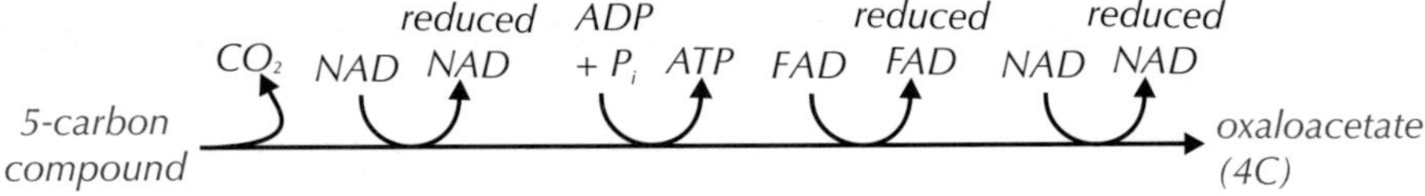


**Tip:** Reduced NAD and reduced FAD may also be written as NADH and $FADH_2$. Don't worry, they still mean the same thing.

### The products of the Krebs cycle

Some products of the Krebs cycle are reused, some are released and others are used for the next stage of respiration — oxidative phosphorylation.

| Product from one Krebs cycle | Where it goes |
|---|---|
| 1 coenzyme A | Reused in the next link reaction |
| Oxaloacetate | Regenerated for use in the next Krebs cycle |
| 2 carbon dioixde | Released as a waste product |
| 1 ATP | Used for energy |
| 3 reduced NAD | To oxidative phosphorylation |
| 1 reduced FAD | To oxidative phosphorylation |

**Tip:** The table only shows the products of one turn of the Krebs cycle. The cycle turns twice for one glucose molecule, so one glucose molecule produces twice as much as what's shown in the table.

## Practice Questions — Application

Q1 The diagram below shows part of the Krebs cycle:

*acetyl CoA + oxaloacetate → citrate → 5C-intermediate*

a) How many carbon atoms do oxaloacetate and citrate each have?

b) What happens to turn the 5C-intermediate back into oxaloacetate?

Q2 If six molecules of glucose were respired, how many molecules of $CO_2$ would be produced from the Krebs cycle?

Q3 Fats can be broken down and converted into acetyl coenzyme A. Explain how this allows fats to be respired.

**Tip:** Remember that the Krebs cycle is just that... a cycle — some of its products need to be recycled for the process to continue.

# Oxidative phosphorylation

Oxidative phosphorylation is the process where the energy carried by electrons, from reduced coenzymes (reduced NAD and reduced FAD), is used to make ATP. (The whole point of the previous stages is to make reduced NAD and reduced FAD for the final stage.) Oxidative phosphorylation involves the **electron transport chain** and **chemiosmosis** (see below).

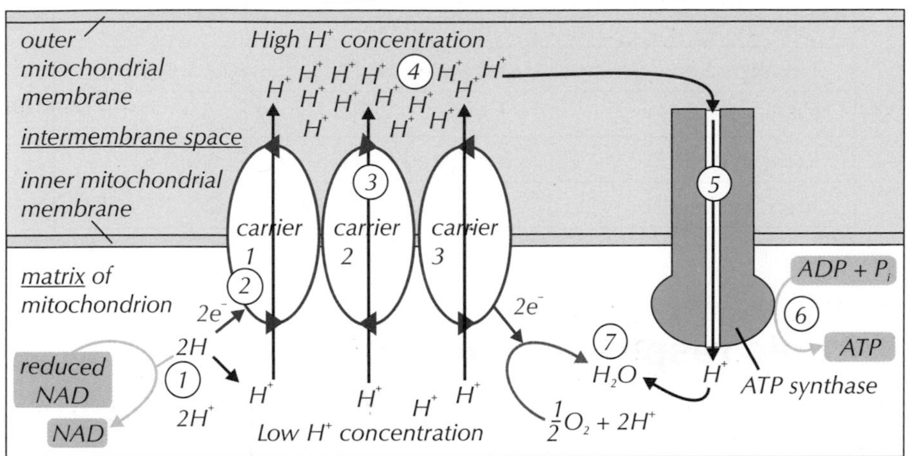


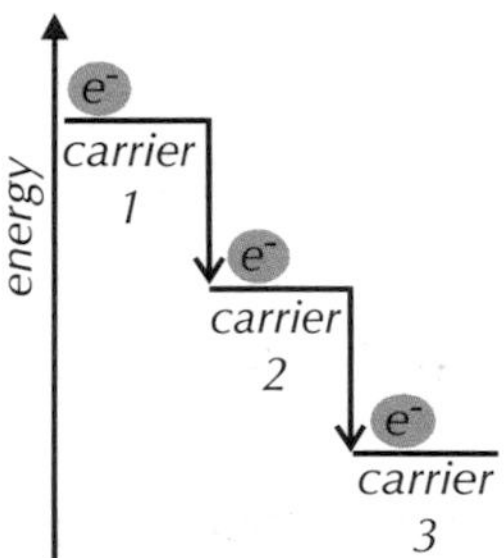


*Figure 2: As electrons move down the electron transport chain, they lose energy.*

**Tip:** The regenerated coenzymes from the electron transport chain are reused in the Krebs cycle.

The numbers of the steps below correspond to the circled numbers in the diagram above.

1. Hydrogen atoms are released from reduced NAD and reduced FAD as they're oxidised to NAD and FAD. The hydrogen atoms split into protons ($H^+$) and electrons ($e^-$).
2. The electrons move down the electron transport chain (made up of electron carriers), losing energy at each carrier (see Figure 2).
3. This energy is used by the electron carriers to pump protons from the mitochondrial matrix into the intermembrane space (the space between the inner and outer mitochondrial membranes).
4. The concentration of protons is now higher in the intermembrane space than in the mitochondrial matrix — this forms an electrochemical gradient (a concentration gradient of ions).
5. Protons then move down the electrochemical gradient, back across the inner mitochondrial membrane and into the mitochondrial matrix, via ATP synthase (which is embedded in the inner mitochondrial membrane). This movement drives the synthesis of ATP from ADP and inorganic phosphate ($P_i$).
6. This process of ATP production driven by the movement of $H^+$ ions across a membrane (due to electrons moving down an electron transport chain) is called chemiosmosis (which is described by the chemiosmotic theory).
7. In the mitochondrial matrix, at the end of the transport chain, the protons, electrons and oxygen (from the blood) combine to form water. Oxygen is said to be the **final electron acceptor**.

**Tip:** The job of a carrier is to transfer electrons. When a carrier receives electrons it's reduced and when it passes on electrons it becomes oxidised again.

**Exam Tip**
Don't write that protons move into or out of the inner mitochondrial membrane — they move across it.

# Aerobic respiration and ATP

As you know, oxidative phosphorylation makes ATP using energy from the reduced coenzymes — 2.5 ATP are made from each reduced NAD and 1.5 ATP are made from each reduced FAD.

**Tip:** The number of ATP produced per reduced NAD or reduced FAD was thought to be 3 and 2, but newer research has shown that the figures are nearer 2.5 and 1.5.

**Tip:** For each molecule of glucose, 28 molecules of ATP are produced by oxidative phosphorylation (i.e. that's the ATP made from reduced NAD and reduced FAD).

The table below shows that a cell can make 32 ATP from 1 molecule of glucose in aerobic respiration. (Remember, 1 molecule of glucose produces 2 pyruvate, so the link reaction and Krebs cycle happen twice.)

| Stage of respiration | Molecules produced | Number of ATP molecules |
|---|---|---|
| Glycolysis | 2 ATP | **2** |
| Glycolysis | 2 reduced NAD | 2 × 2.5 = **5** |
| Link Reaction (×2) | 2 reduced NAD | 2 × 2.5 = **5** |
| Krebs cycle (×2) | 2 ATP | **2** |
| Krebs cycle (×2) | 6 reduced NAD | 6 × 2.5 = **15** |
| Krebs cycle (×2) | 2 reduced FAD | 2 × 1.5 = **3** |
| | | Total ATP = **32** |

## Aerobic respiration summary

Glycolysis, the link reaction and the Krebs cycle are basically a series of reactions which produce ATP, reduced NAD, reduced FAD and $CO_2$. The reduced coenzymes (NAD and FAD) are then used in oxidative phosphorylation, to produce loads more ATP. The overall process is shown below:

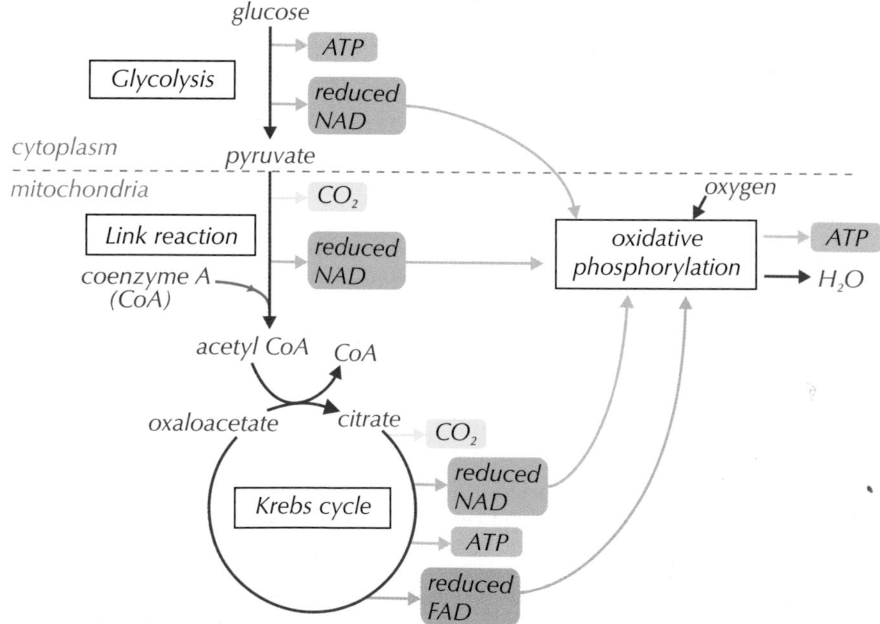


**Tip:** Don't forget oxygen's role in respiration. It's the final electron acceptor in the electron transport chain in oxidative phosphorylation (see previous page).

**Tip:** Remember that the whole purpose of respiration is to produce ATP to fuel biological processes. That's why it's happening continuously in plant and animal cells.

## Mitochondrial diseases

ATP production can be affected by **mitochondrial diseases**. Mitochondrial diseases affect the functioning of mitochondria. They can affect how proteins involved in oxidative phosphorylation or the Krebs cycle function, reducing ATP production. This may cause anaerobic respiration to increase, to try and make up some of the ATP shortage. This results in lots of lactate being produced, which can cause muscle fatigue and weakness. Some lactate will also diffuse into the bloodstream, leading to high lactate concentrations in the blood.

## Practice Questions — Application

Q1 Antimycin A inhibits carrier 2 in the electron transport chain of oxidative phosphorylation.

a) If antimycin A was added to isolated mitochondria, what state (oxidised or reduced) would carriers 1 and 3 be in after its addition? Explain your answers.

b) Suggest why antimycin A can be used as a fish poison.

Q2 Dicyclohexylcarbodiimide (DCC) is an inhibitor that binds to ATP synthase and prevents protons moving through it. When mitochondria are treated with DCC they stop synthesising ATP. Explain how this provides evidence for the chemiosmotic theory.

## Practice Questions — Fact Recall

Q1 a) In the link reaction, pyruvate is converted into acetate. Describe how this happens.

b) The second stage of the link reaction relies on coenzyme A. What is the role of coenzyme A in the link reaction?

c) State what happens to the products of the link reaction.

Q2 In one turn of the Krebs cycle:

a) how many molecules of $CO_2$ are released, and where are they released from?

b) how many molecules of reduced FAD are made?

Q3 During the Krebs cycle ATP is produced by the direct transfer of a phosphate group from an intermediate compound to ADP. What name is given to this process?

Q4 After each turn of the Krebs cycle, what happens to:

a) coenzyme A?

b) oxaloacetate?

Q5 During oxidative phosphorylation, what happens to electrons as they move down the electron transport chain?

Q6 What is said to be the final electron acceptor in oxidative phosphorylation?

Q7 Give one example of a decarboxylation reaction in respiration.

Q8 Draw out the table below and fill it in with crosses to show where the following substances are made in respiration.

| *Substance* | *Glycolysis* | *Link reaction* | *Krebs cycle* | *Oxidative phosphorylation* |
|---|---|---|---|---|
| *ATP* | | | | |
| *reduced NAD* | | | | |
| *reduced FAD* | | | | |
| *$CO_2$* | | | | |

**Exam Tip**
You really need to know this stuff for your exam. If you find you're struggling to answer a question go back to the relevant page and make sure you really understand what's going on.

**Learning Objective:**

- Be able to carry out an investigation into the effect of a named variable on the rate of respiration of cultures of single-celled organisms (Required Practical 9).

**Specification Reference 3.5.2**

# 8. Respiration Experiments

*These pages give you some experiments that you could use to carry out investigations into respiration.*

## Investigating factors affecting respiration in single-celled organisms

REQUIRED PRACTICAL 9

Yeast are single-celled organisms that can be grown in culture. They can respire aerobically when plenty of oxygen is available and anaerobically when oxygen isn't available. Both aerobic and anaerobic respiration in yeast produce $CO_2$ (see page 19). So the rate of $CO_2$ production gives an indication of the yeast's respiration rate. One way to measure $CO_2$ production is by using a gas syringe to collect the $CO_2$.

The methods below and on the next page show you how to investigate the effects of temperature on both aerobic and anaerobic respiration in yeast. You'll need to decide what temperatures you're going to investigate before you start (e.g. 10 °C, 20 °C and 25 °C).

**Tip:** Make sure you think about and address all the risks involved in the experiments on pages 46-48 before you carry them out.

### Example — Aerobic Respiration

1. Put a known volume and concentration of substrate solution (e.g. glucose) in a test tube. Add a known volume of buffer solution to keep the pH constant. (Choose the optimum pH for the yeast you're testing — usually 4-6.)
2. Place the test tube in a water bath set to one of the temperatures being investigated. Leave it there for 10 minutes to allow the temperature of the substrate to stabilise.
3. Add a known mass of dried yeast (e.g. *Saccharomyces cerevisiae*) to the test tube and stir for two minutes.
4. After the yeast has dissolved into the solution, put a bung with a tube attached to a gas syringe in the top of the test tube. The gas syringe should be set to zero.
5. Start a stop watch as soon as the bung has been put in the test tube.
6. As the yeast respire, the $CO_2$ formed will travel up the tube and into the gas syringe, which is used to measure the volume of $CO_2$ released.
7. At regular time intervals (e.g. every minute), record the volume of $CO_2$ that is present in the gas syringe. Do this for a set amount of time (e.g. 10 minutes).
8. A negative control experiment should also be set up at each temperature, where no yeast is present. No $CO_2$ should be formed without the yeast.
9. Repeat the experiment three times at each temperature you're investigating. Use your data to calculate the mean rate of $CO_2$ production at each temperature.

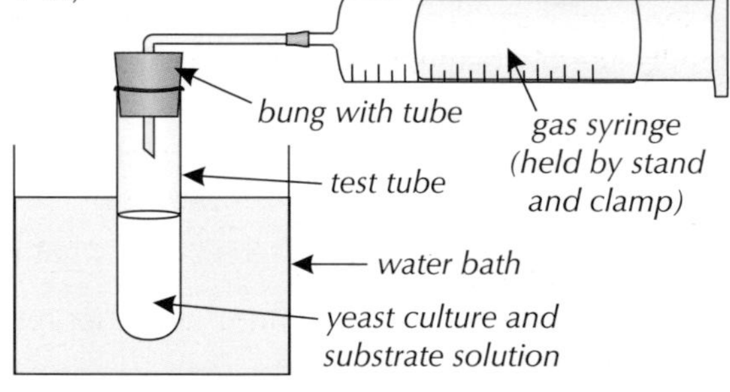


***Figure 1:** Diagram showing how apparatus can be set up to measure aerobic respiration in yeast.*

**Tip:** A buffer solution is able to resist changes in pH when small amounts of acid or alkali are added. You can get acidic buffers (with a pH of less than 7) and alkaline buffers (with a pH of more than 7).

**Tip:** The yeast will only respire aerobically until the oxygen trapped in the tube is all used up. If you wanted to run the experiment for more time or with more yeast or glucose, you could use a conical flask that can trap more oxygen.

**Tip:** To calculate the rate of $CO_2$ production, divide the total volume of $CO_2$ produced at a particular temperature by the number of minutes the apparatus was left for.

**Example — Anaerobic Respiration**

1. Set up the apparatus according to steps 1-3 of the experiment on the previous page.
2. After the yeast has dissolved into the substrate solution, trickle some liquid paraffin down the inside of the test tube so that it settles on and completely covers the surface of the solution. This will stop oxygen getting in, which will force the yeast to respire anaerobically.
3. Put a bung, with a tube attached to a gas syringe, in the top of the test tube. The gas syringe should be set to zero.

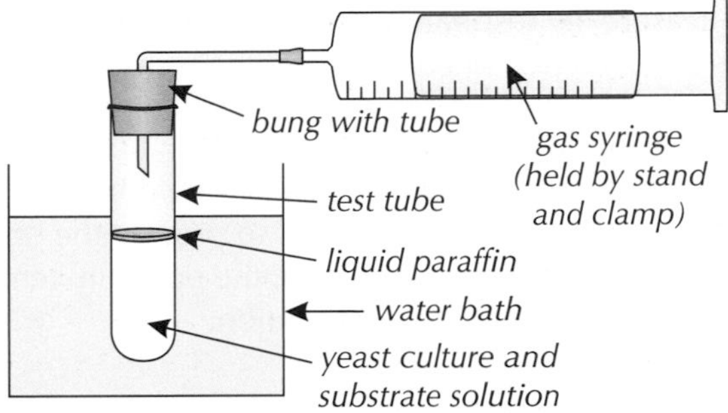


***Figure 2:*** *Diagram showing how apparatus can be set up to measure anaerobic respiration in yeast.*

4. Perform steps 5-9 from the method on the previous page.

**Tip:** To test that the gas produced is definitely $CO_2$, connect the yeast and substrate solution to a test tube of limewater rather than a gas syringe. The limewater will turn cloudy in the presence of $CO_2$.

You can also easily adapt these methods to investigate the effects of other variables, such as substrate concentration and the use of different respiratory substrates (e.g. sucrose) on the respiration rate.

Just remember that you should only change one variable at a time (the independent variable, see page 1). All the other variables that could affect your results need to be controlled (kept the same) or your results won't be valid.

**Tip:** There are other ways of measuring the rate of respiration in yeast. For example, you could use a redox indicator dye (e.g. methylene blue) and a colorimeter to measure the rate of aerobic respiration (the method is similar to the one used in the photosynthesis experiment on pages 36-37). The dye takes the place of electron acceptors in oxidative phosphorylation.

## Practice Question — Application

Q1 A scientist is investigating the effect of pH on aerobic respiration in two different species of yeast. The mean rate of $CO_2$ production is indicative of the respiration rate. Her results are shown in the graph below.

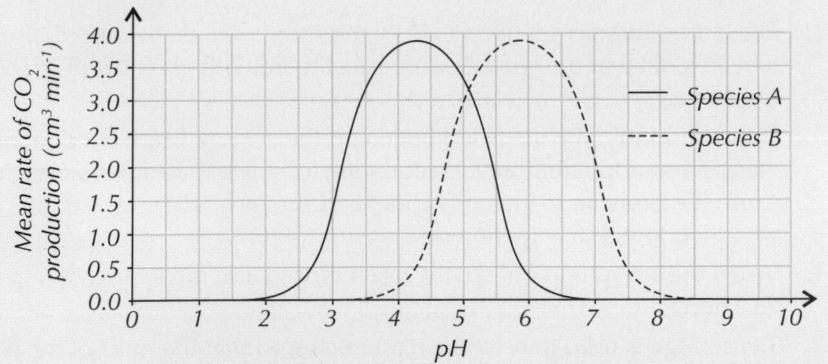


a) Describe an experiment the scientist could have done to obtain the results shown in the graph.

b) The results show that each species has a different optimum pH. Suggest an explanation for this.

c) At pH 5.5, how much faster is the mean rate of $CO_2$ production by species B than species A? Give your answer as a percentage.

d) The scientist also carried out the same experiment using boiled yeast of each species. Explain why.

Tip: Before doing this experiment, you need to think about the ethical issues involved, as well as any safety issues. You must treat the woodlice with respect and ensure that they're not harmed or distressed unnecessarily.

Tip: Wear eye protection and gloves when working with potassium hydroxide, and make sure that the woodlice don't come into contact with it.

*Figure 4:* A respirometer set up to measure the rate of respiration by germinating peas (left). Glass beads are being used as a control (right).

## Using a respirometer to measure oxygen consumption

Respirometers can be used to indicate the rate of aerobic respiration by measuring the amount of oxygen consumed by an organism over a period of time. The example below shows how a respirometer can be used to measure the respiration rate of woodlice. You could also use it to measure the respiration rate of other small organisms or of plant seeds.

**Example**

1. The apparatus is set up as shown in Figure 3, partially submerged in a water bath at 15 °C to provide the optimum temperature for the woodlice and therefore, the optimum temperature for the enzymes involved in their respiration.

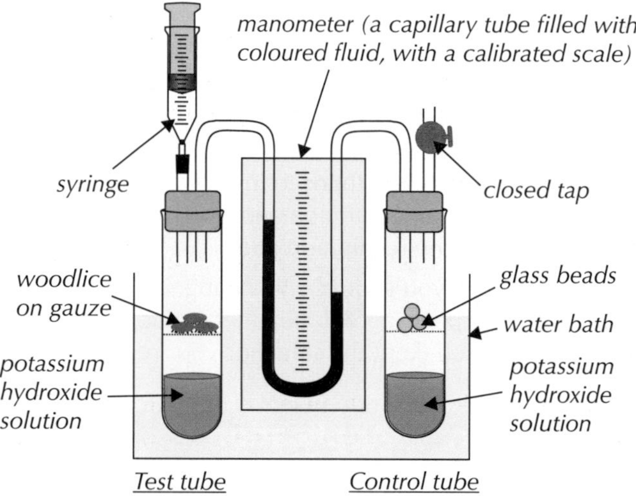


*Figure 3:* Diagram showing how a respirometer can be set up to measure oxygen consumption.

2. The control tube is set up in exactly the same way as the woodlouse tube, except that the woodlice are substituted with glass beads of the same mass.
3. For ten minutes, the tap is left open and the syringe is removed to allow the apparatus to equilibrate (accounting for any expansion that might cause the pressure to change inside) and the respiration rate of the woodlice to stabilise in their new environment.
4. When the ten minutes is up, the tap is closed and the syringe is attached.
5. The syringe is used to reset the manometer, so that the ends of the fluid are at the same level on either side of the 'U' and the reading from the volume scale on the syringe (usually in $cm^3$) is recorded.
6. As respiration occurs, the volume of the air in the test tube containing woodlice will decrease, due to the oxygen consumed during respiration (all the $CO_2$ produced is absorbed by the potassium hydroxide).
7. The decrease in the volume of the air will reduce the pressure in the test tube, causing the coloured fluid in the capillary tube of the manometer to move towards it.

8. After leaving the apparatus to run for a set period of time (e.g. 10 minutes), the syringe is used to reset the manometer and the reading on the syringe's volume scale is recorded again. The difference between this figure and the figure taken at the start of the experiment is the oxygen consumption for this time period. You can use this to calculate a rate of respiration.
9. To check the precision of the results, the experiment is repeated and a mean volume of $O_2$ is calculated.

**Tip:** Oxygen consumption can also be calculated by recording the movement of the fluid in the manometer, read from the scale on the manometer itself.

## Practice Questions — Fact Recall

Q1 If you were measuring anaerobic respiration in yeast, why would you add a layer of liquid paraffin to the yeast solution in the test tube before sealing the tube with a rubber bung?

Q2 Suggest a negative control experiment that could be included when measuring the rate of respiration of yeast in a test tube.

Q3 If you were using a respirometer to measure the oxygen consumed by germinating peas with a mass of 10 g, what mass of glass beads would you have in the control tube?

## Section Summary

Make sure you know...

- That ATP is the immediate source of energy in a cell. It is used to carry out biological processes.
- That the compensation point in plants is the point when the rate of photosynthesis exactly matches the rate of respiration and how to identify the compensation point of a plant from a graph.
- That photosynthesis (where plants convert light energy into chemical energy in the form of glucose) has two stages — the light-dependent reaction and the light-independent reaction.
- That the light-dependent reaction includes non-cyclic photophosphorylation and cyclic photophosphorylation. In both processes, light energy is absorbed by the chlorophyll in photosystems and used to excite electrons, releasing them from the chlorophyll (photoionisation). As the electrons move down the electron transport chain they lose energy, which is used to generate a proton gradient across the thylakoid membrane. The subsequent movement of protons down their concentration gradient is used to produce ATP. In non-cyclic photophosphorylation, reduced NADP is also produced.
- That the process of electrons flowing down the electron transport chain and creating a proton gradient across the membrane to drive ATP synthesis is called chemiosmosis. It's described by the chemiosmotic theory.
- That the photolysis of water is the splitting of water using light and that it produces protons, electrons and oxygen. It happens in non-cyclic photophosphorylation.
- That cyclic photophosphorylation only produces small amounts of ATP and doesn't produce any reduced NADP or oxygen.
- That in the light-independent reaction carbon dioxide ($CO_2$) enters the Calvin cycle, where it is combined with ribulose bisphosphate (RuBP) to form two molecules of glycerate 3-phosphate (GP). This reaction is catalysed by the enzyme rubisco. These two molecules of GP are then reduced to two molecules of triose phosphate (TP), using ATP and reduced NADP from the light-dependent reaction. Five out of every six molecules of TP are used to regenerate RuBP (allowing the Calvin cycle to continue) while the remaining TP is used to produce organic substrates such as carbohydrates, lipids and proteins.

- That a limiting factor is a variable that can slow down the rate of a reaction. The limiting factors of photosynthesis are light intensity, temperature and carbon dioxide concentration.
- That agricultural growers create ideal conditions of light intensity, carbon dioxide concentration and temperature in glasshouses, so that these factors are less likely to limit photosynthesis and that crop yield is increased.
- How to interpret data on agricultural processes used to overcome limiting factors in photosynthesis, e.g. using heaters in glasshouses.
- How to use chromatography to separate the pigments in the leaves of plants to allow you to compare the pigments present in shade-tolerant and shade-intolerant plants or in different coloured leaves (Required Practical 7).
- How to use a redox indicator dye to investigate the effect of a named factor (e.g. light intensity) on the activity of dehydrogenase enzyme in extracts of chloroplasts (Required Practical 8).
- That both aerobic and anaerobic respiration produce ATP, and both begin with glycolysis.
- That respiratory substrates other than glucose can be used for aerobic respiration, including the breakdown products of lipids and amino acids, which enter the Krebs cycle.
- The four stages of aerobic respiration — glycolysis (which happens in the cytoplasm), the link reaction, the Krebs cycle and oxidative phosphorylation (the last three stages happen in the mitochondria).
- That in glycolysis, ATP is used to phosphorylate glucose to glucose phosphate. Glucose phosphate is then converted into hexose bisphosphate, using ATP to add another phosphate. Hexose bisphosphate is then split into two molecules of triose phosphate. Triose phosphate is then oxidised to pyruvate. There is a net gain of two ATP and two reduced NAD, per molecule of glucose.
- That in anaerobic respiration pyruvate (from glycolysis) is converted to ethanol or lactate. Only two ATP per molecule of glucose can be produced by this method and NAD is regenerated.
- That in the link reaction of aerobic respiration, pyruvate is oxidised to acetate (via decarboxylation and the reduction of NAD). Then acetate is combined with coenzyme A to form acetyl coenzyme A.
- That acetyl coenzyme A (a two-carbon molecule) combines with a four-carbon molecule (oxaloacetate) to produce a six-carbon molecule (citrate) in the first reaction of the Krebs cycle. This is followed by a series of oxidation-reduction reactions to produce reduced NAD, reduced FAD (reduced coenzymes) and ATP. $CO_2$ is also produced and lost in the process. The reduced coenzymes are used in oxidative phosphorylation.
- That ATP is produced in the Krebs cycle by substrate-level phosphorylation — a phosphate group is directly transferred from an intermediate molecule to ADP.
- That oxidative phosphorylation uses electrons from reduced NAD and reduced FAD to make ATP. Electrons travel down the electron transport chain, losing energy as they go. This energy is used to form a proton gradient across the inner mitochondrial membrane, which is used to make ATP by chemiosmosis (which is described by the chemiosmotic theory). Water is also produced in this process.
- How to carry out an investigation into the effect of a named variable (e.g. temperature) on the rate of respiration in cultures of single-celled organisms (Required Practical 9).

# Exam-style Questions

1 Petite mutants are yeast cells that have mutations in genes that are important for mitochondrial function. They are called petite mutants because they grow and divide to form unusually small colonies when grown in medium with a low glucose concentration.

**1.1** Petite mutants are unable to produce mitochondrial proteins. Suggest how this could stop the mitochondria from producing ATP.

*(1 mark)*

**1.2** Petite mutants lack functioning mitochondria but they can still produce ATP by glycolysis. Explain why.

*(1 mark)*

**1.3** Triose phosphate is an intermediate compound in glycolysis. Describe how two triose phosphate molecules are formed from a molecule of glucose.

*(3 marks)*

**1.4** Describe the role of the coenzyme NAD in glycolysis.

*(2 marks)*

2 DCPIP is an artificial hydrogen acceptor that can be used to measure the rate of photosynthesis. When DCPIP is reduced it turns from blue to colourless. In the presence of NADP, DCPIP is reduced first. A scientist used DCPIP to investigate the rate of photosynthesis in plant chloroplasts at three different temperatures. DCPIP was incubated with liquid extracts of chloroplasts for 10 minutes. Every minute, the absorbance of the solution was measured. All conditions except the temperature were kept the same. The results are shown in **Figure 1**.

**Figure 1**

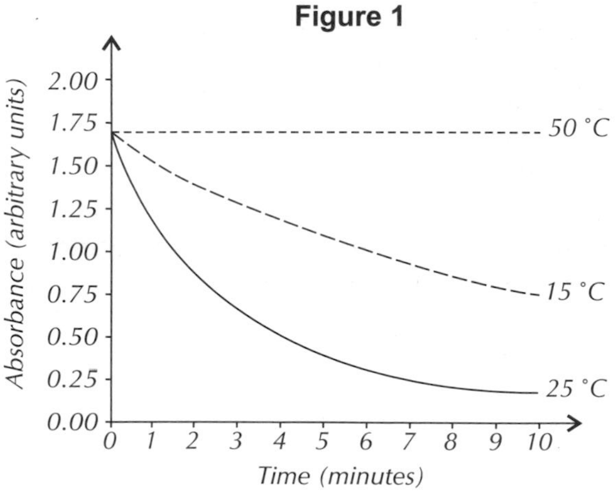


**2.1** Suggest how the absorbance of the solution was measured.

*(2 marks)*

**2.2** Why was measuring the absorbance of the solution over time a suitable way of indicating the rate of photosynthesis?

*(3 marks)*

**2.3** Suggest why the absorbance doesn't change at 50 °C.

*(3 marks)*

**3** In oxidative phosphorylation hydrogen atoms are released from reduced NAD and reduced FAD.

**3.1** Describe the reactions in respiration in which these reduced coenzymes are produced.

*(5 marks)*

**3.2** The hydrogen atoms split up into hydrogen ions and electrons. Describe the movement of electrons in oxidative phosphorylation.

*(2 marks)*

**3.3** DNP is an uncoupler. This means it carries $H^+$ ions from the intermembrane space back into the matrix of mitochondria during oxidative phosphorylation. Describe and explain the effect that DNP would have on the production of ATP in animal cells.

*(4 marks)*

**4** A student carried out a study into the effect of different factors on the rate of photosynthesis in a certain species of plant.

**4.1** The student calculated the rate of photosynthesis by measuring how much oxygen was released by the plants over a period of time. Explain why this is not an accurate way of calculating the rate of photosynthesis.

*(2 marks)*

The student carried out three experiments in his study — the results of which are shown in **Figure 2**. In each experiment the plants had an adequate supply of water.

**Figure 2**

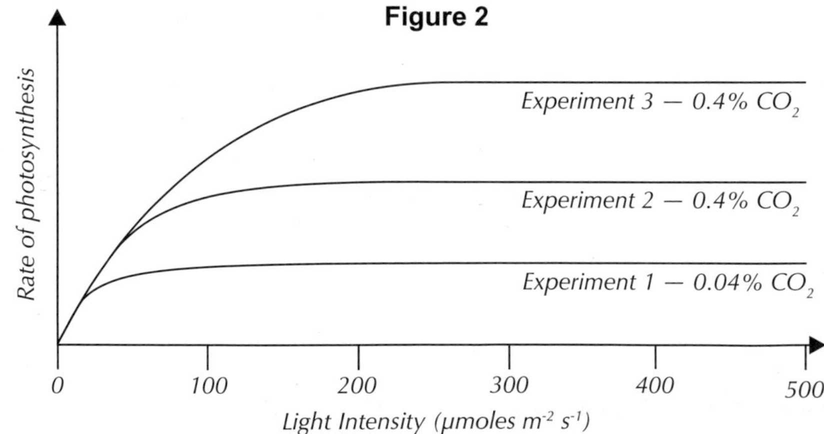


**4.2** What is the limiting factor of photosynthesis in experiment 2? Explain your answer.

*(2 marks)*

**4.3** The student extended experiment 2 by measuring the amount of RuBP and TP produced by the plant over time. After 5 minutes, the student lowered the $CO_2$ concentration of the plants to 0.04%. Describe and explain what effect the lowering of $CO_2$ concentration had on the levels of RuBP and TP in the plants.

*(3 marks)*

# 1. Energy Transfer in Ecosystems

*Plants get their energy from the Sun, and animals get their energy by eating plants or other animals. Some energy gets lost along the way, but you can calculate the energy that gets transferred using some nifty equations.*

**Learning Objectives:**

- Know that in any ecosystem, plants synthesise organic compounds from atmospheric, or aquatic, carbon dioxide.
- Know that most of the sugars synthesised by plants are used by the plant as respiratory substrates, and that the rest are used to make other groups of biological molecules. These biological molecules form the biomass of the plants.
- Know that biomass can be measured in terms of mass of carbon or dry mass of tissue per given area.
- Know that the chemical energy store in dry biomass can be estimated using calorimetry.
- Know that gross primary production (*GPP*) is the chemical energy store in plant biomass, in a given area or volume.
- Know that net primary production (*NPP*) is the chemical energy store in plant biomass after respiratory losses to the environment (*R*) have been taken into account, i.e. $NPP = GPP - R$.
- Know that primary productivity is the rate of primary production and is measured as biomass in a given area, in a given time.

## Ecosystem basics

An ecosystem includes all the organisms living in a particular area and all the non-living (abiotic) conditions (see page 173). In all ecosystems, there are producers — organisms that make their own food.

**Examples**

- In land-based ecosystems, plants (such as trees, shrubs and grasses) produce their own food through photosynthesis.
- In aquatic ecosystems, plants (such as water lilies and watercress) and algae (such as seaweeds) also produce their own food through photosynthesis.

During photosynthesis plants use energy (from sunlight) and carbon dioxide (from the atmosphere in land-based ecosystems, or dissolved in water in aquatic ecosystems) to make glucose and other sugars.

Some of the sugars produced during photosynthesis are used in respiration, to release energy for growth. The rest of the glucose is used to make other biological molecules, such as cellulose (a component of plant cell walls). These biological molecules make up the plant's **biomass** — the mass of living material. Biomass can also be thought of as the chemical energy stored in the plant.

Energy is transferred through the living organisms of an ecosystem when organisms eat other organisms, e.g. producers are eaten by organisms called primary consumers. Primary consumers are then eaten by secondary consumers and secondary consumers are eaten by tertiary consumers. This is a food chain (see page 57).

## Measuring biomass

Biomass can be measured in terms of the mass of carbon that an organism contains or the dry mass of its tissue per unit area. Dry mass is the mass of the organism with the water removed. The water content of living tissue varies, so dry mass is used as a measure of biomass rather than wet mass.

To measure the dry mass, a sample of the organism is dried, often in an oven set to a low temperature. The sample is then weighed at regular intervals (e.g. every day). Once the mass becomes constant you know that all the water has been removed. The mass of carbon present is generally taken to be 50% of the dry mass.

Once you've measured the dry mass of a sample, you can scale up the result to give the dry mass (biomass) of the total population or the area being investigated. So typical units for dry mass might be kg $m^{-2}$.

- Know that net primary production is available for plant growth and reproduction.
- Know that net primary production is also available to other trophic levels in the ecosystem such as herbivores and decomposers.
- Know that the net production of consumers ($N$), such as animals, can be calculated as $N = I - (F + R)$, where $I$ represents the chemical energy store in ingested food, $F$ represents the chemical energy lost to the environment in faeces and urine and $R$ represents the respiratory losses to the environment.
- Know that the net production of consumers is also known as secondary production and that this is called secondary productivity when expressed as a rate.

**Specification Reference 3.5.3**

**Tip:** Remember, plants convert light energy to chemical energy during photosynthesis.

**Tip:** Photosynthesis isn't 100% efficient. Not all of the light energy absorbed by a plant will be converted to chemical energy.

### Calorimetry

You can estimate the amount of chemical energy stored in biomass by burning the biomass in a **calorimeter** (see Figure 1). The amount of heat given off tells you how much energy is in it. Energy is measured in joules (J) or kilojoules (kJ).

A sample of dry biomass is burnt and the energy released is used to heat a known volume of water. The change in temperature of the water is used to calculate the chemical energy of the dry biomass.

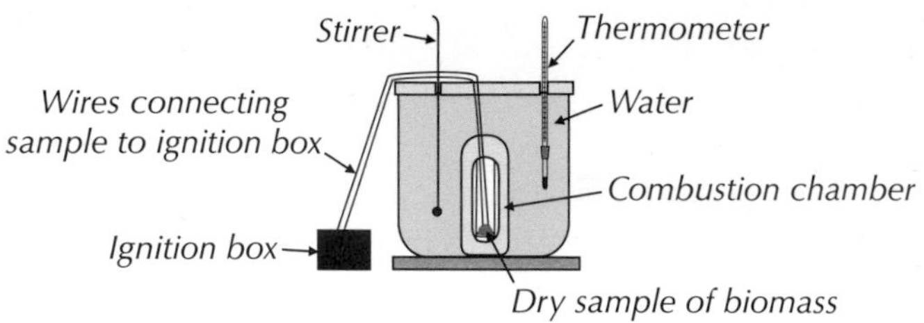


***Figure 1:*** *An example of a calorimeter being used to measure the chemical energy in biomass.*

## Primary production

**Gross primary production** (***GPP***) is the total amount of chemical energy converted from light energy by plants in a given area. Approximately 50% of the gross primary production is lost to the environment as heat when the plants respire. This is called **respiratory loss** (***R***). The remaining chemical energy is called the **net primary production** (***NPP***). This relationship is shown by the following formula:

$$NPP = GPP - R$$

Often, primary production is expressed as a rate — i.e. the total amount of chemical energy (or biomass) in a given area, in a given time. Typical units might be kJ ha$^{-1}$ yr$^{-1}$ (kilojoules per hectare per year) or kJ m$^{-2}$ yr$^{-1}$ (kilojoules per square metre per year). When primary production is expressed as a rate it is called **primary productivity**.

**Examples — Maths Skills**

1. The grass in an ecosystem has a gross primary productivity of 20 000 kJ m$^{-2}$ yr$^{-1}$. It loses 8000 kJ m$^{-2}$ yr$^{-1}$ as heat from respiration.
   **Calculate the net primary productivity of the grass in this ecosystem.**

   net primary productivity = 20 000 – 8000
   = **12 000 kJ m$^{-2}$ yr$^{-1}$**

2. The net primary productivity in an area of tundra is 2800 kJ m$^{-2}$ yr$^{-1}$. It loses 1250 kJ m$^{-2}$ yr$^{-1}$ through respiration.
   **Calculate the gross primary productivity of the area of tundra.**
   - First you need to rearrange the formula: $NPP = GPP - R$, so $GPP = NPP + R$
   - Then you can use it to calculate $GPP$: gross primary productivity = 2800 + 1250
   = **4050 kJ m$^{-2}$ yr$^{-1}$**

The *NPP* is the energy available to the plant for growth and reproduction — the energy is stored in the plant's biomass. It is also the energy available to organisms at the next stage in the food chain (the next trophic level, see page 57). These include herbivores (animals that eat the plants) and decomposers.

## Net production in consumers

Consumers also store chemical energy in their biomass. Consumers get energy by ingesting plant material, or animals that have eaten plant material. However, not all the chemical energy stored in the consumers' food is transferred to the next trophic level — around 90% of the total available energy is lost in various ways. Firstly, not all of the food is eaten (e.g. plant roots, bones) so the energy it contains is not taken in. Then, of the parts that are ingested:

- Some are indigestible, so are egested as faeces. The chemical energy stored in these parts is therefore lost to the environment.
- Some energy is also lost to the environment through respiration or excretion of urine.

The energy that's left after all this is stored in the consumers' biomass and is available to the next trophic level. This energy is the consumers' **net production**. The net production of consumers can be calculated using the following formula:

$$N = I - (F + R)$$

Where:
$N$ = Net production
$I$ = Chemical energy in ingested food
$F$ = Chemical energy lost in faeces and urine
$R$ = Energy lost through respiration

**Example — Maths Skills**

The rabbits in an ecosystem ingest 20 000 kJ m$^{-2}$ yr$^{-1}$ of energy, but lose 12 000 kJ m$^{-2}$ yr$^{-1}$ of it in faeces and urine. They lose a further 6000 kJ m$^{-2}$ yr$^{-1}$ using energy for respiration. You can use this to calculate the net productivity of the rabbits:

net productivity = 20 000 – (12 000 + 6000)
= 20 000 – 18 000 = **2000 kJ m$^{-2}$ yr$^{-1}$**

The net production of consumers can also be called **secondary production** (or secondary productivity when it's expressed as a rate).

## Efficiency of energy transfer

You can use the following equation to calculate how efficient energy transfer is between one trophic level and the next:

$$\text{\% efficiency of energy transfer} = \frac{\text{net production of trophic level}}{\text{net production of previous trophic level}} \times 100$$

**Example — Maths Skills**

The rabbits receive 20 000 kJ m$^{-2}$ yr$^{-1}$, and their net productivity is 2000 kJ m$^{-2}$ yr$^{-1}$. So the percentage efficiency of energy transfer is:

(2000 ÷ 20 000) × 100 = **10%**

As you move up a food chain (from producers to consumers) energy transfer usually becomes more efficient. For example, the efficiency of energy transfer from producer to consumer might only be 5-10%, but from consumer to consumer, it might be 15-20%. This is because plants (producers) contain more indigestible matter than animals (consumers).

**Tip:** There are lots of similar sounding words here. 'Ingest' means 'take in to the body'. 'Indigestible' means 'can't be digested (broken down)'. 'Egest' means 'get rid of from the body'.

**Exam Tip**
You need to know the equations for net primary production and net production for the exam, so learn them both.

**Tip:** Net productivity is just net production expressed as a rate, i.e. per unit time.

**Tip:** If the organisms in the previous trophic level are producers, then use 'net primary production of previous trophic level' rather than 'net production of previous trophic level'.

**Tip:** Increasing efficiency of energy transfer as you go up a food chain is only a general rule of thumb — there are plenty of exceptions.

## Practice Questions — Application

Q1 A scientist wanted to measure the biomass of a crop of wheat. To do so, he took a sample of the wheat and measured its dry mass.

a) Describe how the scientist could have measured the dry mass of the wheat.

b) Once the scientist has a sample of dry mass, he decides to burn it in a calorimeter. What will the results from this procedure tell him about the wheat?

Q2 The mussels in an ecosystem ingest 57 153 kJ $m^{-2} yr^{-1}$. 34 292 kJ $m^{-2} yr^{-1}$ is indigestible or lost through urine and 17 000 kJ $m^{-2} yr^{-1}$ is lost through respiration.

a) Calculate the net productivity of the mussels.

The mussels provide food for crayfish which have a net productivity of 627 kJ $m^{-2} yr^{-1}$.

b) Calculate the efficiency of energy transfer between the mussels and the crayfish.

Q3 The diagram below shows the net primary productivity of plant plankton in a food chain, as well as the net productivity at different trophic levels in the same food chain. Use the diagram to answer the following questions.

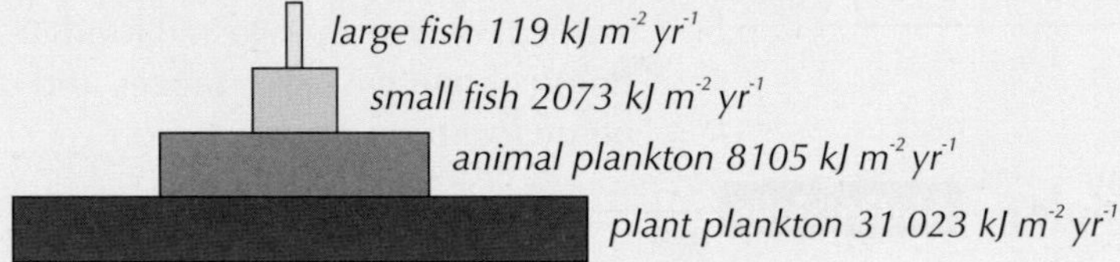


a) The respiratory loss of the plant plankton is 15 604 kJ $m^{-2} yr^{-1}$ Calculate their gross primary productivity.

b) The small fish ingest 8105 kJ $m^{-2} yr^{-1}$ and lose 3988 kJ $m^{-2} yr^{-1}$ in faeces and urine. Calculate the respiratory loss of the small fish.

c) The respiratory loss of the large fish is 879 kJ $m^{-2} yr^{-1}$. Calculate the amount of energy lost in faeces and urine by the large fish.

d) Give two reasons why the net productivity of the large fish is less than the net productivity of the small fish.

e) Calculate the percentage efficiency of energy transfer between each stage of the food chain.

**Tip:** The two equations for net production and net primary production might get a bit confusing — just remember, if you're talking about plants (the first or primary organisms in a food chain), you need the equation for net primary production. Anything else will just be net production.

## Practice Questions — Fact Recall

Q1 What is a plant's biomass?

Q2 What is gross primary production?

Q3 What is meant by the term 'respiratory loss'?

Q4 a) What is net production?

b) State the equation for net production.

# 2. Farming Practices and Production

*Knowing about the efficiency of energy transfer in food chains can help farmers maximise the amount of energy in the food they produce.*

**Learning Objective:**

- Be able to appreciate the ways in which production is affected by farming practices designed to increase the efficiency of energy transfer by:
  - simplifying food webs to reduce energy losses to non-human food chains,
  - reducing respiratory losses within a human food chain.

**Specification Reference 3.5.3**

## Food chains and food webs

Food chains and food webs show how energy is transferred through an ecosystem. Food chains show simple lines of energy transfer. Each of the stages in a food chain is called a **trophic level**. Food webs show lots of food chains in an ecosystem and how they overlap.

**Example**

The example below shows a food chain (red box) and a food web (blue box).

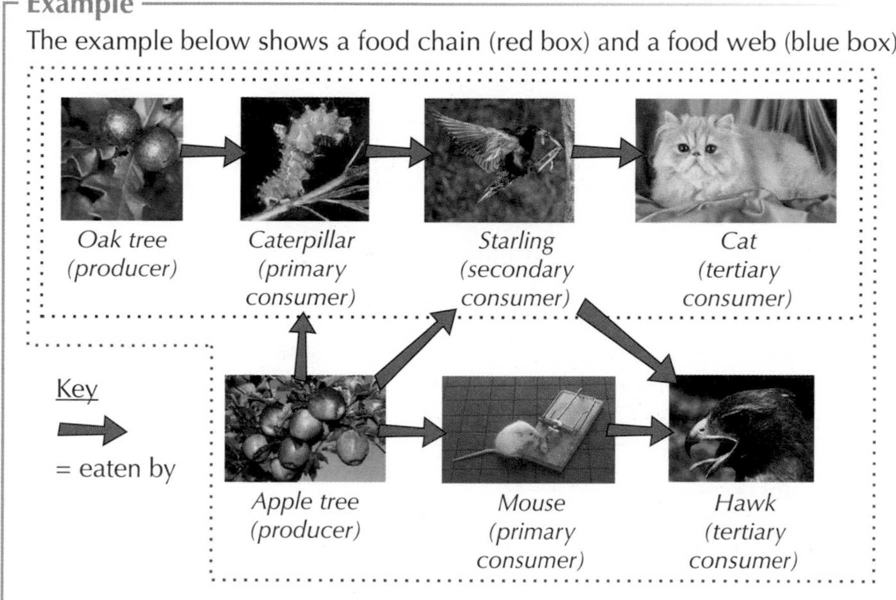


**Tip:** There's more about decomposers on page 60.

Decomposers (e.g. fungi) are also part of food webs. Decomposers break down dead or undigested material, allowing nutrients to be recycled.

## Increasing efficiency

Most farming practices aim to increase the amount of energy that is available for human consumption. This means increasing the net primary production (NPP) of crops and the net production (NP) of livestock. There are different ways this can be done. You need to know about two of them:

- The energy lost to other organisms, e.g. pests, can be reduced through the simplification of food webs.
- The energy lost through the respiration of livestock can be reduced.

**Tip:** NPP is the energy in plants that's available to the next trophic level in a food chain. NP is the energy in consumers that's available to the next trophic level. See pages 54-55 for more.

### Simplifying food webs

Pests are organisms that reduce the amount of energy available for crop growth and therefore the net primary production (NPP) of crops. This ultimately reduces the amount of energy available for humans. By simplifying the food web, i.e. getting rid of food chains that don't involve humans, energy losses will be reduced and the NPP of the crop will increase.

**Tip:** Crops are plants which are grown on a large scale for the benefit of humans, e.g. for human consumption. Livestock are animals which are bred for their produce, e.g milk, or for human consumption.

**Example**

Figure 1 shows a simplified food web involving wheat — a crop plant grown for human consumption. The weed, the mouse and the aphid are pests. By eating the wheat or competing with it for energy, the pests reduce the wheat's biomass and the energy it has for further growth. This means that the wheat's NPP (and the wheat yield) is smaller — so less energy is transferred to humans. Getting rid of food chains involving the weed, the mouse and the aphid will mean that less energy is transferred to pests, increasing the efficiency of transfer to humans.

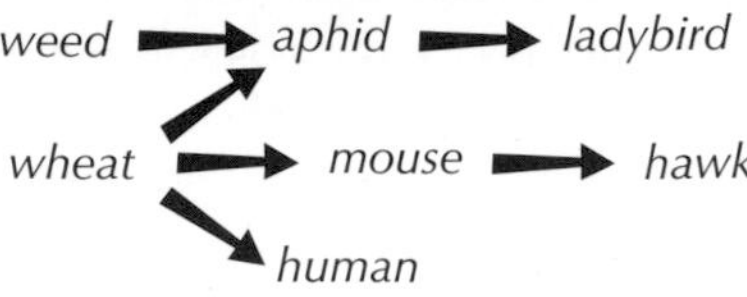


***Figure 1:*** *An example of part of a food web involving a crop.*

To get rid of pests farmers need pest control. Farmers can reduce pest numbers using chemical pesticides.

**Examples**

- Insecticides kill insect pests that eat and damage crops. Killing insect pests means less biomass is lost from crops, so they grow to be larger, which means NPP is greater.
- Herbicides kill weeds (unwanted plant species). Killing weeds can remove direct competition with the crop for energy from the Sun. It can also remove the preferred habitat or food source of the insect pests, helping to further reduce their numbers and simplify the food web.

**Tip:** Weeds also compete with the crop for water, space and nutrients.

Biological agents also reduce the numbers of pests, so crops lose less energy and biomass, increasing the efficiency of energy transfer to humans.

**Examples**

- Parasites live in or lay their eggs on a pest insect. Parasites either kill the insect or reduce its ability to function, e.g. some wasp species lay their eggs inside caterpillars — the eggs hatch and kill the caterpillars.
- Pathogenic (disease-causing) bacteria and viruses are used to kill pests, e.g. the bacterium *Bacillus thuringiensis* produces a toxin that kills a wide range of caterpillars.

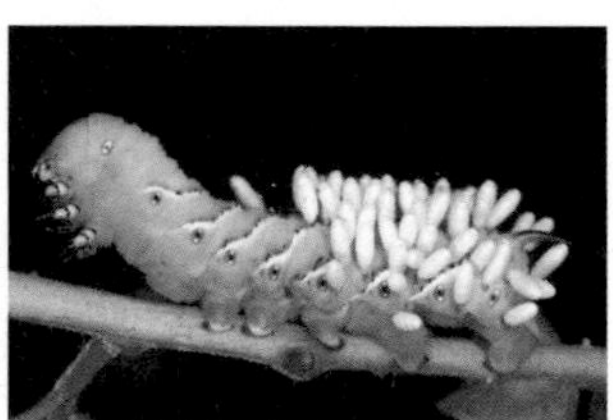

***Figure 2:*** *Braconid wasps lay their eggs in sphinx moth caterpillars.*

Farmers can use integrated systems that combine both chemical and biological methods. The combined effect of using both can reduce pest numbers even more than either method alone, meaning NPP is increased even more.

**Tip:** Natural predators can also be introduced to the ecosystem to eat the pest species, e.g. ladybirds eat aphids — this is useful but doesn't really simplify the food web.

## Reducing respiratory loss

One way that farmers increase the net production of their livestock is by controlling the conditions that they live in, so that more of their energy is used for growth and less is lost through respiration (and activities that increase the rate of respiration).

**Examples**

- Movement increases the rate of respiration, so animals may be kept in pens where their movement is restricted.
- The pens are often indoors and kept warm, so less energy is wasted by generating body heat.

This means that more biomass is produced and more chemical energy can be stored, increasing net production and the efficiency of energy transfer to humans. The benefits are that more food can be produced in a shorter space of time, often at lower cost. However, enhancing net production by keeping animals in pens raises ethical issues. For example, some people think that the conditions intensively reared animals are kept in cause the animals pain, distress or restricts their natural behaviour, so it shouldn't be done.

***Figure 3:*** *Chickens being kept indoors.*

## Practice Question — Application

Q1 A pig farmer wants to maximise production on his farm. He collects data on three different breeds of pig as shown in the table on the right and in the graph below.

| | *Meat yield (% of total body weight)* |
|---|---|
| *Breed 1* | 64 |
| *Breed 2* | 73 |
| *Breed 3* | 66 |

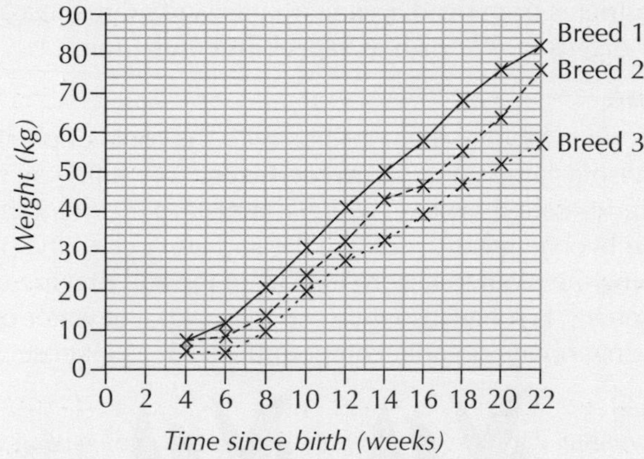


a) Calculate the rate at which breed 3 gained weight between 18 and 22 weeks.

b) Which breed of pig would produce the most meat at 22 weeks?

Antibiotics can be used to treat bacterial diseases in pigs.

c) Suggest how using antibiotics may increase the net production of the pigs.

d) Suggest and explain one other way the farmer could increase the net production of the pigs.

**Tip:** Remember that to find the rate you need to find the gradient of the line — see page 11.

## Practice Questions — Fact Recall

Q1 What does a food chain show?

Q2 What does a food web show?

Q3 Explain how simplifying a food web could increase the efficiency of energy transfer to humans.

Q4 Give two examples of methods of pest control.

# 3. Nutrient Cycles in Natural Ecosystems

**Learning Objectives:**

- Know that nutrients are recycled within natural ecosystems and that the nitrogen cycle and phosphorus cycle are examples of this.
- Know that microorganisms play a vital role in recycling chemical elements such as phosphorus and nitrogen including:
  - the role of saprobionts in decomposition.
  - the role of mycorrhizae in facilitating the uptake of water and inorganic ions by plants.
  - the role of bacteria in the processes of saprobiotic nutrition, ammonification, nitrification, nitrogen fixation and denitrification.

**Specification Reference 3.5.4**

*A natural ecosystem is one that hasn't been changed by human activity. In natural ecosystems, nutrients such as nitrogen and phosphorus are recycled though food webs — but human activity often disrupts this.*

## The role of microorganisms

Microorganisms, such as bacteria and fungi, are an important part of food webs and ecosystems. Many are **saprobionts**. Saprobionts do two things:

- They feed on the remains of dead plants and animals and on their waste products (faeces and urine), breaking them down. This makes saprobionts a type of decomposer and it allows important chemical elements in the remains and waste to be recycled.
- They secrete enzymes and digest their food externally, then absorb the nutrients they need. This is known as **extracellular digestion**. During this process, organic molecules are broken down into inorganic ions.

Obtaining nutrients from dead organic matter and animal waste using extracellular digestion is known as **saprobiotic nutrition**.

### Mycorrhizae

Some fungi form symbiotic relationships with the roots of plants. These relationships are known as **mycorrhizae**. The fungi are made up of long, thin strands called hyphae, which connect to the plant's roots — see Figure 1. The hyphae greatly increase the surface area of the plant's root system, helping the plant to absorb ions from the soil that are usually scarce (e.g. phosphorus). Hyphae also increase the uptake of water by the plant. In turn, the fungi obtain organic compounds, such as glucose, from the plant.

**Tip:** A symbiotic relationship is when two species live closely together and one or both species depends on the other for survival.

***Figure 1:*** *A plant without mycorrhizae (left) and with mycorrhizae (right).*

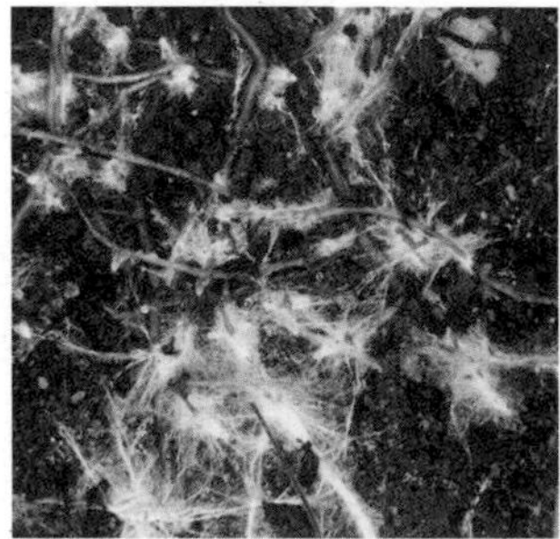

***Figure 2:*** *White hyphae of the fungus* Basidiomycetes, *growing on the roots of a strawberry tree.*

**Example**

The fungus *G. intraradices* can develop mycorrhizal relationships with crops, e.g. wheat, and has been shown to increase the crop's phosphorus uptake.

## The nitrogen cycle

Plants and animals need nitrogen to make proteins and nucleic acids (DNA and RNA). The atmosphere's made up of about 78% nitrogen gas, but plants and animals can't use it in that form — they need bacteria to convert it into nitrogen-containing compounds first.

The nitrogen cycle shows how nitrogen is converted into a usable form and then passed on between different living organisms and the non-living environment. It includes food chains (nitrogen is passed on when organisms are eaten), and four different processes that involve bacteria — nitrogen fixation, ammonification, nitrification and denitrification:

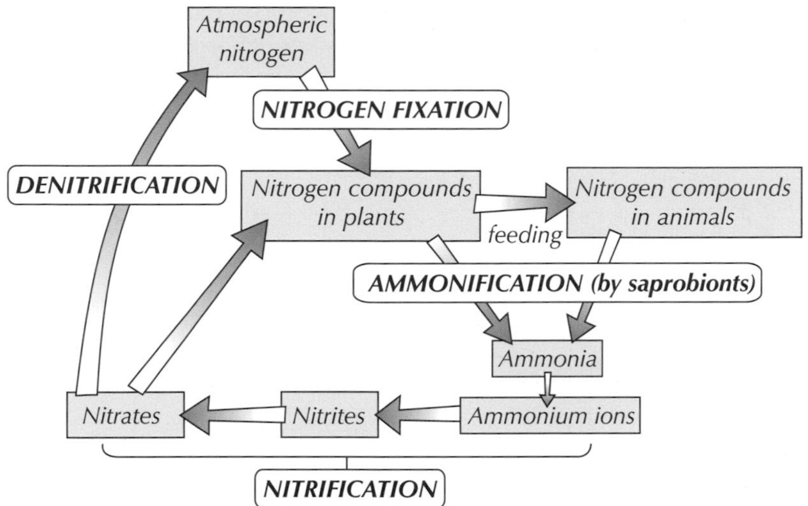


***Figure 3:*** *The four main processes in the nitrogen cycle.*

**Tip:** Don't worry — you don't need to learn the names of the microorganisms.

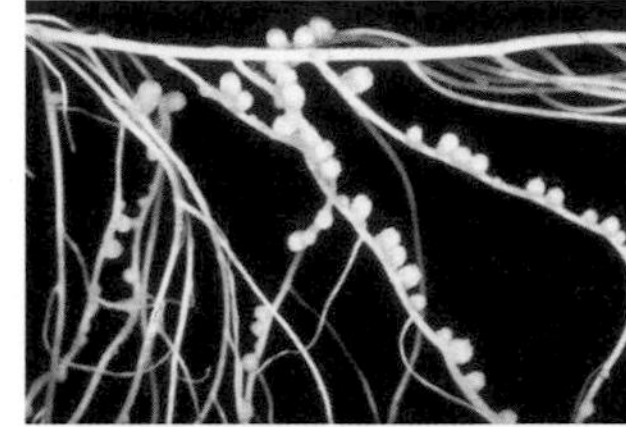

***Figure 4:*** *Pink nodules of* Rhizobium *on plant roots.*

## Nitrogen fixation

Nitrogen fixation is when nitrogen gas in the atmosphere is turned into nitrogen-containing compounds. Biological nitrogen fixation is carried out by bacteria such as *Rhizobium*. It turns nitrogen into ammonia, which goes on to form ammonium ions in solution that can be used by plants. *Rhizobium* are found inside root nodules (growths on the roots) of leguminous plants (e.g. peas, beans and clover). They form a mutualistic relationship with the plants — they provide the plant with nitrogen compounds and the plant provides them with carbohydrates. Other nitrogen-fixing bacteria are found in the soil.

**Tip:** A mutualistic relationship is a type of symbiotic relationship where both species benefit.

## Ammonification

Ammonification is when nitrogen compounds from dead organisms are turned into ammonia by saprobionts, which goes on to form ammonium ions. Animal waste (urine and faeces) also contains nitrogen compounds. These are also turned into ammonia by saprobionts and go on to form ammonium ions.

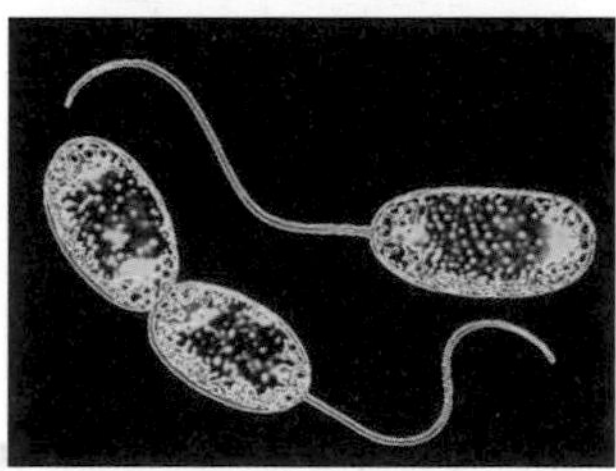

***Figure 5:*** Nitrobacter *bacteria.*

## Nitrification

Nitrification is when ammonium ions in the soil are changed into nitrogen compounds that can then be used by plants (nitrates). First nitrifying bacteria called *Nitrosomonas* change ammonium ions into nitrites. Then other nitrifying bacteria called *Nitrobacter* change nitrites into nitrates.

## Denitrification

Denitrification is when nitrates in the soil are converted into nitrogen gas by denitrifying bacteria — they use nitrates in the soil to carry out respiration and produce nitrogen gas. This happens under anaerobic conditions (where there's no oxygen), e.g. in waterlogged soils.

Other ways that nitrogen gets into an ecosystem are by lightning (which fixes atmospheric nitrogen into nitrogen oxides) or by artificial fertilisers (they're produced from atmospheric nitrogen on an industrial scale in the Haber process).

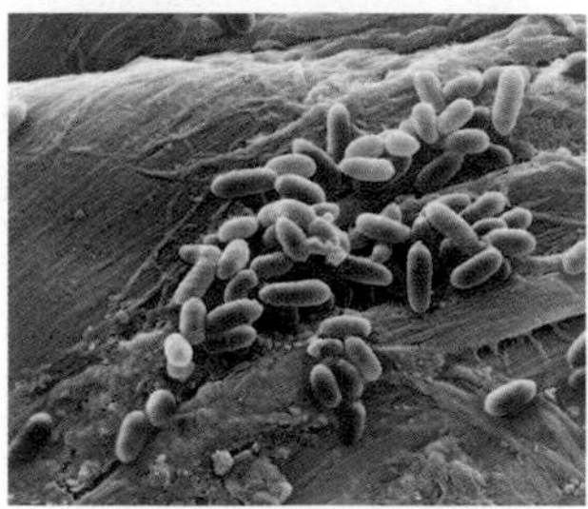

***Figure 6:*** Pseudomonas aeruginosa *are a type of denitrifying bacteria.*

# The phosphorus cycle

Plants and animals need phosphorus to make biological molecules such as phospholipids (which make up cell membranes), DNA and ATP. Phosphorus is found in rocks and dissolved in the oceans in the form of phosphate ions ($PO_4^{3-}$). Phosphate ions dissolved in water in the soil can be assimilated (absorbed and then used to make more complex molecules) by plants and other producers. The phosphorus cycle shows how phosphorus is passed through an ecosystem:

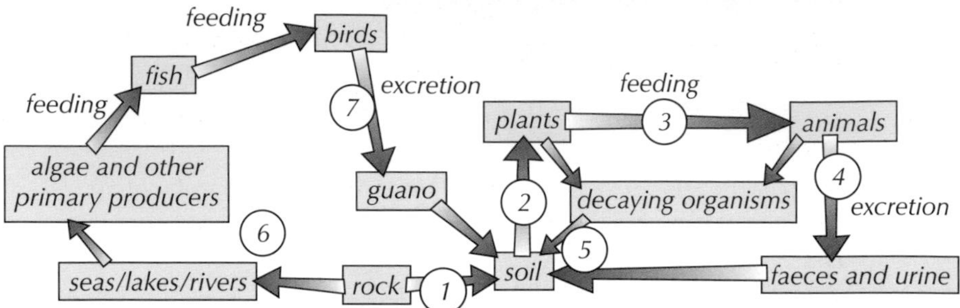


***Figure 7:*** *The phosphorus cycle.*

**Tip:** Weathering is the breakdown of rocks by mechanical, chemical and biological processes.

***Figure 8:*** *Seabirds nesting on a cliff stained white with guano.*

1. Phosphate ions in rocks are released into the soil by weathering.
2. Phosphate ions are taken into the plants through the roots. Mycorrhizae (see page 60) greatly increase the rate at which phosphorus can be assimilated.
3. Phosphate ions are transferred through the food chain as animals eat the plants and are in turn eaten by other animals.
4. Phosphate ions are lost from the animals in waste products.
5. When plants and animals die, saprobionts are involved in breaking down the organic compounds, releasing phosphate ions into the soil for assimilation by plants. These microorganisms also release the phosphate ions from urine and faeces.
6. Weathering of rocks also releases phosphate ions into seas, lakes and rivers. This is taken up by aquatic producers, such as algae, and passed along the food chain to birds.
7. The waste produced by sea birds is known as guano and contains a high proportion of phosphate ions. Guano returns a significant amount of phosphate ions to soils (particularly in coastal areas). It is often used as a natural fertiliser.

## Practice Questions — Application

**Tip:** Tg N $yr^{-1}$ means teragrams of nitrogen per year. 1 teragram is the same as $10^{12}$ grams or 1 million metric tons.

**Tip:** Cultivated land is land that has been used by humans to grow crops.

Q1 The table on the right shows the rate of nitrogen fixation by various sources in the early 1990s.

| Source of nitrogen fixation | Rate of fixation (Tg N $yr^{-1}$) |
|---|---|
| Lightning | 5.4 |
| Bacteria in uncultivated land | 107 |
| Bacteria in cultivated land | 31.5 |
| Fertiliser manufacture | 86 |

a) What percentage of the total amount of nitrogen fixed by all sources was fixed by bacteria?

b) In 1860, 120 Tg N $yr^{-1}$ were fixed by bacteria on uncultivated land. Calculate the overall percentage decrease in the mass of nitrogen fixed per year by bacteria on uncultivated land between 1860 and the early 1990s.

c) Suggest why the mass of nitrogen fixed in uncultivated land decreased between 1860 and the early 1990s.

d) Using the table, suggest one way in which the nitrogen cycle may have been altered by the action of humans.

Q2 Heavy rain combined with poor drainage can lead to soils becoming waterlogged. Suggest and explain what might happen to the amount of nitrogen assimilated by a plant in waterlogged soil.

Q3 Figures A and B below show simplified versions of the nitrogen and phosphorus cycles.

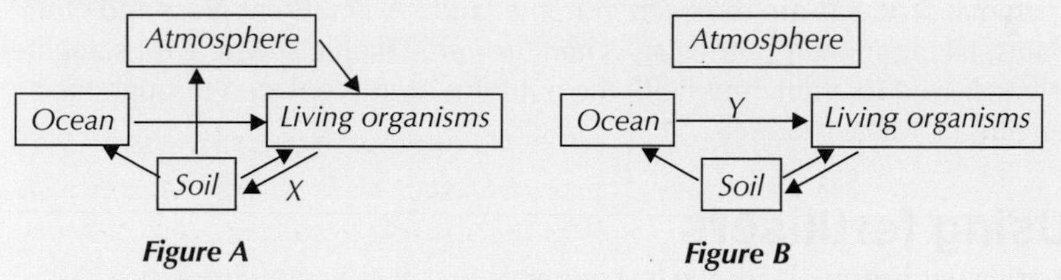


**Figure A** **Figure B**

a) Which Figure, A or B, represents the phosphorus cycle? Give a reason for your answer.

b) In what form is phosphorus assimilated by plants?

c) Name the process labelled X in Figure A.

d) Explain what is happening at the part labelled Y in Figure B.

e) Give two ways in which phosphate ions are returned from living organisms to the soil.

**Exam Tip**
Make sure you know your way around basic maths — you'll be asked some maths questions in the exams, and simple calculations such as percentage decrease are easy marks if you know what you're doing.

## Practice Questions — Fact Recall

Q1 a) Name two types of saprobiont.

b) How do saprobionts digest their food?

Q2 a) What are mycorrhizae?

b) Explain how mycorrhizae increase water and mineral ion uptake by plants.

Q3 Name the four main processes in the nitrogen cycle.

Q4 Describe the role of saprobionts in the phosphorus cycle.

Q5 a) What is guano?

b) Why is guano important in the phosphorus cycle?

**Learning Objectives:**

- Know that natural and artificial fertilisers can be used to replace the nitrates and phosphates lost by harvesting plants and removing livestock.
- Understand the environmental issues arising from the use of fertilisers including leaching and eutrophication.

**Specification Reference 3.5.4**

# 4. Fertilisers and Eutrophication

*Farmers can add extra nutrients, e.g. nitrogen and phosphorus, to the soil to increase the productivity of crops, but this can cause environmental problems. It's a delicate balance between adding too much and too little.*

## Loss of nutrients

Crops take in minerals from the soil as they grow and use them to build their own tissues. When crops are harvested, they're removed from the field where they're grown rather than being allowed to die and decompose there. This means the mineral ions that they contain (e.g. phosphates and nitrates) are not returned to the soil by decomposers in the nitrogen or phosphorus cycles.

Phosphates and nitrates are also lost from the system when animals or animal products are removed from the land. Animals eat grass and other plants, taking in their nutrients. When they are taken elsewhere for slaughter or transferred to a different field, the nutrients aren't replaced through their remains or waste products.

***Figure 1:** Pellets of a chemical fertiliser — diammonium phosphate.*

## Using fertilisers

Adding fertiliser replaces the lost minerals, so more energy from the ecosystem can be used for growth, increasing the efficiency of energy transfer. Fertilisers can be artificial or natural.

- Artificial fertilisers are inorganic — they contain pure chemicals (e.g. ammonium nitrate) as powders or pellets.
- Natural fertilisers are organic matter — they include manure, composted vegetables, crop residues (the parts left over after the harvest) and sewage sludge.

***Figure 2:** A tractor spreading natural fertiliser — liquid manure.*

## Environmental issues

Sometimes more fertiliser is applied than the plants need or are able to use at a particular time. This can lead to the fertilisers **leaching** into waterways. Leaching is when water-soluble compounds in the soil are washed away, e.g. by rain or irrigation systems. They're often washed into nearby ponds and rivers. This can lead to **eutrophication** (see next page).

Inorganic ions in chemical fertilisers are relatively soluble. This means that excess minerals that are not used immediately are more likely to leach into waterways. Leaching is also more likely to occur if the fertiliser is applied just before heavy rainfall.

Leaching is less likely with natural fertilisers — that's because the nitrogen and phosphorus are still contained in organic molecules that need to be decomposed by microorganisms before they can be absorbed by plants. This means that their release into the soil for uptake by plants is more controlled. The leaching of phosphates is less likely than the leaching of nitrates because phosphates are less soluble in water.

Using fertilisers may also change the balance of nutrients in the soil — too much of a particular nutrient can cause crops and other plants to die.

## Eutrophication

Eutrophication is caused by excess nutrients. The process of eutrophication is explained below and illustrated in Figure 3:

1. Mineral ions leached from fertilised fields stimulate the rapid growth of algae in ponds and rivers.
2. Large amounts of algae block light from reaching the plants below.
3. Eventually the plants die because they're unable to photosynthesise enough.
4. Bacteria feed on the dead plant matter. The increased numbers of bacteria reduce the oxygen concentration in the water by carrying out aerobic respiration.
5. Fish and other aquatic organisms die because there isn't enough dissolved oxygen.

**Tip:** Eutrophication is where too many mineral ions in the water cause a sequence of "mega-growth, mega-death and mega-decay" involving most of the plant and animal life in the water.

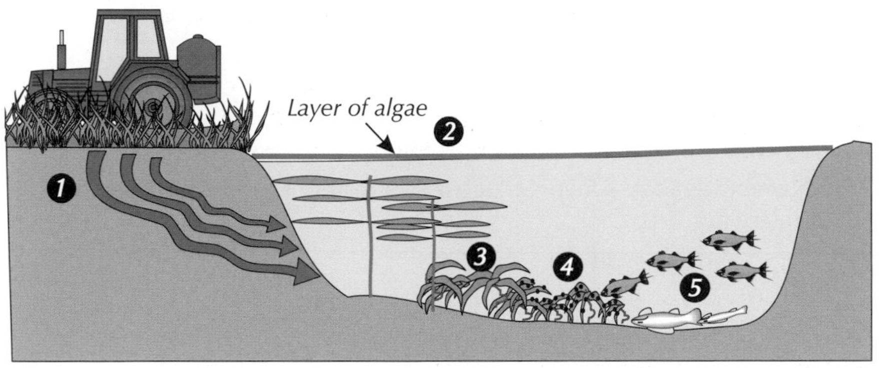


***Figure 3:*** *The process of eutrophication.*

***Figure 4:*** *Algae growing on the Thames estuary.*

## Practice Questions — Application

A study was conducted to investigate the changes in nitrate concentration and algal content down a stretch of river with two farms along it (river A). In the same study, the nitrate concentration and algal content of a river without farmland along it (control river) was also recorded. The results are shown in the graph below:

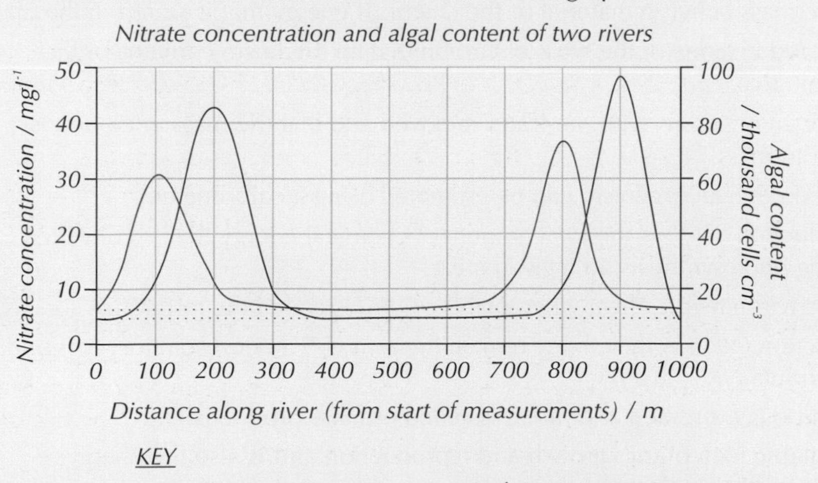


**Tip:** The questions about this graph are on the next page.

Tip: There's more on drawing conclusions on pages 13-14.

Q1 a) Suggest the distance at which the two farms are situated along river A. Explain your answer.

b) i) Calculate the percentage increase in peak nitrate concentration between the first and second farm along the river.

ii) Suggest a reason for this increase.

Q2 What do the results of the control river show?

Q3 a) Draw a conclusion from the data shown in the graph.

b) Suggest an explanation for your conclusion.

Q4 Describe and explain the possible consequences of the peaks in the algal content of river A at 200 m and 900 m.

## Practice Questions — Fact Recall

Q1 Explain how mineral ions are lost from crop fields.

Q2 Give an example of a natural fertiliser.

Q3 By what process do fertilisers get into waterways?

Q4 Name the process that can occur as a result of excess fertilisers in waterways.

## Section Summary

Make sure you know...

- That plants make organic compounds during photosynthesis using light energy from the Sun and carbon dioxide from the atmosphere (in land-based ecosystems) and dissolved in water (in aquatic ecosystems).
- That some of the sugars produced during photosynthesis are used immediately for respiration.
- That the rest of the sugars are used to make biological molecules — these form the plants' biomass.
- That a plant's biomass is the mass of living material or the chemical energy that is stored in the plant.
- That biomass can be measured in terms of the mass of carbon that an organism contains or the dry mass of its tissue per unit area.
- That dry mass is the mass of an organism with the water removed and that the mass of carbon is approximately 50% of the dry mass.
- That the chemical energy stored in an organism can be estimated using a calorimeter.
- That the gross primary production (*GPP*) is the total amount of chemical energy that is converted from light energy by plants during photosynthesis, in a given area.
- That the energy lost to the environment as heat when plants respire is called the respiratory loss (*R*).
- That the net primary production (*NPP*) is the energy remaining from *GPP* after respiratory loss and that this is shown by the formula $NPP = GPP - R$.
- That when primary production is expressed as a rate it is called primary productivity.
- That *NPP* is the energy available for a plant's growth and reproduction and is also the energy available to the next trophic level.
- That consumers also store energy as biomass.

- That about 90% of the energy available to consumers is lost to the environment — some is not ingested (e.g. roots, bones), some is indigestible and is egested as faeces, and some is lost through respiration or the excretion of urine.
- That the remaining energy or net production ($N$) of consumers can be calculated using the following formula: $N = I - (F + R)$, where $I$ is the chemical energy in ingested food, $F$ is the chemical energy lost in faeces and urine and $R$ is the energy lost through respiration.
- That when net production of consumers is expressed as a rate it can be called net or secondary productivity.
- That food chains and webs show how energy is transferred through an ecosystem.
- That farming practices try to maximise production by simplifying food webs to reduce energy losses (e.g. by removing pests using pesticides or biological agents) and by reducing respiratory losses (e.g. by limiting the movement of livestock and keeping livestock warm).
- That microorganisms such as bacteria and fungi are saprobionts and recycle nutrients through food webs through the decomposition of dead plants and animals and waste matter.
- That some fungi form symbiotic relationships with plants known as mycorrhizae, and that these increase the rate of water and mineral ion uptake by plants by increasing the surface area of the plants' root system.
- The role of microorganisms in the four main processes of the nitrogen cycle: nitrogen fixation, ammonification, nitrification and denitrification, including the role of saprobionts.
- How phosphorus is recycled in natural ecosystems, including the role of mycorrhizae.
- That natural and artificial fertilisers are used to replace the nitrates and phosphates that are lost from the soil when crops are harvested or livestock are removed from the area.
- That leaching is when water soluble compounds in the soil are washed away, e.g. by rain.
- That the leaching of fertilisers can cause eutrophication.
- That eutrophication involves the rapid growth of algae, causing plants to die from lack of light, and that bacteria feeding on the dead organic matter decrease the oxygen concentration causing other aquatic organisms to die as well.

# Exam-style Questions

1 **Figure 1** shows the net productivity of some organisms in a food web. All the figures are in kJ $m^{-2}$ $yr^{-1}$.

**Figure 1**

*Box A*

*Producer 38 750*

*Primary consumer 1 2619*

*Secondary consumer 1*

*Primary consumer 2 1265*

*Secondary consumer 2 302*

*Saprobionts*

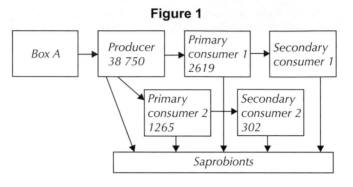

**1.1** Name the source of energy represented by Box A and the process by which this energy is transferred to the producer.

*(2 marks)*

**1.2** The respiratory loss of secondary consumer 1 is 785 kJ $m^{-2}$ $yr^{-1}$ and the energy lost through urine and faeces is 1571 kJ $m^{-2}$ $yr^{-1}$. Calculate the net productivity of secondary consumer 1.

*(1 mark)*

**1.3** Calculate the difference in the percentage efficiency of energy transfer between the producer and primary consumer 1, and the producer and primary consumer 2.

*(2 marks)*

**1.4** Describe the role of the saprobionts in this food web.

*(2 marks)*

2 A group of scientists were investigating the effect of mycorrhizae on the growth of plant seedlings.

The scientists inoculated a group of seedlings with a mycorrhizal culture and grew them under controlled conditions for 60 days. A control group of seedlings was not inoculated with the mycorrhizal culture but was grown under the same conditions. The seedlings in each set were periodically weighed and their mean mass recorded. The results are shown in **Figure 2**.

**Figure 2**

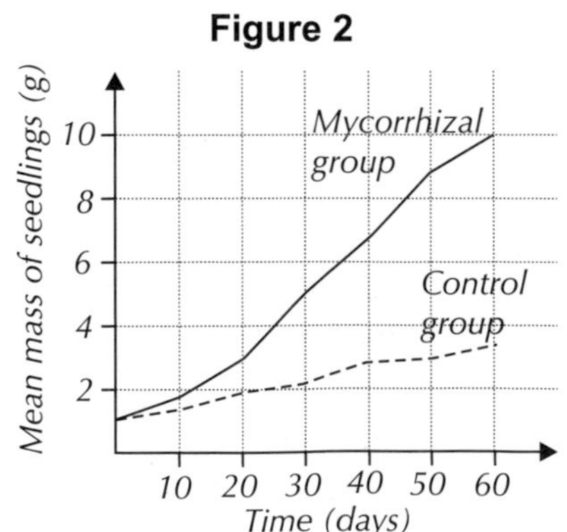


**2.1** Explain what is meant by the term 'mycorrhizae'.

*(1 mark)*

**2.2** Suggest **two** environmental conditions under which the seedlings were grown, which should have been controlled by the scientists.

*(1 mark)*

**2.3** Calculate the average rate of growth in the mycorrhizal group between 30 and 60 days. Give your answer in g day$^{-1}$.

*(1 mark)*

**2.4** Suggest an explanation for the differences between the mycorrhizal group and the control group shown in **Figure 2**.

*(3 marks)*

**3** A study was carried out to investigate the effect of different types of pest control on greenfly — a pest species.

Three fields of potato crops, each with a greenfly infestation, were treated with a different type of pest control — one with a pesticide, the other with lacewing insects (a natural predator of greenfly) and the third with an integrated system that made use of both a pesticide and lacewings.

The study included a negative control. The number of greenfly in each field was recorded over time. The net primary production of each field was also measured. The graphs below show the results.

**Figure 3**

Number of greenfly

KEY
— negative control
····· pesticide
····· lacewings
- · - integrated system

0 100 200
Time / days

**Figure 4**

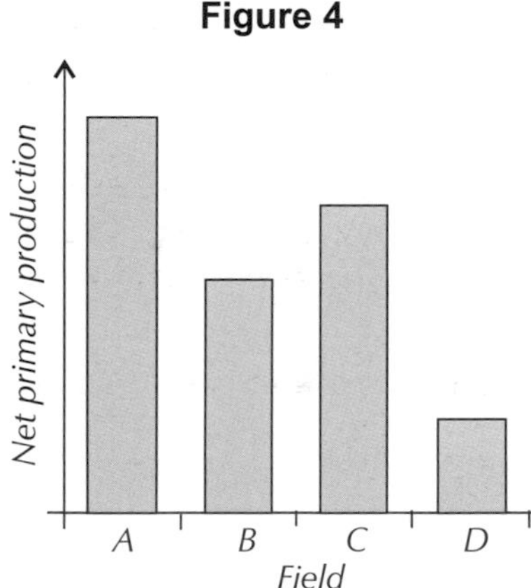

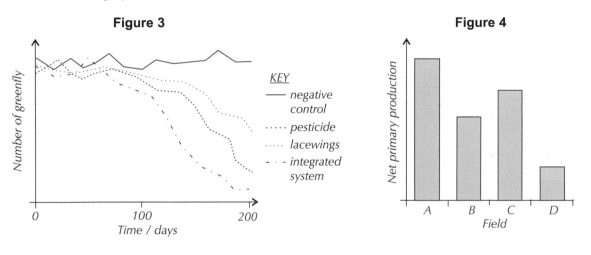


**3.1** Suggest what the negative control would have been in this study.

*(1 mark)*

**3.2** Using the results of **Figure 3** and your own knowledge, identify which field in **Figure 4** is the negative control field and which is the field treated with the integrated system. Explain your answers.

*(4 marks)*

Net productivity can be thought of as the rate at which energy is stored or the rate at which biomass is added.

**3.3** Suggest and explain a method for determining the rate at which biomass is added by a potato crop over a study period.

*(4 marks)*

# Topic 6 A: Stimuli and Responses

**Learning Objectives:**
- Know that organisms increase their chance of survival by responding to changes in their environment.
- Know that taxes and kineses are simple responses that maintain a mobile organism in a favourable environment.
- Be able to investigate the effect of an environmental variable on the movement of an animal using either a choice chamber or a maze (Required Practical 10).

**Specification Reference 3.6.1.1**

## 1. Survival and Response

*In order to survive, organisms need to respond to what's going on around them. Otherwise they'd find themselves in a pretty unfavourable position...*

### Responding to the environment

Organisms increase their chances of survival by responding to changes in their external environment. Animals and plants respond in different ways.

**Examples**
- Animals can move away from harmful environments such as places that are too hot or too cold.
- Plants can't actually move themselves, but they can change the way they grow in an attempt to find more favourable environmental conditions. E.g. seedlings growing in dark conditions can rapidly develop very long, thin stems to increase their chances of finding light.

Organisms also respond to changes in their internal environment to make sure that the conditions are always optimal for their metabolism (all the chemical reactions that go on inside them).

Any change in the internal or external environment, e.g. a change in temperature, light intensity or pressure, is called a **stimulus**.

### Simple responses

Simple mobile organisms, e.g. woodlice, have simple responses to keep them in a favourable environment. Their response can either be tactic or kinetic:

**Tactic response (taxis)** — directional movement in response to a stimulus. The direction of the stimulus affects the response.

**Example**

Woodlice show a tactic response to light — they move away from a light source. This helps them survive as it keeps them concealed under stones during the day (where they're safe from predators) and keeps them in damp conditions (which reduces water loss).

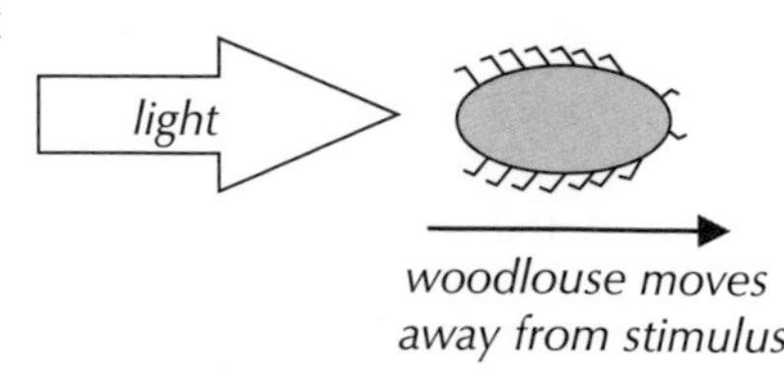


**Kinetic response (kinesis)** — non-directional (random) movement in response to a stimulus. The intensity of the stimulus affects the response.

**Example**

Woodlice show a kinetic response to humidity. In high humidity they move slowly and turn less often, so that they stay where they are. As the air gets drier, they move faster and turn more often, so that they move into a new area. This response helps woodlice move from drier air to more humid air, and then stay put. This improves their chances of survival — it reduces their water loss and it helps to keep them concealed.

**Tip:** If an organism moves towards a stimulus it's a positive taxis, and if it moves away from a stimulus it's a negative taxis. So in the first example, woodlice show a negative taxis to light.

**Tip:** Taxes is the plural of taxis, kineses is the plural of kinesis.

**Tip:** The word before 'taxis' tells you what the organism is responding to, e.g. phototaxis is a response to light.

# Investigating simple animal responses

**REQUIRED PRACTICAL 10**

A choice chamber is a container with different compartments, in which you can create different environmental conditions. It can be used to investigate how animals, such as woodlice or maggots, respond to conditions like light intensity or humidity in the laboratory. Here's how you can use a choice chamber:

> **Tip:** Simple responses are automatic responses to a stimulus — the organism doesn't 'choose' where to move.

1. Construct a choice chamber using the equipment shown in Figure 1.

> **Tip:** Don't forget to assess all the risks involved before you begin your experiment.

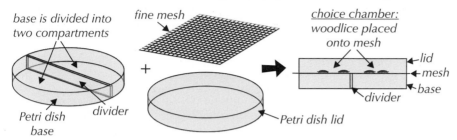

**Figure 1:** *How to construct a choice chamber.*

2. To investigate the effect of light intensity on woodlouse movement, cover one half of the lid (including the sides) with black paper. This will make one side of the chamber dark. Put damp filter paper in both sides of the base to make the humidity constant throughout the chamber.
3. Place 10 woodlice on the mesh in the centre of the chamber and position the lid on the mesh so it's lined up with the base below.
4. After 10 minutes, take off the lid and record the number of woodlice on each side of the chamber. Try to minimise the amount of time the lid is off, so that the environmental conditions created aren't disturbed.
5. Repeat the experiment after gently moving the woodlice back to the centre. You can use a small, soft paintbrush to help with moving the woodlice if necessary. You should find that most woodlice end up on the dark side of the choice chamber (a tactic response to light).
6. To investigate humidity, place some damp filter paper in one side of the base and a desiccating (drying) agent (such as anhydrous calcium chloride) in the other side. Don't cover the lid with paper. Put the lid on and leave the chamber for 10 minutes for the environmental conditions to stabilise before carrying out steps 3-5 above.

> **Tip:** For ethical reasons, you should handle the woodlice carefully and return them to their natural habitat as soon as possible. Make sure you wash your hands after handling the woodlice.

> **Tip:** Be careful if you use anhydrous calcium chloride. It's an irritant to the eyes and skin and generates heat on contact with water. Make sure you're wearing eye protection.

You can also investigate simple animal responses using a maze. For example, a paper maze can be used to investigate turning behaviour in woodlice and whether it's affected by light intensity.

> **Tip:** After being forced to turn in a particular direction, woodlice will often turn in the opposite direction next time they have a free choice. This turn alternation can increase the chances of them finding more favourable conditions because it means that they move into different areas.

## Practice Question — Application

Q1 *E. coli*, a type of bacteria, have been observed to move towards the highest concentration of oxygen in their surroundings.

a) What type of simple response is this?

b) Suggest why *E. coli* move in this way.

## Practice Questions — Fact Recall

Q1 Why is it important that organisms respond to stimuli?

Q2 What is a tactic response?

Q3 What is a kinetic response?

**Learning Objective:**

- Know that a simple reflex has a protective effect, exemplified by a three-neurone simple reflex.

**Specification Reference 3.6.1.1**

# 2. Nervous Communication

*In order to respond to changes in the environment, an organism needs to pass information between different areas of its body. In animals some of this communication is carried out using nerve impulses.*

## Receptors and effectors

Receptors detect stimuli — they can be cells, or proteins on cell surface membranes. There are loads of different types of receptors that detect different stimuli, e.g. baroreceptors are a type of receptor that detect changes in blood pressure, but receptors are specific to one type of stimulus (see page 78).

Effectors are cells that bring about a response to a stimulus, to produce an effect. Effectors include muscle cells and cells found in glands, e.g. the pancreas. Receptors communicate with effectors via the nervous system or the hormonal system, or sometimes using both.

## The nervous system

### Neurones (nerve cells)

The nervous system is made up of a complex network of cells called neurones. There are three main types of neurone:

1. **Sensory neurones** transmit electrical impulses from receptors to the central nervous system (CNS) — the brain and spinal cord.
2. **Motor neurones** transmit electrical impulses from the CNS to effectors.
3. **Relay neurones** (also called intermediate neurones, interneurones or association neurones) transmit electrical impulses between sensory neurones and motor neurones.

**Tip:** For more information about the CNS see page 82.

### Nervous communication

A stimulus is detected by receptor cells and an electrical impulse is sent along a sensory neurone. When an electrical impulse reaches the end of a neurone chemicals called **neurotransmitters** take the information across the gap (called a synapse) to the next neurone, where another electrical impulse is generated (see p. 93). The CNS (the coordinator) processes the information and sends impulses along motor neurones to an effector (see Figure 1).

**Tip:** The electrical impulses sent along neurones are also called nerve impulses or action potentials — see page 89.

**Tip:** The coordinator formulates an appropriate response to a stimulus before sending impulses to an effector.

***Figure 1:*** *The pathway of nervous communication.*

**Example**

A real-life example of nervous communication is when you see a friend waving to you and you wave back in response:

- **Stimulus** — you see a friend waving.
- **Receptors** — light receptors (photoreceptors) in your eyes detect the wave. The electrical impulse is carried by a sensory neurone to the CNS.
- **CNS** — processes information and sends an electrical impulse along a motor neurone.
- **Effectors** — muscle cells are stimulated by the motor neurone.
- **Response** — muscles contract to make your arm wave.

### The nervous response

When an electrical impulse reaches the end of a neurone, chemical messengers called neurotransmitters are secreted directly onto cells (e.g. muscle cells) — so the nervous response is localised. Neurotransmitters are quickly removed once they've done their job, so the response is short-lived. Electrical impulses are really fast, so the response is usually rapid — this allows animals to react quickly to stimuli.

**Tip:** The cells that neurotransmitters are released onto are called target cells — they have specific receptors for the neurotransmitters (see page 93 for more).

## Simple reflexes

A simple reflex is a rapid, involuntary response to a stimulus. The pathway of communication goes through the spinal cord but not through conscious parts of the brain, so the response happens automatically. Because you don't have to spend time deciding how to respond, information travels really fast from receptors to effectors.

Simple reflexes are protective — they help organisms to avoid damage to the body because the response happens so quickly.

**Tip:** Nervous impulses that involve the conscious brain are voluntary responses — you have to think about them. Reflexes don't involve the conscious brain so they're involuntary responses — your body responds without thinking about it first.

### The reflex arc

The pathway of neurones linking receptors to effectors in a simple reflex is called a reflex arc. Three neurones are involved — a sensory neurone, a relay neurone and a motor neurone (see Figure 2).

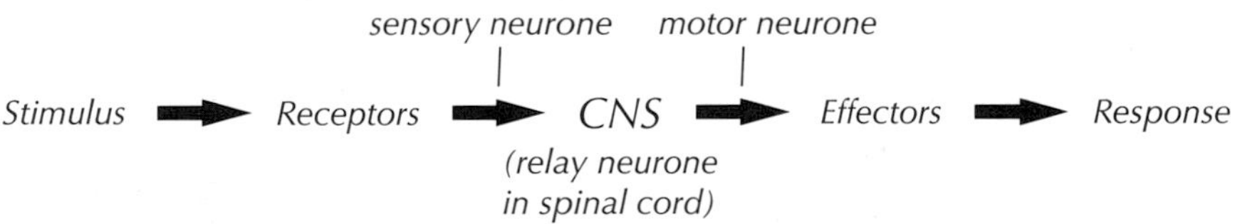


***Figure 2:*** *The pathway of nervous communication in a simple reflex arc.*

**Example**

A real-life example of a simple reflex is the hand-withdrawal response to heat:

- **Stimulus** — you touch a hot surface.
- **Receptors** — thermoreceptors (heat receptors) in your skin detect the heat stimulus. A sensory neurone carries the impulse to the CNS.
- **CNS** — a relay neurone in your spinal cord carries the impulse to a motor neurone.
- **Effectors** — the motor neurone carries the impulse to muscle cells in your biceps.
- **Response** — your biceps muscle contracts to pull your hand away from the heat source and stop your hand from being damaged.

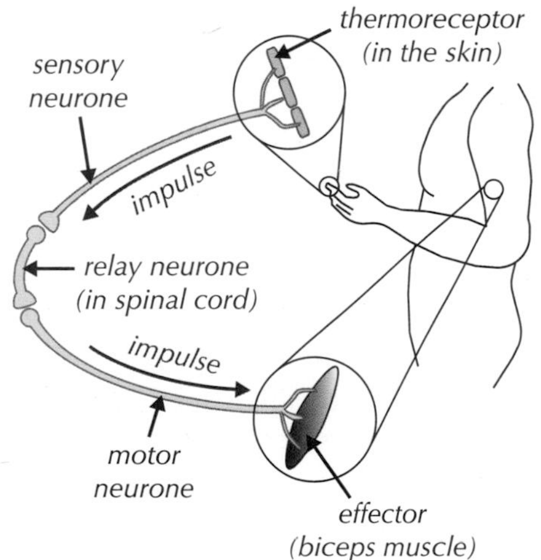


**Exam Tip**
You need to learn a simple reflex arc involving three neurones for your exam. The hand-withdrawal response to heat is a really common example.

If there's a relay neurone involved in the simple reflex arc then it's possible to override the reflex, e.g. in the example above your brain could tell your hand to withstand the heat.

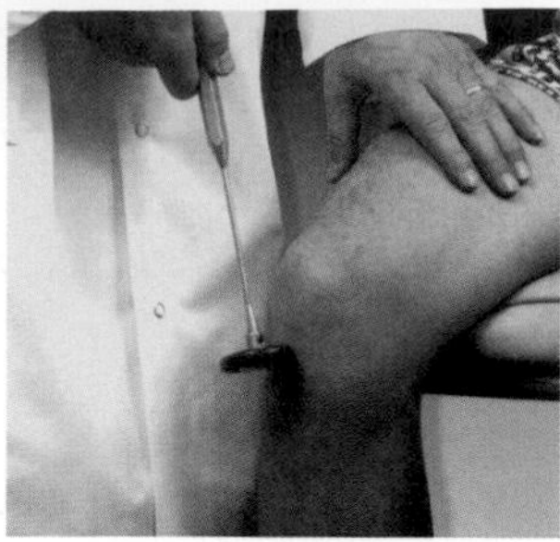

*Figure 3:* *A doctor testing the knee-jerk reflex of a patient.*

**Tip:** When you're asked to 'suggest' answers, you're not expected to be able to give an exact, detailed answer. Instead, you're expected to use your knowledge to make educated and plausible suggestions.

## Practice Questions — Application

Q1 The knee-jerk reflex involves lightly tapping a person on the patellar tendon (just below the knee-cap) with a tendon hammer. When this happens, the quadriceps muscle (in the thigh) immediately contracts, causing the person's lower leg to jerk forward.

a) This response is a reflex. Suggest one way in which the response would differ if it was not a reflex.

b) Name the stimulus and the effector in the knee-jerk reflex.

c) The knee-jerk reflex is unusual because the sensory neurone synapses directly onto the motor neurone in the spinal cord.

i) Describe how this differs from a simple reflex, such as the hand-withdrawal response to heat.

ii) Suggest what effect tapping the patellar tendon might have in someone with a spinal cord injury. Explain your answer.

Q2 Many nociceptors (pain receptors) are located in the skin.

a) Describe the pathway of nervous communication that would take place in a healthy person if they pricked their finger with a pin.

Congenital insensitivity to pain is a condition where the body does not feel physical pain. The condition is a result of non-functional nociceptors. The ability of sufferers to feel a light touch is usually normal.

b) Suggest why people with this condition are able to feel a light touch even though they're unable to feel pain.

c) Suggest why it's beneficial to an organism to be able to detect and respond to pain.

## Practice Questions — Fact Recall

Q1 What is the role of a receptor?

Q2 Give two types of cell that act as effectors.

Q3 Describe the roles of the following types of neurone:

a) sensory,

b) motor,

c) relay.

Q4 a) Describe the pathway of nervous communication from stimulus to response, in a voluntary response.

b) Which part of the pathway acts as the coordinator in this response?

Q5 Explain why nervous communication leads to a localised and short-lived response.

Q6 Reflexes are involuntary responses to stimuli. Explain why they are involuntary.

Q7 Why do simple reflexes help an organism to avoid damage to their body?

# 3. Responses in Plants

*Just like animals, plants also respond to stimuli. Not surprisingly they use a different system to animals — it's all about tropisms and growth factors in the plant world...*

## Tropisms

Flowering plants, like animals, increase their chances of survival by responding to changes in their environment.

**Examples**

- They sense the direction of light and grow towards it to maximise light absorption for photosynthesis.
- They can sense gravity, so their roots and shoots grow in the right direction.
- Climbing plants have a sense of touch, so they can find things to climb and reach the sunlight.

A tropism is the response of a plant to a directional stimulus (a stimulus coming from a particular direction). Plants respond to stimuli by regulating their growth. A positive tropism is growth towards the stimulus, whereas a negative tropism is growth away from the stimulus.

### Phototropism

Phototropism is the growth of a plant in response to light. Shoots are positively phototropic and grow towards light (see Figure 1). Roots are negatively phototropic and grow away from light (see Figure 2).

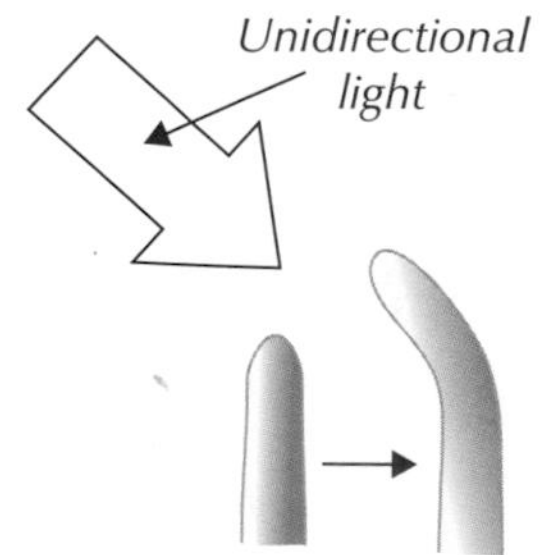


***Figure 1:*** *Phototropism in shoots.*

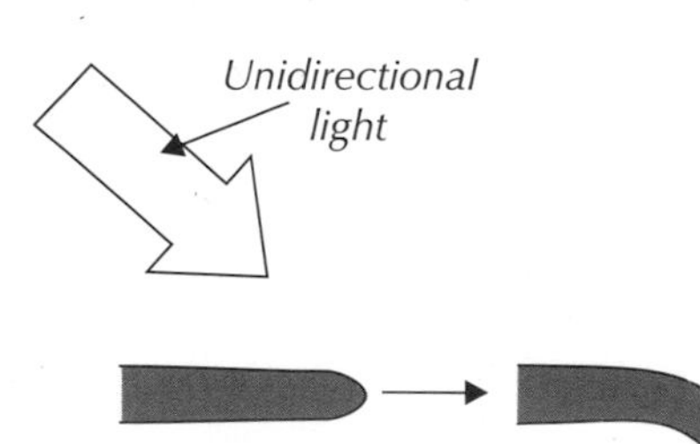


***Figure 2:*** *Phototropism in roots.*

### Gravitropism

Gravitropism is the growth of a plant in response to gravity. Shoots are negatively gravitropic and grow upwards (see Figure 4). Roots are positively gravitropic and grow downwards (see Figure 5).

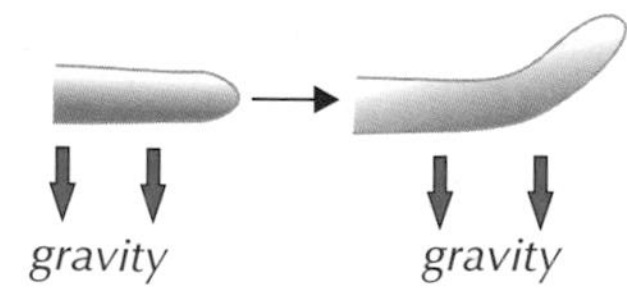


***Figure 4:*** *Gravitropism in shoots.*

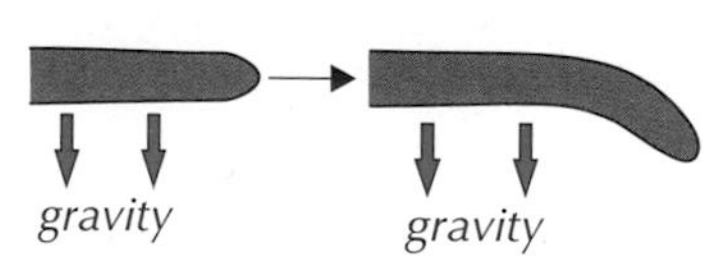


***Figure 5:*** *Gravitropism in roots.*

## Auxins

Plants respond to directional stimuli using specific growth factors — these are hormone-like chemicals that speed up or slow down plant growth. Plant growth factors are produced in the growing regions of the plant (e.g. shoot and root tips) and they move to where they're needed in the other parts of the plant.

**Learning Objectives:**

- Know that in flowering plants, specific growth factors move from growing regions to other tissues, where they regulate growth in response to directional stimuli.
- Know the effect of different concentrations of indoleacetic acid (IAA) on cell elongation in the roots and shoots of flowering plants as an explanation of gravitropism and phototropism in flowering plants.

**Specification Reference 3.6.1.1**

***Figure 3:*** *A radish seedling showing positive phototropism.*

**Tip:** Gravitropism is sometimes referred to as geotropism.

***Figure 6:*** *A radish seedling showing negative gravitropism.*

> **Tip:** There are other classes of growth factors that affect growth in different ways, e.g. a growth factor called gibberellin stimulates flowering and seed germination.

Growth factors called **auxins** are produced in the tips of shoots and diffuse backwards to stimulate the cell just behind the tips to elongate — this is where cell walls become loose and stretchy, so the cells get longer (see Figure 7). If the tip of a shoot is removed, no auxin will be available and the shoot stops growing.

Auxins stimulate growth in shoots but high concentrations inhibit growth in roots.

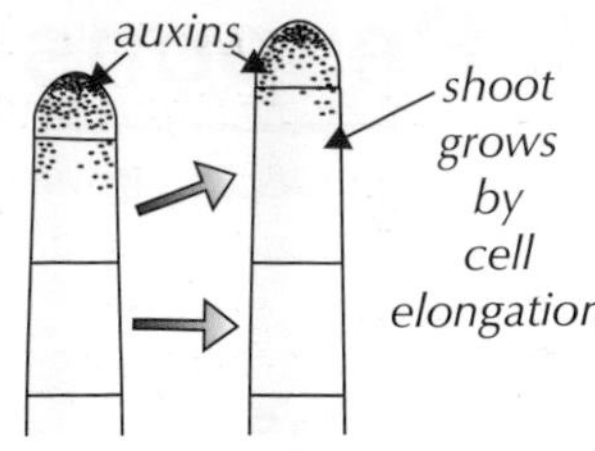


***Figure 7:** Effect of auxins on shoot growth.*

### Indoleacetic acid (IAA)

Indoleacetic acid (IAA) is an important auxin that's produced in the tips of shoots and roots in flowering plants. It's moved around the plant to control tropisms — it moves by diffusion and active transport over short distances, and via the phloem over long distances. This results in different parts of the plant having different concentrations of IAA. The uneven distribution of IAA means there's uneven growth of the plant.

> **Tip:** Phloem is a tissue which transports sugars around a plant.

**Example — phototropism**

IAA moves to the more shaded parts of the shoots and roots, so there's uneven growth.

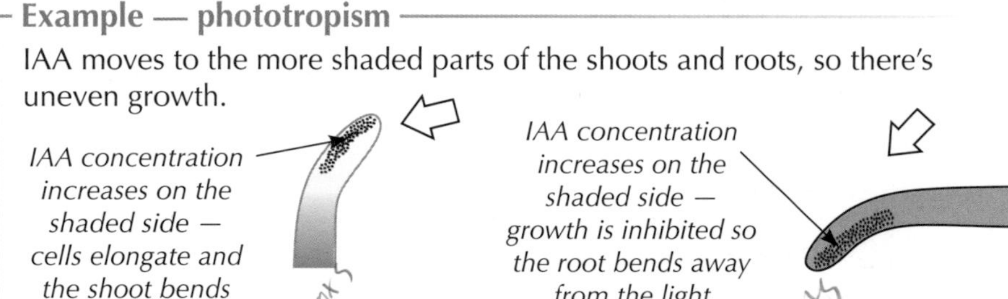


> **Exam Tip**
> You need to learn these examples for the exam.

> **Tip:** Remember, root growth is inhibited by high concentrations of IAA. The opposite is true in shoots — high concentrations of IAA promote shoot growth.

**Example — gravitropism**

IAA moves to the underside of shoots and roots, so there's uneven growth.

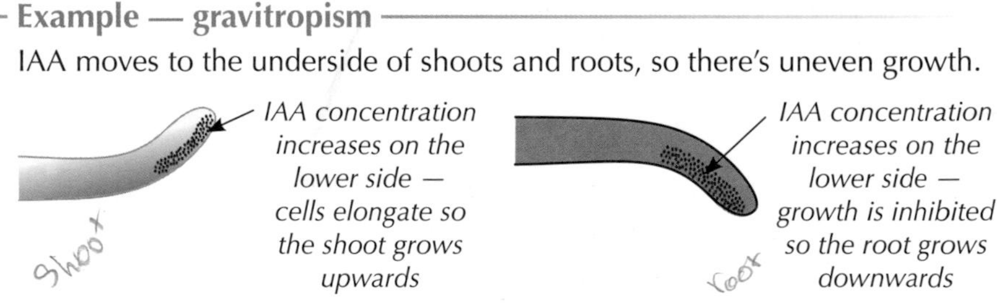

IAA concentration increases on the lower side — cells elongate so the shoot grows upwards
IAA concentration increases on the lower side — growth is inhibited so the root grows downwards


> **Tip:** Remember, gravitropism is the growth of a plant in response to gravity.

## Interpreting experimental data about IAA

In the exam, you could be given some experimental data on IAA and then be asked to interpret the data. You could get something that looks a little like this:

**Example**

An experiment was carried out to investigate the role of IAA in shoot growth. Eight shoots, equal in height and mass, had their tips removed. Sponges soaked in glucose and either IAA or water were then placed where the tip should be. Four shoots were then placed in the dark (experiment A) and the other four shoots were exposed to a light source, directed at them from the right (experiment B) — see Figure 8 (next page).

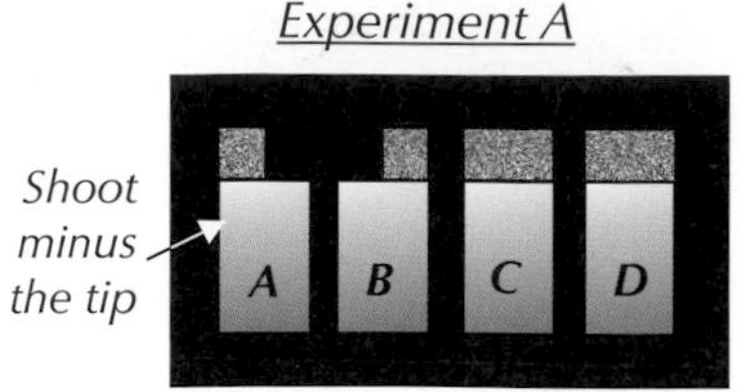

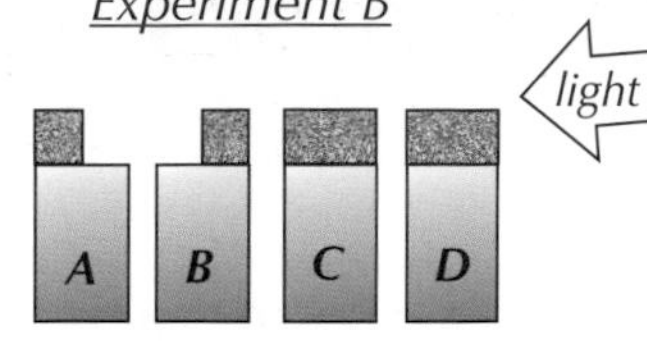


Sponge soaked in IAA and glucose   Sponge soaked in water and glucose

***Figure 8:*** *An investigation into the role of IAA.*

After two days the amount of growth (in mm) and direction of growth was recorded. The results are shown in the table on the right.

| | Growth / mm | | | |
|---|---|---|---|---|
| | Shoot A | Shoot B | Shoot C | Shoot D |
| Experiment A (dark) | 6, right | 6, left | 6, straight | 1, straight |
| Experiment B (light) | 8, right | 8, right | 8, right | 3, straight |

**You could be asked to explain the data...**

The results show how the movement of IAA controls phototropism in plant shoots. In experiment A shoot A, the IAA diffused straight down from the sponge into the left-hand side of the shoot. This stimulated the cells on this side to elongate, so the shoot grew towards the right. In shoot B, the opposite occurred, making the shoot grow towards the left. In shoot C, equal amounts of IAA diffused down both sides, making all the cells elongate at the same rate.

In experiment B, the shoots were exposed to a light source. The IAA diffused into the shoot and accumulated on the shaded side (left-hand side) regardless of where the sponge was placed. Shoots A, B and C all grew towards the right because most IAA accumulated on the left, stimulating cell elongation there.

**Tip:** Remember, growth factors are produced in shoot tips. So by removing the tips, any IAA already present is removed.

**Exam Tip**
You might be asked about experimental design in the exam. A good thing to think about is the use of controls. In this experiment the negative control treatment was the sponge soaked in water (and glucose) which was included to show that it was the IAA causing the observed effects and nothing else.

**Tip:** All sponges used were soaked in glucose to provide energy for growth of shoots. Photosynthesis can't take place in the dark so the growth of seedlings in experiment A might have been limited if they weren't provided with glucose (an external energy source).

## Practice Question — Application

Q1 Thigmotropism is a plant growth response to touch.

a) In the diagram on the right, does the shoot display positive or negative thigmotropism?

b) Is the concentration of auxins, such as IAA, likely to be highest at the point labelled X or Y? Explain why.

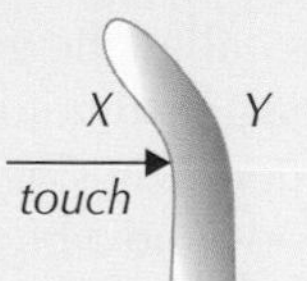


## Practice Questions — Fact Recall

Q1 What name is given to the growth of a plant in response to light?

Q2 Plant shoots are negatively gravitropic. What does this mean?

Q3 What parts of a plant produce growth factors?

Q4 How do auxins affect plant growth?

Q5 What is indoleacetic acid (IAA) and where is it produced?

Q6 How does IAA move around a plant?

Q7 Explain how the distribution of IAA affects the growth of:

a) shoots in response to light.

b) roots in response to gravity.

# 4. Receptors

*Receptors detect stimuli. They pass information about stimuli along the nervous pathway... and you need to know how they work.*

**Learning Objectives:**

- Know that the Pacinian corpuscle is an example of a receptor and illustrates that:
  - receptors only respond to specific stimuli.
  - stimulation of a receptor leads to the establishment of a generator potential.
- Know that deformation of stretch-mediated sodium ion channels in a Pacinian corpuscle leads to the establishment of a generator potential.
- Know the basic structure of a Pacinian corpuscle.
- Understand the human retina in sufficient detail to show how differences in sensitivity to light, sensitivity to colour and visual acuity are explained by differences in the optical pigments of rods and cones and the connections rods and cones make in the optic nerve.

**Specification Reference 3.6.1.2**

## How receptors work

Receptors are specific — they only detect one particular stimulus, e.g. light or glucose concentration or pressure (e.g. Pacinian corpuscles — see next page). There are many different types of receptor that each detect a different type of stimulus. Some receptors are cells, e.g. photoreceptors are receptor cells that connect to the nervous system (see p. 80). Some receptors are proteins on cell surface membranes, e.g. glucose receptors are proteins found in the cell membranes of some pancreatic cells.

Receptors in the nervous system convert the energy of the stimulus into the electrical energy used by neurones. Here's how they work...

### The resting potential

When a nervous system receptor is in its resting state (not being stimulated), there's a difference in charge between the inside and the outside of the cell — the inside is negatively charged relative to the outside (see Figure 1). This means there's a **voltage** across the membrane. Voltage is also known as **potential difference**. The potential difference when a cell is at rest is called its **resting potential**. The resting potential is generated by ion pumps and ion channels (see p. 88).

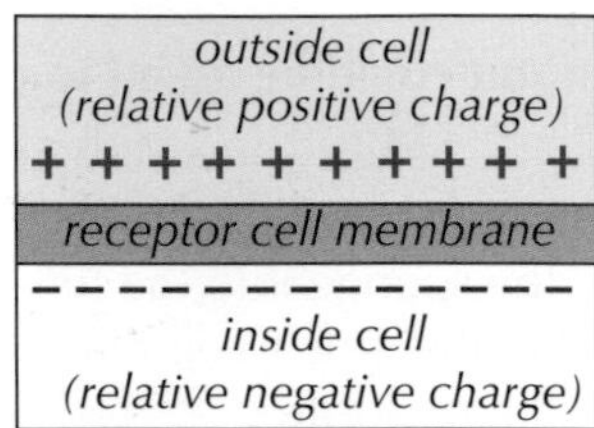


***Figure 1:** Relative charges either side of a receptor cell membrane at rest.*

**Tip:** Potential difference across a cell membrane is usually measured in millivolts (mV).

### The generator potential

When a stimulus is detected, the cell membrane is excited and becomes more permeable, allowing more ions to move in and out of the cell — altering the potential difference. The change in potential difference due to a stimulus is called the **generator potential**. A bigger stimulus excites the membrane more, causing a bigger movement of ions and a bigger change in potential difference — so a bigger generator potential is produced (see Figure 2).

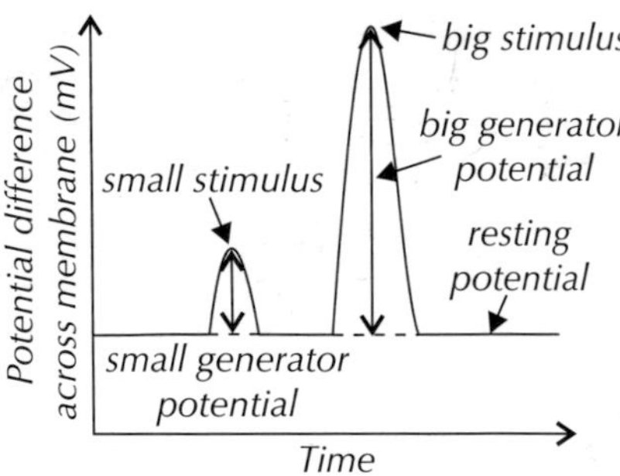


***Figure 2:** The bigger stimulus produces the bigger generator potential.*

### The action potential

If the generator potential is big enough it'll trigger an action potential — an electrical impulse along a neurone. An action potential is only triggered if the generator potential reaches a certain level called the **threshold level**. Action potentials are all one size, so the strength of the stimulus is measured by the frequency of action potentials (the number of action potentials triggered during a certain time period). If the stimulus is too weak the generator potential won't reach the threshold, so there's no action potential (Figure 3).

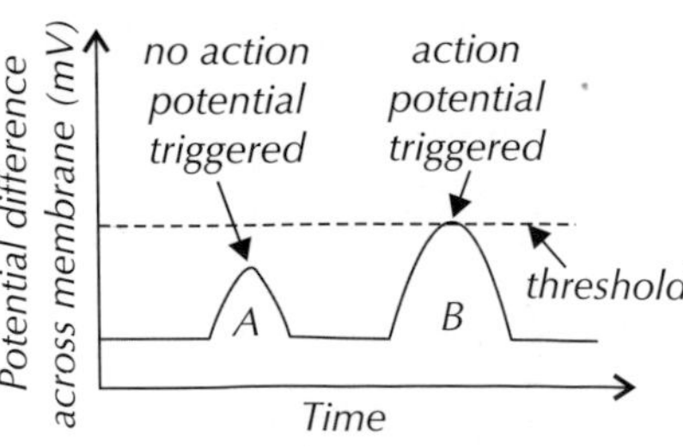


***Figure 3:** Generator potential not reaching the threshold (A) and reaching the threshold (B).*

**Tip:** There's much more on action potentials on pages 89-91.

# Pacinian corpuscles

Pacinian corpuscles are mechanoreceptors — they detect mechanical stimuli, e.g. pressure and vibrations. They're found in your skin. Pacinian corpuscles contain the end of a sensory neurone, imaginatively called a sensory nerve ending. The sensory nerve ending is wrapped in loads of layers of connective tissue called lamellae (see Figure 4).

When a Pacinian corpuscle is stimulated, e.g. by a tap on the arm, the lamellae are deformed and press on the sensory nerve ending. This causes the sensory neurone's cell membrane to stretch, deforming the **stretch-mediated sodium ion channels**. The channels open and sodium ions diffuse into the cell, creating a generator potential. If the generator potential reaches the threshold, it triggers an action potential.

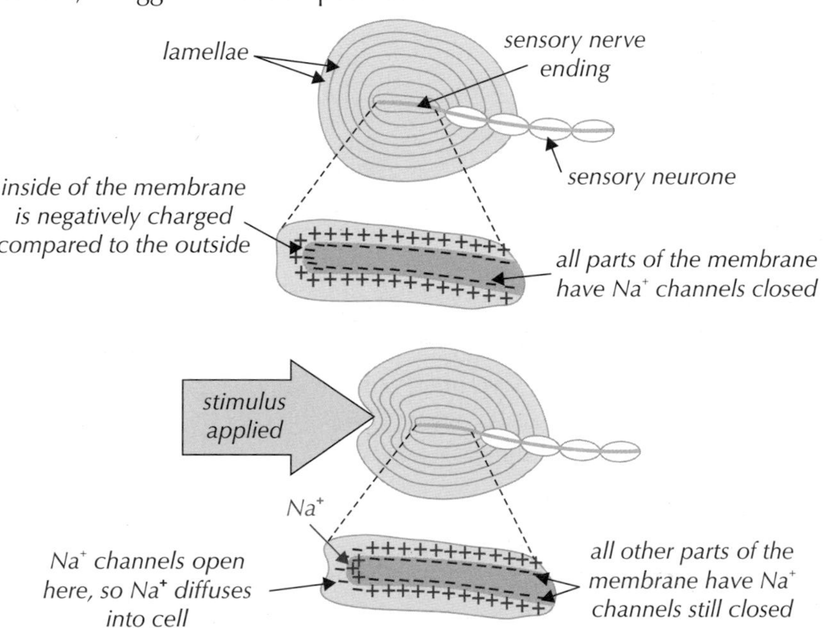


***Figure 4:*** *A Pacinian corpuscle at rest (top) and during stimulation (bottom).*

**Tip:** Pacinian corpuscles only respond to mechanical stimuli, not to any other type of stimulus — this is a good example of how receptors only respond to specific stimuli.

**Tip:** Stretch-mediated sodium ion channels get their name because they only open and let sodium ions pass through when they're stretched.

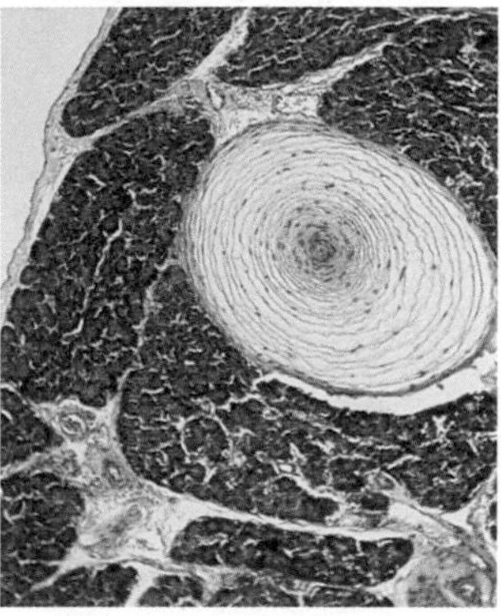

***Figure 5:*** *Light micrograph showing a section of a Pacinian corpuscle at rest.*

**Tip:** The bigger the stimulus (i.e. the more pressure that's applied), the more sodium channels open. This creates a bigger generator potential, which is more likely to reach the threshold and cause an action potential.

## Practice Questions — Application

Q1 For a particular receptor cell, an action potential is triggered when the generator potential reaches –60 mV.

a) What name is given to the value at which an action potential will be triggered?

The graph below shows generator potentials in the receptor cell.

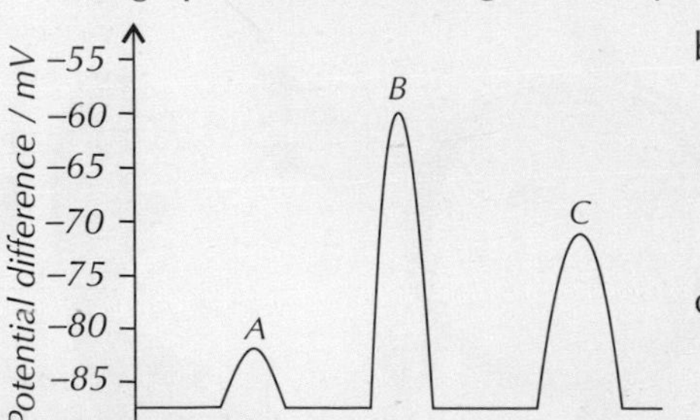


b) Which curve shows a generator potential that would trigger an action potential? Give a reason for your answer.

c) What is the resting potential of this receptor cell?

Q2 Suggest how a person's perception of touch might be affected by drugs that block stretch-mediated sodium ion channels in cell membranes.

## Photoreceptors

Photoreceptors are receptors in your eye that detect light. Light enters the eye through the pupil, and the amount of light that enters is controlled by the muscles of the iris. Light rays are focused by the lens onto the retina, which lines the inside of the eye. The retina contains the photoreceptor cells. The fovea is an area of the retina where there are lots of photoreceptors. Nerve impulses from the photoreceptor cells are carried from the retina to the brain by the optic nerve, which is a bundle of neurones. Where the optic nerve leaves the eye is called the blind spot — there aren't any photoreceptor cells, so it's not sensitive to light.

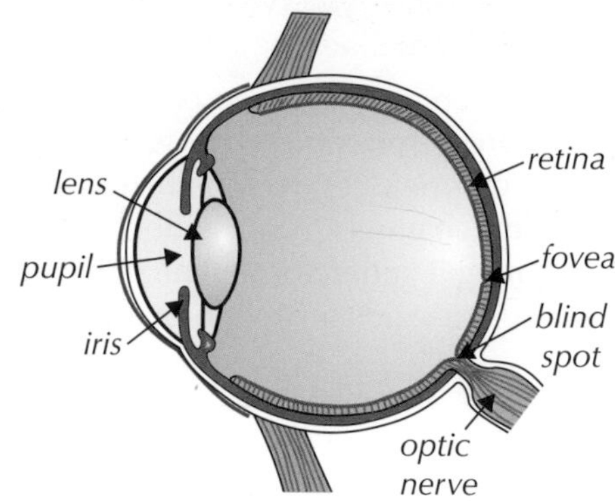


**Figure 6:** *Cross-section of an eye.*

**Figure 7:** *A section through a human retina. Light entering the eye from the left hits the photoreceptors (yellow), which connect to neurones (red).*

### How photoreceptors work

Light enters the eye, hits the photoreceptors and is absorbed by light-sensitive optical pigments. Light bleaches the pigments, causing a chemical change and altering the membrane permeability to sodium ions. A generator potential is created and if it reaches the threshold, a nerve impulse is sent along a bipolar neurone. Bipolar neurones connect photoreceptors to the optic nerve, which takes impulses to the brain (see Figure 8).

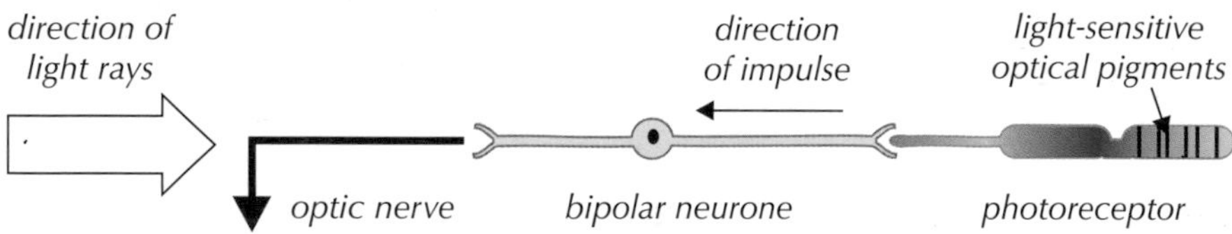


**Figure 8:** *Nervous communication in the eye.*

**Tip:** Light passes straight through the optic nerve and bipolar neurone to get to the photoreceptors.

### Rods and cones

The human eye has two types of photoreceptor — rods and cones. Rods are mainly found in the peripheral parts of the retina, and cones are mainly found packed together in the fovea — see Figure 9. Rods and cones contain different optical pigments making them sensitive to different wavelengths of light. Rods only give information in black and white (monochromatic vision), but cones give information in colour (trichromatic vision). There are three types of cones each containing a different optical pigment — red-sensitive, green-sensitive and blue-sensitive. When they're stimulated in different proportions you see different colours.

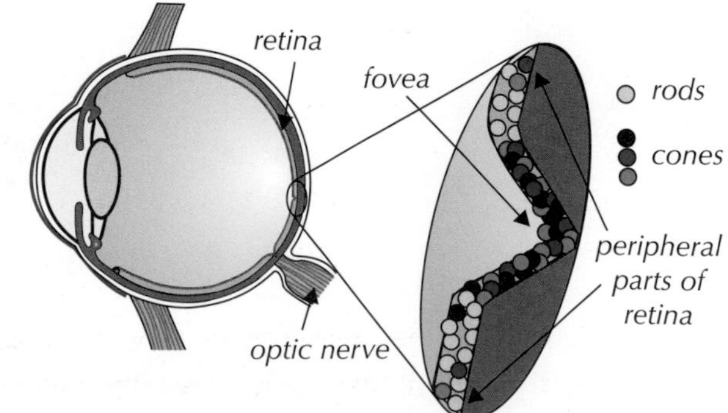


**Figure 9:** *Diagram showing the location of rods and cones.*

**Tip:** You are able to see yellow because this frequency of light (which falls between the wavelengths for red and green) stimulates both red and green-sensitive cones a bit — the brain converts this into seeing yellow.

**Sensitivity**

Rods are very sensitive to light (they work well in dim light).
This is because many rods join one bipolar neurone, so many weak generator potentials combine to reach the threshold and trigger an action potential.

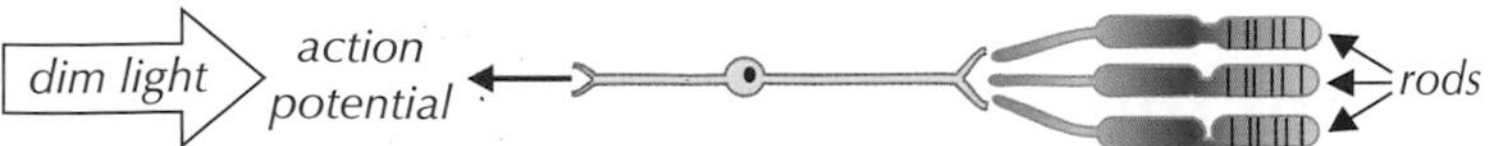


Cones are less sensitive than rods (they work best in bright light).
This is because one cone joins one bipolar neurone, so it takes more light to reach the threshold and trigger an action potential.

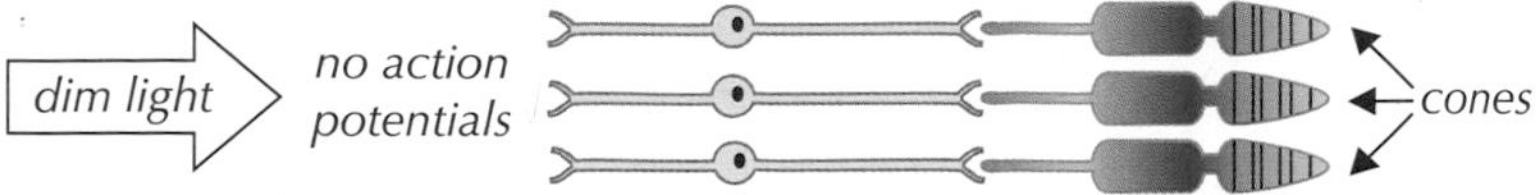


**Visual acuity**

Visual acuity is the ability to tell apart points that are close together.
Rods give low visual acuity because many rods join the same bipolar neurone, which means light from two points close together can't be told apart.

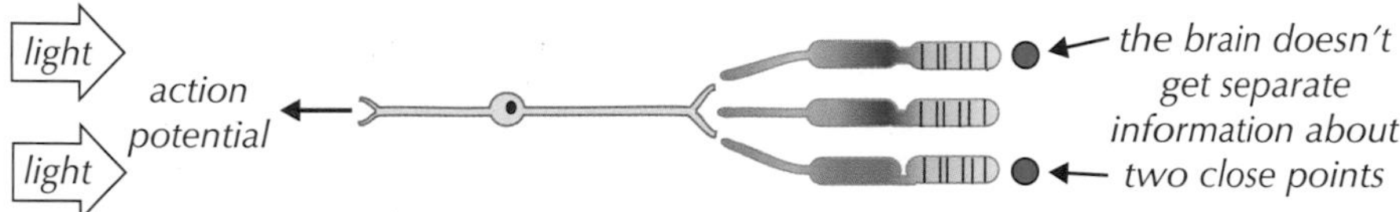


Cones give high visual acuity because cones are close together and one cone joins one bipolar neurone. When light from two points hits two cones, two action potentials (one from each cone) go to the brain — so you can distinguish two points that are close together as two separate points.

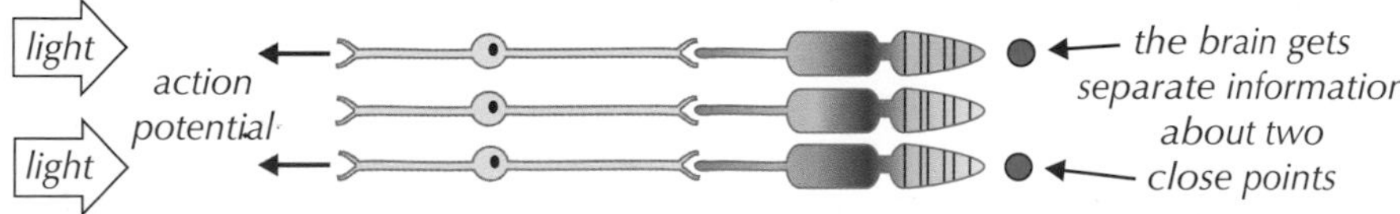


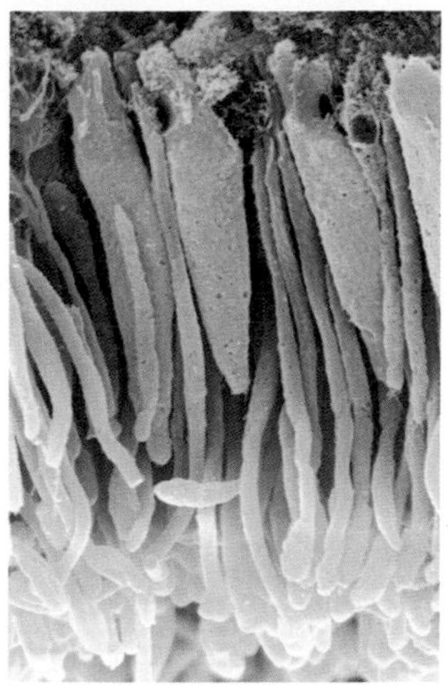

***Figure 10:*** *A scanning electron microscope (SEM) image of rod (white) and cone (green) cells in the retina.*

**Tip:** Someone with a low visual acuity will have blurry vision.

## Summary table of rods and cones

| Rods | Cones |
|---|---|
| Mainly located in the peripheral parts of the retina | Mainly located in the fovea |
| Give information in black and white | Give information in colour |
| Many rods join one bipolar neurone | One cone joins one bipolar neurone |
| High sensitivity to light | Low sensitivity to light |
| Give low visual acuity | Give high visual acuity |

**Tip:** Remember, cones are packed closely together.

## Practice Questions — Fact Recall

Q1 Explain how a generator potential is produced.

Q2 What type of stimulus does a Pacinian corpuscle respond to?

Q3 Describe the structure of a Pacinian corpuscle.

Q4 Explain how the presence of a stimulus triggers an action potential in a Pacinian corpuscle.

Q5 Explain why cones give a higher visual acuity than rods.

Q6 Other than visual acuity, give three differences between rods and cones.

# 5. Control of Heart Rate

*You can't consciously control your heart rate — it's controlled by a part of the nervous system called the autonomic nervous system, which does it for you.*

**Learning Objectives:**

- Know about myogenic stimulation of the heart and the transmission of a subsequent wave of electrical activity.
- Know the roles of the sinoatrial node (SAN), atrioventricular node (AVN) and Purkyne tissue in the bundle of His.
- Know the roles and locations of chemoreceptors and pressure receptors and the roles of the autonomic nervous system and effectors in controlling heart rate.

**Specification Reference 3.6.1.3**

## Structure of the nervous system

The nervous system is split into two different systems — the central nervous system (CNS) and the peripheral nervous system. The CNS is made up of the brain and spinal cord, whereas the peripheral nervous system is made up of the neurones that connect the CNS to the rest of the body.

The peripheral nervous system also has two different systems — the somatic and autonomic nervous systems. The somatic nervous system controls conscious activities, e.g. running and playing video games. The autonomic nervous system controls unconscious activities, e.g. digestion.

The autonomic nervous system is split into the sympathetic and parasympathetic nervous systems, which have opposite effects on the body. The sympathetic nervous system is the 'fight or flight' system that gets the body ready for action. The parasympathetic system is the 'rest and digest' system that calms the body down. The autonomic nervous system is involved in the control of heart rate (see next page). The structure of the nervous system is summarised below:

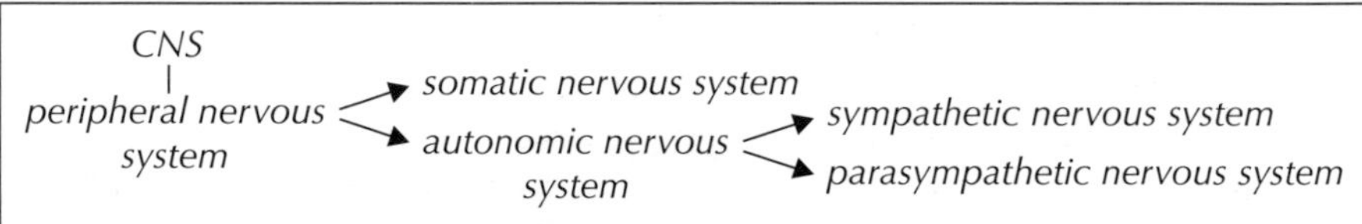


***Figure 1:*** *The structure of the nervous system.*

**Tip:** You don't need to learn the structure of the nervous system, but understanding it'll help you with the rest of this section.

**Tip:** To help you remember the difference between the sympathetic and parasympathetic nervous systems, remember: sympathetic for stress, parasympathetic for peacefulness.

## Control of heart beat

Cardiac (heart) muscle is '**myogenic**' — this means that it can contract and relax without receiving signals from nerves. This pattern of contractions controls the regular heartbeat.

The process starts in the **sinoatrial node (SAN)**, which is a small mass of tissue in the wall of the right atrium (see Figure 2). The SAN is like a pacemaker — it sets the rhythm of the heartbeat by sending out regular waves of electrical activity to the atrial walls. This causes the right and left atria to contract at the same time. A band of non-conducting collagen tissue prevents the waves of electrical activity from being passed directly from the atria to the ventricles. Instead, these waves of electrical activity are transferred from the SAN to the **atrioventricular node (AVN)**.

The AVN is responsible for passing the waves of electrical activity on to the bundle of His. But, there's a slight delay before the AVN reacts, to make sure the atria have emptied before the ventricles contract. The **bundle of His** is a group of muscle fibres responsible for conducting the waves of electrical activity between the ventricles to the apex (bottom) of the heart. The bundle splits into finer muscle fibres in the right and left ventricle walls, called the **Purkyne tissue**. The Purkyne tissue carries the waves of electrical activity into the muscular walls of the right and left ventricles, causing them to contract simultaneously, from the bottom up.

**Exam Tip**
Remember that there's a delay before the AVN reacts. Don't write in the exam that there is a delay in the wave of electrical activity reaching the AVN.

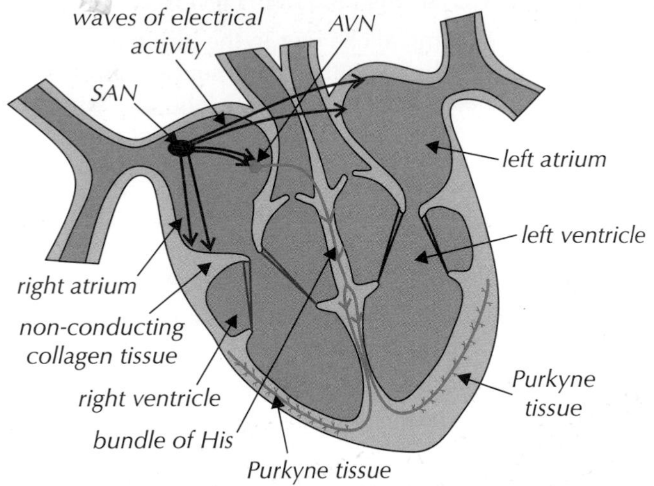


***Figure 2:*** *The pathway of electrical activity in the heart.*

**Tip:** Remember the route of the waves of electrical activity by Silly Ants Have Pants — SAN, AVN, bundle of His, Purkyne fibres.

## Communication between the heart and brain

The SAN generates electrical impulses that cause the cardiac muscles to contract. The rate at which the SAN fires (i.e. heart rate) is unconsciously controlled by a part of the brain called the medulla.

**Tip:** The medulla's full name is the medulla oblongata.

Animals need to alter their heart rate to respond to internal stimuli, e.g. to prevent fainting due to low blood pressure or to make sure the heart rate is high enough to supply the body with enough oxygen. Internal stimuli are detected by pressure receptors and chemical receptors:

- There are **pressure receptors** called baroreceptors in the aorta and carotid arteries. They're stimulated by high and low blood pressure.
- There are chemical receptors called **chemoreceptors** in the aorta, the carotid arteries and in the medulla. They monitor the oxygen level in the blood and also carbon dioxide and pH (which are indicators of $O_2$ level).

**Tip:** The carotid arteries are major arteries in the neck.

Electrical impulses from receptors are sent to the medulla along sensory neurones. The medulla processes the information and sends impulses to the SAN along sympathetic or parasympathetic neurones.

### Control of heart rate in response to different stimuli

**1. High blood pressure**

Baroreceptors detect high blood pressure and send impulses along sensory neurones to the medulla, which sends impulses along parasympathetic neurones. These secrete acetylcholine, which binds to receptors on the SAN. This causes the heart rate to slow down in order to reduce blood pressure back to normal.

**Tip:** Acetylcholine is a type of neurotransmitter. (see page 93 for more).

**2. Low blood pressure**

Baroreceptors detect low blood pressure and send impulses along sensory neurones to the medulla, which sends impulses along sympathetic neurones. These secrete noradrenaline, which binds to receptors on the SAN. This causes the heart rate to speed up in order to increase blood pressure back to normal.

**Tip:** Noradrenaline is another type of neurotransmitter.

Tip: The effectors in all of these situations are the cardiac muscles of the heart.

### 3. High blood $O_2$, low $CO_2$ or high blood pH levels

Chemoreceptors detect chemical changes in the blood and send impulses along sensory neurones to the medulla, which sends impulses along parasympathetic neurones. These secrete acetylcholine, which binds to receptors on the SAN. This causes the heart rate to decrease in order to return oxygen, carbon dioxide and pH levels back to normal.

Tip: Low blood $O_2$, high $CO_2$ or low blood pH levels are a result of increased respiration.

### 4. Low blood $O_2$, high $CO_2$ or low blood pH levels

Chemoreceptors detect chemical changes in the blood and send impulses along sensory neurones to the medulla, which sends impulses along sympathetic neurones. These secrete noradrenaline, which binds to receptors on the SAN. This causes the heart rate to increase in order to return oxygen, carbon dioxide and pH levels back to normal.

The control of heart rate by the medulla is summarised in Figure 3.

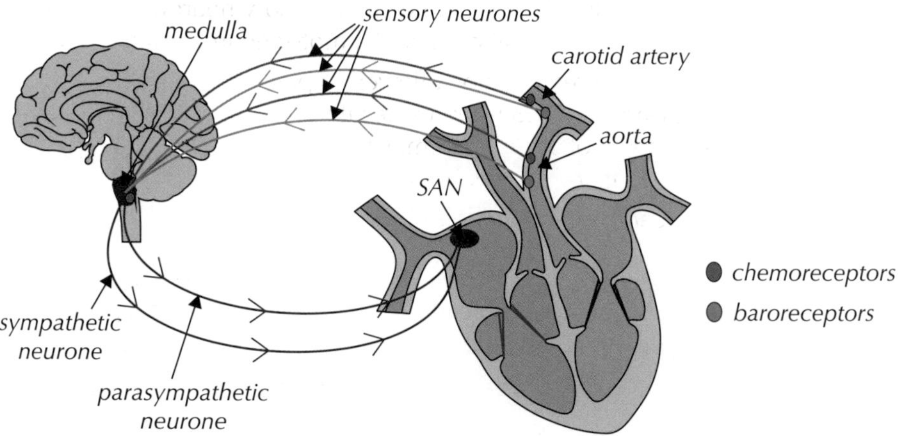


**Figure 3:** *The control of heart rate.*

## Practice Question — Application

Q1 Anaemia is a condition in which the oxygen carrying capacity of the blood is reduced.
Use your knowledge of the control of heart rate to explain why a person with anaemia is likely to have a more rapid heart rate than someone without anaemia.

Tip: There are lots of receptors in the body that detect changes in blood chemistry — these questions refer to the ones that are used in controlling heart rate.

## Practice Questions — Fact Recall

Q1 a) What is the overall role of the autonomic nervous system?
b) Name the two divisions of the autonomic nervous system.

Q2 Heart muscle is described as being 'myogenic'. What does this mean?

Q3 What is the role of the sinoatrial node (SAN)?

Q4 Name the part of the brain that controls heart rate.

Q5 a) What type of receptor detects a fall in blood pressure?
b) Where are these receptors located in the body?

## Section Summary

Make sure you know...

- That organisms increase their chance of survival by responding to changes in their environment.
- That simple responses keep mobile organisms in a favourable environment and can be tactic (directional movement in response to a stimulus) or kinetic (non-directional movement in response to a stimulus).
- How to investigate animal responses using a choice chamber or maze, e.g. the movement of woodlice in a choice chamber under different environmental conditions (Required Practical 10).
- That receptors detect stimuli.
- That the coordinator (e.g. the CNS) processes information from receptors, formulates an appropriate response to the stimulus and passes it to an effector (e.g. a muscle), which then produces a response.
- That simple reflexes are rapid, involuntary responses to stimuli which help protect the body from damage. They involve three neurones — a sensory neurone (that connects the receptor to the CNS), a relay neurone (in the spinal cord) and a motor neurone (that connects the CNS to the effector).
- That a tropism is the response of a flowering plant to a change in the environment (a positive tropism is a growth towards a stimulus and a negative tropism is a growth away from a stimulus). These changes are a result of specific hormone-like growth factors that move from growing regions to other tissues and speed up or slow down growth.
- That high concentrations of indoleacetic acid (IAA) promote cell elongation in shoots and inhibit cell elongation in roots. IAA controls the direction of plant growth in response to light (phototropism) by increasing in concentration in shaded parts of shoots and roots, and controls the direction of plant growth in response to gravity (gravitropism) by moving to the underside of shoots and roots.
- That a receptor only responds to a specific stimulus and that when a receptor is stimulated it causes a change in the potential difference across a membrane, called a generator potential.
- That a Pacinian corpuscle is a mechanoreceptor that is made up of a sensory nerve ending wrapped in layers of connective tissue called lamellae. Pressure on the lamellae causes stretch-mediated sodium ion channels to deform, allowing sodium ions to diffuse into the cell and establish a generator potential.
- That photoreceptors are found on the retina of the human eye. There are two types which contain different optical pigments — rods (which give information in black and white) and cones (which give information in colour). Rods and cones have different distributions on the retina.
- That many rods join one bipolar neurone, which makes them very sensitive to light but gives a low visual acuity. One cone joins one bipolar neurone, which makes them less sensitive to light than rods but gives a high visual acuity.
- That cardiac (heart) muscle is myogenic, which means it can contract and relax without receiving signals from nerves.
- That the sinoatrial node (SAN) sends out regular waves of electrical activity that spread across the atria causing them to contract. This electrical activity is transferred to the ventricles by the atrioventricular node (AVN), which connects to the bundle of His and the Purkyne tissue. The Purkyne tissue carries the waves of electrical activity to the left and right ventricles, causing them to contract simultaneously.
- That the autonomic nervous system is involved in the control of heart rate. Stimuli detected by pressure and chemical receptors result in the rate of cardiac muscle contraction, and therefore heart rate, being altered.
- That pressure receptors (baroreceptors) are located in the aorta and carotid arteries and cause heart rate to speed up when low blood pressure is detected and slow down when high blood pressure is detected. Chemical receptors (chemoreceptors) are located in the aorta, carotid arteries and medulla and cause heart rate to speed up when low oxygen, high carbon dioxide or low pH levels are detected and slow down when high oxygen, low carbon dioxide or high pH levels are detected.

# Exam-style Questions

**1** Scientists took three Goosegrass seedlings and planted them in individual pots with soil taken from the same source. They let each seedling grow for 15 days in the conditions shown in **Figure 1**.

**Figure 1**

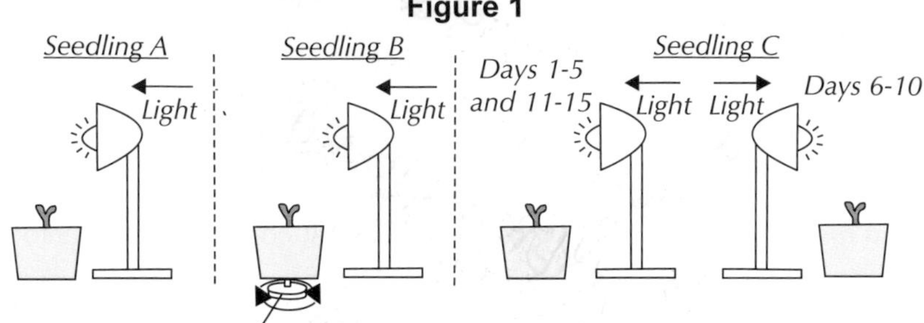


**1.1** Suggest what response the scientists were testing with this experiment.

*(1 mark)*

**1.2** The scientists didn't include a negative control in their experiment. Describe the conditions that should have been used for a seedling acting as a negative control.

*(2 marks)*

**1.3** Suggest why the scientists used soil taken from the same source for each seedling.

*(1 mark)*

**1.4** Describe and explain the pattern of growth in the three plants you would expect to see by the end of the experiment.

*(3 marks)*

**1.5** Explain the role of growth factors in controlling the direction of growth in this experiment.

*(3 marks)*

**2** Protanopia is a type of colour blindness where the photoreceptor that perceives red light is absent.

**2.1** Explain how photoreceptors in the eye enable coloured light to be perceived.

*(4 marks)*

**2.2** Explain why having protanopia doesn't necessarily affect the ability to see in low light conditions.

*(5 marks)*

**2.3** Pupils respond to light intensity by a reflex action which causes the diameter of the pupil to change. The pupil widens in low intensity light and contracts in bright light, as a result of muscles in the eye relaxing and contracting. Suggest how this reflex protects the body from damage.

*(2 marks)*

**2.4** Describe the pathway of nervous communication in the pupil reflex when bright light is shone in the eyes.

*(3 marks)*

3 Some people suffer from a condition called third-degree atrioventricular (AV) block — the waves of electrical activity from the atrioventricular node (AVN) are not relayed to the ventricles. A pacemaker can be fitted to take over this role. **Figure 2** shows a heart with a pacemaker attached.

**Figure 2**

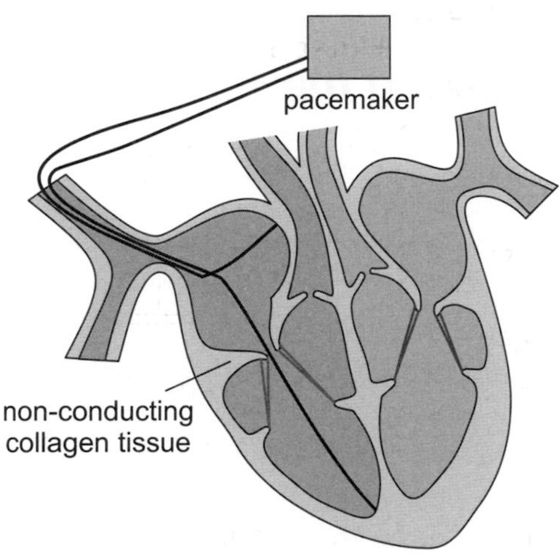


**3.1** The pacemaker is programmed to have a delay between receiving waves of electrical activity from the SAN and producing an electrical impulse in the ventricles. Explain the purpose of this delay.

*(1 mark)*

**3.2** Explain the role of the non-conducting collagen tissue.

*(1 mark)*

**3.3** Explain how waves of electrical activity from the AVN lead to blood being pumped out of the heart in a healthy person.

*(3 marks)*

**3.4** AV block can lead to an abnormally slow heart rate. Patients suspected of having the condition are asked about any medication they are taking when being assessed by a doctor.

Drugs called beta-blockers block the action of noradrenaline. Suggest why a doctor might ask if these drugs are being taken.

*(3 marks)*

**3.5** Third-degree AV block is a complete block of the function of the AVN. Second-degree AV block is a partial blockage which causes a delay in the time taken for the wave of electrical activity to pass through the AVN. People with second-degree AV block may experience dizziness or fainting. Suggest why this might be the case.

*(3 marks)*

**3.6** Where are the chemoreceptors that detect low oxygen levels located?

*(1 mark)*

# 1. Neurones

**Learning Objectives:**

- Understand how a resting potential is established in terms of differential membrane permeability, electrochemical gradients and the movement of sodium and potassium ions.
- Understand how changes in membrane permeability lead to depolarisation and the generation of an action potential.
- Understand the nature and importance of the refractory period in producing discrete impulses and in limiting the frequency of impulse transmission.
- Understand the all-or-nothing principle of an action potential.
- Know the structure of a myelinated motor neurone.
- Understand how an action potential is passed along non-myelinated and myelinated axons, resulting in nerve impulses.
- Know how myelination, saltatory conduction, axon diameter and temperature affect the speed of conductance.

**Specification Reference 3.6.2.1**

**Tip:** Remember, sodium-potassium pumps are SOPI — Sodium Out, Potassium In.

*Nervous impulses are the electrical charges transmitted along a neurone. They're created by the movement of sodium and potassium ions.*

## The resting membrane potential

In a neurone's resting state (when it's not being stimulated), the outside of the membrane is positively charged compared to the inside. This is because there are more positive ions outside the cell than inside. So the membrane is polarised — there's a difference in charge (called a potential difference or voltage) across it. The voltage across the membrane when it's at rest is called the resting potential — it's about –70 mV (millivolts).

### Movement of sodium and potassium ions

The resting potential is created and maintained by **sodium-potassium pumps** and **potassium ion channels** in a neurone's membrane (see Figure 1).

- Sodium-potassium pumps use **active transport** to move three sodium ions ($Na^+$) out of the neurone for every two potassium ions ($K^+$) moved in. ATP is needed to do this.
- Potassium ion channels allow **facilitated diffusion** of potassium ions ($K^+$) out of the neurone, down their concentration gradient.

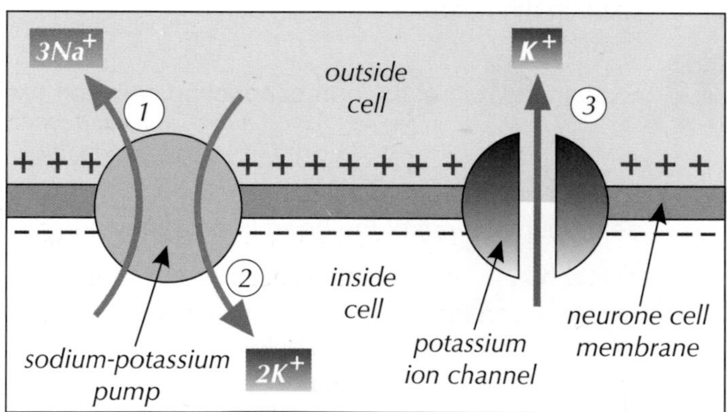


***Figure 1:*** *Movement of sodium and potassium ions across a resting cell membrane.*

1. The sodium-potassium pumps move sodium ions out of the neurone, but the membrane isn't permeable to sodium ions, so they can't diffuse back in. This creates a sodium ion **electrochemical gradient** (a concentration gradient of ions) because there are more positive sodium ions outside the cell than inside.
2. The sodium-potassium pumps also move potassium ions in to the neurone.
3. When the cell's at rest, most potassium ion channels are open. This means that the membrane is permeable to potassium ions, so some diffuse back out through potassium ion channels.

Even though positive ions are moving in and out of the cell, in total more positive ions move out of the cell than enter. This makes the outside of the cell positively charged compared to the inside.

# Action potentials

When a neurone is stimulated, other ion channels in the cell membrane, called sodium ion channels, open. If the stimulus is big enough, it'll trigger a rapid change in potential difference. This causes the cell membrane to become **depolarised** (it's no longer polarised). The sequence of events that happens is known as an action potential — see Figure 2.

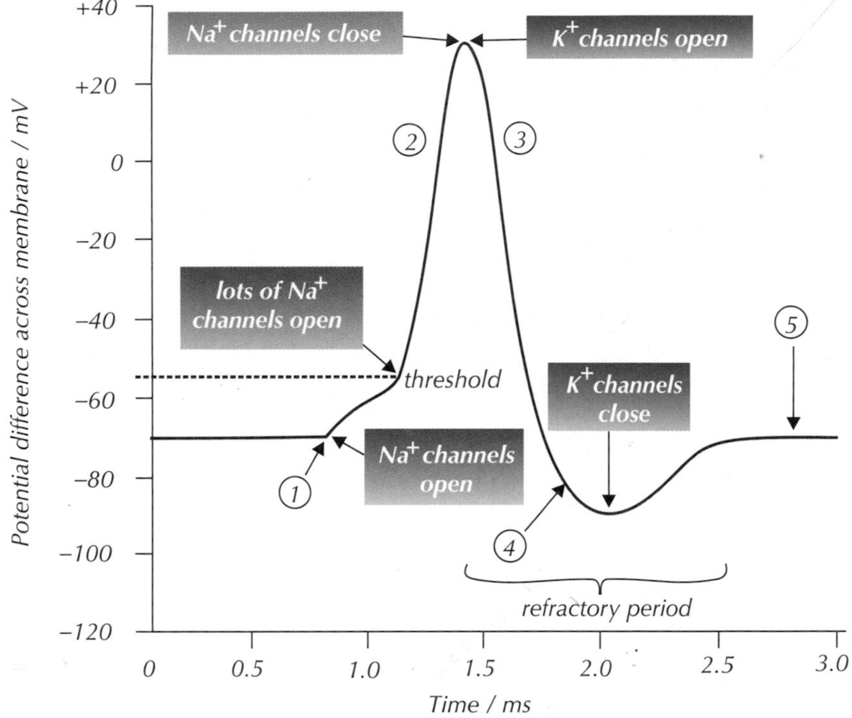


***Figure 2:*** *A graph to show the changes in potential difference across a neurone cell membrane during an action potential.*

1. **Stimulus** — this excites the neurone cell membrane, causing sodium ion channels to open. The membrane becomes more permeable to sodium, so sodium ions diffuse into the neurone down the sodium ion electrochemical gradient. This makes the inside of the neurone less negative.
2. **Depolarisation** — if the potential difference reaches the threshold (around –55 mV), more sodium ion channels open. More sodium ions diffuse into the neurone.
3. **Repolarisation** — at a potential difference of around +30 mV the sodium ion channels close and potassium ion channels open. The membrane is more permeable to potassium so potassium ions diffuse out of the neurone down the potassium ion concentration gradient. This starts to get the membrane back to its resting potential.
4. **Hyperpolarisation** — potassium ion channels are slow to close so there's a slight 'overshoot' where too many potassium ions diffuse out of the neurone. The potential difference becomes more negative than the resting potential (i.e. less than –70 mV).
5. **Resting potential** — the ion channels are reset. The sodium-potassium pump returns the membrane to its resting potential by pumping sodium ions out and potassium ions in, and maintains the resting potential until the membrane's excited by another stimulus.

**Tip:** These sodium ion channels are voltage-gated — they only open when the potential difference reaches a certain voltage.

**Tip:** The sodium-potassium pump, potassium ion channel and sodium ion channel are all types of transport protein.

**Exam Tip**
You don't have to learn these mV values for your exams — they're only approximate and vary from neurone to neurone.

**Tip:** ms = milliseconds, 1000 ms = 1 second.

**Tip:** The graph below shows when the sodium ion channels (orange) are open during an action potential (dotted line):

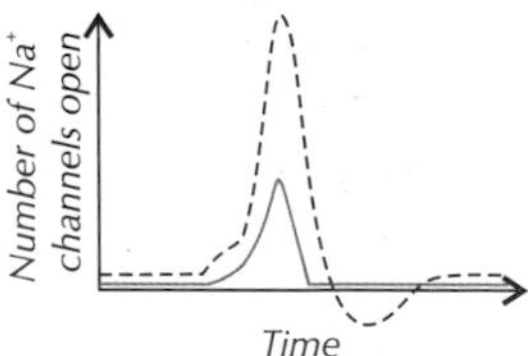


And this graph shows when the potassium ion channels (blue) are open:

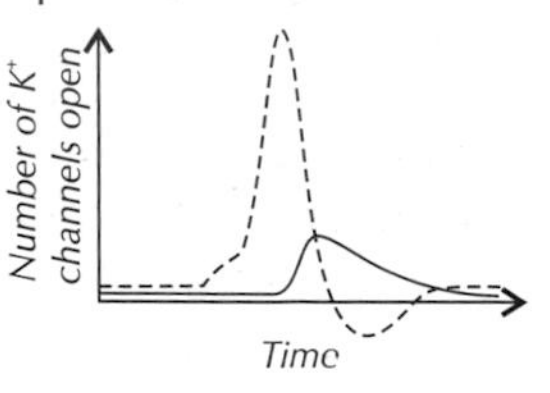


**Tip:** During repolarisation the sodium channels have to close or the membrane will remain depolarised.

### The refractory period

After an action potential, the neurone cell membrane can't be excited again straight away. This is because the ion channels are recovering and they can't be made to open — sodium ion channels are closed during repolarisation and potassium ion channels are closed during hyperpolarisation. This period of recovery is called the refractory period (see Figure 3).

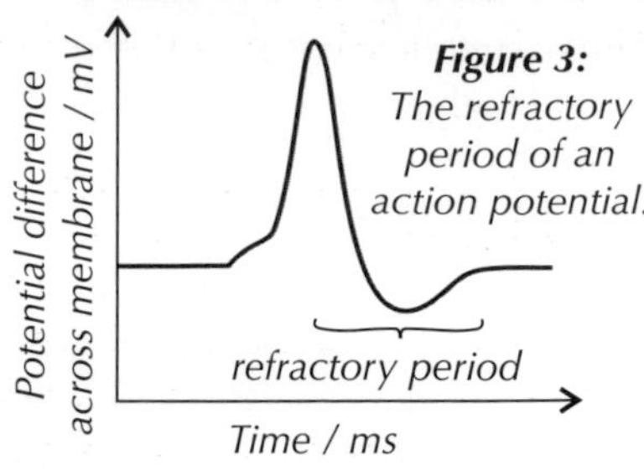


***Figure 3:*** *The refractory period of an action potential.*

The refractory period acts as a time delay between one action potential and the next. This makes sure that action potentials don't overlap but pass along as discrete (separate) impulses. The refractory period also means that there's a limit to the frequency at which the nerve impulses can be transmitted, and that action potentials are unidirectional (they only travel in one direction).

## Waves of depolarisation

**Tip:** A wave of depolarisation is like a Mexican wave travelling through a crowd — sodium ions rushing inwards causes a wave of activity along the membrane.

When an action potential happens, some of the sodium ions that enter the neurone diffuse sideways. This causes sodium ion channels in the next region of the neurone to open and sodium ions diffuse into that part. This causes a wave of depolarisation to travel along the neurone. The wave moves away from the parts of the membrane in the refractory period because these parts can't fire an action potential.

**Tip:** The electrical impulse can be said to 'propagate' along the neurone. This just describes the wave-like movement of the action potential.

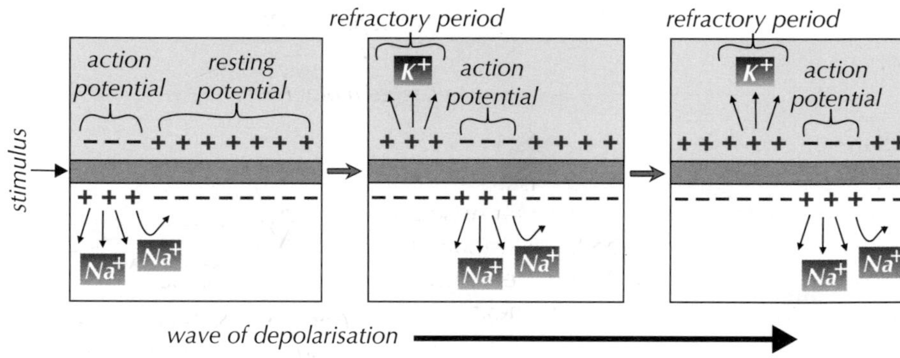


***Figure 4:*** *The movement of ions across a neurone cell membrane during a wave of depolarisation.*

## All-or-nothing principle

**Tip:** The all-or-nothing principle stops the brain from getting over-stimulated by not responding to very small stimuli.

Once the threshold is reached, an action potential will always fire with the same change in voltage, no matter how big the stimulus is. If the threshold isn't reached, an action potential won't fire (see Figure 5). This is the **all-or-nothing** nature of action potentials.

A bigger stimulus won't cause a bigger action potential but it will cause them to fire more frequently (see Figure 6).

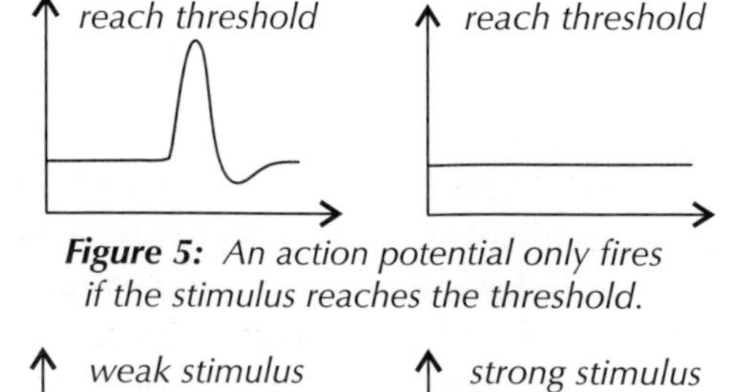


***Figure 5:*** *An action potential only fires if the stimulus reaches the threshold.*

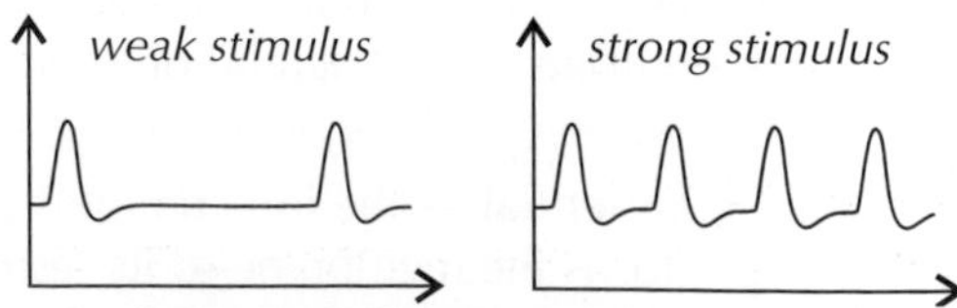


***Figure 6:*** *A bigger stimulus causes more frequent action potentials.*

## Speed of conduction

Three factors affect the speed of conduction of action potentials:

### 1. Myelination

Some neurones, including many motor neurones, are myelinated — they have a **myelin sheath** (see Figure 8). The myelin sheath is an electrical insulator. In the peripheral nervous system (see page 82), the sheath is made of a type of cell called a **Schwann cell**. Between the Schwann cells are tiny patches of bare membrane called the **nodes of Ranvier**. Sodium ion channels are concentrated at the nodes of Ranvier.

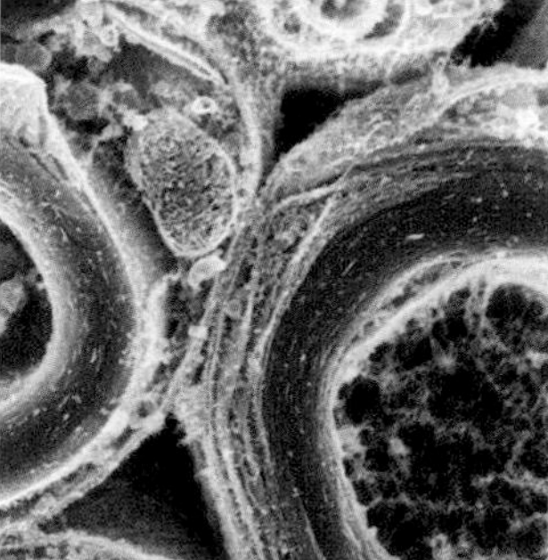

*Figure 7: A cross-section through a myelinated neurone. The myelin sheath (orange/brown) surrounds the axon (dark brown).*

**Exam Tip**
You need to learn the structure of a myelinated motor neurone for your exams.

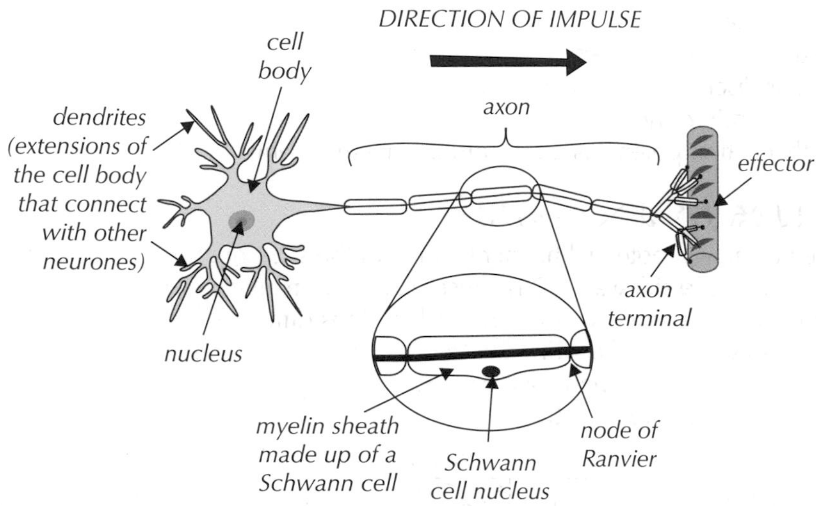


*Figure 8: Structure of a myelinated motor neurone.*

#### Saltatory conduction

In a myelinated neurone, depolarisation only happens at the nodes of Ranvier (where sodium ions can get through the membrane). The neurone's cytoplasm conducts enough electrical charge to depolarise the next node, so the impulse 'jumps' from node to node. This is called saltatory conduction and it's really fast — see Figure 10.

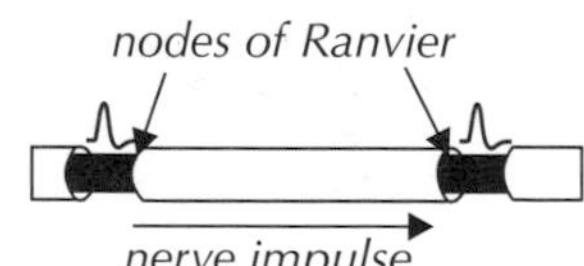


*Figure 10: Saltatory conduction along a myelinated neurone.*

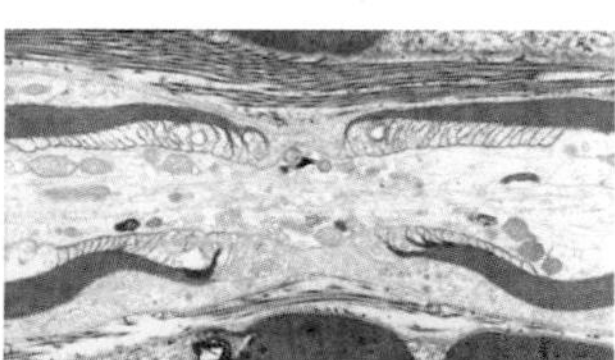

*Figure 9: A section through a myelinated neurone. The myelin sheath appears blue — the area where there is no myelin sheath is a node of Ranvier.*

In a non-myelinated neurone, the impulse travels as a wave along the whole length of the axon membrane — so you get depolarisation along the whole length of the membrane (see Figure 11). This is slower than saltatory conduction (although it's still pretty quick).

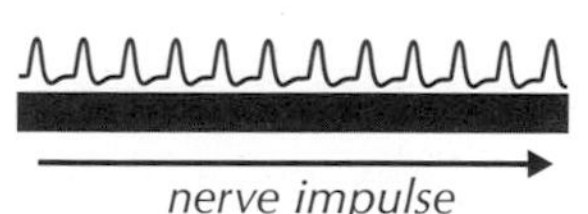


*Figure 11: Conduction along a non-myelinated neurone.*

**Tip:** If you imagine a Mexican wave travelling through a crowd, then saltatory conduction is like every tenth person doing the wave instead of everyone doing the wave — so it travels much faster.

### 2. Axon diameter

Action potentials are conducted quicker along axons with bigger diameters because there's less resistance to the flow of ions than in the cytoplasm of a smaller axon. With less resistance, depolarisation reaches other parts of the neurone cell membrane quicker.

### 3. Temperature

The speed of conduction increases as the temperature increases too, because ions diffuse faster. The speed only increases up to around 40 °C though — after that the proteins begin to denature and the speed decreases.

**Tip:** The pumps and channels that move ions across the membrane are proteins, so these will denature at high temperatures.

**Tip:** Remember, the potential difference is the voltage across the membrane.

**Exam Tip**
You might be asked questions like this in your exams, i.e. ones that get you to explain the shape of the graph on page 89. Make sure you really understand what's happening at each point.

**Exam Tip**
Always be clear in your exam answers as to whether you're talking about sodium ions ($Na^+$) or potassium ions ($K^+$) — don't just write 'sodium', 'potassium' or 'ions'.

**Tip:** The sodium ion channels are closed when the cell's at rest — they only open following the arrival of a stimulus.

**Exam Tip**
In your exams, be careful not to use phrases like 'ions move across the membrane' — you need to make it clear whether they're moving into or out of the cell.

## Practice Questions — Application

The graph below shows the changes in potential difference across a neurone cell membrane during an action potential.

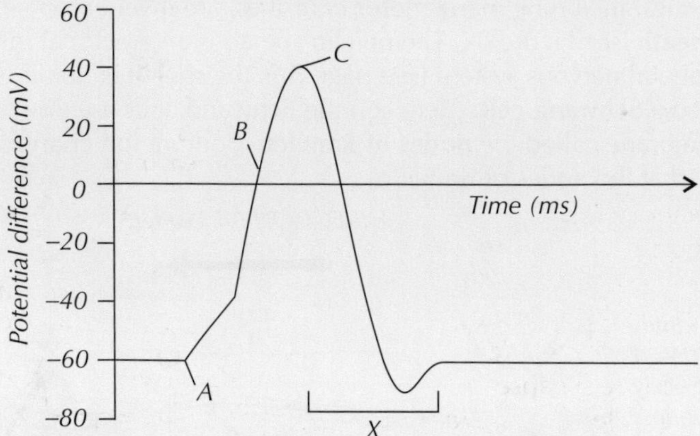


Q1 Describe the different events occurring at points A, B and C.

Q2 What is the threshold level for this action potential?

Q3 What is the resting potential of this neurone cell membrane?

Q4 a) Explain the shape of the curve during the period marked X.
b) What name is given to the period marked X?

Q5 How would the graph look if a bigger stimulus triggered the action potential? Explain your answer.

## Practice Questions — Fact Recall

Q1 Which two proteins in a neurone's cell membrane are responsible for creating and maintaining the resting membrane potential?

Q2 Following a stimulus, explain how the opening of sodium ion channels affects the potential difference across a neurone cell membrane.

Q3 Describe and explain the movement of sodium ions if the potential difference across a neurone cell membrane reaches the threshold level.

Q4 a) After an action potential, why can't the neurone cell membrane be excited again straight away?
b) What three effects does this have on the conduction of action potentials along a neurone?

Q5 Explain how waves of depolarisation are produced.

Q6 Describe the structure of a myelinated neurone in the peripheral nervous system.

Q7 How does conduction along a myelinated neurone differ compared to conduction along a non-myelinated neurone?

Q8 Give two factors, other than myelination, that affect the conduction of action potentials.

# 2. Synaptic Transmission

*If you've ever wanted to know more about neurones and how they pass on information, well now's your chance...*

**Learning Objectives:**

- Know the detailed structure of a synapse.
- Understand the sequence of events involved in transmission across a cholinergic synapse in sufficient detail to be able to explain unidirectionality, inhibition by inhibitory synapses, and spatial and temporal summation.
- Know the detailed structure of a neuromuscular junction.
- Be able to compare transmission across a cholinergic synapse and across a neuromuscular junction.
- Be able to predict and explain the effects of specific drugs on a synapse, when provided with information.

**Specification Reference 3.6.2.2**

## Synapses and neurotransmitters

A synapse is the junction between a neurone and another neurone, or between a neurone and an effector cell, e.g. a muscle or gland cell. The tiny gap between the cells at a synapse is called the synaptic cleft. The presynaptic neurone (the one before the synapse) has a swelling called a synaptic knob. This contains synaptic vesicles filled with chemicals called neurotransmitters — see Figure 1.

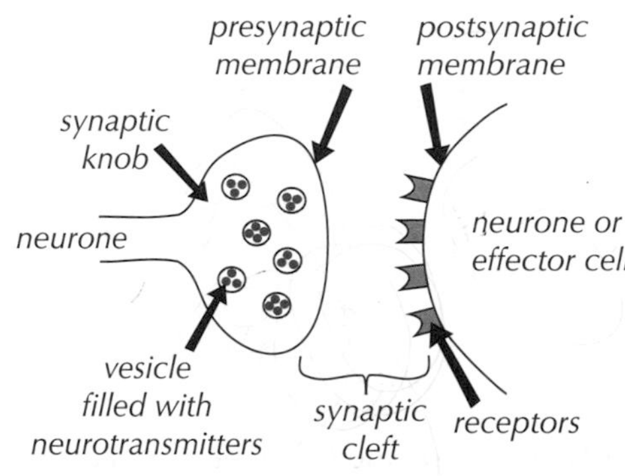


**Figure 1:** *The structure of a typical synapse.*

### Effect of an action potential

When an action potential reaches the end of a neurone it causes neurotransmitters to be released into the synaptic cleft. They diffuse across to the postsynaptic membrane (the one after the synapse) and bind to specific receptors. When neurotransmitters bind to receptors they might trigger an action potential (in a neurone), cause muscle contraction (in a muscle cell), or cause a hormone to be secreted (from a gland cell).

Because the receptors are only on the postsynaptic membranes, synapses make sure impulses are **unidirectional** — the impulse can only travel in one direction. Neurotransmitters are removed from the cleft so the response doesn't keep happening, e.g. they're taken back into the presynaptic neurone or they're broken down by enzymes (and the products are taken into the neurone).

### Acetylcholine

There are many different neurotransmitters. You need to know about one called **acetylcholine** (**ACh**), which binds to cholinergic receptors. Synapses that use acetylcholine are called **cholinergic synapses**.

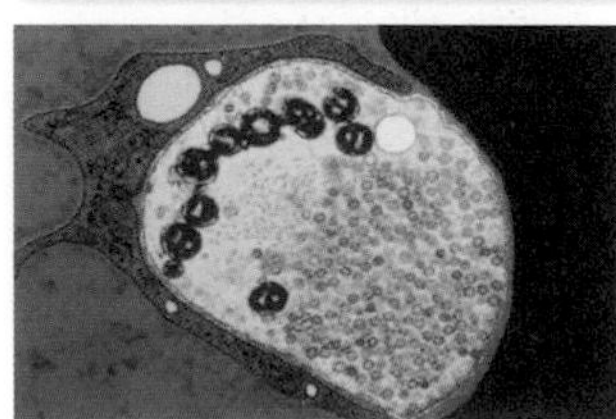

**Figure 2:** *A synaptic knob (yellow) containing vesicles (large red circles).*

**Tip:** Noradrenaline is another example of a neurotransmitter — see pages 83-84.

## Cholinergic synapses

This is how a nerve impulse is transmitted across a cholinergic synapse:

### 1. Arrival of an action potential

An action potential arrives at the synaptic knob of the presynaptic neurone. The action potential stimulates voltage-gated calcium ion channels in the presynaptic neurone to open. Calcium ions ($Ca^{2+}$) diffuse into the synaptic knob. (They're pumped out afterwards by active transport.)

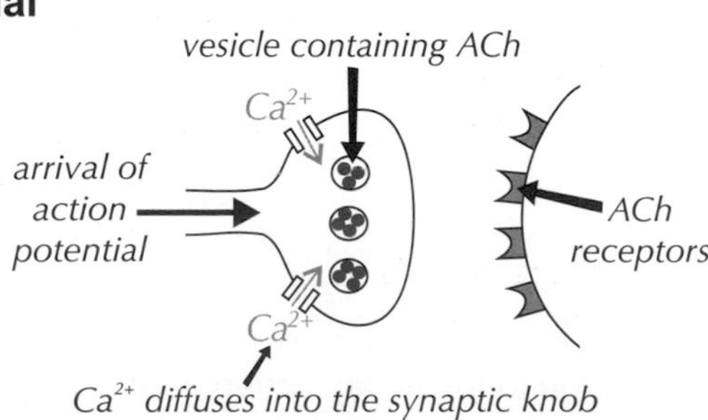


**Tip:** Voltage-gated ion channels are channels that only open when the potential difference across a membrane reaches a certain voltage.

**Exam Tip**
"The influx of calcium ions..." means that the calcium ions have flowed into the synaptic knob. You'll lose out on marks in the exam if you talk about an influx of calcium ions out of the synaptic knob.

**Tip:** Exocytosis is the process by which a vesicle inside a cell moves to the cell-surface membrane, fuses with the membrane and releases its contents outside the cell.

**Tip:** Look back at page 89 if you need a reminder of how action potentials are generated.

### 2. Fusion of the vesicles

The influx of calcium ions into the synaptic knob causes the synaptic vesicles to fuse with the presynaptic membrane. The vesicles release the neurotransmitter acetylcholine (ACh) into the synaptic cleft by exocytosis.

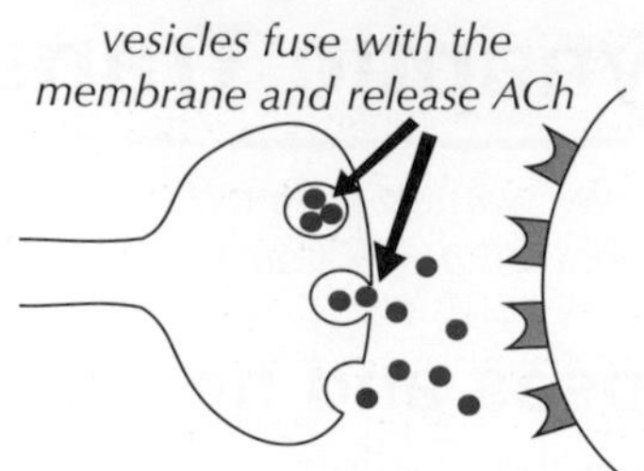
vesicles fuse with the membrane and release ACh

### 3. Diffusion of ACh

ACh diffuses across the synaptic cleft and binds to specific cholinergic receptors on the postsynaptic membrane. This causes sodium ion channels in the postsynaptic neurone to open. The influx of sodium ions into the postsynaptic membrane causes depolarisation. An action potential on the postsynaptic membrane is generated if the threshold is reached. ACh is removed from the synaptic cleft so the response doesn't keep happening. It's broken down by an enzyme called acetylcholinesterase (AChE) and the products are re-absorbed by the presynaptic neurone and used to make more ACh.

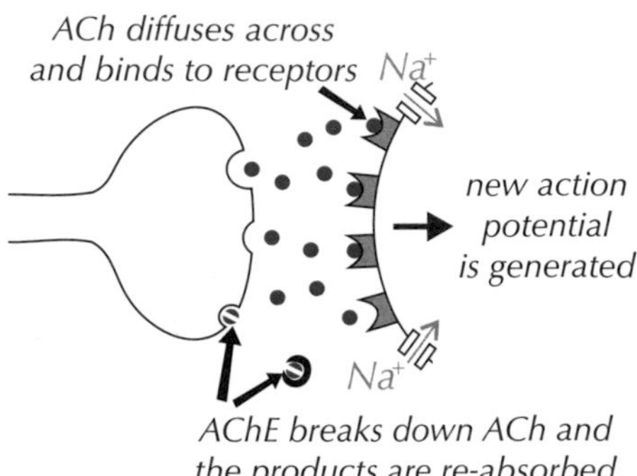
ACh diffuses across and binds to receptors
$Na^+$
new action potential is generated
$Na^+$
AChE breaks down ACh and the products are re-absorbed

## Excitatory and inhibitory neurotransmitters

Neurotransmitters can be excitatory, inhibitory or both. Excitatory neurotransmitters depolarise the postsynaptic membrane, making it fire an action potential if the threshold is reached.

**Example**

Acetylcholine is an excitatory neurotransmitter (it binds to cholinergic receptors to cause an action potential in the postsynaptic membrane) at cholinergic synapses in the CNS and at neuromuscular junctions (see page 96).

**Tip:** 'Depolarise' means making the potential difference across the neurone membrane more positive. 'Hyperpolarise' means making the potential difference across the membrane more negative. (See page 89 for more.)

Inhibitory neurotransmitters hyperpolarise the postsynaptic membrane (make the potential difference more negative), preventing it from firing an action potential.

**Examples**

- GABA is an inhibitory neurotransmitter — when it binds to its receptors it causes potassium ion channels to open on the postsynaptic membrane, hyperpolarising the neurone.
- Acetylcholine is an inhibitory neurotransmitter at cholinergic synapses in the heart. When it binds to receptors here, it can cause potassium ion channels to open on the postsynaptic membrane, hyperpolarising it.

**Tip:** Acetylcholine is both an excitatory and an inhibitory neurotransmitter

A synapse where inhibitory neurotransmitters are released from the presynaptic membrane following an action potential is called an **inhibitory synapse**.

# Summation at synapses

If a stimulus is weak, only a small amount of neurotransmitter will be released from a neurone into the synaptic cleft. This might not be enough to excite the postsynaptic membrane to the threshold level and stimulate an action potential. Summation is where the effect of neurotransmitters released from many neurones (or one neurone that's stimulated a lot in a short period of time) is added together. It means synapses accurately process information, finely tuning the response. There are two types of summation:

**Tip:** Summation is where the sum total of lots of smaller impulses triggers an action potential.

### 1. Spatial summation

Spatial summation is where two or more presynaptic neurones release their neurotransmitters at the same time onto the same postsynaptic neurone. The small amount of neurotransmitter released from each of these neurones can be enough altogether to reach the threshold in the postsynaptic neurone and trigger an action potential — see Figure 3.

**Tip:** Remember, only excitatory neurotransmitters can trigger an action potential (see previous page).

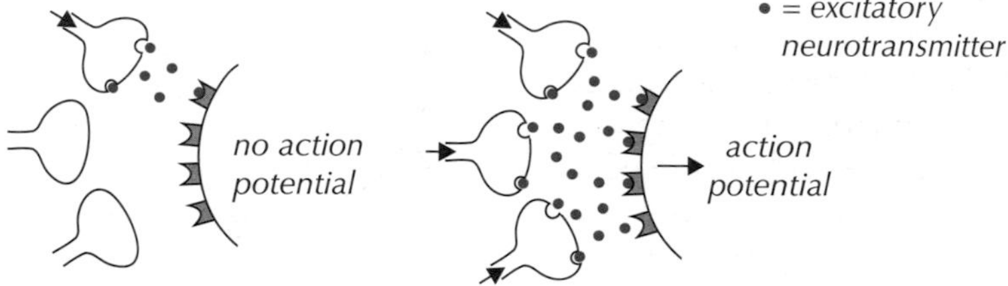


***Figure 3:*** *One presynaptic neurone only releases a few neurotransmitters (left) but three presynaptic neurones release enough to trigger an action potential (right).*

If some neurones release an inhibitory neurotransmitter then the total effect of all the neurotransmitters might be no action potential — see Figure 4.

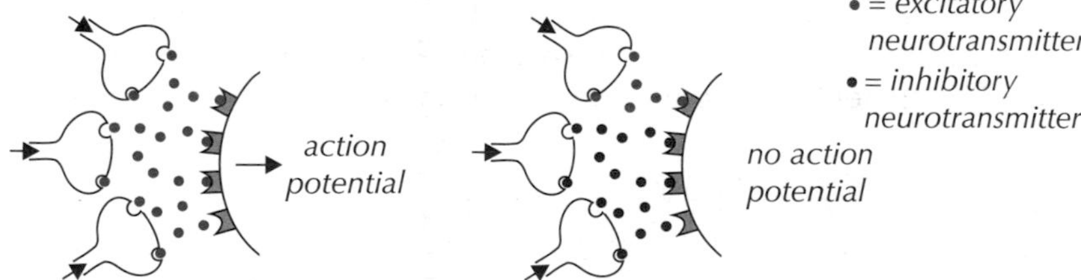


***Figure 4:*** *If some presynaptic neurones release inhibitory neurotransmitters, it might prevent an action potential from being triggered (right).*

### 2. Temporal summation

Temporal summation is where two or more nerve impulses arrive in quick succession from the same presynaptic neurone. This makes an action potential more likely because more neurotransmitter is released into the synaptic cleft — see Figure 5.

**Tip:** Impulses have to follow each other very quickly, otherwise the neurotransmitter will be removed from the cleft before it's reached a level high enough to trigger an action potential.

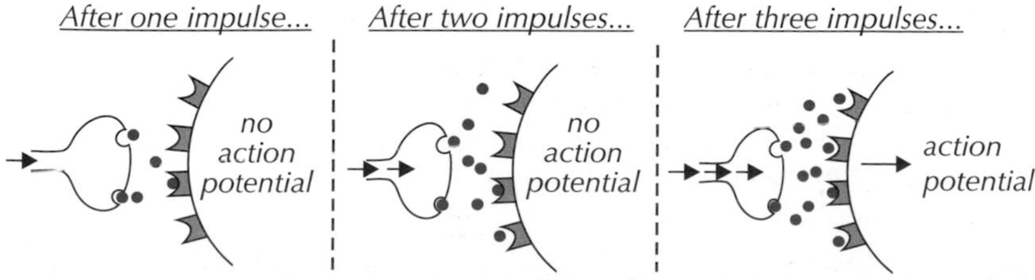


***Figure 5:*** *The effects of temporal summation at a synapse.*

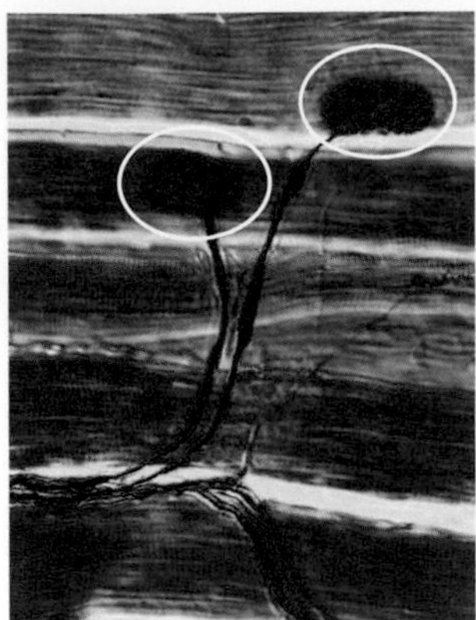

*Figure 6:* A light micrograph showing neuromuscular junctions (circled) in skeletal muscle.

**Exam Tip**
You need to be able to compare transmission across a neuromuscular junction and a cholinergic synapse (see pages 93-94 for a reminder of cholinergic synapses).

## Neuromuscular junctions

A neuromuscular junction is a specialised cholinergic synapse between a motor neurone and a muscle cell. Neuromuscular junctions use the neurotransmitter acetylcholine (ACh), which binds to cholinergic receptors called nicotinic cholinergic receptors.

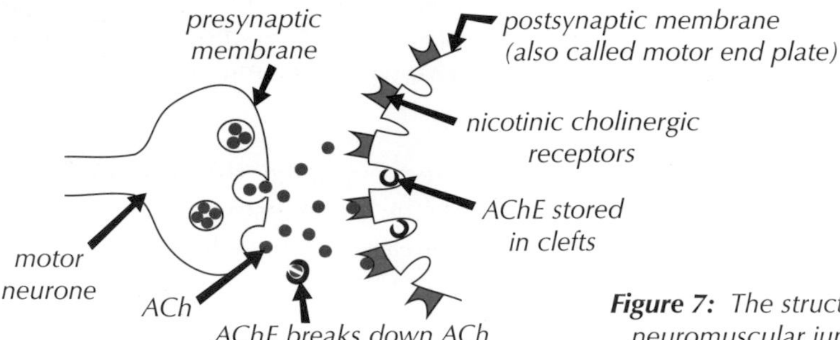


*Figure 7:* The structure of a neuromuscular junction.

Neuromuscular junctions work in basically the same way as cholinergic synapses, i.e. they both release ACh from vesicles in the presynaptic membrane, ACh then diffuses across the synaptic cleft and binds to cholinergic receptors on the postsynaptic membrane, and this triggers an action potential if the threshold is reached. In both types of synapse, ACh is broken down in the synaptic cleft by the enzyme acetylcholinesterase (AChE).

There are a few differences between the two types of synapse too. For example, at a neuromuscular junction:

- The postsynaptic membrane has lots of folds that form clefts. These clefts store AChE.
- The postsynaptic membrane has more receptors than other synapses.
- ACh is always excitatory, so when a motor neurone fires an action potential, it normally triggers a response in a muscle cell. This isn't always the case for a synapse between two neurones.

## Drugs at synapses

**Exam Tip**
You don't have to learn the names of all the drugs given here (and on the next page), but make sure you understand how they affect synaptic transmission. In the exam, you could be given information about a particular drug you've not come across before and be asked to predict the effects the drug would have at a synapse.

Drugs can affect synaptic transmission. They can do this in various ways. For example, some drugs are the same shape as neurotransmitters so they mimic their action at receptors (these drugs are called agonists). This means more receptors are activated.

**Example**

Nicotine mimics acetylcholine so binds to nicotinic cholinergic receptors in the brain.

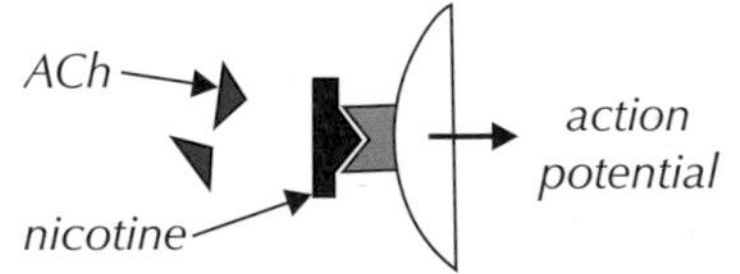


Some drugs block receptors so they can't be activated by neurotransmitters (these drugs are called antagonists). This means fewer receptors (if any) can be activated.

**Example**

Curare blocks the effects of acetylcholine by blocking nicotinic cholinergic receptors at neuromuscular junctions, so muscle cells can't be stimulated. This results in the muscle being paralysed.

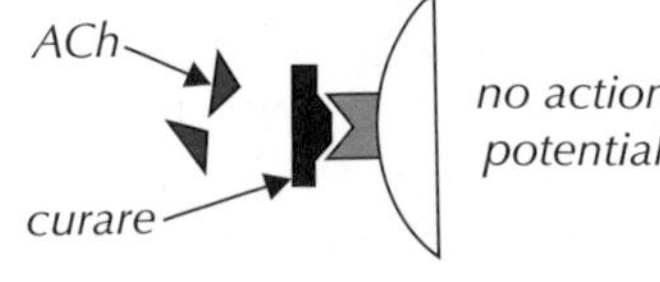

Some drugs inhibit the enzyme that breaks down neurotransmitters (they stop it from working). This means there are more neurotransmitters in the synaptic cleft to bind to receptors and they're there for longer.

**Example**

Nerve gases stop acetylcholine from being broken down in the synaptic cleft. This can lead to loss of muscle control.

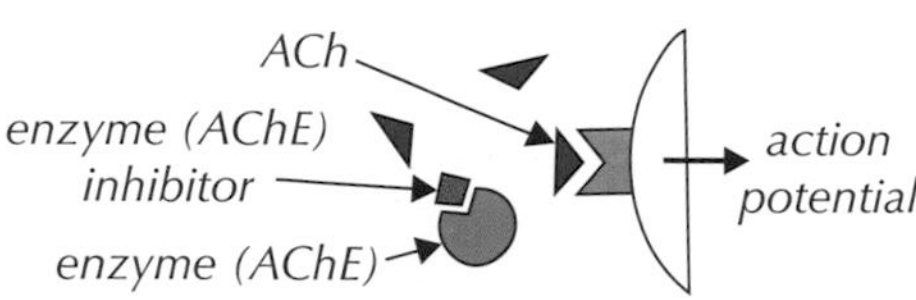

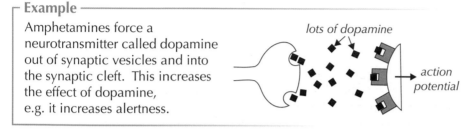

Some drugs stimulate the release of neurotransmitter from the presynaptic neurone so more receptors are activated.

**Example**

Amphetamines force a neurotransmitter called dopamine out of synaptic vesicles and into the synaptic cleft. This increases the effect of dopamine, e.g. it increases alertness.

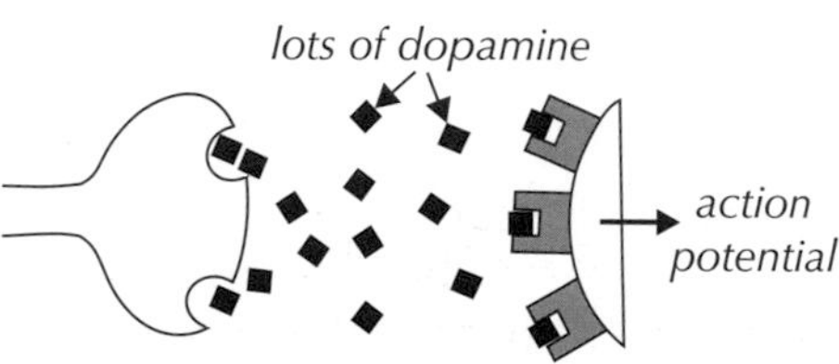


Some drugs inhibit the release of neurotransmitters from the presynaptic neurone so fewer receptors are activated.

**Example**

Opioids block calcium ion channels in the presynaptic neurone. This means fewer vesicles fuse with the presynaptic membrane so less neurotransmitter is released.

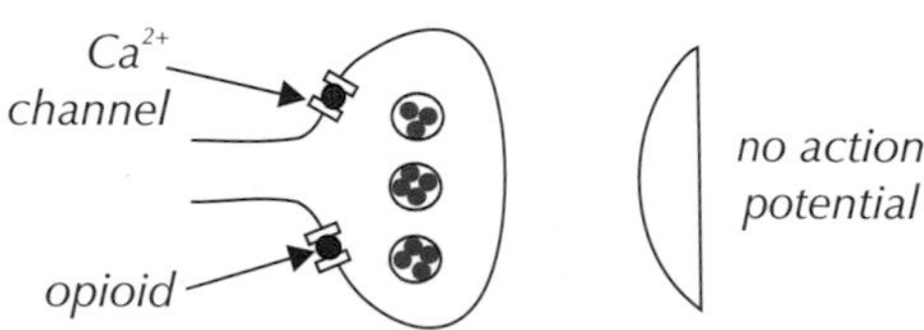


## Practice Questions — Application

Q1 Lambert–Eaton myasthenic syndrome (LEMS) is an autoimmune disorder where antibodies are formed against calcium ion channels in the neuromuscular junction, preventing the channels from working properly. Suggest what the main symptom of LEMS might be. Explain your answer.

Q2 Endorphins are endogenous opioid peptides that function as inhibitory neurotransmitters. Endorphins bind to opioid receptors on neurones that transmit pain signals.

a) Suggest what effect endorphins have on the sensation of pain. Explain your answer.

b) Morphine is an opioid drug that's very similar in structure to an endorphin molecule. Suggest what effect taking morphine will have on a person's sensation of pain. Explain your answer.

Q3 Acetylcholine (ACh) is involved in many functions in the body, including saliva production. Carbachol is a drug that binds and activates cholinergic receptors. Predict the effect of carbachol on saliva production and explain your answer.

**Tip:** An autoimmune disease is where a person's immune system mistakes their own cells for pathogens, so it starts to attack them.

**Tip:** Endogenous just means it's produced naturally by the body.

## Practice Questions — Fact Recall

Q1 The diagram on the right shows a cholinergic synapse. Name the structures labelled A to G on the diagram.

Q2 Give three types of cell that have receptors for neurotransmitters.

Q3 Explain why impulses at a synapse are unidirectional.

Q4 At a cholinergic synapse:

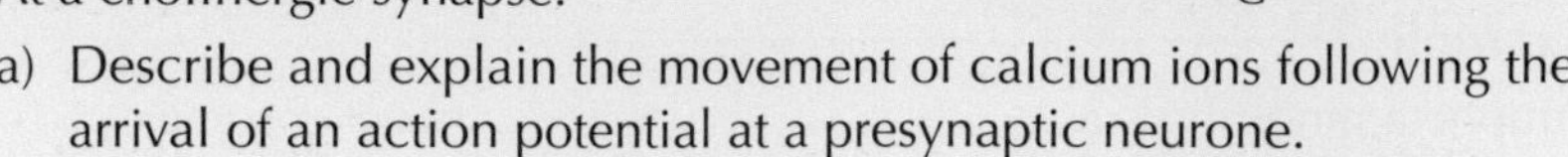

a) Describe and explain the movement of calcium ions following the arrival of an action potential at a presynaptic neurone.

b) Explain how acetylcholine (ACh) leaves the presynaptic neurone and causes an action potential in the postsynaptic neurone.

Q5 Why is it important that ACh is removed from the synaptic cleft by being broken down by the enzyme AChE?

Q6 What effect does an inhibitory neurotransmitter have on a postsynaptic membrane?

Q7 Explain how an action potential may be more likely as a result of:

a) spatial summation,

b) temporal summation.

Q8 What is a neuromuscular junction?

Q9 Give three ways in which a neuromuscular junction is similar to a cholinergic synapse.

**Tip:** Don't get the presynaptic and postsynaptic neurones mixed up — remember 'pre' means before and 'post' means after.

# 3. Muscle Structure

*Muscles are effectors — they contract in response to nervous impulses. To understand how muscles contract, first you need to know about their structure...*

**Learning Objectives:**
- Understand that muscles act in antagonistic pairs against an incompressible skeleton.
- Know the gross and microscopic structure of skeletal muscle.
- Know the ultrastructure of a myofibril.

**Specification Reference 3.6.3**

## Types of muscle

There are three different types of muscle in the body:
- **Smooth muscle** contracts without conscious control. It's found in walls of internal organs (apart from the heart), e.g. stomach, intestine and blood vessels.
- **Cardiac muscle** contracts without conscious control (like smooth muscle) but it's only found in the heart.
- **Skeletal muscle** (also called striated, striped or voluntary muscle) is the type of muscle you use to move, e.g. the biceps and triceps move the lower arm.

You need to know the ins and outs of skeletal muscle for the exams...

## Role of skeletal muscle

Skeletal muscles are attached to bones by tendons. Ligaments attach bones to other bones, to hold them together. Pairs of skeletal muscles contract and relax to move bones at a joint — the bones of the skeleton are incompressible (rigid) so they act as levers, giving the muscles something to pull against.

**Tip:** Ligaments are bands of strong connective tissue.

### Antagonistic pairs

Muscles that work together to move a bone are called antagonistic pairs. The contracting muscle is called the agonist and the relaxing muscle is called the antagonist.

**Example — Biceps and triceps**

The bones of your lower arm are attached to a biceps muscle and a triceps muscle by tendons. The biceps and triceps work together to move your arm — as one contracts, the other relaxes.

When your biceps contracts your triceps relaxes. This pulls the bone so your arm bends (flexes) at the elbow — see Figure 1. Here, the biceps is the agonist and the triceps is the antagonist.

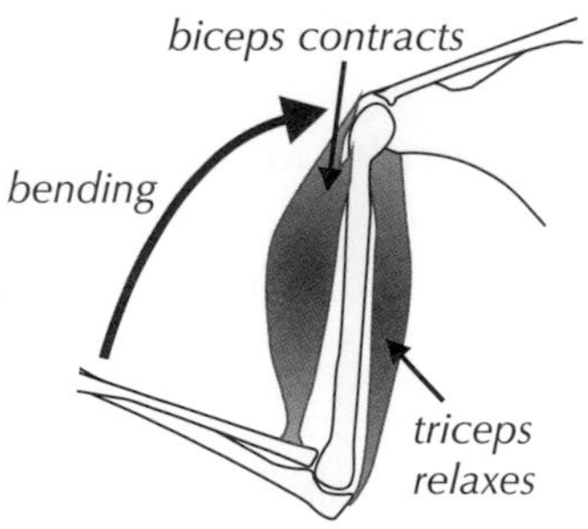


***Figure 1:*** *Arm bending.*

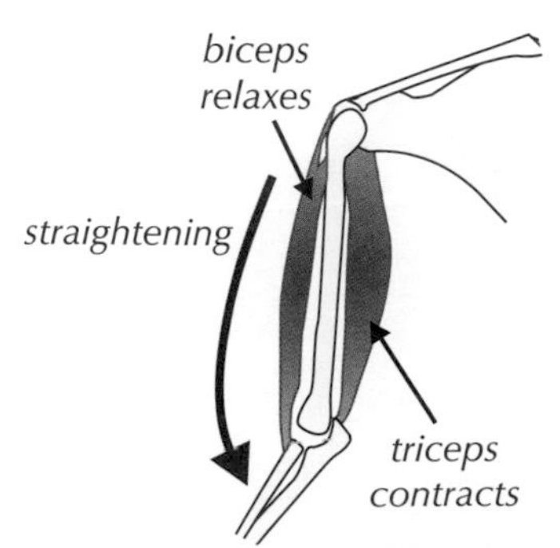


***Figure 2:*** *Arm straightening.*

When your triceps contracts your biceps relaxes. This pulls the bone so your arm straightens (extends) at the elbow — see Figure 2. Here, the triceps is the agonist and the biceps is the antagonist.

**Tip:** Muscles work in pairs because they can only pull when they contract — they can't push.

# Structure of skeletal muscle

Skeletal muscle is made up of large bundles of long cells, called muscle fibres. The cell membrane of muscle fibre cells is called the sarcolemma. Bits of the sarcolemma fold inwards across the muscle fibre and stick into the sarcoplasm (a muscle cell's cytoplasm). These folds are called transverse (T) tubules and they help to spread electrical impulses throughout the sarcoplasm so they reach all parts of the muscle fibre — see Figure 4.

A network of internal membranes called the sarcoplasmic reticulum runs through the sarcoplasm. The sarcoplasmic reticulum stores and releases calcium ions that are needed for muscle contraction. Muscle fibres have lots of mitochondria to provide the ATP that's needed for muscle contraction. They are multinucleate (contain many nuclei) and have lots of long, cylindrical organelles called **myofibrils**. Myofibrils are made up of proteins and are highly specialised for contraction (see next page).

***Figure 3:*** *A scanning electron microscope (SEM) image of a section of muscle fibre with myofibrils (pink and yellow) bundled together.*

**Tip:** Myofibrils are organelles within the cell (muscle fibre).

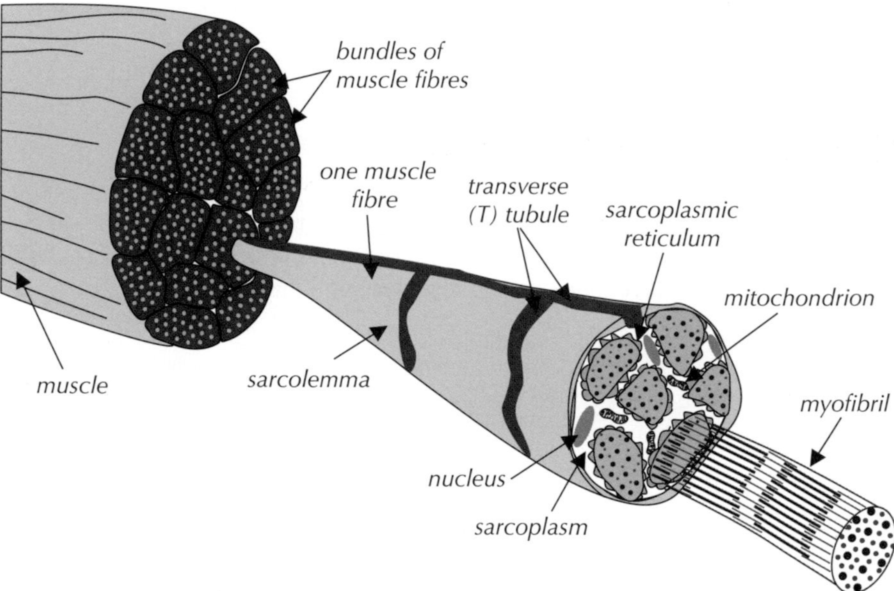


***Figure 4:*** *Diagram showing the structure of skeletal muscle and a muscle fibre.*

## Examination under an optical microscope

You could look at skeletal muscle under an optical microscope. What you see will depend on how the sample has been stained and whether you're looking at a longitudinal or transverse cross-section.

**Tip:** Longitudinal cross-sections are taken along the length of a structure, whereas transverse cross-sections cut through the structure at a right angle to its length.

**Example**

This photomicrograph shows a longitudinal cross-section of skeletal muscle. You can see six muscle fibres. The blue parts are nuclei — there are many in each muscle fibre. The cross-striations (alternating darker and lighter pink stripes) are the A-bands and I-bands of the myofibrils, see next page.

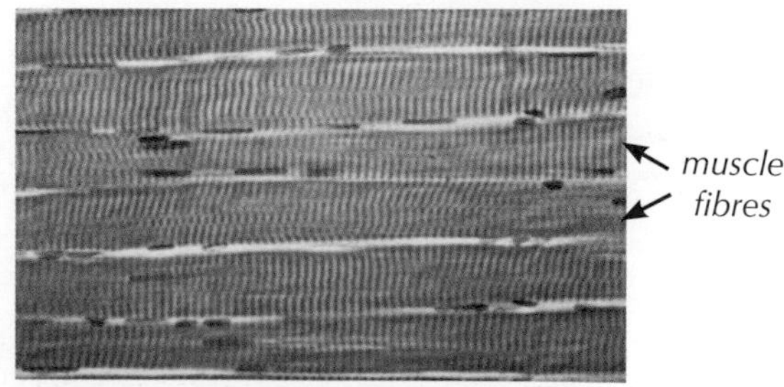

# Myofibrils

Myofibrils contain bundles of thick and thin myofilaments that move past each other to make muscles contract. The thick myofilaments are made of the protein **myosin** and the thin myofilaments are made of the protein **actin**.

If you look at a myofibril under an electron microscope, you'll see a pattern of alternating dark and light bands (see Figures 5 and 6). Dark bands contain the thick myosin filaments and some overlapping thin actin filaments — these are called A-bands. Light bands contain thin actin filaments only — these are called I-bands.

A myofibril is made up of many short units called **sarcomeres**. The ends of each sarcomere are marked with a Z-line. In the middle of each sarcomere is an M-line. The M-line is the middle of the myosin filaments. Around the M-line is the H-zone. The H-zone only contains myosin filaments.

**Tip:** You need to know the 'ultrastructure' of a myofibril — this just means the fine structure that can only be seen using an electron microscope.

**Tip:** To remember which band is which, think: d**a**rk = **A**-bands and l**i**ght = **I**-bands.

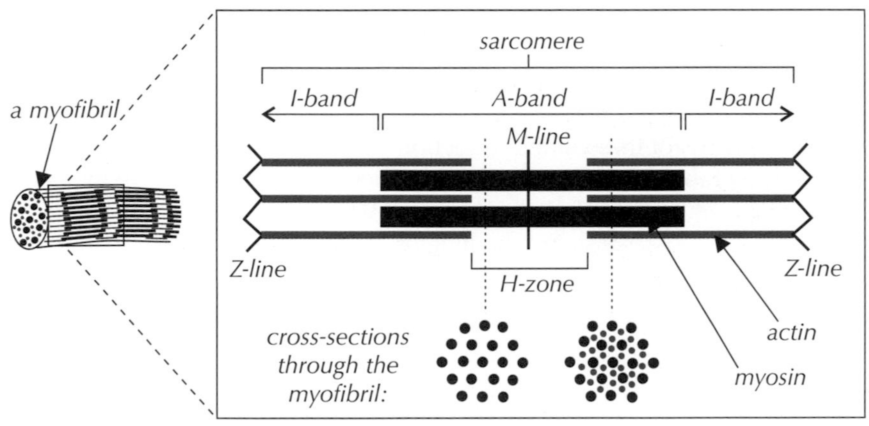


*Figure 5: The structure of a sarcomere — a unit of a myofibril.*

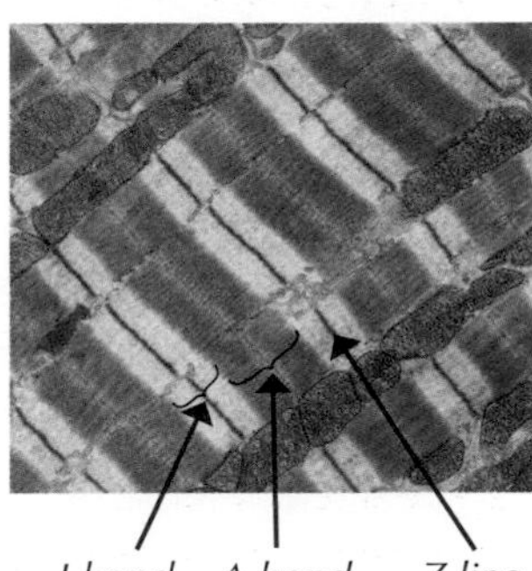


*Figure 6: A transmission electron microscope (TEM) of myofibrils showing the banding of myosin (red) and actin (yellow).*

# The sliding filament theory

Muscle contraction is explained by the sliding filament theory. This is where myosin and actin filaments slide over one another to make the sarcomeres contract — the myofilaments themselves don't contract. The simultaneous contraction of lots of sarcomeres means the myofibrils and muscle fibres contract. Sarcomeres return to their original length as the muscle relaxes.

**Tip:** There's a lot more detail on muscle contraction coming up (see pages 103-105).

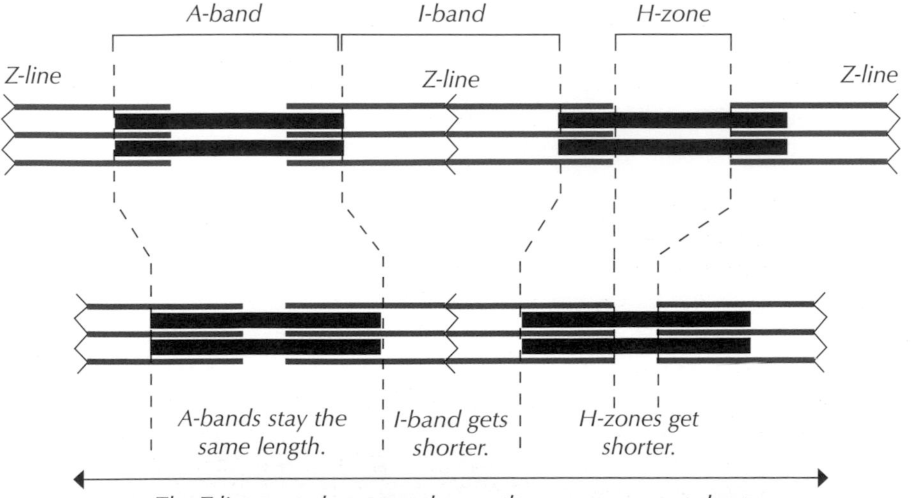


*Figure 7: Sarcomeres during relaxation (top) and contraction (bottom).*

**Tip:** A bands are the only ones that stay the same length.

**Tip:** If you're struggling with Q1, look closely at which bones the muscles are attached to and think how the contraction of each muscle would move the bones.

**Tip:** The diagrams in Q2 might look a bit odd at first, but with a bit of logical thinking you should be able to work out the answers. It might help if you sketch out the sarcomere structure with the bands on, so you can see what's happening.

## Practice Questions — Application

Q1 The quadriceps and hamstrings are antagonistic muscles that are attached to bones in the leg. In the diagram on the right, which muscle is acting as the antagonist? Explain your answer.

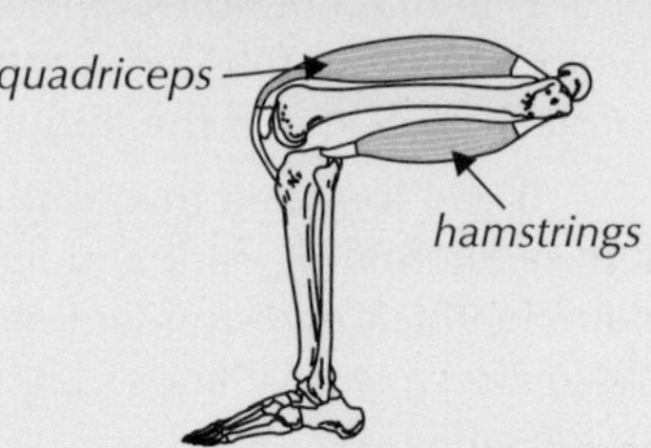


Q2 Cross sections from three different sites along a sarcomere are shown below. Which cross-section(s) could be from:

a) an I-band?
b) an M-line?
c) an A-band?
d) a Z-line?

A
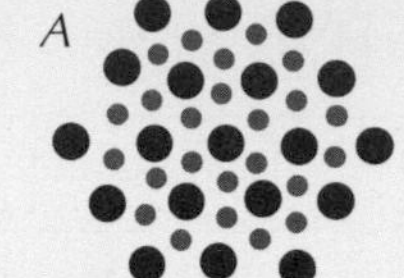
B
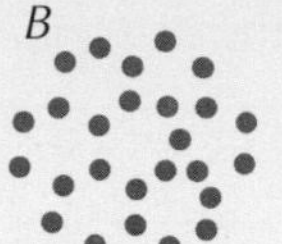
C
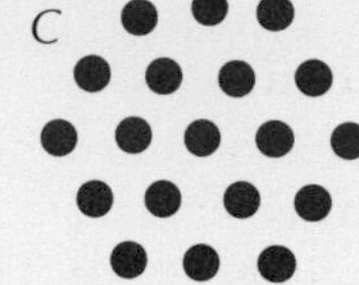

Q3 The lengths of three different sections of a sarcomere were measured when a rabbit muscle was relaxed. These values are given in the first column of the table below. Work out which other set of values in the table (options 1-3) shows the lengths of the sections when the muscle was contracted. Explain your answer.

| | *Relaxed (μm)* | *Option 1 (μm)* | *Option 2 (μm)* | *Option 3 (μm)* |
|---|---|---|---|---|
| *A-band* | *1.5* | *1.5* | *1.2* | *1.5* |
| *I-band* | *0.8* | *0.5* | *0.5* | *1* |
| *H-zone* | *0.7* | *0.2* | *0.7* | *0.2* |

## Practice Questions — Fact Recall

Q1 What is meant by an 'antagonistic pair' of muscles?

Q2 Describe the structure and function of T-tubules.

Q3 Why do muscle fibres contain lots of mitochondria?

Q4 Describe the structure of an A-band in a myofibril and describe its appearance under an electron microscope.

Q5 What is the sliding filament theory of muscle contraction?

# 4. Muscle Contraction

*So now you know all about the structure of muscle it's time to find out just how it contracts...*

**Learning Objectives:**

- Understand the roles of calcium ions and tropomyosin in the cycle of actin-myosin cross bridge formation.
- Understand the roles of actin, myosin, calcium ions and ATP in myofibril contraction.
- Understand the role of ATP and phosphocreatine in muscle contraction.
- Know the structure, location and general properties of slow and fast skeletal muscle fibres.

**Specification Reference 3.6.3**

## Myosin and actin filaments

Muscle contraction involves myosin and actin filaments sliding over one another. Here's a bit more detail about the two types of filament:

**Myosin filaments**

Myosin filaments have globular heads that are hinged, so they can move back and forth. Each myosin head has a binding site for actin and a binding site for ATP — see Figure 1.

**Actin filaments**

Actin filaments have binding sites for myosin heads, called actin-myosin binding sites. Another protein called **tropomyosin** is found between actin filaments. It helps myofilaments move past each other (see Figure 1).

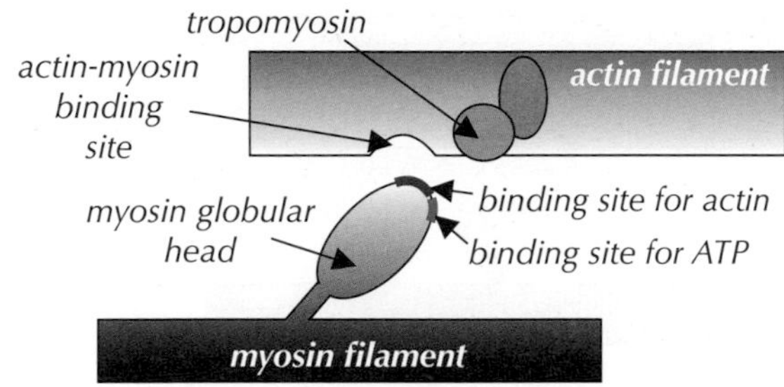


***Figure 1:*** *The structure of myosin and actin filaments.*

**Tip:** This diagram has been simplified — tropomyosin molecules actually form part of a long chain that coils round the actin filament.

## Binding sites in resting muscles

For myosin and actin filaments to slide past each other, the myosin head needs to bind to the actin-myosin binding site on the actin filament. In a resting (unstimulated) muscle the actin-myosin binding site is blocked by tropomyosin — see Figure 2. This means myofilaments can't slide past each other because the myosin heads can't bind to the actin filaments.

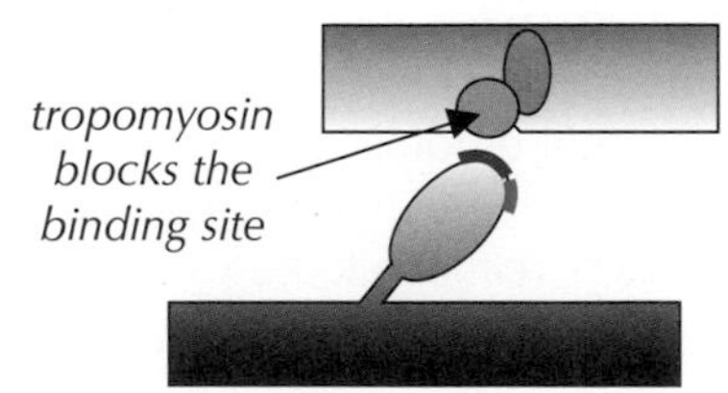


***Figure 2:*** *Actin and myosin filaments in resting muscle.*

## The process of muscle contraction

### Arrival of an action potential

When an action potential from a motor neurone stimulates a muscle cell, it depolarises the sarcolemma. Depolarisation spreads down the T-tubules to the sarcoplasmic reticulum. This causes the sarcoplasmic reticulum to release stored calcium ions ($Ca^{2+}$) into the sarcoplasm. This influx of calcium ions into the sarcoplasm triggers muscle contraction.

Calcium ions bind to a protein attached to tropomyosin, causing the protein to change shape. This pulls the attached tropomyosin out of the actin-myosin binding site on the actin filament. This exposes the binding site, which allows the myosin head to bind. The bond formed when a myosin head binds to an actin filament is called an **actin-myosin cross bridge** — see Figure 3 on the next page.

**Tip:** If you can't remember your sarcolemma from your sarcoplasmic reticulum then take a look back at page 100.

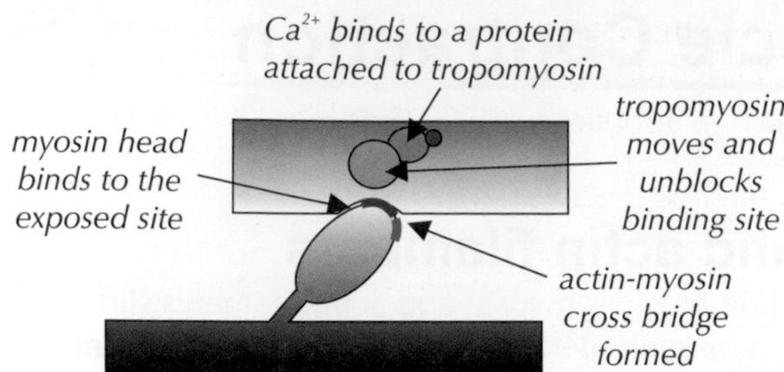


***Figure 3:*** *Formation of an actin-myosin cross bridge.*

## Movement of the actin filament

Calcium ions also activate the enzyme ATP hydrolase, which hydrolyses (breaks down) ATP (into ADP + $P_i$) to provide the energy needed for muscle contraction. The energy released from ATP causes the myosin head to bend, which pulls the actin filament along in a kind of rowing action (see Figure 4).

**Tip:** The movement of the myosin head to the side is called a 'power stroke'.

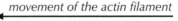

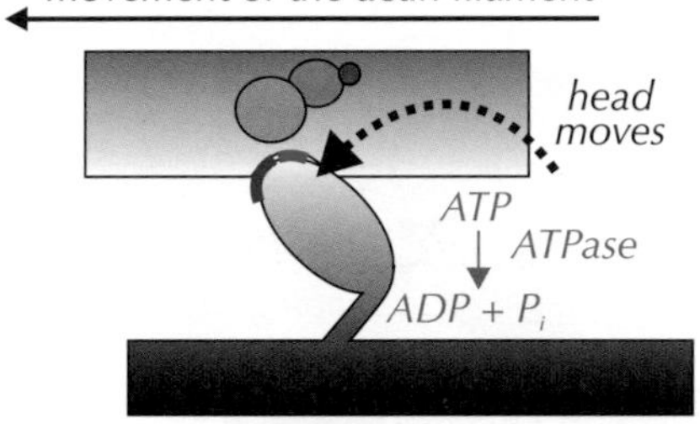

*movement of the actin filament*

*head moves*

*ATP → ATPase → ADP + $P_i$*

***Figure 4:*** *Movement of the myosin head.*

## Breaking of the cross bridge

Another ATP molecule provides the energy to break the actin-myosin cross bridge, so the myosin head detaches from the actin filament after it's moved. The myosin head then returns to its starting position, and reattaches to a different binding site further along the actin filament — see Figure 5. A new actin-myosin cross bridge is formed and the cycle is repeated (attach, move, detach, reattach to new binding site...).

Many actin-myosin cross bridges form and break very rapidly, pulling the actin filament along — which shortens the sarcomere, causing the muscle to contract. The cycle will continue as long as calcium ions are present.

**Tip:** A good supply of ATP is essential for muscle contraction. There's more how ATP stores and releases energy on page 20.

**Tip:** As the actin filaments are being moved along, the I-bands are getting shorter and the Z-lines are moving closer together.

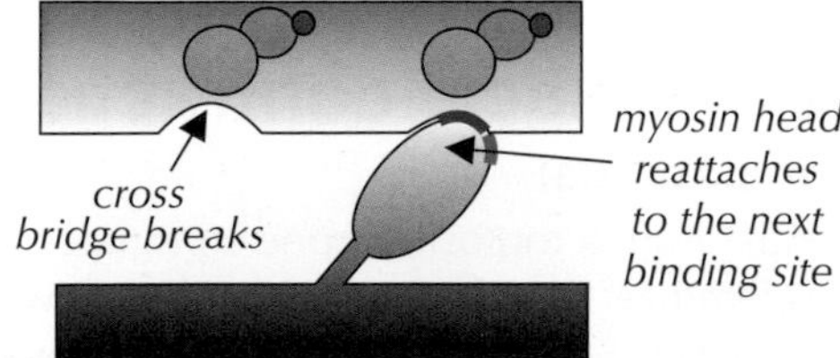


***Figure 5:*** *Myosin head forms a new actin-myosin cross bridge.*

## Return to resting state

When the muscle stops being stimulated, calcium ions leave their binding sites and are moved by active transport back into the sarcoplasmic reticulum (this needs ATP too).

This causes the tropomyosin molecules to move back, so they block the actin-myosin binding sites again — see Figure 6. Muscles aren't contracted because no myosin heads are attached to actin filaments (so there are no actin-myosin cross bridges). The actin filaments slide back to their relaxed position, which lengthens the sarcomere.

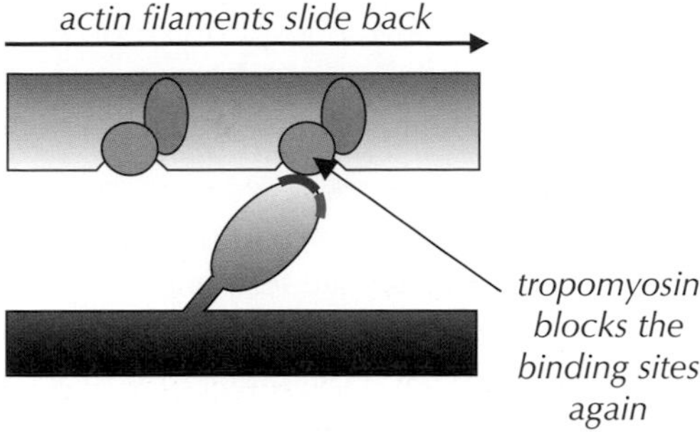


***Figure 6:*** *Blocking of the actin-myosin binding sites as the muscle returns to its resting state.*

## Practice Questions — Application

Q1 The graph below shows the calcium ion concentration in the sarcoplasm of a muscle fibre over time.

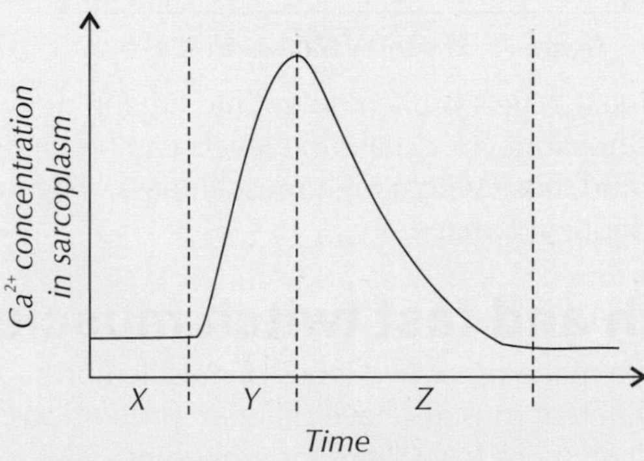


a) During what time period (X, Y or Z):

i) is the muscle fibre the longest length? Explain your answer.

ii) would $Ca^{2+}$ ions be bound to the protein attached to tropomyosin? Explain your answer.

iii) would ATP hydrolase be activated? Explain your answer.

b) Describe the movement of calcium ions during time period Z.

c) Describe the event that causes an increase in $Ca^{2+}$ ions in the sarcoplasm at the beginning of time period Y.

Q2 Cardiac muscle in the heart has some similarities to skeletal muscle, for example, it has both actin and myosin filaments. Patients who suffer from heart failure may be given positive inotropic agents — these are substances which increase the level of calcium ions in the cytoplasm of muscle cells.

Use your knowledge of muscle contraction to explain why this treatment may be used.

**Exam Tip**
Remember, it's dead easy to lose marks in the exam by rushing headlong into answering a question without reading it through properly first. Take your time — make sure you understand any information in a table or a graph before attempting the question.

**Tip:** Heart failure is where the heart is unable to pump enough blood around the body.

**Tip:** Have a flick back to pages 38-44 if you need to remind yourself of the processes involved in aerobic and anaerobic respiration.

# Energy for muscle contraction

So much energy is needed when muscles contract that ATP gets used up very quickly. ATP has to be continually generated so exercise can continue — this happens in three main ways:

### 1. Aerobic respiration

Most ATP is generated via oxidative phosphorylation in the cell's mitochondria. Aerobic respiration only works when there's oxygen so it's good for long periods of low-intensity exercise, e.g. a long walk.

### 2. Anaerobic respiration

ATP is made rapidly by glycolysis. The end product of glycolysis is pyruvate, which is converted to lactate by lactate fermentation. Lactate can quickly build up in the muscles and cause muscle fatigue. Anaerobic respiration is good for short periods of hard exercise, e.g. a 400 m sprint.

**Tip:** Many activities use a combination of these systems.

### 3. ATP-phosphocreatine (PCr) system

ATP is made by phosphorylating ADP — adding a phosphate group taken from PCr. The equation for this is shown in Figure 7. PCr is stored inside cells and the ATP-PCr system generates ATP very quickly. PCr runs out after a few seconds so it's used during short bursts of vigorous exercise, e.g. a tennis serve. The ATP-PCr system is anaerobic (it doesn't need oxygen) and it's alactic (it doesn't form any lactate).

$$\text{ADP} + \text{PCr} \rightarrow \text{ATP} + \text{Cr (creatine)}$$

***Figure 7:*** *Phosphorylation of ADP by PCr.*

Some of the creatine (Cr) gets broken down into creatinine, which is removed from the body via the kidneys. Creatinine levels can be higher in people who exercise regularly and those with a high muscle mass. High creatinine levels may also indicate kidney damage.

# Slow twitch and fast twitch muscle fibres

Skeletal muscles are made up of two types of muscle fibres — slow twitch and fast twitch. Different muscles have different proportions of slow and fast twitch fibres. The two types have different properties:

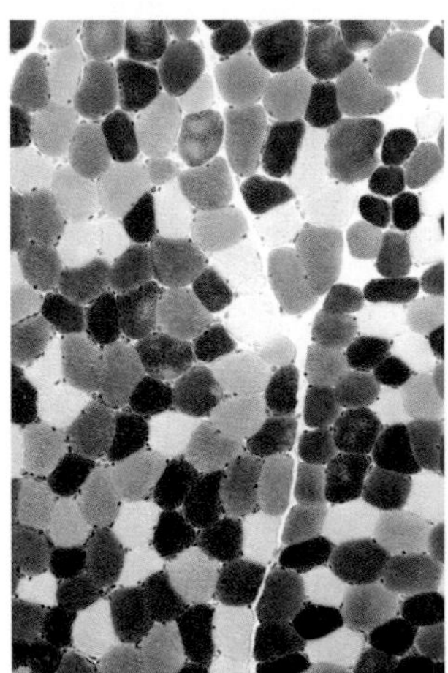

***Figure 8:*** *A light micrograph showing a transverse cross-section of a muscle. The dark fibres are slow twitch and the light fibres are fast twitch.*

### Slow twitch muscle fibres

Slow twitch muscle fibres contract slowly and can work for a long time without getting tired. This makes them good for endurance activities, e.g. long-distance running and maintaining posture. High proportions of slow twitch muscle fibres are found in the muscles you use for posture, such as the muscles in the back and in the calves.

Energy is released slowly through aerobic respiration (see above) in slow twitch muscle fibres. They have lots of mitochondria and blood vessels to supply the muscles with oxygen. The mitochondria are mainly found near to the edge of muscle fibres, so that there's a short diffusion pathway for oxygen from the blood vessels to the mitochondria. Slow twitch muscle fibres are also rich in myoglobin, a red-coloured protein that stores oxygen, so they're reddish in colour.

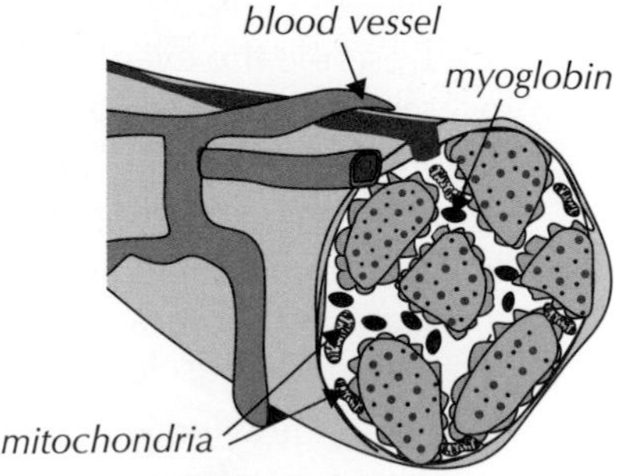


***Figure 9:*** *A slow twitch muscle fibre.*

### Fast twitch muscle fibres

Fast twitch muscle fibres contract very quickly but also get tired quickly. This makes them good for short bursts of speed and power, e.g. sprinting and eye movement. High proportions of fast twitch muscle fibres are found in muscles you use for fast movement, such as the legs, arms and eyes.

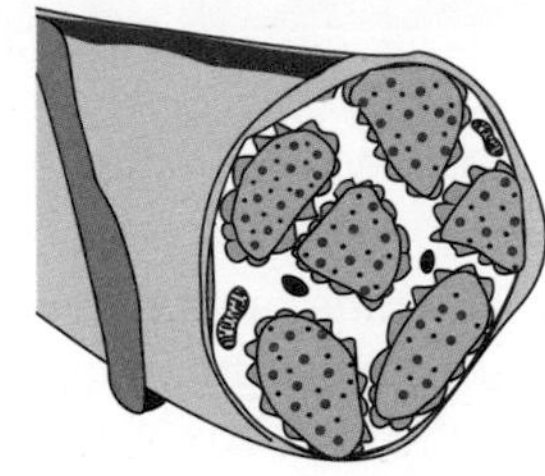

***Figure 10:*** *A fast twitch muscle fibre, with few blood vessels, myoglobin or mitochondria.*

Energy is released quickly through anaerobic respiration using glycogen in fast twitch muscle fibres. They also have stores of PCr so that energy can be generated very quickly when needed (see previous page). Fast twitch muscle fibres have few mitochondria or blood vessels. They don't have much myoglobin either, so they can't store much oxygen — this gives them more of a whitish colour.

**Tip:** Cells are able to store excess glucose as glycogen, which can be converted back into glucose when needed.

## Practice Question — Application

Q1 A marathon runner runs 25 miles at a steady pace. She then speeds up for the 26th mile and sprints the last 385 yards to the finish line.

a) Discuss the ways in which the marathon runner is most likely to generate ATP during the course of the race.

b) Is the marathon runner likely to have a greater proportion of fast twitch or slow twitch muscle fibres in her leg muscles? Give a reason for your answer.

## Practice Questions — Fact Recall

Q1 Name a protein found between actin filaments that help myofilaments slide past each other.

Q2 Explain how calcium ions in the sarcoplasm allow the formation of actin-myosin cross bridges.

Q3 Describe the role of ATP in muscle contraction.

Q4 a) Describe how ATP is generated in the ATP-phosphocreatine system.

b) Give one advantage and one disadvantage of generating ATP via the ATP-phosphocreatine system.

c) Give two other ways in which ATP can be generated.

Q5 Give two ways in which slow twitch muscle fibres are adapted for their function.

## Section Summary

Make sure you know...

- How a resting membrane potential is established and maintained by sodium-potassium pumps and potassium ion channels in a neurone's cell membrane.
- That when sodium ion channels in the membrane open the membrane becomes more permeable to sodium ions and this causes depolarisation (the potential difference of the membrane becomes more positive), resulting in an action potential if the threshold level is reached.
- That the refractory period is when sodium and potassium ion channels can't be made to open again, and that this is important to ensure action potentials form discrete impulses, have a limited frequency and are unidirectional.
- That the all-or-nothing principle means that if the threshold is reached, an action potential will always fire with the same change in voltage and if the threshold isn't reached there'll be no action potential.
- The structure of a myelinated neurone including the dendrites, axon, axon terminal and myelin sheath.
- Why action potentials are passed more quickly along myelinated neurones than unmyelinated neurones.
- That bigger diameters and higher temperatures speed up the rate of conduction along a neurone.
- The detailed structure of a synapse including the synaptic knob, vesicles and postsynaptic membrane.
- That impulses at a synapse are unidirectional because only the postsynaptic membrane has receptors.
- How a nerve impulse is transmitted across a cholinergic synapse, including the role of voltage-gated calcium channels, calcium ions, acetylcholine (ACh), cholinergic receptors on the postsynaptic membrane, sodium ion channels and sodium ions.
- That at inhibitory synapses, inhibitory neurotransmitters are released from the presynaptic neurone, which hyperpolarise the postsynaptic membrane (make the potential difference more negative), preventing it from firing an action potential.
- That spatial summation is the total effect of all the neurotransmitters released from many neurones present at a synapse and that temporal summation is where two or more nerve impulses arrive in quick succession from the same presynaptic neurone.
- The detailed structure of a neuromuscular junction.
- The similarities and differences in transmission across a cholinergic synapse and a neuromuscular junction.
- How to use information given about a drug to predict and explain the effects it will have at a synapse.
- That muscles work in antagonistic pairs to move bones at a joint — as one muscle (the agonist) contracts and pulls the bone, the other muscle (the antagonist) relaxes.
- That skeletal muscle is made up of large bundles of muscle fibres that contain transverse tubules, sarcolemma, sarcoplasm, sarcoplasmic reticulum, myofibrils, and lots of mitochondria and nuclei.
- That myofibrils contain thick myosin and thin actin filaments, and are divided into sarcomeres. A-bands on sarcomeres contain myosin and actin filaments, I-bands only contain actin filaments.
- That, during muscle contraction, calcium ions bind to a protein attached to tropomyosin, which pulls tropomyosin out of the actin-myosin binding site so that actin-myosin cross bridges can be formed.
- How actin, myosin, calcium ions and ATP work together to make a myofibril contract.
- That energy from ATP is used for muscle contraction and that ATP generation may involve the ATP-phosphocreatine (PCr) system.
- That slow twitch muscle fibres are good for endurance activities, release energy slowly through aerobic respiration and are found in muscles such as those used for posture.
- That fast twitch muscle fibres are good for short bursts of speed and power, release energy quickly through anaerobic respiration and are found in muscles, such as those in the eyes and legs, which are used for fast movement.

# Exam-style Questions

**1** Human skeletal muscle is made up of both slow twitch and fast twitch muscle fibres, the proportions of which can vary depending on the location of the muscle and a person's activity levels. Both types of muscle fibres contain GLUT4, a membrane protein that helps glucose to be transported across a plasma membrane.

**1.1** A person who performs a lot of low-intensity training may have a higher proportion of slow twitch muscle fibres than fast twitch muscle fibres. Suggest a reason for this.

*(1 mark)*

**1.2** Sprinters often have more fast twitch muscle fibres than marathon runners. Give one function of fast twitch muscle fibres and explain how they are adapted for this function.

*(3 marks)*

**1.3** During muscle contraction, the content of GLUT4 in muscle cell membranes increases. Explain why.

*(3 marks)*

**1.4** Muscle contraction involves the movement of actin and myosin filaments. Describe the structure of a myosin filament.

*(2 marks)*

**2** **Figure 1** shows three action potentials recorded across the membrane of a myelinated axon (axon X).

**Figure 1**

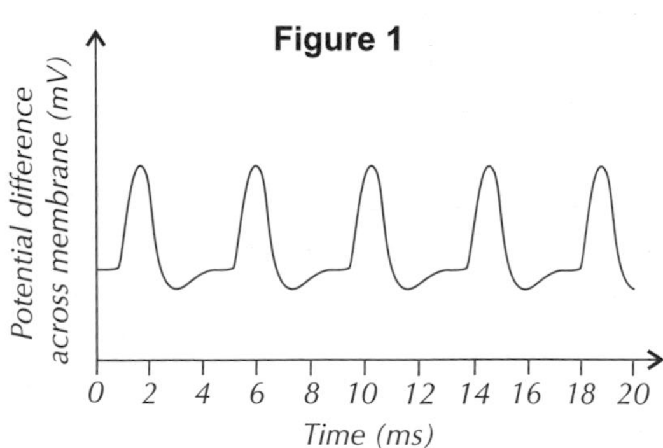


**2.1** Explain why the action potentials don't overlap.

*(3 marks)*

**2.2** If the action potentials continue at the same frequency, calculate the number of action potentials along the axon in 0.5 s.

*(2 marks)*

**2.3** At the same temperature, another myelinated axon (axon Y) conducted 140 action potentials in 0.5 s. Use your answer to **2.2** to suggest whether axon X or axon Y has the biggest diameter. Explain your answer.

*(3 marks)*

3 **Figure 2** shows the structure of a myelinated motor neurone in the peripheral nervous system.

Figure 2

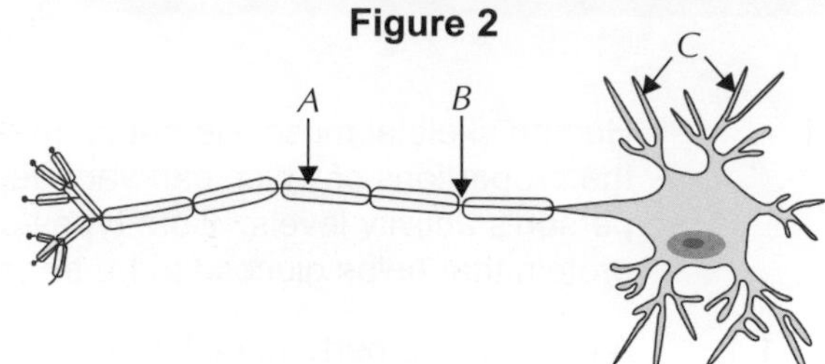


3.1 Name the type of cell that forms structure A.

*(1 mark)*

3.2 Name the structures labelled B and C.

*(2 marks)*

Guillain-Barré syndrome is an autoimmune disease whereby the myelin sheath around certain neurones is damaged.

3.3 Explain the function of myelin in a normal motor neurone.

*(2 marks)*

3.4 Use your knowledge of myelination to explain how Guillain-Barré syndrome can result in muscle weakness and paralysis.

*(2 marks)*

4 A bodybuilder lifts weights to increase the size of the muscles in his arms.

4.1 Describe how the biceps and triceps muscles work together to bend the arm.

*(3 marks)*

4.2 Explain the role of acetylcholine in causing depolarisation of cells in the biceps muscle following a nervous impulse.

*(5 marks)*

**Figure 3** shows part of a myofibril in the biceps muscle when it is **contracted**.

Figure 3

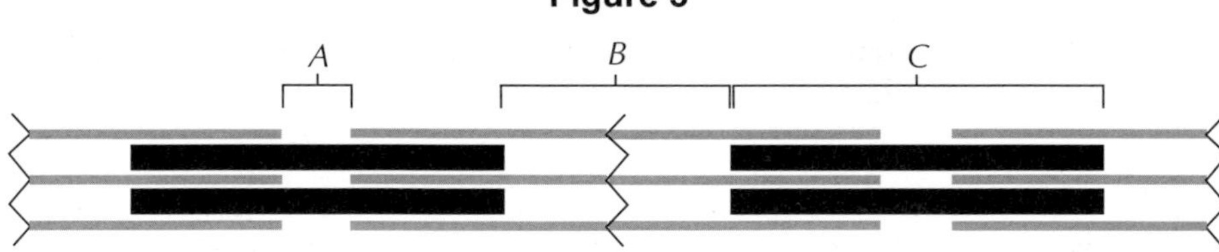


4.3 Name the sections of the myofibril labelled **A-C**.

*(3 marks)*

4.4 For each of the sections **A-C**, state how it will appear when the biceps relaxes, compared to how it appears in **Figure 3**.

*(2 marks)*

The bodybuilder manages to lift an extremely heavy weight with a short burst of explosive power. He can only sustain the lift for a few seconds.

4.5 Describe how ATP is likely to be generated in the bodybuilder's arm muscles when he lifts the heavy weight.

*(2 marks)*

4.6 Give **one** advantage of ATP being generated in this way.

*(1 mark)*

5 **Figure 4** shows a neurone cell membrane at two different times during one action potential.

**Figure 4**

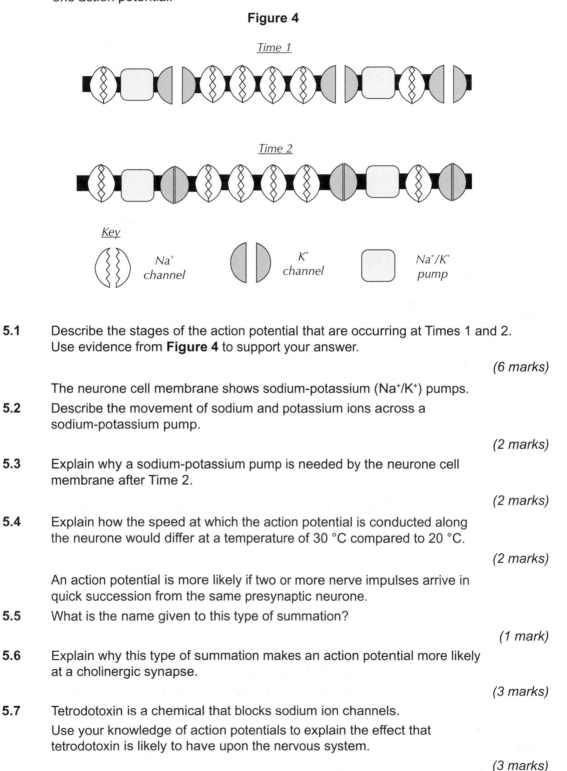

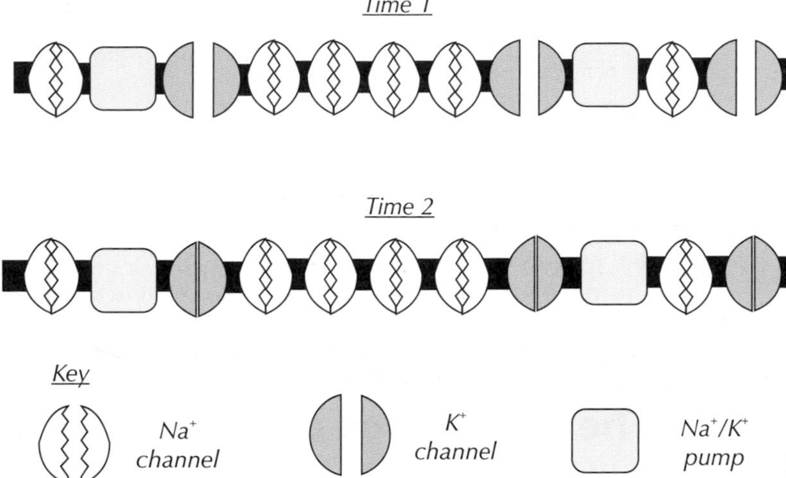


**5.1** Describe the stages of the action potential that are occurring at Times 1 and 2. Use evidence from **Figure 4** to support your answer.

*(6 marks)*

The neurone cell membrane shows sodium-potassium ($Na^+/K^+$) pumps.

**5.2** Describe the movement of sodium and potassium ions across a sodium-potassium pump.

*(2 marks)*

**5.3** Explain why a sodium-potassium pump is needed by the neurone cell membrane after Time 2.

*(2 marks)*

**5.4** Explain how the speed at which the action potential is conducted along the neurone would differ at a temperature of 30 °C compared to 20 °C.

*(2 marks)*

An action potential is more likely if two or more nerve impulses arrive in quick succession from the same presynaptic neurone.

**5.5** What is the name given to this type of summation?

*(1 mark)*

**5.6** Explain why this type of summation makes an action potential more likely at a cholinergic synapse.

*(3 marks)*

**5.7** Tetrodotoxin is a chemical that blocks sodium ion channels.

Use your knowledge of action potentials to explain the effect that tetrodotoxin is likely to have upon the nervous system.

*(3 marks)*

**Learning Objectives:**

- Understand that homeostasis in mammals involves physiological control systems that maintain the internal environment within restricted limits.
- Understand the importance of maintaining a stable core temperature and stable blood pH in relation to enzyme activity.
- Understand the importance of maintaining a stable blood glucose concentration in terms of the water potential of blood and of availability of respiratory substrate.
- Know that negative feedback restores systems to their original level.
- Understand that the possession of separate mechanisms involving negative feedback controls departures in different directions from the original state, giving a greater degree of control.
- Be able to interpret information relating to examples of negative and positive feedback.

**Specification Reference 3.6.4.1**

# 1. Homeostasis Basics

*The body has some pretty clever systems to control its internal environment...*

## What is homeostasis?

Changes in your external environment can affect your internal environment — the blood and tissue fluid that surrounds your cells. Homeostasis is the maintenance of a stable internal environment. It involves control systems that keep your internal environment roughly constant (within certain limits). This means your internal environment is kept in a state of dynamic equilibrium (i.e. fluctuating around a normal level). Keeping your internal environment stable is vital for cells to function normally and to stop them being damaged.

## The importance of homeostasis

It's particularly important to maintain the right core body temperature and blood pH. This is because temperature and pH affect enzyme activity, and enzymes control the rate of **metabolic reactions** (chemical reactions in living cells). It's also important to maintain the right blood glucose concentration because cells need glucose for energy and blood glucose concentration affects the water potential of blood — see page 114.

### Temperature

The rate of metabolic reactions increases when the temperature's increased. More heat means more kinetic energy, so molecules move faster. This makes the substrate molecules more likely to collide with the enzymes' active sites. The energy of these collisions also increases, which means each collision is more likely to result in a reaction.

But, if the temperature gets too high (e.g. over 40 °C), the reaction essentially stops. The rise in temperature makes the enzyme's molecules vibrate more. If the temperature goes above a certain level, this vibration breaks some of the hydrogen bonds that hold the enzyme in its 3D shape. The active site changes shape and the enzyme and substrate no longer fit together. At this point, the enzyme is denatured — it no longer functions as a catalyst (see Figure 1).

If body temperature is too low enzyme activity is reduced, slowing the rate of metabolic reactions. The highest rate of enzyme activity happens at their optimum temperature — about 37 °C in humans (see Figure 1).

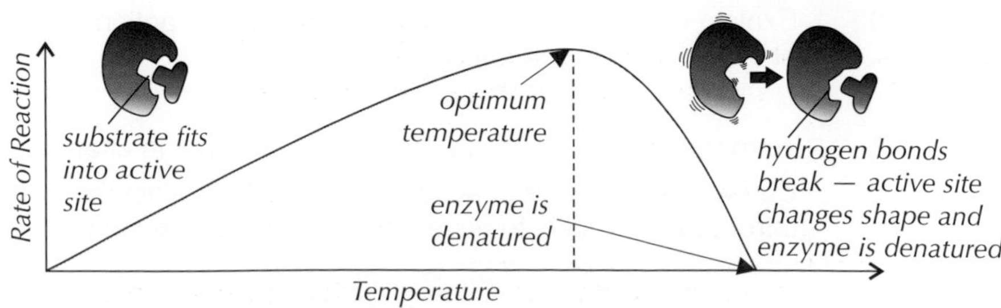


***Figure 1:*** *Effect of temperature on the rate of a metabolic reaction.*

## pH

If blood pH is too high or too low (highly alkaline or acidic) enzymes become denatured (see Figure 2). The ionic bonds and hydrogen bonds that hold them in their 3D shape are broken, so the shape of the enzyme's active site is changed and it no longer works as a catalyst. The highest rate of enzyme activity happens at their optimum pH, so this is when metabolic reactions are fastest. Optimum pH is usually around pH 7 (neutral), but some enzymes work best at other pHs, e.g. enzymes found in the stomach work best at a low pH.

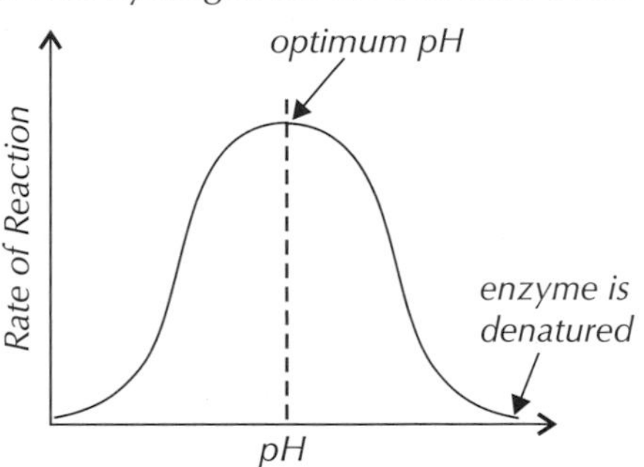


***Figure 2:*** *Effect of pH on a metabolic reaction.*

**Tip:** When an enzyme is denatured the reaction may still happen but it'll be too slow for the body's needs.

pH is calculated based on the concentration of hydrogen ions ($H^+$) in the environment. The greater the concentration of $H^+$, the lower the pH will be (and the more acidic the environment). You can work out the pH of a solution using the following equation:

$$pH = -\log_{10}[H^+]$$

$\text{Log}_{10}$ tells you the pH is expressed on a **logarithmic scale.** You could get asked to use a logarithmic scale in the exam so here's a bit more about them:

A logarithmic scale is a scale that uses the **logarithm** of a number instead of the number itself. Each value on a logarithmic scale using $\log_{10}$ is ten times larger than the value before — so a solution of pH 3 contains ten times more $H^+$ ions than a solution of pH 4. This is because the concentration of $H^+$ can vary enormously and so it's easier to compare values on a logarithmic scale. Converting values to a logarithmic scale also makes it easier to plot both very small and very large values (e.g. both 0.1 and 1000) on the same axis of a graph.

$[H^+]$ is the concentration of hydrogen ions in a solution, measured in mol dm$^{-3}$. So, if you know the hydrogen ion concentration of a solution, you can calculate its pH by sticking the numbers into the formula above.

**Tip:** Increasing the number by 1 on a $\log_{10}$ scale is the same as multiplying by 10 on a linear (normal) scale. So the numbers 1, 2, 3 and 4 on a $\log_{10}$ scale represent 10, 100, 1000 and 10,000 on a linear scale:

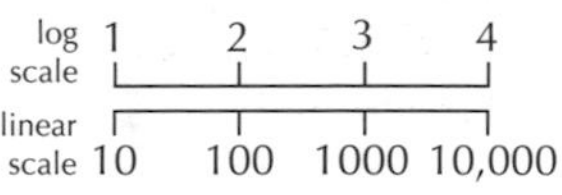

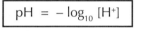

**Tip:** Another situation where logarithms come in handy is with microbial growth, where the number of organisms increases exponentially (see page 179).

**Examples — Maths Skills**

1. A solution has a hydrogen ion concentration of 0.01 mol dm$^{-3}$. Calculate its pH.

$pH = -\log_{10}[H^+]$
$= -\log_{10}(0.01)$
$= \mathbf{2}$

*Just substitute the [H⁺] value into the pH formula and solve.*

2. A blood sample has a hydrogen ion concentration of $3.9 \times 10^{-8}$ mol dm$^{-3}$. What is the pH of the blood?

$pH = -\log_{10}[H^+]$
$= -\log_{10}(3.9 \times 10^{-8})$
$= \mathbf{7.4}$

To calculate logarithms you need to use the 'log' button on your calculator. On most calculators, 'log' will stand for $\log_{10}$, but different calculators work differently so make sure you know how to calculate logs on yours.

**Tip:** The values being expressed on a logarithmic scale are often very large or very small quantities, so standard form is often used. See pages 7 and 8 for more on standard form.

Tip: Water potential is the potential (likelihood) of water molecules to diffuse out of or into a solution.

Tip: Glucose is a solute. It lowers the water potential of the blood. If the blood glucose concentration is too high, water molecules move by osmosis from the cells (an area of higher water potential) to the blood (an area of lower water potential).

Tip: Glucose is a respiratory substrate — a substance that can be broken down during respiration to release energy.

### Blood glucose concentration

If blood glucose concentration is too high, the water potential of blood is reduced to a point where water molecules diffuse out of cells into the blood by osmosis (the diffusion of water molecules from an area of higher water potential to an area of lower water potential, across a partially permeable membrane). This can cause the cells to shrivel up and die (see Figure 3).

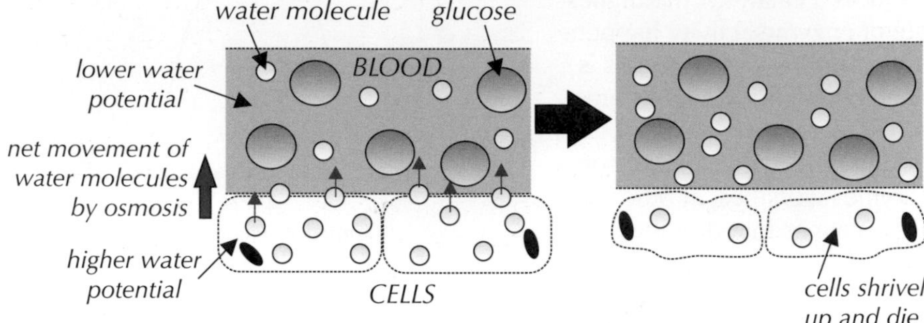


***Figure 3:*** *Effect of high blood glucose concentration on cells.*

If blood glucose concentration is too low, cells are unable to carry out normal activities because there isn't enough glucose for respiration to provide energy.

## Negative feedback

Tip: The 'level' in Figure 4 refers to something inside the body that needs to be controlled, e.g. temperature level, pH level, blood glucose level.

Homeostatic systems involve receptors, a communication system and effectors (see page 72). Receptors detect when a level is too high or too low, and the information's communicated via the nervous system or the hormonal system to effectors. The effectors respond to counteract the change — bringing the level back to normal. The mechanism that restores the level to normal is called a **negative feedback mechanism** — see Figure 4.

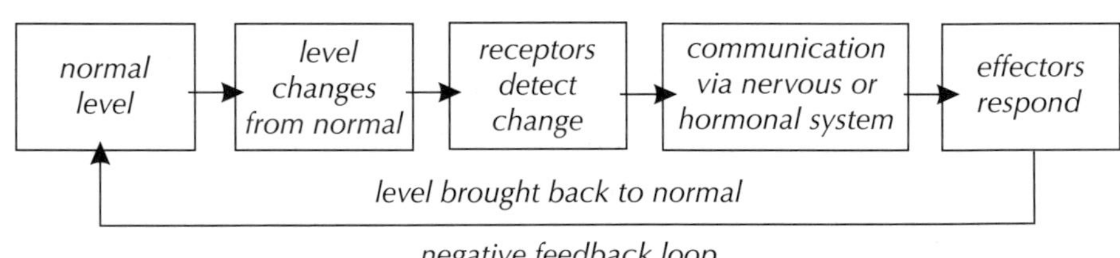


***Figure 4:*** *A negative feedback mechanism.*

Negative feedback keeps things around the normal level.

Tip: Negative feedback keeps the pH of the blood within the range 7.35 - 7.45 and blood glucose within the range 82 - 110 mg/100 $cm^3$.

**Example**

Body temperature is usually kept within 0.5 °C above or below 37 °C.

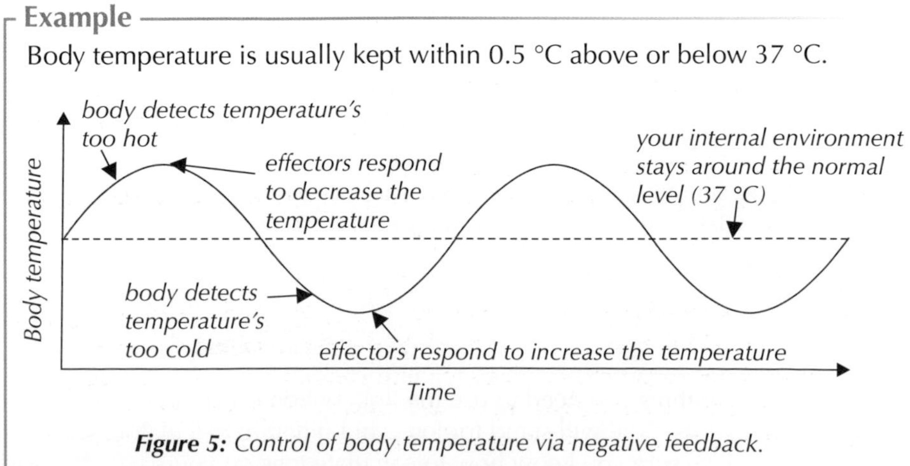


***Figure 5:*** *Control of body temperature via negative feedback.*

Negative feedback only works within certain limits though — if the change is too big then the effectors may not be able to counteract it, e.g. a huge drop in body temperature caused by prolonged exposure to cold weather may be too large to counteract.

### Multiple negative feedback mechanisms

Homeostasis involves multiple negative feedback mechanisms for each thing being controlled. This is because having more than one mechanism gives more control over changes in your internal environment than just having one negative feedback mechanism.

Having multiple negative feedback mechanisms means you can actively increase or decrease a level so it returns to normal, e.g. you have feedback mechanisms to reduce your body temperature and you also have mechanisms to increase it. If you only had one negative feedback mechanism, all you could do would be turn it on or turn it off. You'd only be able to actively change a level in one direction so it returns to normal. Only one negative feedback mechanism means a slower response and less control.

**Tip:** Think of this as trying to slow down a car with only an accelerator — all you can do is take your foot off the accelerator (you'd have more control with a brake too).

## Positive feedback

Some changes trigger a positive feedback mechanism, which amplifies the change. The effectors respond to further increase the level away from the normal level. The mechanism that amplifies a change away from the normal level is called a **positive feedback mechanism** — see Figure 6.

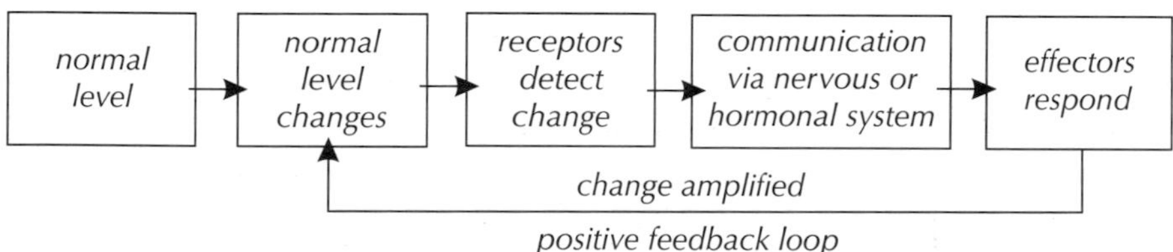


***Figure 6:*** *A positive feedback mechanism.*

Positive feedback isn't involved in homeostasis because it doesn't keep your internal environment stable. Positive feedback is useful to rapidly activate processes in the body.

**Example**

During the formation of a blood clot after an injury, platelets become activated and release a chemical — this triggers more platelets to be activated, and so on. This means platelets very quickly form a blood clot at the injury site. (The process ends with negative feedback, when the body detects the blood clot has been formed.)

### Breakdown of homeostatic systems

Positive feedback can also happen when a homeostatic system breaks down.

**Example**

Hypothermia is low body temperature (below 35 °C). It happens when heat's lost from the body quicker than it can be produced. As body temperature falls the brain doesn't work properly and shivering stops — this makes body temperature fall even more (see Figure 8 — next page). Positive feedback takes body temperature further away from the normal level, and it continues to decrease unless action is taken.

**Tip:** 'Hypo' is often used to describe a condition where something being controlled (in this case body temperature) has fallen below its normal level —'hyper' is when it's gone above its normal level.

*Figure 7: A person with hypothermia could be helped by being wrapped in a foil blanket as shown above. The foil blanket minimises further heat loss from the body so internal temperature should increase back to within normal limits.*

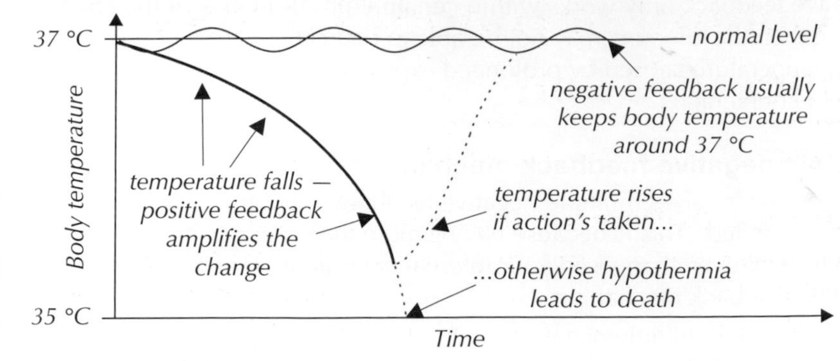


***Figure 8:*** *Positive feedback takes body temperature away from its normal level in people with hypothermia.*

## Practice Questions — Application

Q1 The range of normal blood pH is between 7.35 and 7.45. Metabolic acidosis is a condition that occurs when blood pH falls below 7.35.

a) Analysis of a patient's blood revealed that their hydrogen ion concentration $[H^+]$ was $5.50 \times 10^{-8}$ mol dm$^{-3}$. Use the formula $pH = -\log_{10} [H^+]$ to calculate the pH of the patient's blood. Use your answer to determine whether the patient could be suffering from metabolic acidosis.

b) Why is it important to maintain a blood pH in the normal range?

Q2 Read the following two passages about control systems in the body:

Passage A

A high blood concentration of carbon dioxide lowers the pH of the blood. Chemoreceptors in the blood vessels detect this change and send signals to the brain to increase the respiration rate.

Passage B

When oestrogen concentration is high it stimulates the anterior pituitary gland to release LH. LH stimulates the ovaries to release more oestrogen.

For each passage, state whether it's an example of negative or positive feedback and explain your answer.

**Tip:** Oestrogen and LH are both hormones — you don't need to know anything about their effects in the body to answer the question.

## Practice Questions — Fact Recall

Q1 What is homeostasis?

Q2 Explain why is it important for the body to maintain its internal temperature within normal limits.

Q3 Why is it important that a stable blood glucose concentration is maintained?

Q4 Describe how positive feedback mechanisms differ from negative feedback mechanisms.

# 2. Control of Blood Glucose Concentration

*Blood glucose concentration is under tight control by a hormonal system.*

## Glucose concentration in the blood

All cells need a constant energy supply to work — so blood glucose concentration must be carefully controlled. The concentration of glucose in the blood is normally around 90 mg per 100 $cm^3$ of blood. It's monitored by cells in the **pancreas**. Blood glucose concentration rises after eating food containing carbohydrate. It falls after exercise, as more glucose is used in respiration to release energy.

## Hormonal control of blood glucose concentration

The hormonal system controls blood glucose concentration using two hormones called **insulin** and **glucagon**. Like all hormones, insulin and glucagon are chemical messengers that travel in the blood to their target cells (effectors). They're both secreted by clusters of cells in the pancreas called the **islets of Langerhans**.

The islets of Langerhans contain **beta** (β) **cells** and **alpha** (α) **cells** (see Figure 1). β cells secrete insulin into the blood.

α cells secrete glucagon into the blood. Insulin and glucagon act on effectors, which respond to restore the blood glucose concentration to the normal level.

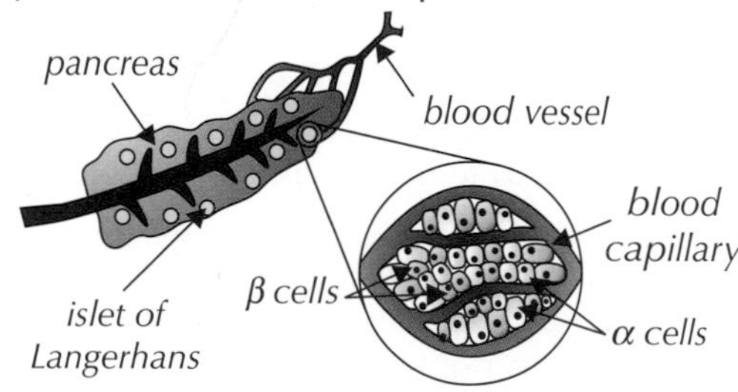


***Figure 1:*** *The location of α and β cells in the islets of Langerhans.*

### Insulin

Insulin lowers blood glucose concentration when it's too high. It binds to specific receptors on the cell membranes of muscle cells and liver cells (hepatocytes). It increases the permeability of muscle-cell membranes to glucose, so the cells take up more glucose. This involves increasing the number of channel proteins in the cell membranes (see page 119 for more).

Insulin also activates enzymes in muscle and liver cells that convert glucose into glycogen. The cells are able to store glycogen in their cytoplasm, as an energy source. The process of forming glycogen from glucose is called **glycogenesis** (see Figure 2). Insulin also increases the rate of respiration of glucose, especially in muscle cells.

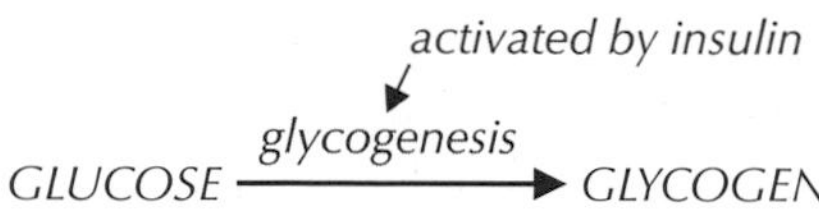


***Figure 2:*** *The process of glycogenesis.*

### Glucagon

Glucagon raises blood glucose concentration when it's too low. It binds to specific receptors on the cell membranes of liver cells and activates enzymes that break down glycogen into glucose. The process of breaking down glycogen is called **glycogenolysis**.

**Learning Objectives:**

- Know the factors that influence blood glucose concentration.
- Understand the role of the liver in glycogenesis, glycogenolysis and gluconeogenesis.
- Understand the action of insulin by attaching to receptors on the surfaces of target cells and activating enzymes involved in the conversion of glucose to glycogen.
- Understand the action of glucagon by attaching to receptors on the surfaces of target cells, activating enzymes involved in the conversion of glycogen to glucose and activating enzymes involved in the conversion of glycerol and amino acids into glucose.
- Understand the action of insulin in controlling the uptake of glucose by regulating the inclusion of channel proteins in the surface membranes of target cells.
- Understand the role of adrenaline by attaching to receptors on the surfaces of target cells and activating enzymes involved in the conversion of glycogen to glucose.
- Know the second messenger model of adrenaline and glucagon action, involving adenylate cyclase, cyclic AMP (cAMP) and protein kinase.

**Specification Reference 3.6.4.2**

Glucagon also activates enzymes that are involved in the formation of glucose from glycerol (a component of lipids) and amino acids. The process of forming glucose from non-carbohydrates is called **gluconeogenesis** (see Figure 3). Glucagon decreases the rate of respiration of glucose in cells.

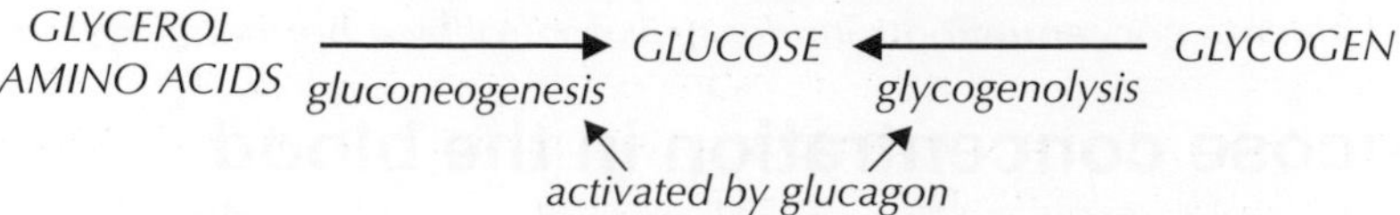


***Figure 3:*** *The processes of glycogenolysis and gluconeogenesis.*

**Tip:** Hormones (like insulin and glucagon) only bind to cells with specific receptors (target cells).

Because they travel in the blood to their target cells, the responses produced by hormones are slower than those produced by nervous impulses (which are very quick — see page 73). It also means that responses to hormones can occur all over the body if their target cells are widespread, unlike nervous impulses that are localised to one area. Hormones are not broken down as quickly as neurotransmitters though, so their effects tend to last for longer.

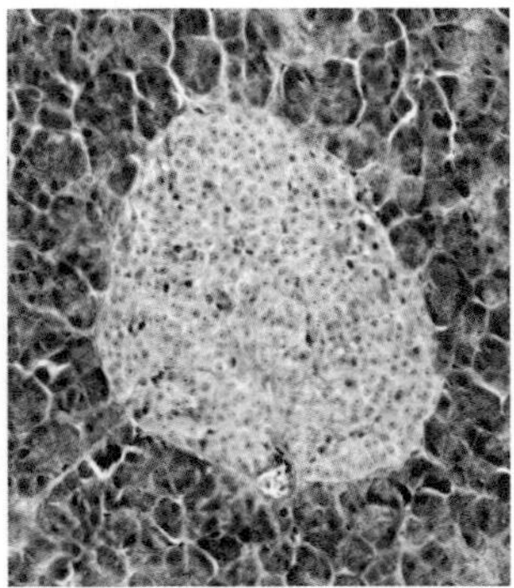

***Figure 4:*** *Islet of Langerhans (white) in the pancreas containing α cells and β cells.*

## Negative feedback mechanisms and glucose concentration

Negative feedback mechanisms keep blood glucose concentration normal.

### Rise in blood glucose concentration

When the pancreas detects blood glucose concentration is too high, the β cells secrete insulin and the α cells stop secreting glucagon. Insulin then binds to receptors on liver and muscle cells (the effectors). The liver and muscle cells respond to decrease the blood glucose concentration, e.g. glycogenesis is activated (see previous page). Blood glucose concentration then returns to normal.

**Tip:** 'Genesis' means 'making' — so glycogenesis means making glycogen.

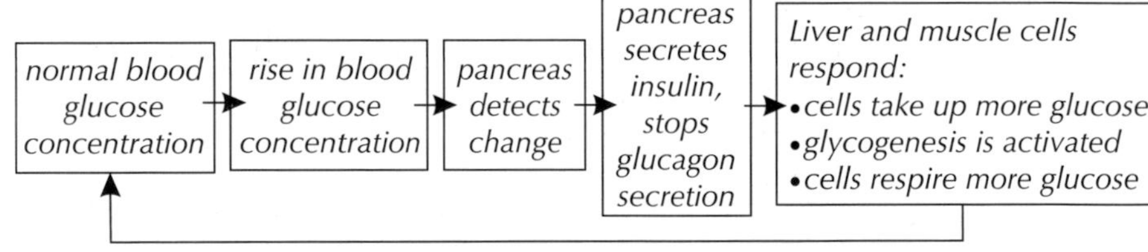


***Figure 5:*** *Negative feedback mechanism activated by a rise in blood glucose.*

### Fall in blood glucose concentration

When the pancreas detects blood glucose is too low, the α cells secrete glucagon and the β cells stop secreting insulin. Glucagon then binds to receptors on liver cells (the effectors). The liver cells respond to increase the blood glucose concentration, e.g. glycogenolysis is activated (see previous page). Blood glucose concentration then returns to normal.

**Tip:** 'Lysis' means 'splitting' — so glycogenolysis means splitting glycogen.

**Tip:** 'Neo' means 'new' — so gluconeogenesis means making new glucose.

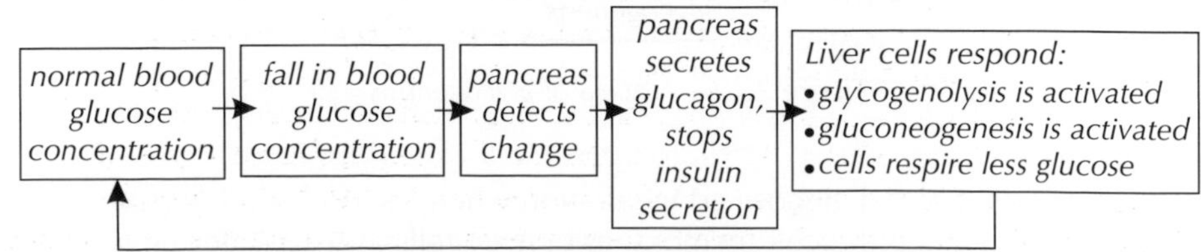


***Figure 6:*** *Negative feedback mechanism activated by a fall in blood glucose.*

# Glucose transporters

Glucose transporters are **channel proteins** which allow glucose to be transported across a cell membrane. Skeletal and cardiac muscle cells contain a glucose transporter called GLUT4. When insulin levels are low, GLUT4 is stored in vesicles in the cytoplasm of cells, but when insulin binds to receptors on the cell-surface membrane, it triggers the movement of GLUT4 to the membrane. Glucose can then be transported into the cell through the GLUT4 protein by facilitated diffusion.

**Tip:** Facilitated diffusion transports large or charged particles across a cell membrane down a concentration gradient (from a higher concentration to a lower concentration). It's a passive process so it doesn't require any energy.

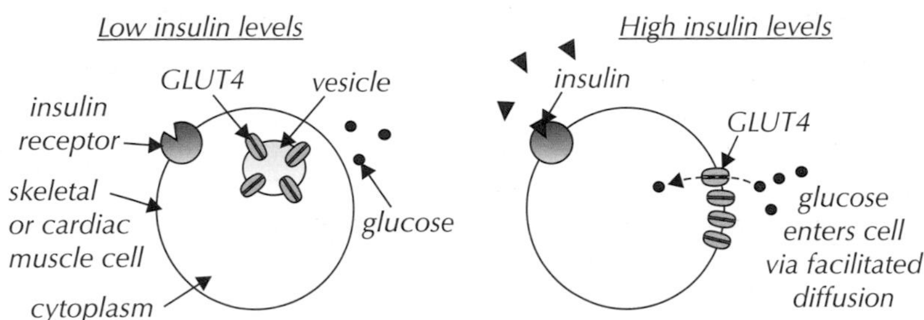


***Figure 7:*** *The effect of insulin on the availability of GLUT4.*

# Adrenaline

Adrenaline is a hormone that's secreted from your adrenal glands (found just above your kidneys). It's secreted when there's a low concentration of glucose in your blood, when you're stressed and when you're exercising. Adrenaline binds to receptors in the cell membrane of liver cells and does these things to increase blood glucose concentration:

- It activates glycogenolysis (the breakdown of glycogen to glucose).
- It inhibits glycogenesis (the synthesis of glycogen from glucose).

It also activates glucagon secretion and inhibits insulin secretion, which increases glucose concentration. Adrenaline gets the body ready for action by making more glucose available for muscles to respire.

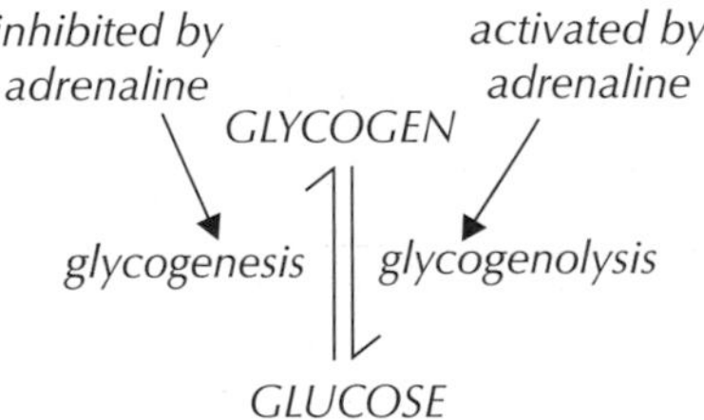


***Figure 8:*** *The effect of adrenaline on glycogenesis and glycogenolysis.*

## Second messengers

Both adrenaline and glucagon can activate glycogenolysis inside a cell even though they bind to receptors on the outside of the cell. They do this by the **second messenger model** — the binding of the hormone to cell receptors activates an enzyme on the inside of the cell membrane, which then produces a chemical known as a second messenger. The second messenger activates other enzymes in the cell to bring about a response.

**Tip:** Remember, adrenaline and glucagon bind to receptors on the cell membranes of liver cells.

The receptors for adrenaline and glucagon have specific tertiary structures that make them complementary in shape to their respective hormones. To activate glycogenolysis, adrenaline and glucagon bind to their receptors and activate an enzyme called **adenylate cyclase**. Activated adenylate cyclase converts ATP into a chemical called **cyclic AMP** (**cAMP**), which is a second messenger. cAMP activates an enzyme called **protein kinase A**. Protein kinase A activates a cascade (a chain of reactions) that breaks down glycogen into glucose (glycogenolysis) — see Figure 9 on the next page.

**Tip:** Adenylate cyclase is also known as adenylyl cyclase.

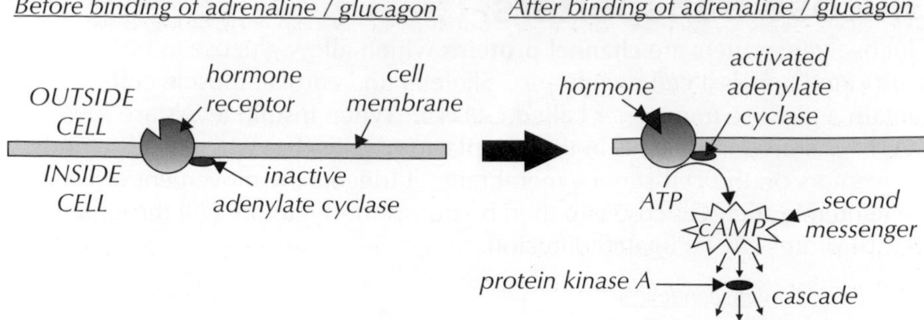


***Figure 9:*** *Second messenger model of adrenaline and glucagon action.*

**Exam Tip**
There's lots of similar sounding words in this section so you need to make sure you get your spelling spot on in the exam, e.g. if you write 'glycogon' the examiner won't know whether you mean glucagon or glycogen so you won't get the marks.

## Summary of blood glucose control

| Process | Converts | Activated by | Inhibited by |
|---|---|---|---|
| Glycogenesis | Glucose to glycogen | Insulin | Adrenaline |
| Glycogenolysis | Glycogen to glucose | Glucagon and adrenaline | — |
| Gluconeogenesis | Glycerol / amino acids to glucose | Glucagon | — |

**Tip:** Hypoglycaemia means low blood glucose concentration.

### Practice Questions — Application

Q1 Describe how a person's blood glucose concentration will change after eating a big bowl of pasta and explain how their body returns it back to normal.

Q2 Von Gierke's disease is a glycogen storage disease. It's caused by an enzyme deficiency, which means the processes of glycogenolysis and gluconeogenesis can't work properly. Explain why someone with von Gierke's disease might suffer from hypoglycaemia if they don't eat regularly.

### Practice Questions — Fact Recall

Q1 Where are insulin and glucagon secreted from?

Q2 Give three ways in which insulin reduces blood glucose concentration.

Q3 Name the process that converts glucose to glycogen.

Q4 Name and describe two processes activated by glucagon.

Q5 Describe the negative feedback mechanism that is activated by a fall in blood glucose concentration.

Q6 Describe how insulin regulates the uptake of glucose into skeletal and cardiac muscle cells.

Q7 Explain how adrenaline brings about glycogenolysis when blood glucose concentration is low.

# 3. Diabetes and Blood Glucose Concentration

*Diabetes is an example of when homeostasis goes awry...*

**Learning Objectives:**

- Understand the causes of Types I and II diabetes and their control by insulin and/or manipulation of the diet.
- Be able to evaluate the positions of health advisers and the food industry in relation to the increased incidence of Type II diabetes.
- Be able to produce a dilution series of a glucose solution and use colorimetric techniques to produce a calibration curve with which to identify the concentration of glucose in an unknown 'urine' sample (Required Practical 11).

**Specification Reference 3.6.4.2**

## What is diabetes?

Diabetes mellitus is a condition where blood glucose concentration can't be controlled properly. There are two types:

### Type I

In Type I diabetes, the immune system attacks the β cells in the islets of Langerhans so they can't produce any insulin. After eating, the blood glucose level rises and stays high — this is called hyperglycaemia and can result in death if left untreated. The kidneys can't reabsorb all this glucose, so some of it's excreted in the urine. Type I diabetes is treated with insulin therapy. Most people with Type I diabetes need regular insulin injections throughout the day, but some people use an insulin pump to deliver insulin continuously instead. Insulin therapy has to be carefully controlled because too much can produce a dangerous drop in blood glucose levels — this is called hypoglycaemia. Eating regularly and controlling simple carbohydrate intake (intake of sugars) helps to avoid a sudden rise in glucose.

No one knows exactly what causes the immune system to attack the β cells and cause Type I diabetes. Scientists have found that some people have a genetic predisposition to developing Type I diabetes. They also think that the disease may be triggered by a viral infection.

**Tip:** Simple carbohydrates are more easily broken down to glucose, which is then absorbed by the digestive system, than complex carbohydrates.

### Type II

Type II diabetes is usually acquired later in life than Type I. It is often linked with obesity and is more likely in people with a family history of the condition. Other risk factors include lack of exercise, age and poor diet. Type II diabetes occurs when the β cells don't produce enough insulin or when the body's cells don't respond properly to insulin. Cells don't respond properly because the insulin receptors on their membranes don't work properly, so the cells don't take up enough glucose. This means the blood glucose concentration is higher than normal. It can be treated by eating a healthy, balanced diet, losing weight (if necessary) and regular exercise. Glucose-lowering medication can be taken if diet and exercise can't control it. Eventually, insulin injections may be needed.

## Responses to Type II diabetes

Type II diabetes is becoming increasingly common in the UK. This has been linked to increasing levels of obesity, a move towards more unhealthy diets and low levels of physical activity. Type II diabetes can cause additional health problems, including visual impairment and kidney failure, so health advisors are understandably keen to educate people about the risks and reduce the incidence of the disease. Some people also think the food industry has a role to play in tackling the problem.

You need to understand the various responses to the increase in Type II diabetes and be able to evaluate them.

### Response of health advisors

To reduce the risk of developing Type II diabetes, health advisors recommend that people eat a diet that's low in fat, sugar and salt, with plenty of whole grains, fruit and vegetables, take regular exercise and lose weight if necessary.

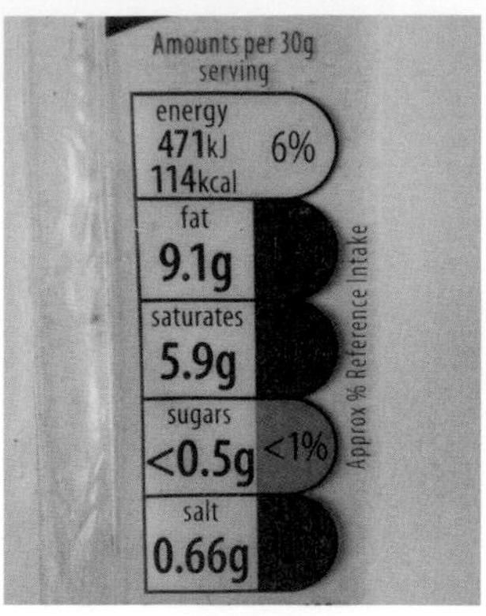


***Figure 1:*** *Clearer labelling can help people make healthier choices.*

Campaigns like the NHS's 'Change4Life', aim to educate people on how to have a healthier diet and lifestyle, and so reduce their risk of developing conditions like Type II diabetes. Health advisors have also challenged the food industry to reduce the advertising of junk food (particularly to children), to improve the nutritional value of their products, and to use clearer labelling on products — allowing consumers to make healthier choices about what to buy.

### Response of food companies

In response to criticism, some food companies have attempted to make their products more healthy. For example, by using sugar alternatives to sweeten food and drinks, and by reducing the sugar, fat and salt content of products.

However, there is pressure on companies to increase profits — they're reluctant to spend money developing new, healthier alternatives if the more unhealthy products are still popular and generate lots of profit. They say that the industry will only respond fully in the long term, as public perception about healthy eating changes.

**Tip:** Some people believe that diet varieties are not as good for health as they are claimed to be, e.g. there is some evidence to suggest that artificial sweeteners are linked to weight gain.

## Glucose in urine

If it is suspected that a person has diabetes, a doctor may request that a sample of their urine is tested for glucose. Normally, the concentration of glucose in urine is very low — between 0 and 0.8 mM. Higher concentrations than this may indicate diabetes (although a blood test would be needed to confirm it).

### Determining the concentration of a glucose solution

REQUIRED PRACTICAL 11

You need to be able to determine the concentration of glucose in a 'urine' sample, using **colorimetry**.

To do this you can use a quantitative Benedict's test. Quantitative Benedict's reagent is different to normal Benedict's reagent. When heated with glucose, the initial blue colour is lost, but a brick-red precipitate is not produced. You can use a colorimeter to measure the light absorbance of the solution after the quantitative Benedict's test has been carried out. The higher the concentration of glucose, the more blue colour will be lost (i.e. the paler the solution will become), decreasing the absorbance of the solution.

**Tip:** Don't worry, it won't be real urine! You'll be given a fake sample by your teacher.

**Tip:** Make sure you do a risk assessment before starting this experiment. The Benedict's test requires you to heat test tubes in a water bath, so take care not to touch them when they're hot. You should also wear safety goggles when working with Benedict's reagent.

### Making serial dilutions

Initially you need to make up several glucose solutions of different, known concentrations. You can do this using a serial dilution technique:

**Example**

This is how you'd make five serial dilutions with a dilution factor of 2, starting with an initial glucose concentration of 4 mM:

1. Line up five test tubes in a rack.
2. Add 10 cm$^3$ of the initial 4 mM glucose solution to the first test tube and 5 cm$^3$ of distilled water to the other four test tubes.
3. Then, using a pipette, draw 5 cm$^3$ of the solution from the first test tube, add it to the distilled water in the second test tube and mix the solution thoroughly. You now have 10 cm$^3$ of solution that's half as concentrated as the solution in the first test tube (it's 2 mM).
4. Repeat this process three more times to create solutions of 1 mM, 0.5 mM and 0.25 mM (see Figure 2 — next page).

**Tip:** When you're testing for a low concentration of glucose in a solution, quantitative Benedict's reagent can give a more accurate result than normal Benedict's reagent.

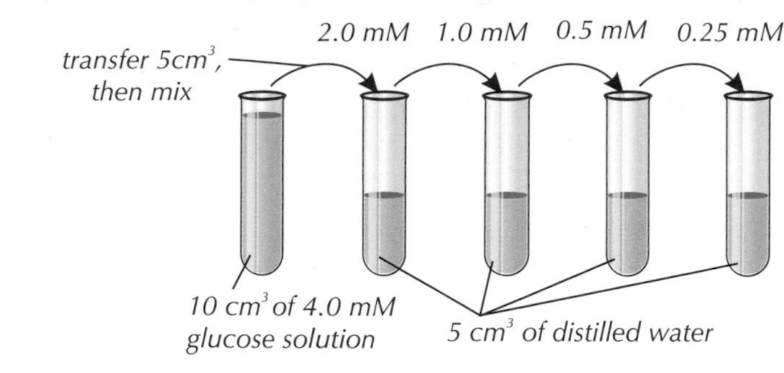


***Figure 2:*** *How to make serial dilutions.*

## Measuring the absorbance of glucose solutions

Once you've got your glucose solutions, you need to find out the absorbance of each one. Here's how:

1. Make sure you are using equal volumes of each of the solutions. You should also set up a test tube containing only pure water, which will act as a negative control.
2. Add the same amount of quantitative Benedict's reagent to each test tube and stir gently to mix.
3. Heat the test tubes for 4-5 minutes in a water bath that's been brought to the boil. Make sure you heat them all for the same amount of time.
4. Carefully remove the test tubes from the water bath and leave to cool.
5. Next, use a colorimeter to measure the absorbance of the solution in each test tube (see below).

**Tip:** There's no glucose in the negative control, so there's nothing for the Benedict's reagent to react with. This means the solution will remain blue — this should give you the highest absorbance value in the experiment.

## Using a colorimeter

A colorimeter is a device that measures absorbance (the amount of light absorbed by a solution). You've probably come across one before, but here's a quick recap:

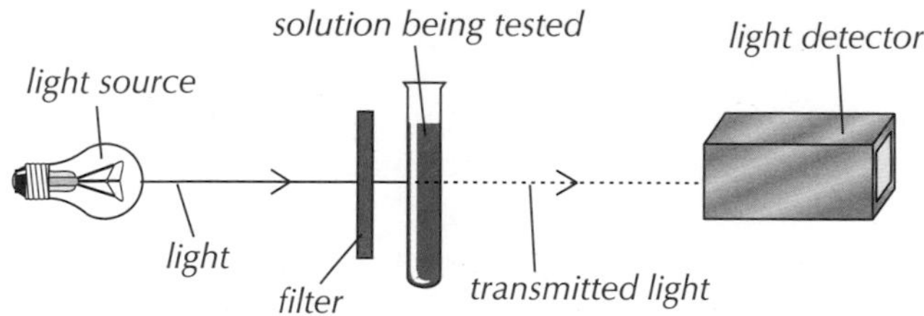


***Figure 3:*** *A diagram showing how a colorimeter works.*

For this experiment, you will need to set up the colorimeter with a red filter (or a wavelength of 635 nm).

After turning on the machine and allowing it time to stabilise, calibrate it to zero using a cuvette of distilled water. Then use a pipette to transfer a sample of the solution you would like to test into a clean cuvette and measure the absorbance of the solution. For each solution you test, use a clean pipette and cuvette.

**Tip:** Don't forget to zero the colorimeter between each reading.

## Making and using a calibration curve

Once you've measured the absorbance of each glucose solution, you can make a calibration curve. To do this, plot a graph of your results showing absorbance (on the *y*-axis) against glucose concentration (on the *x*-axis). Draw a smooth line/curve of best fit through your data points to create a calibration curve.

Then you can test the unknown solution (the 'urine' sample) in the same way as the known concentrations — i.e. use the same volume of solution and quantitative Benedict's reagent, and heat the solution for the same amount of time. Once you've measured the absorbance of the unknown solution you can use the calibration curve to find its concentration.

**Tip:** When drawing a calibration curve, the curve should go through or near as many points as possible.

**Example — Maths Skills**

Use the calibration curve below to find the glucose concentration of an unknown glucose solution with an absorbance value of 0.7.

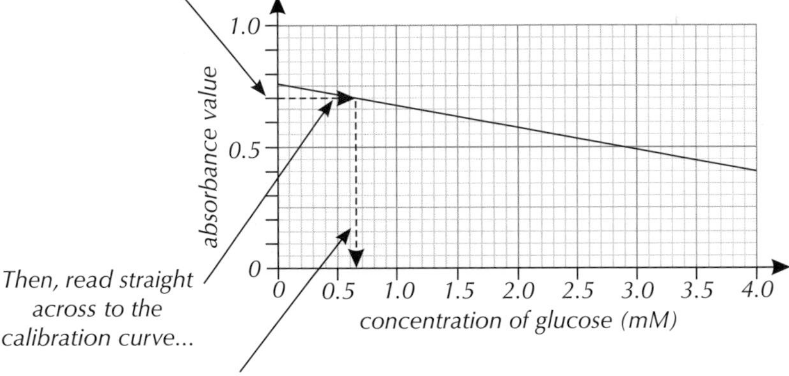

Firstly, find the absorbance value of the unknown solution on the y-axis.
1.0
0.5
0
absorbance value
Then, read straight across to the calibration curve...
0
0.5
1.0
1.5
2.0
2.5
3.0
3.5
4.0
concentration of glucose (mM)
...and then straight down to the x-axis.

So here, an unknown solution with an absorbance value of 0.7 has a glucose concentration of **0.65 mM**.

**Tip:** A calibration curve doesn't actually have to be a 'curve' — it can be a straight line (but you still call it a calibration curve).

## Practice Questions — Application

Q1 The table below shows the blood glucose concentration of a person with Type I diabetes taken at various times throughout the day. The person controls her diabetes with insulin injections after meals and aims to keep her blood glucose concentration between 4 and 7 mM.

| | Blood glucose concentration (mM) | | |
|---|---|---|---|
| | Before lunch | One hour after lunch | Before evening meal |
| Day 1 | 4.2 | 8.7 | 5.0 |
| Day 2 | 3.5 | 7.3 | 6.7 |

a) On which day do you think the person ate a lunch with the highest proportion of simple carbohydrates? Explain your answer.

b) Give one assumption that you have made in your answer to a) about the insulin injections.

**Tip:** There is a time delay between an insulin injection and the reduction of blood glucose concentration. This is because the insulin first needs to travel in the blood to its target cells.

Q2 A student used a colorimeter to measure the absorbance of known concentrations of glucose, after doing a quantitative Benedict's test on each solution, and used the results to draw the calibration curve below. The student also carried out the test on a 'urine' sample with an unknown glucose concentration.

a) The 'urine' sample gave an absorbance reading of 0.4. Using the calibration curve, find the glucose concentration of the sample.

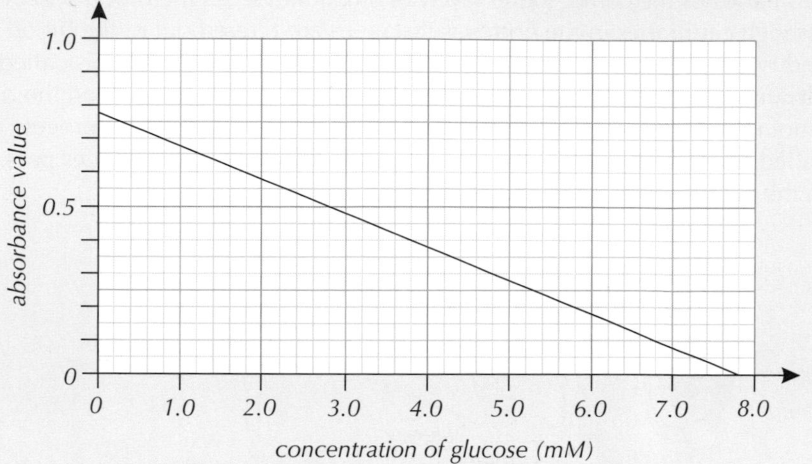


b) The glucose concentration in urine is normally between 0 and 0.8 mM. What range of absorbance values would the student expect normal urine samples to give in this investigation?

**Exam Tip**
Remember to be really careful when reading values from a graph in the exams — you don't want to throw away marks because you've rushed and misread the scale.

## Practice Questions — Fact Recall

Q1 What causes Type I diabetes?

Q2 Give two risk factors associated with Type II diabetes.

Q3 Describe how Type II diabetes can be controlled.

Q4 Give three actions that health advisors think the food industry needs to do to reduce the risk of people developing Type II diabetes.

Q5 Describe how you could use serial dilutions of a glucose solution of known concentration to find the glucose concentration of a urine sample.

# 4. The Kidneys

*One of the main functions of the kidneys is to filter waste products out of the blood and reabsorb useful solutes (e.g. glucose).*

**Learning Objective:**

- Recall the structure of the nephron and its role in:
  - the formation of glomerular filtrate,
  - reabsorption of glucose and water by the proximal convoluted tubule,
  - reabsorption of water by the distal convoluted tubule and collecting ducts.

**Specification Reference 3.6.4.3**

## Excretion of waste products

Blood enters the kidney through the renal artery and then passes through capillaries in the cortex (outer layer) of the kidneys. As the blood passes through capillaries in the cortex, substances are filtered out of the blood and into long tubules that surround the capillaries. This process is called **ultrafiltration** (see below). Useful substances, such as glucose and the right amount of water, are then reabsorbed back into the blood. This process is called **selective reabsorption**. The remaining unwanted substances pass along to the bladder and are excreted as urine.

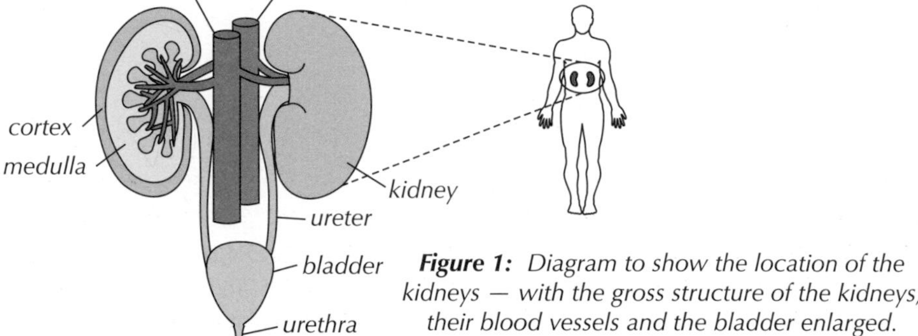


**Figure 1:** *Diagram to show the location of the kidneys — with the gross structure of the kidneys, their blood vessels and the bladder enlarged.*

**Tip:** The kidneys also regulate the body's water content — there's more about this on pages 129-131.

## The nephrons

The long tubules along with the bundles of capillaries where the blood is filtered are called nephrons — there are around one million nephrons in each kidney. You need to learn the structure of a nephron (see Figure 3).

### Ultrafiltration

Blood from the renal artery enters smaller arterioles in the cortex of the kidney. Each arteriole splits into a structure called a glomerulus (plural, glomeruli) — a bundle of capillaries looped inside a hollow ball called a Bowman's capsule (see Figure 3). This is where ultrafiltration takes place.

**Tip:** 'Renal' means anything to do with the kidney.

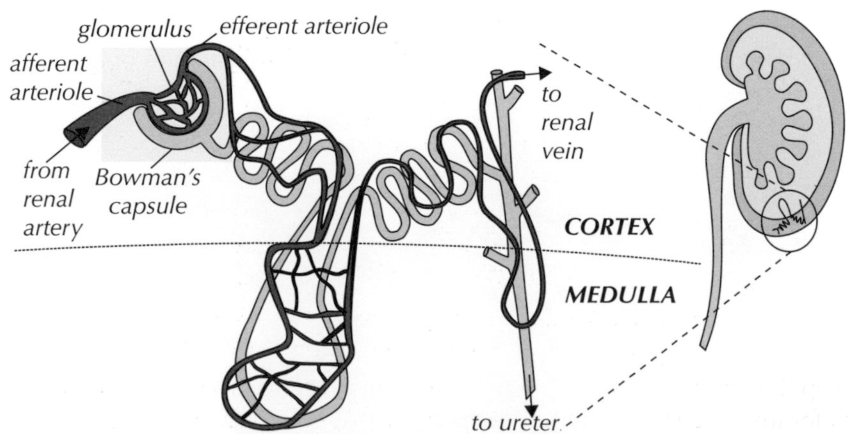


**Figure 3:** *The location and structure of one nephron. Ultrafiltration takes place in the glomerulus and Bowman's capsule (highlighted in blue).*

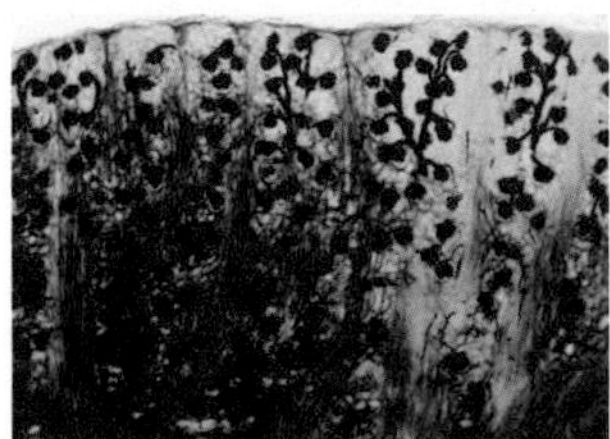

**Figure 2:** *Light micrograph of a section through the cortex, showing the glomeruli (tiny balls) and the vessels that supply them.*

The arteriole that takes blood into each glomerulus is called the afferent arteriole, and the arteriole that takes the filtered blood away from the glomerulus is called the efferent arteriole (see Figure 3 on the previous page). The efferent arteriole is smaller in diameter than the afferent arteriole, so the blood in the glomerulus is under high pressure. The high pressure forces liquid and small molecules in the blood out of the capillary and into the Bowman's capsule.

The liquid and small molecules pass through three layers to get into the Bowman's capsule and enter the nephron tubules — the capillary endothelium, a membrane (called the basement membrane) and the epithelium of the Bowman's capsule (see Figure 4).

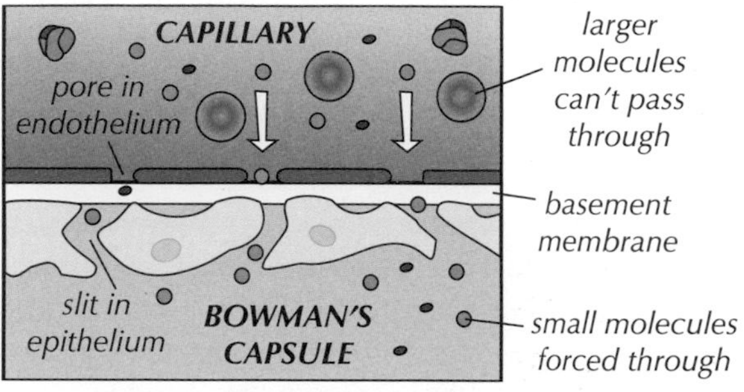


***Figure 4:*** *Diagram to show the three layers separating the glomerular capillary and the Bowman's capsule.*

**Tip:** The cells that make up the epithelium of the Bowman's capsule are called podocytes.

Larger molecules like proteins and blood cells can't pass through so stay in the blood. The substances that enter the Bowman's capsule are known as the **glomerular filtrate**. The glomerular filtrate passes along the rest of the nephron and useful substances are reabsorbed along the way — see below. Finally, the filtrate flows through the collecting duct and passes out of the kidney along the ureter.

**Tip:** The glomerular filtrate can also be called the tubular fluid.

### Selective reabsorption

Selective reabsorption of useful substances takes place as the glomerular filtrate flows along the proximal convoluted tubule (PCT), through the loop of Henle, and along the distal convoluted tubule (DCT) — see Figure 5. Useful substances leave the tubules of the nephrons and enter the capillary network that's wrapped around them.

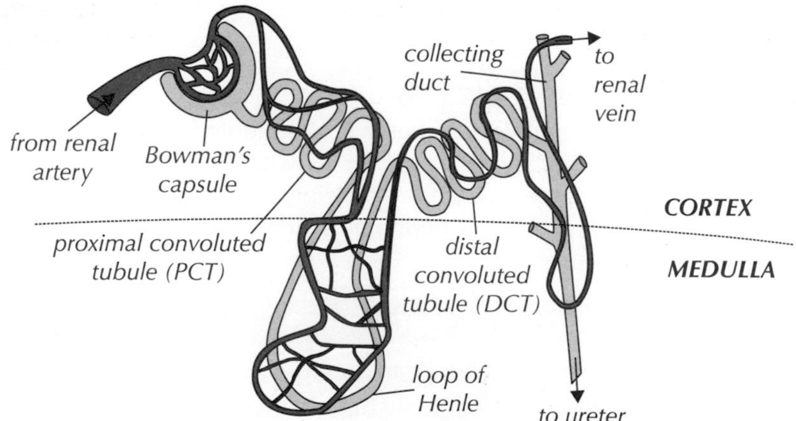

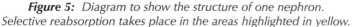

***Figure 5:*** *Diagram to show the structure of one nephron. Selective reabsorption takes place in the areas highlighted in yellow.*

The epithelium of the wall of the PCT has microvilli to provide a large surface area for the reabsorption of useful materials from the glomerular filtrate (in the tubules) into the blood (in the capillaries) — see Figure 7 on the next page. Useful solutes, like glucose, are reabsorbed along the PCT by **active transport** and **facilitated diffusion**.

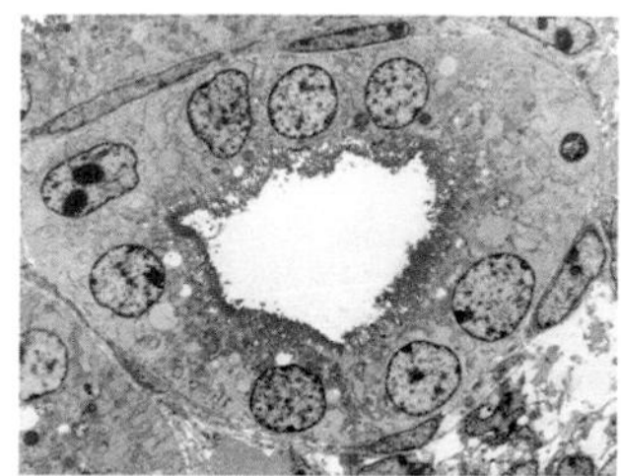

***Figure 6:*** *Electron micrograph of a cross-section through the proximal convoluted tubule (PCT). Microvilli (shown in reddish-brown) line the inside of the tubule, increasing the surface area for reabsorption.*

Tip: Remember, water potential describes the tendency of water to move from one area to another. Water will move from an area of higher water potential to an area of lower water potential — it moves down the water potential gradient.

Tip: Urea is a waste product produced from the breakdown of amino acids in the liver.

Tip: The volume of water in urine varies depending on how much you've drunk (see pages 129-131).

Water enters the blood by **osmosis** because the water potential of the blood is lower than that of the filtrate. Water is reabsorbed from the PCT, loop of Henle, DCT and the collecting duct (see next page). The filtrate that remains is urine, which passes along the ureter to the bladder.

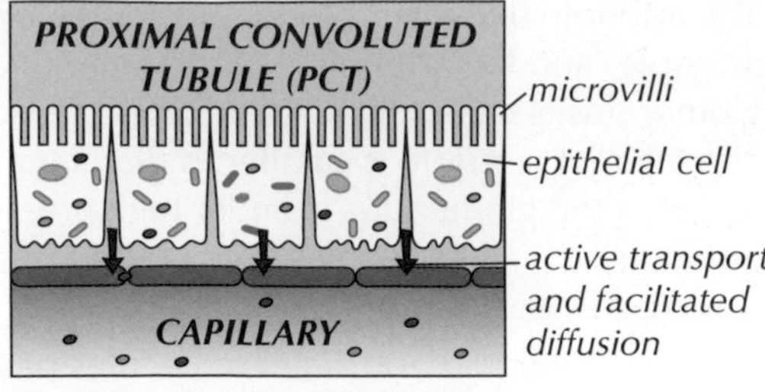


**Figure 7:** *Epithelial wall of the proximal convoluted tubule (PCT).*

## Urine

Urine is usually made up of water and dissolved salts, urea and other substances such as hormones and excess vitamins. Urine doesn't usually contain proteins or blood cells as they're too big to be filtered out of the blood. Glucose is actively reabsorbed back into the blood (see previous page), so it's not usually found in the urine either.

## Practice Questions — Application

Q1 The kidneys filter the blood in order to produce urine. The flow diagram below shows the sequence of urine production. Name the missing structures, A to D.

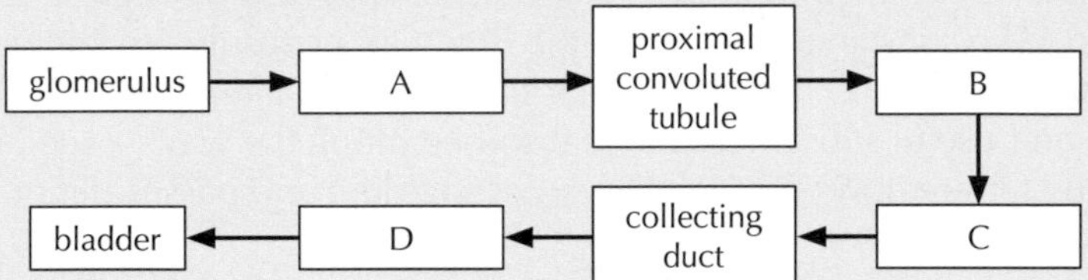


Q2 The diagram below shows an electron micrograph of a cross-section of the barrier between the Bowman's capsule and the blood supply.

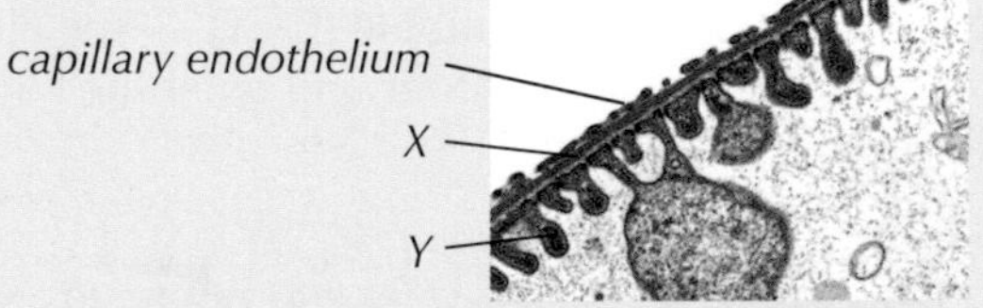


a) Name the structures labelled X and Y.

b) Hereditary nephrotic syndrome is an inherited disease which affects the structure of the barrier shown above, resulting in the presence of large amounts of protein in the urine (proteinuria). Suggest why hereditary nephrotic syndrome causes proteinuria.

## Practice Questions — Fact Recall

Q1 The diagram below shows a glomerulus and surrounding structures.

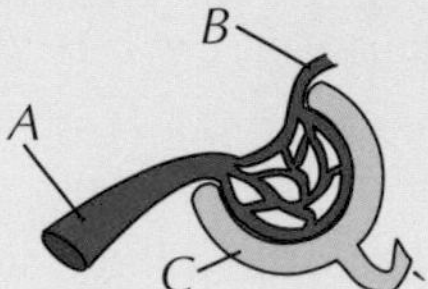


a) Name blood vessel A.

b) Name the structure labelled C.

c) Vessel A has a larger diameter than vessel B. Explain why this is important in the process of ultrafiltration.

Q2 Name two substances that are reabsorbed in the proximal convoluted tubule.

# 5. Controlling Blood Water Potential

*After the last few pages you might feel like you know all there is to know about nephrons — but there's more. Now it's time to see how they're involved in controlling the water potential of the blood.*

**Learning Objectives:**

- Be able to explain osmoregulation as control of the water potential of the blood.
- Recall the role of the nephron in maintaining a gradient of sodium ions in the medulla by the loop of Henle.
- Recall the roles of the hypothalamus, posterior pituitary and antidiuretic hormone (ADH) in osmoregulation.

**Specification Reference 3.6.4.3**

## Regulation of water content

Water is essential to keep the body functioning, so the amount of water in the blood (and so the water potential of the blood) needs to be kept constant. Mammals excrete urea (and other waste products) in solution, which means water is lost during excretion. Water is also lost in sweat. The kidneys regulate the water potential of the blood (and urine), so the body has just the right amount of water — this is called **osmoregulation**:

- If the water potential of the blood is too low (the body is dehydrated), more water is reabsorbed by osmosis into the blood from the tubules of the nephrons. This means the urine is more concentrated, so less water is lost during excretion.
- If the water potential of the blood is too high (the body is too hydrated), less water is reabsorbed by osmosis into the blood from the tubules of the nephrons. This means the urine is more dilute, so more water is lost during excretion.

Water is reabsorbed into the blood along almost all of the nephron (see previous page), but regulation of water potential mainly takes place in the loop of Henle, DCT and collecting duct (see below). The volume of water reabsorbed by the DCT and collecting duct is controlled by hormones (see next page).

**Tip:** For more on reabsorption in the nephrons, see pages 127-128.

## The loop of Henle

The loop of Henle is located in the medulla (inner layer) of the kidneys. It's made up of two 'limbs' — the descending limb and the ascending limb. The limbs control the movement of sodium ions so that water can be reabsorbed by the blood.

**Tip:** Figure 1 is explained in detail on the next page.

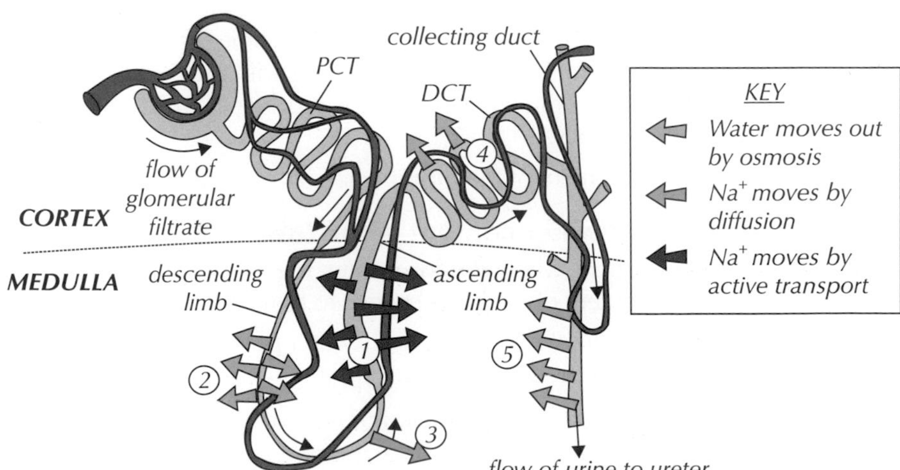


***Figure 1:*** *The movement of water and $Na^+$ in the loop of Henle, DCT and collecting duct.*

**Tip:** $Na^+$ is a sodium ion. These ions help establish the water potential that drives the reabsorption of water from the glomerular filtrate back into the blood.

Here's how the system works:

1. Near the top of the ascending limb, $Na^+$ ions are actively pumped out into the medulla. The ascending limb is impermeable to water, so the water stays inside the tubule. This creates a low water potential in the medulla, because there's a high concentration of ions.
2. Because there's a lower water potential in the medulla than in the descending limb, water moves out of the descending limb (which is permeable to water) into the medulla by osmosis. This makes the glomerular filtrate more concentrated (the ions can't diffuse out — the descending limb isn't permeable to them). The water in the medulla is reabsorbed into the blood through the capillary network.
3. Near the bottom of the ascending limb $Na^+$ ions diffuse out into the medulla, further lowering the water potential in the medulla. (The ascending limb is impermeable to water, so it stays in the tubule.)
4. Water moves out of the distal convoluted tubules (DCT) by osmosis and is reabsorbed into the blood.
5. The first three stages massively increase the ion concentration in the medulla, which lowers the water potential. This causes water to move out of the collecting duct by osmosis. As before, the water in the medulla is reabsorbed into the blood through the capillary network.

The volume of water reabsorbed into the capillaries is controlled by changing the permeability of the DCT and the collecting duct (see below).

**Tip:** Different animals have different length loops of Henle. The longer an animal's loop of Henle, the more water they can reabsorb from the glomerular filtrate.

## Antidiuretic hormone (ADH)

The water potential of the blood is monitored by cells called **osmoreceptors** in a part of the brain called the **hypothalamus**. When the water potential of the blood decreases, water will move out of the osmoreceptor cells by osmosis. This causes the cells to decrease in volume. This sends a signal to other cells in the hypothalamus, which send a signal to the **posterior pituitary gland**. This causes the posterior pituitary to release a hormone called antidiuretic hormone (ADH) into the blood.

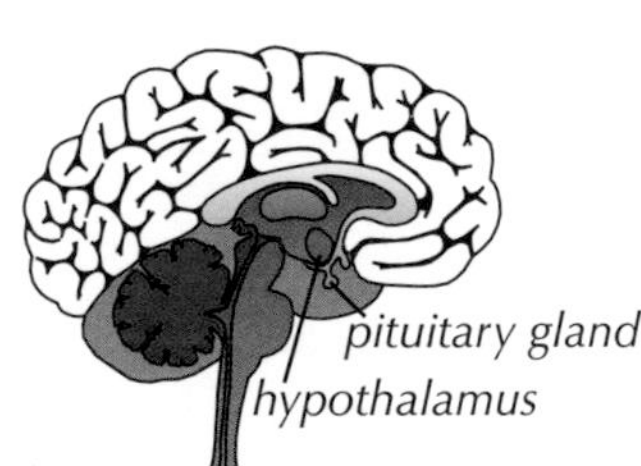


***Figure 2:*** *Location of the hypothalamus and the pituitary gland in the brain.*

ADH molecules bind to receptors on the plasma membranes of cells in the DCT and the collecting duct. When this happens, protein channels called aquaporins are inserted into the plasma membrane. These channels allow water to pass through via osmosis, making the walls of the DCT and collecting duct more permeable to water. This means more water is reabsorbed from these tubules into the medulla and into the blood by osmosis. A small amount of concentrated urine is produced, which means less water is lost from the body.

**Tip:** Diuresis is when lots of dilute urine is produced. Antidiuretic hormone is so called because it causes a small amount of concentrated urine to be produced (the opposite of diuresis).

ADH changes the water content of the blood when it's too low or too high:

### Dehydration — blood water content is too low

Dehydration is what happens when you lose water, e.g. by sweating during exercise, so the water content of the blood needs to be increased:

- The water content of the blood drops, so its water potential drops.
- This is detected by osmoreceptors in the hypothalamus.
- The posterior pituitary gland is stimulated to release more ADH into the blood.
- More ADH means that the DCT and collecting duct are more permeable, so more water is reabsorbed into the blood by osmosis.

- A small amount of highly concentrated urine is produced and less water is lost.

### Hydration — blood water content is too high

If you're hydrated, you've taken in lots of water, so the water content of the blood needs to be reduced:

- The water content of the blood rises, so its water potential rises.
- This is detected by the osmoreceptors in the hypothalamus.
- The posterior pituitary gland releases less ADH into the blood.
- Less ADH means that the DCT and collecting duct are less permeable, so less water is reabsorbed into the blood by osmosis.
- A large amount of dilute urine is produced and more water is lost.

**Tip:** Like many hormones, ADH is a protein. Once it's had its effect, it travels in the bloodstream to the liver where it's broken down.

## Practice Questions — Application

Q1 A runner is dehydrated whilst running on a hot, sunny day. He left his drink at home and is producing a lot of sweat during his run.

a) Why is the runner dehydrated?

b) How does the runner's body detect that he is dehydrated?

c) The runner's posterior pituitary gland releases antidiuretic hormone (ADH). Explain what effect ADH has on the distal convoluted tubule and the collecting duct of the runner's kidneys.

d) When he returns home, he rehydrates by drinking a sports drink containing sodium ions. Explain how the presence of these ions helps the runner's kidneys to conserve water.

Q2 Exercise-associated hyponatremia (EAH) is a condition experienced by some athletes who drink excessive amounts of fluid when competing in endurance events like marathons. The condition affects the balance of fluid in cells and is potentially fatal if it affects the brain cells.

a) Explain what normally happens when a person consumes too much fluid.

b) Athletes who experience EAH are often unable to suppress their ADH production. Explain why this can cause problems if they have consumed too much fluid.

Q3 The fennec fox lives in a hot, dry environment. It has evolved a long loop of Henle to help it survive in this environment.

a) Suggest and explain the advantage that having a longer loop of Henle gives the fennec fox in its environment.

b) Frogs and toads don't have any loops of Henle. Suggest why this is the case.

## Practice Questions — Fact Recall

Q1 What is osmoregulation?

Q2 Name the layer of the kidney in which the loop of Henle is located.

Q3 Which limb of the loop of Henle is impermeable to water?

Q4 Which part of the brain monitors the water potential of the blood?

## Section Summary

Make sure you know...

- That homeostasis in mammals involves physiological control systems that maintain a stable internal environment (within certain limits).
- That it's important to maintain a stable core body temperature and stable blood pH to provide the optimum conditions for enzymes to work.
- That it's important to maintain a stable blood glucose concentration to prevent the water potential of the blood becoming too low (if blood glucose concentration becomes too high) and to ensure there's enough glucose available for respiration.
- That negative feedback mechanisms return systems in the body back to their normal level.
- That multiple separate negative feedback mechanisms give more control over systems in the body.
- That positive feedback amplifies a change and is often involved in the breakdown of control systems.
- How to interpret information relating to positive and negative feedback.
- That diet and exercise affect blood glucose concentration.
- That glycogenesis is the conversion of glucose to glycogen, glycogenolysis is the conversion of glycogen to glucose, and gluconeogenesis is the conversion of glycerol or amino acids to glucose, and that all of these processes can occur in liver cells.
- That insulin lowers blood glucose level when it's too high by binding to receptors on liver and muscle cells and activating enzymes involved in glycogenesis, causing the cells to take up more glucose and causing the cells to respire more glucose.
- That glucagon raises blood glucose level when it's too low by binding to receptors on liver cells and activating enzymes involved in glycogenolysis and gluconeogenesis, and causing the cells to respire less glucose.
- That insulin increases the uptake of glucose by skeletal and cardiac muscle cells by increasing the amount of glucose transporters (channel proteins) in the cell membranes of those cells.
- The second messenger model of adrenaline and glucagon action — when adrenaline and glucagon bind to specific receptors on liver-cell membranes it activates an enzyme called adenylate cyclase, which then converts ATP into a second messenger called cyclic AMP (cAMP). This then activates an enzyme called protein kinase A, which activates a cascade inside the cell resulting in glycogenolysis.
- That Type I diabetes is caused when the immune system attacks the β cells in the islets of Langerhans meaning that no insulin is produced by the pancreas, and that Type II diabetes is caused when the β cells don't produce enough insulin or body cells no longer respond properly to it.
- That Type I diabetes is controlled by insulin therapy and Type II diabetes can often be controlled by eating a healthy, balanced diet, losing weight (if necessary), and regular exercise.
- The positions of health advisors and the food industry on the increasing incidence of Type II diabetes.
- How to use a colorimeter to determine the glucose concentration of a 'urine' sample, including how to make serial dilutions of a solution with a known concentration of glucose and use the absorbance values of the dilutions to produce a calibration curve (Required Practical 11).
- The structure of a nephron.
- That glomerular filtrate is the liquid and small molecules that pass into the Bowman's capsule following ultrafiltration of the blood entering the nephron.
- That glucose is reabsorbed into the blood from the proximal convoluted tubule and that water is reabsorbed from the proximal convoluted tubule, distal convoluted tubule and collecting ducts.
- That osmoregulation is the control of the water potential of the blood.
- How a gradient of sodium ions is maintained in the medulla by the loop of Henle.
- That the water content of the blood is monitored by osmoreceptors in the hypothalamus, and how the release of antidiuretic hormone (ADH) from the posterior pituitary gland is used to control the reabsorption of water in the nephrons.

# Exam-style Questions

**1** When low blood calcium concentration is detected, the secretion of parathyroid hormone (PTH) from the parathyroid gland is stimulated. When high blood calcium concentration is detected, the secretion of the hormone calcitonin, from the thyroid gland, is stimulated. These two hormones work via negative feedback mechanisms to control the blood calcium concentration. Their effects are shown in **Figure 1**.

**Figure 1**

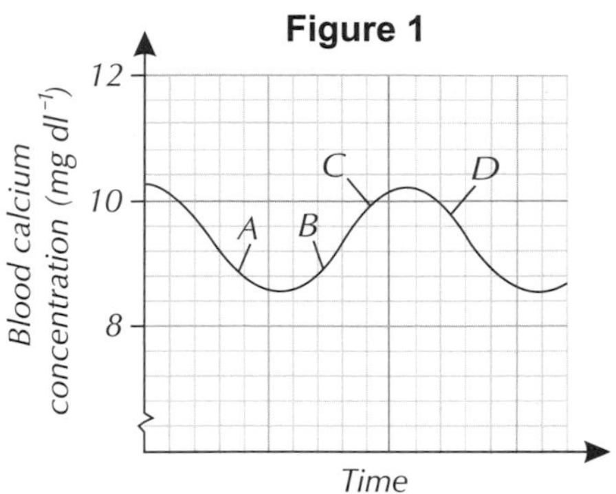


**1.1** Suggest an explanation for the shape of the graph between points A and D.

*(4 marks)*

**1.2** Why is it beneficial to have both PTH and calcitonin controlling the concentration of calcium in the blood?

*(2 marks)*

**1.3** Suggest what could happen to the blood calcium concentration of someone who has had a parathyroid gland removed. Explain your answer.

*(2 marks)*

**2** **Figure 2** is an electron micrograph showing a section through the proximal convoluted tubule of the kidney.

**Figure 2**

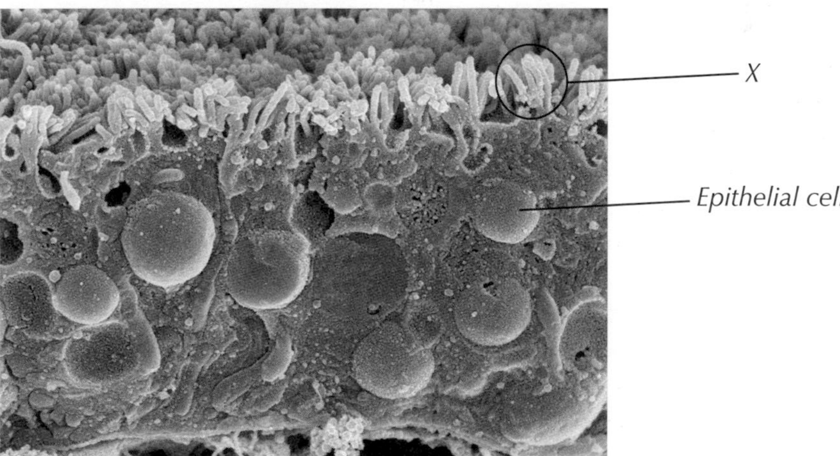


**2.1** Outline what happens to glomerular filtrate in the proximal convoluted tubule.

*(1 mark)*

**2.2** Name the structure labelled **X** on **Figure 2** and explain how this structure helps the epithelial cells of the proximal convoluted tubule to carry out their function.

*(2 marks)*

Figure 3 shows a nephron.

**2.3** What name is given to structure **A**?

*(1 mark)*

**2.4** Which **two** letters (**A** to **F**) indicate the locations where antidiuretic hormone (ADH) acts?

*(1 mark)*

**2.5** Name structure **D** and describe its main function in the process of reabsorption.

*(2 marks)*

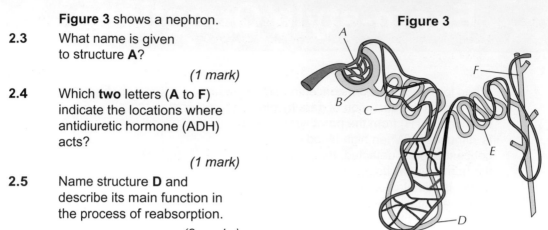

**Figure 3**

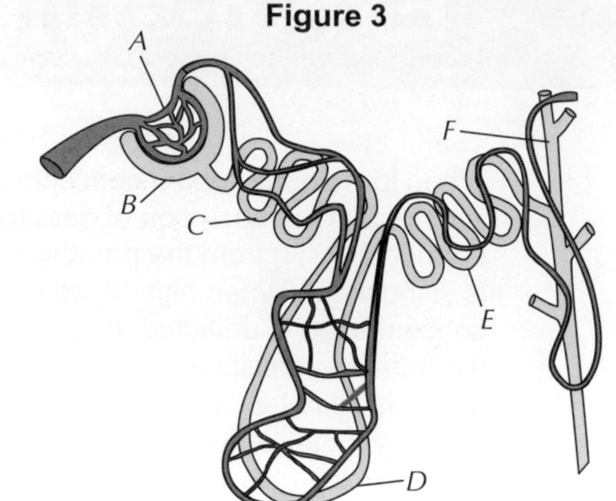


**3** In an experiment, the blood glucose concentrations of a Type II diabetic and a non-diabetic were recorded at regular intervals in a 150 minute time period. 15 minutes into the experiment a glucose drink was given. The normal range for blood glucose concentration in a healthy individual is between 82 and 110 mg/100 cm$^3$. The results of the experiment are shown in **Figure 4**.

**Figure 4**

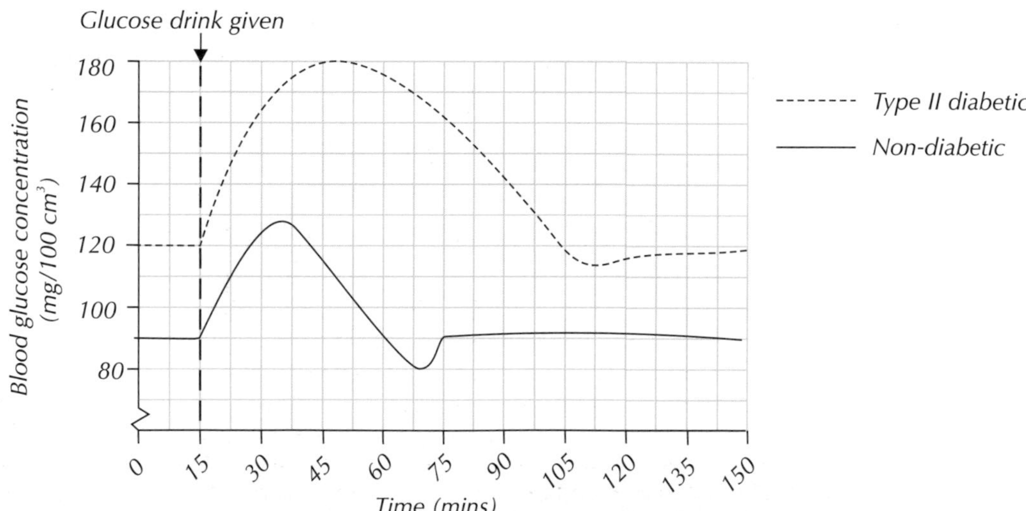


**3.1** Describe how cells in the non-diabetic's islets of Langerhans are responding between 65 and 75 minutes.

*(2 marks)*

**3.2** Explain why the Type II diabetic's blood glucose concentration takes longer to decrease after they take the glucose drink than the non-diabetic's.

*(2 marks)*

**3.3** If the diabetic person had exercised after taking the glucose drink would their blood glucose concentration have decreased more quickly or more slowly? Explain your answer.

*(1 mark)*

**3.4** Suggest how the blood glucose concentration of a Type I diabetic would differ from the Type II diabetic after having the glucose drink.

*(2 marks)*

**3.5** Suggest what time insulin is released in the non-diabetic.
Explain your answer.

*(2 marks)*

**3.6** Blood glucose concentration continues to rise after the release of insulin.
Why is this?

*(1 mark)*

**3.7** Describe how insulin initiates the uptake of glucose by binding to a target cell.

*(2 marks)*

**3.8** Describe how glycogenolysis is activated by hormones through the second messenger model.

*(5 marks)*

**4** The tubular fluid to blood plasma concentration ratio (TF/P ratio) is an index used to measure how well the kidney is working. If substances are able to pass freely from the glomerulus into the Bowman's capsule they will have a TF/P ratio of 1.0, as their concentration in the plasma is the same as in the initial tubular fluid.

**4.1** Complete **Table 1** to show which of the following substances will have a TF/P ratio of 1.0 in a healthy kidney. The first two have been done for you.

**Table 1**

| ***Substance*** | ***TF/P ratio of 1.0*** |
|---|---|
| *urea* | ✓ |
| *serum albumin (protein)* | X |
| *sodium ions ($Na^+$)* | |
| *glucose* | |
| *red blood cells* | |

*(2 marks)*

**4.2** The TF/P ratio of the protein serum albumin is normally less than 1.0 in a healthy kidney, meaning that the concentration of serum albumin is higher in the plasma than the tubular fluid. Explain why this is the case.

*(1 mark)*

**4.3** A patient has kidney failure as a result of high blood pressure.
Her doctor prescribes diuretics to reduce her blood volume,
which will reduce her blood pressure.
Diuretics can reduce the amount of $Na^+$ that is reabsorbed from the nephron.

Suggest how diuretics can be used to decrease blood volume.

*(4 marks)*

# Topic 7 A: Genetics

**Learning Objectives:**

- Understand that there may be many alleles of a single gene.
- Know that genotype is the genetic constitution of an organism.
- Know that phenotype is the expression of the genetic constitution and its interaction with the environment.
- Know that alleles may be dominant, recessive or codominant.
- Know that in a diploid organism, alleles at a specific locus may be either homozygous or heterozygous.

**Specification Reference 3.7.1**

**Tip:** 'Loci' is the plural of 'locus'.

## 1. Genetic Terms

*This section is all about genes and how organisms pass them on to their offspring. But before you start exploring it, you really need to get to grips with the basic terms described below.*

## Basic terms and definitions

### Genes and alleles

A **gene** is a sequence of bases on a DNA molecule that codes for a protein (polypeptide) which results in a characteristic.

You can have one or more versions of the same gene. These different versions are called **alleles**. There can be many different alleles of a single gene, but most plants and animals, including humans, only carry two alleles of each gene, one from each parent. The order of bases in each allele is slightly different — that's because each allele codes for different versions of the same characteristic. Alleles are represented using letters.

**Examples**

- There are many different alleles for eye colour. The allele for brown eyes is shown using a B, and the allele for blue eyes uses b.
- Pea plants have a gene for seed shape. The allele for a round seed is shown using a R, and the allele for a wrinkled seed uses r.

### Loci

Humans are **diploid organisms**. This means we have two copies of each chromosome — one from each parent. It's why we have two alleles of each gene. The allele of each gene is found at a fixed position, called a **locus**, on each chromosome in a pair (see Figure 1).

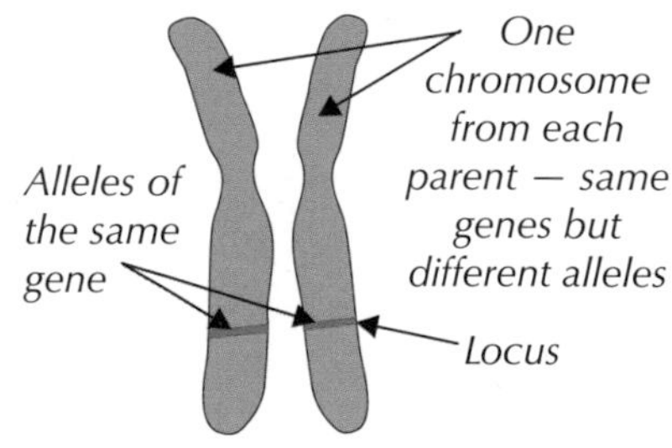


***Figure 1:*** *Diagram showing a locus on a pair of chromosomes.*

### Genotype

The genotype of an organism is its genetic constitution, or put another way, the different alleles an organism has. This could be a list of all its alleles but usually it's just the alleles for one characteristic at a time.

**Examples**

- One person may have the genotype BB for eye colour and another person Bb.
- One pea plant might have the genotype RR for seed shape and another pea plant rr.

### Phenotype

The phenotype of an organism is 'the expression of the genetic constitution and its interaction with the environment'. This just means what characteristics an organism has as a result of both its genes and the effect the environment has on its genes.

Examples

- One person may have brown eyes and another may have blue eyes.
- One pea plant may have round seeds and another may have wrinkled seeds.

**Exam Tip**
You don't need to learn these examples for the exam — they're just here to help you understand the different terms.

### Dominant and recessive alleles

A dominant allele is always expressed in the phenotype, even when there's only one copy of it. Dominant alleles are shown by a capital letter. Recessive alleles are those with characteristics that only appear in the phenotype if two copies are present. They're shown by lower case letters.

Examples

- The allele for brown eyes, B, is dominant, so if a person's genotype is Bb or BB they'll have brown eyes. The allele for blue eyes, b, is recessive, so a person will only have blue eyes if their genotype is bb.
- The allele for round seed shape, R, is dominant, so if a pea plant's genotype is Rr or RR it will have round seeds. The allele for wrinkled seed shape, r, is recessive, so a pea plant will only have wrinkled seeds if its genotype is rr.

### Codominant alleles

Some alleles are both expressed in the phenotype because neither one is recessive. They are said to be codominant alleles.

Example

Horses can have alleles for white hair or coloured hair. Neither allele is recessive, so a horse with one copy of each allele will have a roan coat — a coat with a mixture of white hairs and coloured hairs.

***Figure 2:*** *A horse with a roan coat.*

### Homozygous and heterozygous

At each locus in a diploid organism, the genotype can be homozygous or heterozygous. If an organism carries two copies of the same allele, it's said to be homozygous at that locus. If an organism carries two different alleles for a gene, then it's heterozygous.

Examples

- The genotypes BB and bb are homozygous and the genotype Bb is heterozygous.
- The genotypes RR and rr are homozygous and the genotype Rr is heterozygous.

**Tip:** An organism can be homozygous at one locus and heterozygous at another.

## Practice Questions — Application

Q1 In owl monkeys, the allele T codes for a tufted tail and t codes for a non-tufted tail. For each of the following genotypes, give the owl monkey's phenotype: A — Tt, B — TT, C — tt.

Q2 The yellow colour pea seed allele is dominant to the green allele.

a) What would be the phenotype of a pea seed with the genotype Yy?

b) Give the genotype of a homozygous pea seed that's yellow.

c) Give the genotype of a green pea seed.

**Exam Tip**
Make sure you can answer these questions before you move on. If you don't understand these genetic terms now, you'll struggle with the rest of the section.

**Learning Objective:**

- Be able to use fully labelled genetic diagrams to interpret or predict the results of monohybrid crosses involving dominant, recessive and codominant alleles.

**Specification Reference 3.7.1**

# 2. Genetic Diagrams — Simple Monohybrid Crosses

*Genetic diagrams show how alleles could be passed on to the next generation.*

## What are genetic diagrams?

Diploid organisms have two alleles for each gene (see page 136). Gametes (sex cells) contain only one allele for each gene — they're **haploid**. When haploid gametes from two parents fuse together, the alleles they contain form the genotype of the diploid offspring that is produced.

Genetic diagrams can be used to predict the genotypes and phenotypes of the offspring produced if two parents are crossed (bred). You need to know how to use genetic diagrams to interpret or predict the results of various crosses, including monohybrid crosses.

## Monohybrid inheritance

Monohybrid inheritance is the inheritance of a characteristic controlled by a single gene. **Monohybrid crosses** show the likelihood of the different alleles of that gene (and so different versions of the characteristic) being inherited by offspring of certain parents. The example below shows how wing length can be inherited in fruit flies.

***Figure 1a:** Photo of a fruit fly with normal wings.*

***Figure 1b:** Photo of a fruit fly with vestigial wings.*

**Tip:** The first set of offspring is called the $F_1$ generation.

**Tip:** A monohybrid cross with two homozygous parents will always produce all heterozygous offspring in the $F_1$ generation.

**Example**

The allele for normal wings is dominant, so it's shown by a capital letter N. Any flies that have even one N allele will have normal wings. The allele for vestigial (little) wings is recessive, so it's shown by the letter n. Only flies that have two n alleles will have vestigial wings.

The genetic diagram in Figure 2 shows a cross between one homozygous parent with normal wings (NN) and one homozygous parent with vestigial wings (nn). The normal winged parent can only produce gametes with the allele for normal wings (N). The vestigial winged parent can only produce gametes with the allele for vestigial wings (n).

Here's how to draw a genetic diagram for this cross:

**Step 1:** Make sure you're clear what the letters mean.

*N — normal wings allele*
*n — vestigial (little) wings allele*

**Step 2:** Show the parents' genotypes at the top.

**Step 3:** The middle circles show the possible gametes. Put one of each letter into a circle.

**Step 4:** The lines show all the possible ways the gametes could combine. Fill in the possible combinations in the bottom boxes.

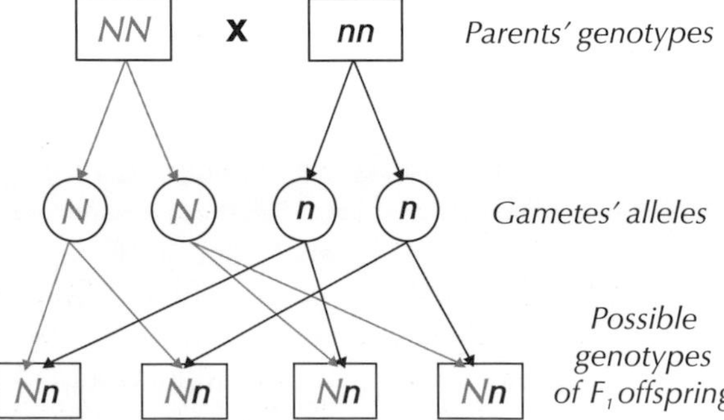

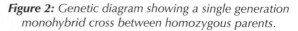

***Figure 2:** Genetic diagram showing a single generation monohybrid cross between homozygous parents.*

All offspring produced are heterozygous (Nn), as one allele is inherited from each parent.

The genetic diagram in Figure 3 shows a cross between two parents from the $F_1$ generation (both heterozygous). Just follow the same steps as on the previous page, but this time the gametes produced by each $F_1$ offspring may contain the allele for either normal (N) or vestigial wings (n).

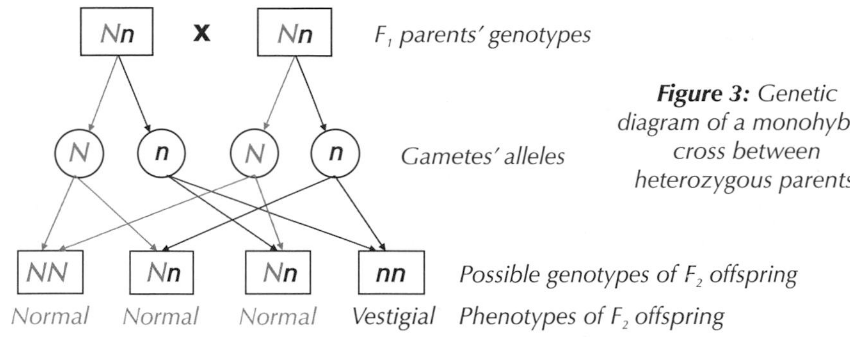


***Figure 3:** Genetic diagram of a monohybrid cross between heterozygous parents.*

**Exam Tip**
If you draw a genetic diagram in the exam and you use letters that haven't been given to you in the question, you'll need to include a key to explain what those letters mean.

### Phenotypic ratios

The phenotypic ratio is the ratio of different phenotypes in the offspring. Genetic diagrams allow you to predict the phenotypic ratios in $F_1$ and $F_2$ offspring.

**Tip:** The second set of offspring is called the $F_2$ generation.

**Example — Maths Skills**

Using the example above, there's a 75% chance the $F_2$ offspring will have the normal wings phenotype (genotype NN or Nn) and a 25% chance they'll have the vestigial wings phenotype (genotype nn). So you'd expect a 3 : 1 ratio of normal : vestigial wings in the offspring. This is the phenotypic ratio.

Usually whenever you do a monohybrid cross with two heterozygous parents you get a 3 : 1 ratio of dominant : recessive characteristics in the offspring. However, sometimes you won't get the expected (predicted) phenotypic ratio. For example, codominant alleles (see next page) and sex linkage (see p. 144) can both alter phenotypic ratios in the offspring of monohybrid crosses.

**Tip:** The 3 : 1 ratio is only an expected ratio. In practice, the phenotypic ratio in the offspring will probably be slightly different to this anyway, just by chance.

## Punnett squares

A Punnett square is just another way of showing a genetic diagram. The Punnett squares below show the same crosses as p. 138 and above.

**Example**

**Step 1:** Work out the alleles the gametes would have.

*Parents' genotypes* NN nn

*Gametes' alleles* N N n n

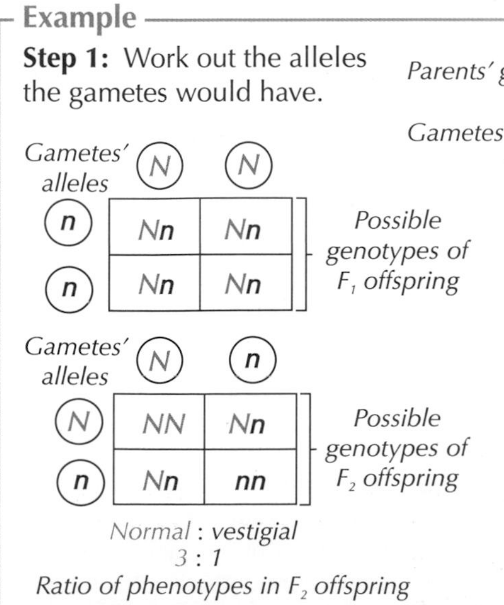

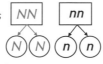

**Step 2:** Cross the parents' gametes to show the possible genotypes of the $F_1$ generation — all heterozygous, Nn.

**Step 3:** Cross the gametes of the $F_1$ generation to show the possible genotypes of the $F_2$ generation. The Punnett square shows a 75% chance that offspring will have normal wings and a 25% chance that they'll have vestigial wings, i.e. a 3 : 1 ratio.

**Exam Tip**
It's up to you whether you draw a diagram or a Punnett square in the exam, whichever you find easier. You must make sure you label your diagram though, so it's clear what you're trying to show.

# Monohybrid inheritance of codominant alleles

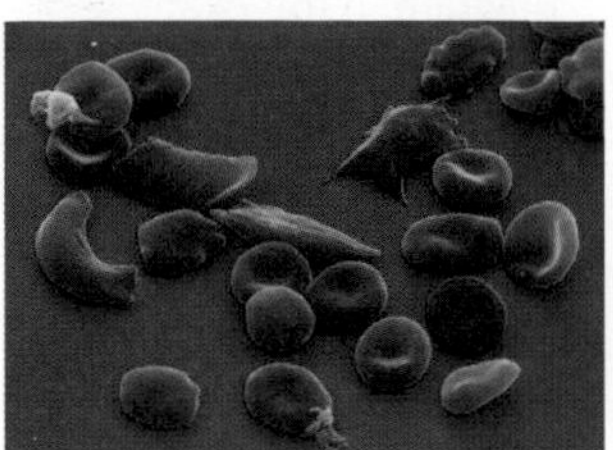

*Figure 4:* *A coloured scanning electron micrograph (SEM) of normal red blood cells (red) and sickle-shaped cells (pink).*

Occasionally, alleles show codominance — both alleles are expressed in the phenotype, and neither one is recessive. One example in humans is the allele for sickle-cell anaemia, a genetic disorder caused by a mutation in the haemoglobin gene. It causes red blood cells to be sickle-shaped.

**Example**

People who are homozygous for normal haemoglobin ($H^NH^N$) don't have the disease. People who are homozygous for sickle haemoglobin ($H^SH^S$) have sickle-cell anaemia — all their blood cells are sickle shaped. People who are heterozygous ($H^NH^S$) have an in-between phenotype, called the sickle-cell trait — they have some normal haemoglobin and some sickle haemoglobin. The two alleles are codominant because they're both expressed in the phenotype. The genetic diagram in Figure 5 shows the possible offspring from crossing two parents with sickle-cell trait (heterozygous).

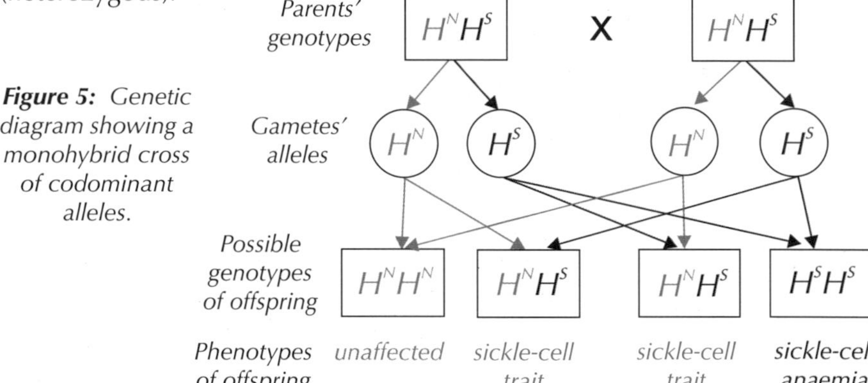


*Figure 5:* *Genetic diagram showing a monohybrid cross of codominant alleles.*

This cross has produced a 1 : 2 : 1 phenotypic ratio of 1 unaffected : 2 sickle-cell trait : 1 sickle-cell anaemia, or 1 unaffected homozygous : 2 heterozygous : 1 disorder homozygous.

Whenever you do a monohybrid cross with two heterozygous parents involving codominant alleles, you would expect to see a 1 : 2 : 1 ratio in the offspring.

**Tip:** When alleles show codominance they're represented in a slightly different way to normal — you show the main gene as a normal capital letter (H) and then the alleles as superscript capitals ($H^S$ or $H^N$), because neither is recessive.

**Exam Tip**
If you're not given letters to use for a genetic diagram, just choose sensible ones yourself, e.g. T for tall dominant allele and t for dwarf recessive allele. Try to avoid using letters that look similar as capital and lower case letters, e.g. C and c.

**Exam Tip**
If you're asked to find the probability of something, you can write it as a fraction (e.g. ¾), a decimal (e.g. 0.75) or a percentage (e.g. 75%).

## Practice Questions — Application

Q1 The allele for tall pea plants is dominant over the allele for dwarf pea plants. Give the possible genotype(s) of offspring produced if a homozygous tall pea plant is crossed with a homozygous dwarf pea plant. Show your working.

Q2 Polydactyly is a genetic disorder where a baby is born with extra fingers or toes. The disorder is caused by a dominant allele. What is the probability of a baby being born with the condition if a person heterozygous for the disorder and a person without the disorder have a child? Show your working.

Q3 In one organism, the alleles for skin colour show codominance. Any organisms that are homozygous with blue alleles are blue in colour. Organisms that are homozygous with yellow alleles are yellow in colour. Heterozygous organisms are yellow and blue striped. What colour ratio of organisms would be produced if a heterozygous parent was crossed with a homozygous blue parent? Show your working.

# 3. Genetic Diagrams — Multiple Allele and Dihybrid Crosses

*Multiple allele crosses aren't much different to the monohybrid crosses you've already come across. They still only involve one gene, it's just the gene can have more than two alleles. If you want to, you can also use genetic diagrams to look at the inheritance of two genes simultaneously — this is called a dihybrid cross.*

**Learning Objectives:**

- Be able to use fully labelled genetic diagrams to interpret or predict the results of crosses involving multiple alleles.
- Be able to use fully labelled genetic diagrams to interpret or predict the results of dihybrid crosses involving dominant, recessive and codominant alleles.

**Specification Reference 3.7.1**

## Multiple allele crosses

Inheritance is more complicated when there are more than two alleles of the same gene (multiple alleles).

**Example**

In the ABO blood group system in humans there are three alleles for blood type:

- $I^O$ is the allele for blood group O.
- $I^A$ is the allele for blood group A.
- $I^B$ is the allele for blood group B.

Allele $I^O$ is recessive. Alleles $I^A$ and $I^B$ are codominant — people with genotype $I^AI^B$ will have blood group AB.

Figure 1 shows a cross between a heterozygous person with blood group A and a heterozygous person with blood group B.

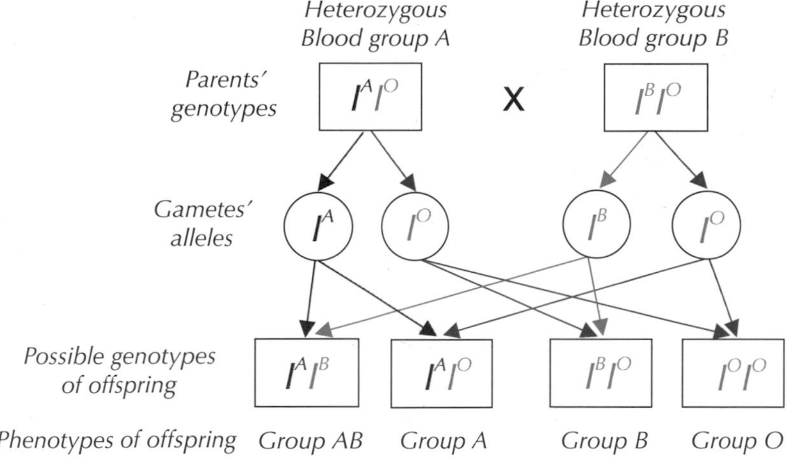


***Figure 1:*** *Genetic diagram showing the inheritance of blood group.*

Any offspring could have one of four different blood groups (A, B, O or AB). So the expected phenotypic ratio is 1 : 1 : 1 : 1.

**Tip:** Recessive blood groups are normally really rare, but it just so happens that loads of people in Britain are descended from people who were $I^O I^O$, so O's really common.

**Tip:** Monohybrid crosses (see p. 138) look at the inheritance of one characteristic only.

## Dihybrid crosses

Dihybrid inheritance is the inheritance of two characteristics, which are controlled by different genes. Each of the two genes will have different alleles. **Dihybrid crosses** can be used to show the likelihood of offspring inheriting certain combinations of the two characteristics from particular parents. The example on the next page is a dihybrid cross showing how seed shape and colour are inherited in pea plants.

*Figure 2:* Pea seeds can be wrinkled or round.

**Tip:** Each gamete should have one letter to represent each gene in the cross. So in a dihybrid cross, each gamete has two letters.

**Tip:** A dihybrid cross between a homozygous dominant parent and a homozygous recessive parent (e.g. RRYY × rryy) will produce all heterozygous offspring in the $F_1$ generation.

**Example**

As you saw on page 136, the gene for seed shape has two alleles. The allele for round seeds (R) is dominant and the allele for wrinkled seeds (r) is recessive. The seed colour gene also has two alleles. The allele for a yellow seed (Y) is dominant and the allele for a green seed (y) is recessive.

The genetic diagram in Figure 3 shows a cross between two heterozygous parents — both have round and yellow seeds (RrYy).

Here's how to draw a genetic diagram for this cross:

**Step 1:** Make sure you're clear what the letters mean.

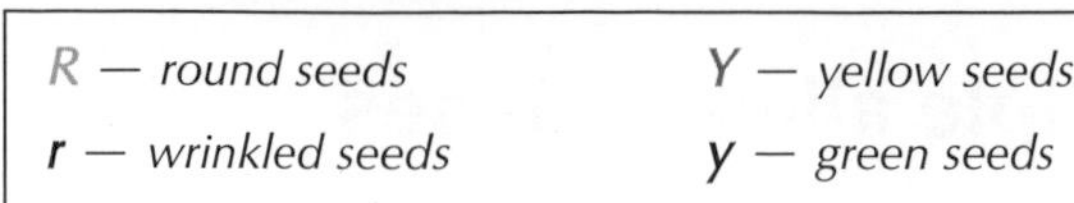

R — round seeds
Y — yellow seeds
r — wrinkled seeds
y — green seeds


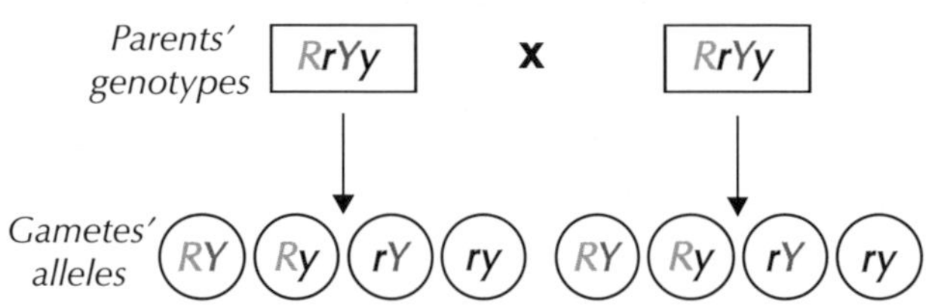


**Step 2:** Work out the alleles the gametes would have.

**Step 3:** Cross the parents' gametes to show the possible offspring.

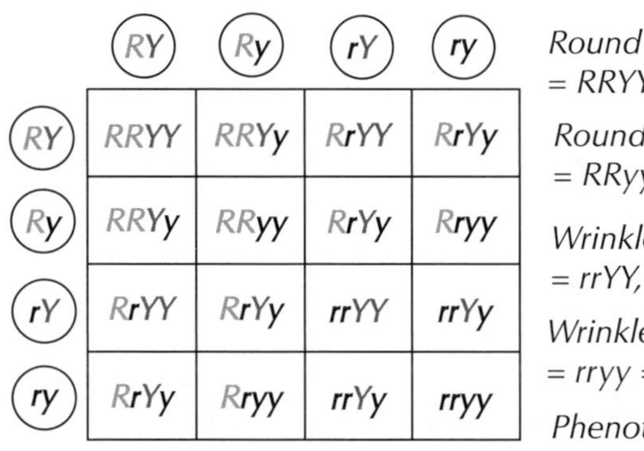

| | RY | Ry | rY | ry |
|---|---|---|---|---|
| RY | RRYY | RRYy | RrYY | RrYy |
| Ry | RRYy | RRyy | RrYy | Rryy |
| rY | RrYY | RrYy | rrYY | rrYy |
| ry | RrYy | Rryy | rrYy | rryy |

*Round and yellow seeds = RRYY, RrYY, RrYy, RRYy = 9*

*Round and green seeds = RRyy, Rryy = 3*

*Wrinkled and yellow seeds = rrYY, rrYy = 3*

*Wrinkled and green seeds = rryy = 1*

*Phenotypic ratio: 9 : 3 : 3 : 1*

***Figure 3:*** *Genetic diagram showing a dihybrid cross between two heterozygous parents.*

Usually, whenever you do a dihybrid cross with two heterozygous parents you get a 9 : 3 : 3 : 1 phenotypic ratio — that's 9 dominant both : 3 dominant first, recessive second : 3 recessive first, dominant second : 1 recessive both.

## Dihybrid crosses and codominance

You can also do dihybrid crosses involving codominant alleles. They work in exactly the same way as the example above, but the phenotypic ratios produced are quite different (there are more than four possible phenotypes in the offspring).

## Changes to phenotypic ratios

Even if neither of the genes involved in the dihybrid cross is codominant, you won't always get the expected 9 : 3 : 3 : 1 phenotypic ratio in the offspring of two heterozygous parents. This could be because of linkage or epistasis, both of which are covered on pages 144-150.

## Practice Questions — Application

Q1 The colour of one species of moth is controlled by three alleles — pale typical (m), darkly mottled insularia (M′) and nearly black melanic (M). The table below shows all possible genotype combinations and their phenotypic outcomes.

| ***Genotype*** | ***Phenotype*** |
|---|---|
| *mm* | *Typical* |
| *MM* | *Melanic* |
| *M′M′* | *Insularia* |
| *mM* | *Melanic* |
| *mM′* | *Insularia* |
| *MM′* | *Melanic* |

a) Describe the dominance of the different alleles.

b) A homozygous melanic and a typical pale moth breed. Show all the possible results of this cross.

Q2 The striping pattern of cats can be determined by three alleles — Ta for Abyssinian, T for the mackerel phenotype and tb for blotched. Abyssinian is dominant to both of the other alleles, mackerel is dominant to blotched only and blotched is recessive to all. (So the dominance of the alleles is Ta > T > tb.)

What are the possible striping patterns of offspring if a TaT cat and a tbtb cat breed together?

Q3 In tomato plants, the allele for round fruit (F) is dominant to the allele for pear-shaped fruit (f). The allele for red fruit colour (R) is dominant to the allele for yellow fruit colour (r).

a) Two tomato plants, heterozygous for fruit shape and colour, are crossed. Draw a Punnett square for this cross.

b) What is the expected ratio of round, red tomatoes to pear-shaped, yellow tomatoes?

Q4 In cattle, the alleles for black colouring (B) and polled (no horns) (P) are dominant and the alleles for red colouring (b) and horns (p) are recessive.

a) A black bull with no horns (BBPP) is crossed with a red cow with horns. What would the phenotypic ratio of the $F_1$ generation be?

b) Use a genetic diagram to show the expected phenotypic ratio in the offspring of a cross between two heterozygous black cattle with no horns.

# 4. Linkage

*There are two types of gene linkage, and they can both affect the phenotypic ratios of monohybrid and dihybrid crosses. You can use this variation from the expected ratios to identify that genes are linked.*

**Learning Objective:**

- Be able to use fully labelled genetic diagrams to interpret or predict the results of crosses involving sex-linkage or autosomal linkage.

**Specification Reference 3.7.1**

## Inheritance of sex-linked characteristics

The genetic information for biological sex is carried on two sex chromosomes. In mammals, females have two X chromosomes (XX) and males have one X chromosome and one Y chromosome (XY).

Figure 1 is a genetic diagram that shows how sex is inherited. From this you can see that the probability of having male offspring is 50% and the probability of having female offspring is 50%.

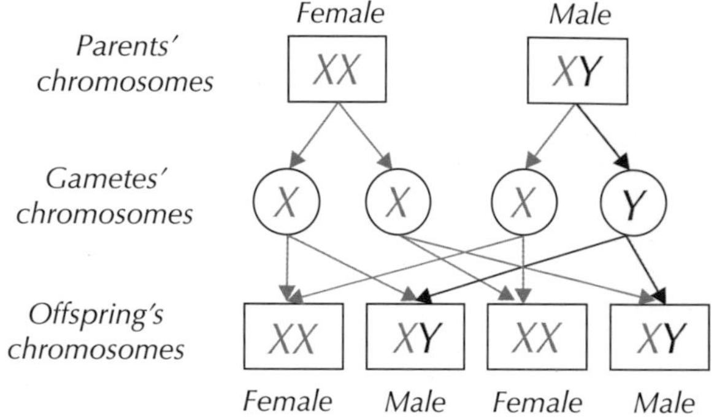


***Figure 1:*** *Genetic diagram showing the inheritance of gender.*

**Exam Tip**
In the exam you could be asked to give the probability of producing a certain sex with a particular genotype, for example, a boy with blue eyes. You work out the probability of a child having blue eyes first and then divide it by 2, to include the 1 in 2 chance of having a boy. (This isn't the same thing as a sex-linked characteristic though.)

Some characteristics are **sex-linked**. That means the alleles that code for them are located on a sex chromosome. The Y chromosome is smaller than the X chromosome and carries fewer genes. So most genes on the sex chromosomes are only carried on the X chromosome (called X-linked genes).

As males only have one X chromosome they often only have one allele for sex-linked genes. So because they only have one copy, they express the characteristic of this allele even if it's recessive. This makes males more likely than females to show recessive phenotypes for genes that are sex-linked.

Genetic disorders caused by faulty alleles located on sex chromosomes include colour blindness and haemophilia. The faulty alleles for both of these disorders are carried on the X chromosome and so are called X-linked disorders. Y-linked disorders do exist but are less common.

**Example**

Figure 2 on the next page shows a genetic diagram for colour blindness. Colour blindness is a sex-linked disorder caused by a faulty allele carried on the X chromosome. As it's sex-linked both the chromosome and the allele are represented in the genetic diagram, e.g. $X^n$, where X represents the X chromosome and n the faulty allele for colour vision. The Y chromosome doesn't have an allele for colour vision so is just represented by Y.

Females would need two copies of the recessive allele to be colour blind, while males only need one copy. This means colour blindness is much rarer in women than men. Females with one copy of the recessive allele are said to be **carriers**. A carrier is a person carrying an allele which is not expressed in the phenotype but that can be passed on to offspring.

**Tip:** The faulty allele for colour vision is represented by a lower case 'n', so you know it's a recessive allele.

Here's how to draw a Punnett square for the sex-linked cross between a carrier female and an unaffected male:

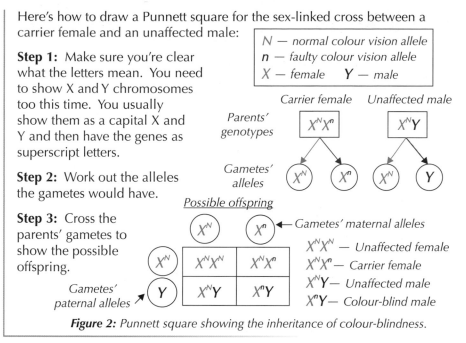

*N — normal colour vision allele*
*n — faulty colour vision allele*
*X — female  Y — male*

**Step 1:** Make sure you're clear what the letters mean. You need to show X and Y chromosomes too this time. You usually show them as a capital X and Y and then have the genes as superscript letters.

**Step 2:** Work out the alleles the gametes would have.

**Step 3:** Cross the parents' gametes to show the possible offspring.

| | *Carrier female* | *Unaffected male* |
|---|---|---|
| *Parents' genotypes* | $X^NX^n$ | $X^NY$ |
| *Gametes' alleles* | $X^N$, $X^n$ | $X^N$, $Y$ |

*Possible offspring*

| Gametes' paternal alleles ↓ / Gametes' maternal alleles → | $X^N$ | $X^n$ |
|---|---|---|
| $X^N$ | $X^NX^N$ | $X^NX^n$ |
| $Y$ | $X^NY$ | $X^nY$ |

*$X^NX^N$ — Unaffected female*
*$X^NX^n$ — Carrier female*
*$X^NY$ — Unaffected male*
*$X^nY$ — Colour-blind male*

***Figure 2:*** *Punnett square showing the inheritance of colour-blindness.*

In the example above, there's a 3 : 1 ratio of offspring without colour blindness : offspring with colour-blindness. But when a female carrier and a male without colour-blindness have children (as in this example), only their male offspring are at risk of being colour-blind. So you can also say that there's a predicted 2 : 1 : 1 ratio — of female offspring without colour-blindness : male offspring without colour-blindness : male offspring with colour-blindness. This ratio will change if a female carrier ($X^NX^n$) and a male with colour-blindness ($X^nY$) have children. The predicted ratio will then be 1 : 1 — of offspring with colour-blindness : offspring without colour-blindness. The ratio will be the same for offspring of each sex. You only end up with this predicted ratio for a monohybrid $F_2$ cross with a sex-linked characteristic.

## Linkage of autosomal genes

**Autosome** is the fancy name for any chromosome that isn't a sex chromosome. Autosomal genes are the genes located on the autosomes. Genes on the same autosome are said to be **linked** — that's because they'll stay together during the independent segregation of chromosomes in meiosis I, and their alleles will be passed on to the offspring together. The only reason this won't happen is if crossing over splits them up first. The closer together two genes are on the autosome, the more closely they are said to be linked. This is because crossing over is less likely to split them up.

*A pair of homologous autosomes.*

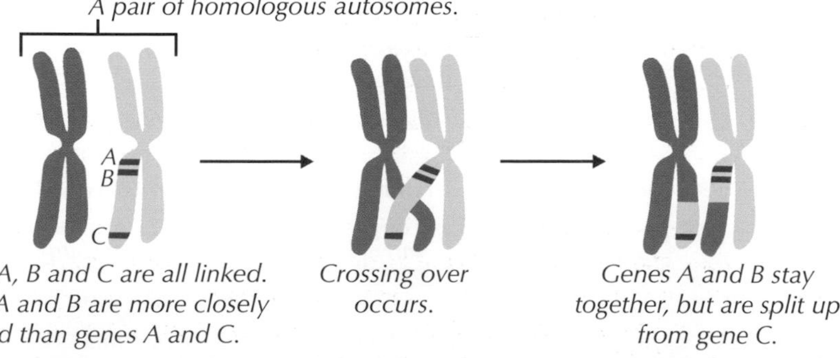

A
B
C
Genes A, B and C are all linked. Genes A and B are more closely linked than genes A and C.
Crossing over occurs.
Genes A and B stay together, but are split up from gene C.


***Figure 3a:*** *Autosomal genes being split up during crossing over.*

**Tip:** Males can't be carriers of X-linked disorders because they only have one copy of each chromosome, so if they have the allele they have the disease — whether it's recessive or not.

**Tip:** Here's a diagram to show the predicted phenotypic ratio of offspring if a female carrier and male with colour-blindness have children:

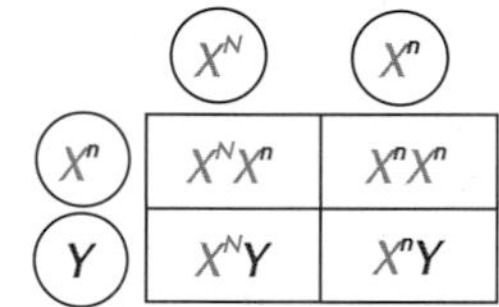


*$X^NX^n$ — Unaffected (carrier) female*
*$X^nX^n$ — Colour-blind female*
*$X^NY$ — Unaffected male*
*$X^nY$ — Colour-blind male*

Two offspring are predicted to have colour-blindness and two aren't. This simplifies to a 1 : 1 ratio.

**Tip:** Independent segregation is the random division of homologous (paired) chromosomes into separate daughter cells during meiosis. Crossing over is when two homologous chromosomes 'swap bits'. It happens in meiosis I before independent segregation. You'll have learnt about both of these in Year 1 of your course.

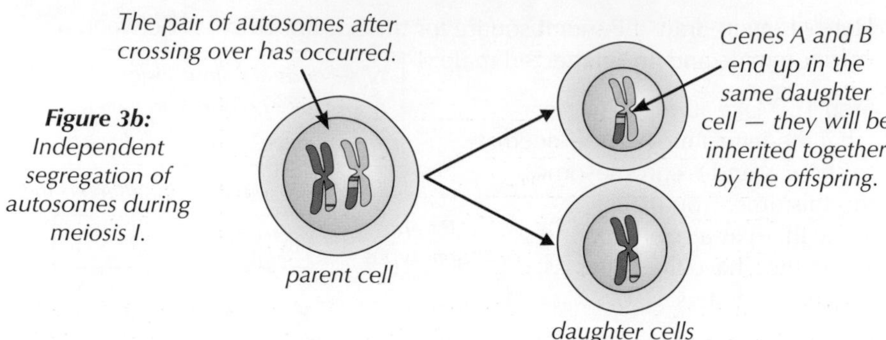


**Figure 3b:** *Independent segregation of autosomes during meiosis I.*

If two genes are autosomally linked, you won't get the phenotypic ratio you expect in the offspring of a cross.

**Example**

In a dihybrid cross between two heterozygous parents you'd expect a 9 : 3 : 3 : 1 ratio in the offspring. Instead, the phenotypic ratio is more likely to be that expected for a monohybrid cross between two heterozygous parents (3 : 1) because the two autosomally-linked alleles are inherited together. This means that a higher proportion of the offspring will have their parents' (heterozygous) genotype and phenotype.

**Tip:** There's more about the expected phenotypic ratios for dihybrid and monohybrid crosses on pages 142 and 139.

So you can use the predicted phenotypic ratio to identify autosomal linkage.

**Example**

A scientist was investigating autosomal linkage between the genes for eye colour and wing length in fruit flies. The gene for normal wings (N) is dominant to the gene for vestigial wings (n) and the gene for red eyes (R) is dominant to the gene for purple eyes (r).

The first cross the scientist carried out was between flies homozygous dominant for both normal wings and red eyes (NNRR) and flies homozygous recessive for both vestigial wings and purple eyes (nnrr). The resulting offspring were all heterozygous for normal wings and red eyes (NnRr).

**Tip:** Crossing the offspring with one of the parents is known as a back cross.

The second cross the scientist carried out was between these offspring (NnRr) and the flies homozygous recessive for vestigial wings and purple eyes (nnrr). He expected a 1 : 1 : 1 : 1 ratio as shown in Figure 4:

**Tip:** Watch out — a 1 : 1 : 1 : 1 ratio is expected here because the cross is between a <u>homozygous</u> parent and a <u>heterozygous</u> parent <u>not</u> two heterozygous parents (which would be a 9 : 3 : 3 : 1 ratio).

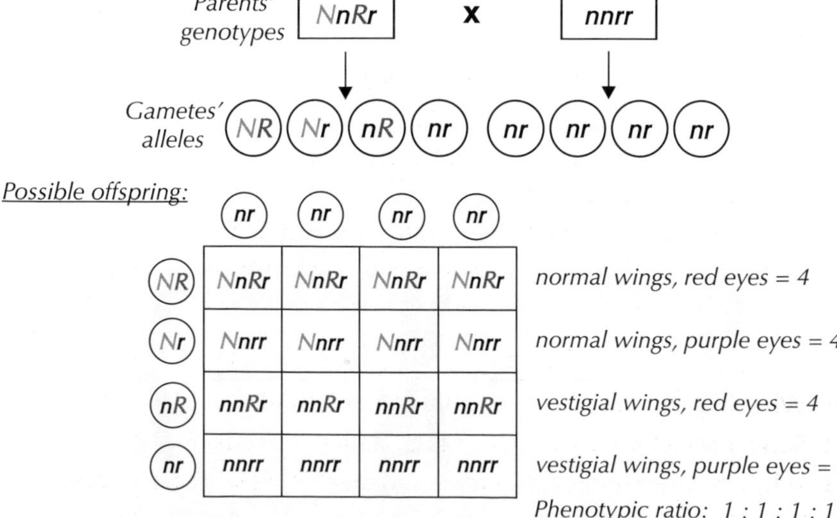


**Figure 4:** *Genetic diagram showing the expected phenotypic ratio for a dihybrid cross between one heterozygous parent and one homozygous parent.*

However, the results the scientist got for the NnRr × nnrr cross showed an 8 : 1 : 1 : 8 ratio, as in the table:

| | *Number of offspring* |
|---|---|
| *Normal wings, red eyes (NnRr)* | *1216* |
| *Normal wings, purple eyes (Nnrr)* | *152* |
| *Vestigial wings, red eyes (nnRr)* | *148* |
| *Vestigial wings, purple eyes (nnrr)* | *1184* |

*Phenotypic ratio = 8 : 1 : 1 : 8*

In order for the NnRr and nnrr genotypes to be so common in the offspring, the NR alleles and the nr alleles in the NnRr parent must have been linked. This means that the NnRr parent produced mostly NR and nr gametes. Some Nr and nR gametes were still made due to crossing over, but there were fewer Nnrr and nnRr offspring overall. As a result, a higher proportion of the offspring have their parents' phenotypes.

**Tip:** To give the ratio 1216 : 152 : 148 : 1184 in its simplest form, divide each number by the smallest number in the ratio (i.e. 148).

**Exam Tip**
In the exam you might get some genetic cross results that show linkage and have to explain them.

## Practice Questions — Application

Q1 Fragile X syndrome is an X-linked dominant disorder. A male and female, each with Fragile X syndrome, have a child. The female is heterozygous for the disorder. Give the possible genotypes and phenotypes of the child.

Q2 Hypertrichosis pinnae (extremely hairy ears) was once thought to be a Y-linked characteristic. If this were true, why might a father with 'bald' ears whose child has hairy ears, be suspicious of his wife?

Q3 In corn plants, the allele for glossy leaves (G) is dominant to the allele for normal leaves (g) and the allele for branching of ears (B) is dominant to the allele for no branching (b). A cross is carried out between a plant that is heterozygous for glossy leaves and branching of ears (GgBb) and a plant that is homozygous recessive for normal leaves and no branching (ggbb).

a) Use a genetic diagram to work out the expected phenotypic ratio in the offspring.

b) The results of the cross are shown in the table below.

| | Number of offspring |
|---|---|
| Glossy leaves, lots of branching (GgBb) | 126 |
| Glossy leaves, no branching (Ggbb) | 81 |
| Normal leaves, lots of branching (ggBb) | 74 |
| Normal leaves, no branching (ggbb) | 133 |

What is the observed phenotypic ratio in the offspring?

c) Suggest why the observed ratio differs from the expected ratio.

***Figure 5:*** *A photo showing normal leaves and no branching in two ears of corn.*

## Practice Questions — Fact Recall

Q1 What is the probability of having a female child?

Q2 Some characteristics are sex-linked. What does this mean?

Q3 Why are X-linked disorders more common in males than females?

Q4 What is an autosome?

Q5 Why are genes on the same autosome said to be linked?

# 5. Epistasis

*Just like linkage, epistasis affects the phenotypic ratios of dihybird crosses.*

**Learning Objective:**

- Be able to use fully labelled genetic diagrams to interpret or predict the results of crosses involving epistasis.

**Specification Reference 3.7.1**

## What is epistasis?

Many different genes can control the same characteristic — they interact to form the phenotype. This can be because the allele of one gene masks (blocks) the expression of the alleles of other genes — this is called **epistasis**.

**Example 1 — Widow's peak**

In humans a widow's peak (see Figure 1) is controlled by one gene and baldness by others. If you have the alleles that code for baldness, it doesn't matter whether you have the allele for a widow's peak or not, as you have no hair. The baldness genes are epistatic to the widow's peak gene, as the baldness genes mask the expression of the widow's peak gene.

***Figure 1:*** *A man with a widow's peak (a V-shaped hair growth). If this man were bald, you wouldn't be able to tell whether he had a widow's peak or not.*

**Example 2 — Flower colour**

Flower pigment in a plant is controlled by two genes. Gene 1 codes for a yellow pigment (Y is the dominant yellow allele) and gene 2 codes for an enzyme that turns the yellow pigment orange (R is the dominant orange allele). If you don't have the Y allele it won't matter if you have the R allele or not as the flower will be colourless. Gene 1 is epistatic to gene 2 as it can mask the expression of gene 2.

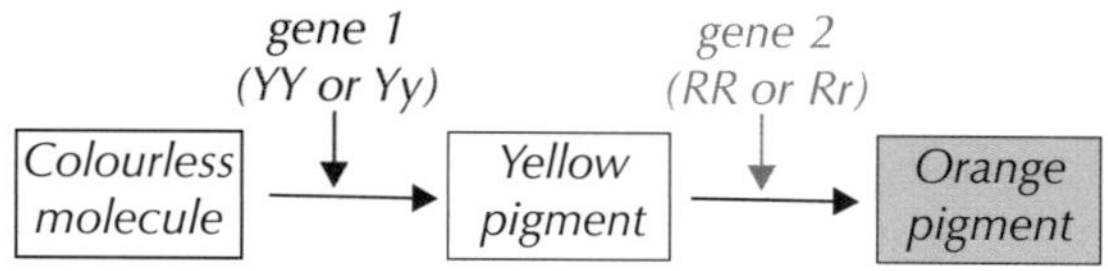


**Tip:** Epistatic genes are usually at different loci (different positions on chromosomes).

## Phenotypic ratios for epistatic genes

Crosses involving epistatic genes don't result in the expected phenotypic ratios, e.g. if you cross two heterozygous orange flowered plants (YyRr) from the example above you wouldn't get the expected 9 : 3 : 3 : 1 phenotypic ratio for a normal dihybrid cross.

The phenotypic ratio you would expect to get from a dihybrid cross involving an epistatic allele depends on whether the epistatic allele is recessive or dominant.

### Recessive epistatic alleles

If the epistatic allele is recessive then two copies of it will mask (block) the expression of the other gene. If you cross a homozygous recessive parent with a homozygous dominant parent you will produce a 9 : 3 : 4 phenotypic ratio of dominant both : dominant epistatic, recessive other : recessive epistatic in the $F_2$ generation.

**Tip:** Remember the $F_1$ generation is the first generation and the $F_2$ generation is the second generation.

**Example**

The flower colour example above is an example of a recessive epistatic allele. If a plant is homozygous recessive for the epistatic gene (yy) then it will be colourless, masking the expression of the orange gene. So if you cross homozygous parents you should get a 9 : 3 : 4 ratio of orange : yellow : white in the $F_2$ generation. You can check the phenotypic ratio is right using a genetic diagram, like the one in Figure 2 (see next page).

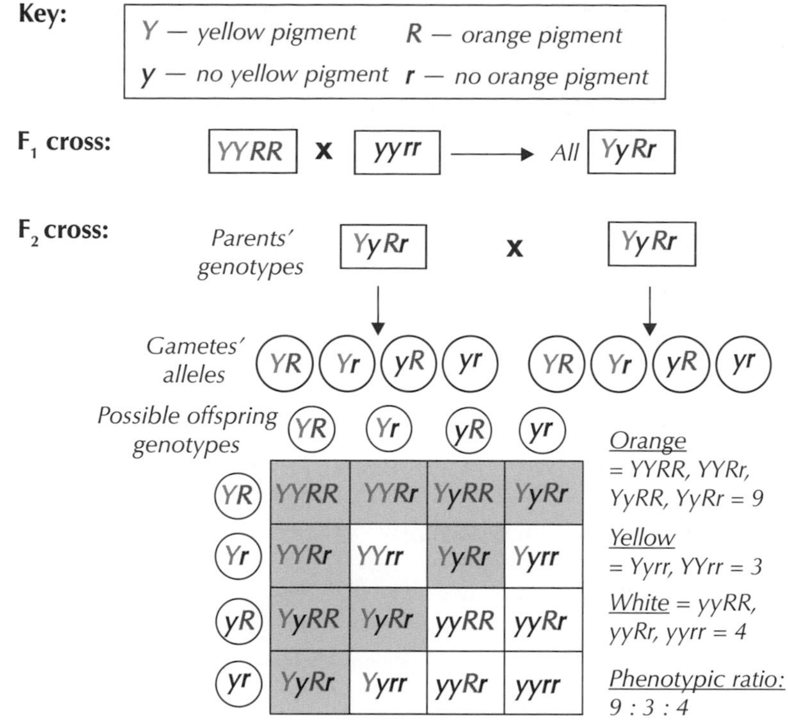


***Figure 2:** Genetic diagram of a dihybrid cross with two heterozygous parents, involving a recessive epistatic gene.*

**Tip:** All of the $F_1$ offspring have to have the genotype YyRr because the only gametes you can get from the parents are YR and yr.

**Tip:** You should be familiar with Punnett squares by now but if not, see page 139 for a recap.

**Tip:** This is a dihybrid cross because you're looking at the inheritance of two genes.

## Dominant epistatic alleles

If the epistatic allele is dominant, then having at least one copy of it will mask (block) the expression of the other gene. Crossing a homozygous recessive parent with a homozygous dominant parent will produce a 12 : 3 : 1 phenotypic ratio of dominant epistatic : recessive epistatic, dominant other : recessive both in the $F_2$ generation.

**Example**

Squash colour is controlled by two genes — the colour epistatic gene (W/w) and the yellow gene (Y/y). The no-colour, white allele (W) is dominant over the coloured allele (w), so WW or Ww will be white and ww will be coloured. The yellow gene has the dominant yellow allele (Y) and the recessive green allele (y). So if the plant has at least one W, then the squash will be white, masking the expression of the yellow gene.

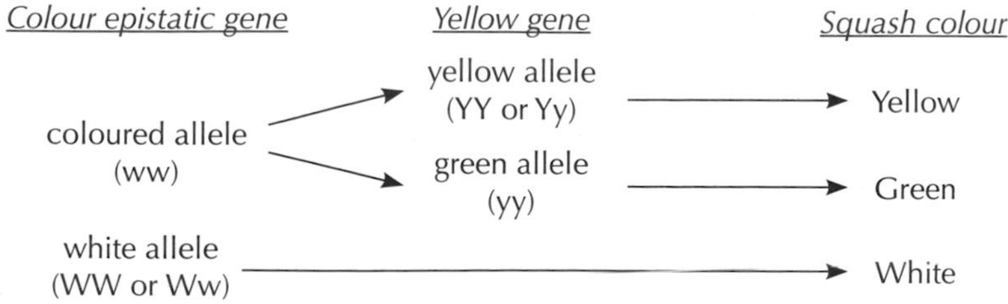


***Figure 3:** Diagram to show how squash colour is controlled by two genes.*

So if you cross wwyy with WWYY, you'll get a 12 : 3 : 1 ratio of white : yellow : green in the $F_2$ generation. The genetic diagram to prove it is shown in Figure 5 (see next page).

**Exam Tip:**
Make sure you know the difference between dominant and recessive epistatic alleles. The phenotypic ratios you'd expect to get are different for each.

***Figure 4:** These squash are yellow in colour so they must have the genotype wwYY or wwYy.*

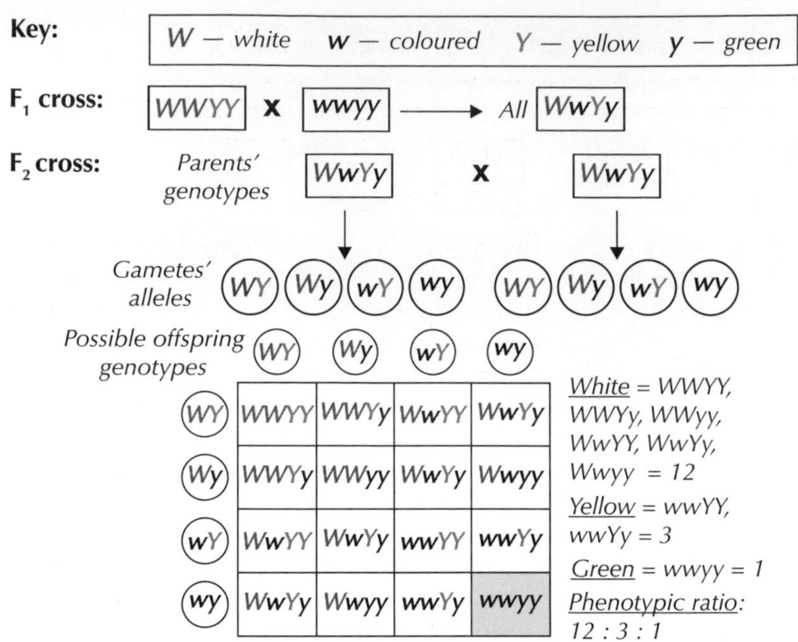


| | WY | Wy | wY | wy |
|---|---|---|---|---|
| WY | WWYY | WWYy | WwYY | WwYy |
| Wy | WWYy | WWyy | WwYy | Wwyy |
| wY | WwYY | WwYy | wwYY | wwYy |
| wy | WwYy | Wwyy | wwYy | wwyy |

***Figure 5:*** *Genetic diagram of a dihybrid cross with two heterozygous parents, involving a dominant epistatic gene.*

**Exam Tip**
If you set your crosses out like this in the exam, it'll help you keep track of what you're doing and it'll help the examiner follow your working out.

***Figure 6:*** *Chocolate and black coated Labrador retrievers.*

## Practice Questions — Application

Q1 Coat colour in Labrador retrievers is controlled by two genes. Gene 1 controls whether the dog can express dark pigment in its coat (E) or not (e). Gene 1 is epistatic over gene 2, which controls whether the dark pigment is black (B) or chocolate (b). Dogs that can't express dark pigment in their coat are yellow (golden) in colour.

a) Write down all the possible genotypes for:
 i) a black Labrador, ii) a chocolate Labrador,
 iii) a yellow Labrador.

b) Describe and explain the phenotypic ratio produced in the $F_2$ generation if a black Labrador retriever (EEBB) breeds with a yellow Labrador retriever (eebb).

Q2 Petal colour in a species of flower is controlled by this pathway:

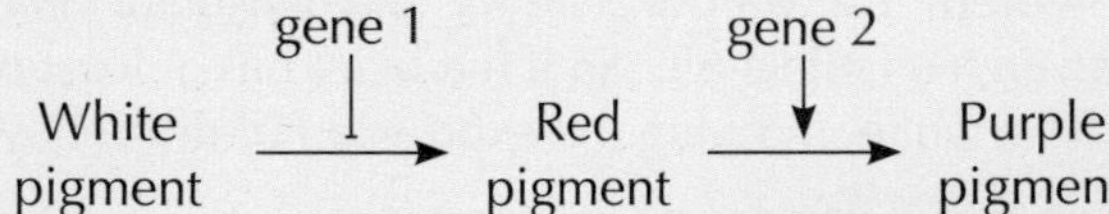


Gene 1 codes for a protein that prevents the formation of the red pigment. This means the dominant allele for gene 1 (W) causes the petals to be white and the recessive allele (w) causes red pigment to be made. Gene 2 codes for a protein that turns the red pigment into purple pigment. This means the dominant allele for gene 2 (P), causes the petals to be purple and the recessive allele (p) causes the petals to stay red. When a white flower (WWPP) is crossed with a red flower (wwpp), 48 white flowers, 12 purple flowers and 4 red flowers are produced in the $F_2$ generation.

a) Is this an example of dominant or recessive epistasis?

b) Explain the phenotypic ratio shown by the cross.

c) Draw a genetic diagram to show this cross.

# 6. The Chi-Squared Test

*The chi-squared test can be a bit tricky to get your head around, but take some time to work through these pages and you'll be fine.*

**Learning Objective:**

- Be able to use the chi-squared ($\chi^2$) test to compare the goodness of fit of observed phenotypic ratios with expected ratios.

**Specification Reference 3.7.1**

## What is the chi-squared test?

The chi-squared ($\chi^2$) test is a statistical test that's used to see if the results of an experiment support a theory. First, the theory is used to predict a result — this is called the expected result. Then, the experiment is carried out and the actual result is recorded — this is called the observed result.

To see if the results support the theory you have to make a hypothesis called the **null hypothesis**. The null hypothesis is always that there's no significant difference between the observed and expected results. Your experimental result will usually be a bit different from what you expect, but you need to know if the difference is just due to chance, or because your theory is wrong. The $\chi^2$ test is then carried out to compare the 'goodness of fit' of the observed and expected results (i.e. to compare how well the observed results match the expected results). The outcome either supports or rejects the null hypothesis.

**Exam Tip**
In the exams, you could be asked to explain when you'd use a chi-squared test to analyse results. The test can be used whenever you have categorical data and you want to compare observed and expected results. See page 9 for more.

### Using the chi-squared test

You can use the $\chi^2$ test in genetics to test theories about the inheritance of characteristics.

**Example — inheritance of wing length experiment**

**Theory:** Wing length in fruit flies is controlled by a single gene with two alleles (monohybrid inheritance). The dominant allele (N) gives normal wings, and the recessive allele (n) gives vestigial wings.

**Expected results:** With monohybrid inheritance, if you cross a homozygous dominant parent with a homozygous recessive parent, you'd expect a 3 : 1 phenotypic ratio of normal : vestigial wings in the $F_2$ generation.

**Observed results:** The experiment (of crossing a homozygous dominant parent with a homozygous recessive parent) is carried out on fruit flies and the number of offspring with normal and vestigial wings is counted.

**Null hypothesis:** There's no significant difference between the observed and expected results.

**Chi-squared test:** To find out if the results are significant, the **chi-squared value** is calculated (see below) and then compared to the **critical value** (see page 153). If the $\chi^2$ test shows the observed and expected results are not significantly different, then we are unable to reject the null hypothesis — the data supports the theory that wing length is controlled by monohybrid inheritance.

***Figure 1:*** *Karl Pearson — the English statistician who developed the chi-squared test.*

## Calculating the chi-squared value

Chi-squared ($\chi^2$) is calculated using this formula:

$$\chi^2 = \sum \frac{(O - E)^2}{E}$$

O = observed result
E = expected result
$\Sigma$ = the sum of...

The best way to understand the $\chi^2$ test is to work through an example — there's one for testing the wing length of fruit flies, as explained above, on the next page.

**Exam Tip**
Don't worry, you won't be expected to calculate a $\chi^2$ value in the written exams. You do need to be able to interpret the results of a chi-squared test though, so it's a good idea to understand how the test itself works.

**Example** — **Maths Skills**

Homozygous dominant flies (NN) are crossed with homozygous recessive flies (nn) and 160 offspring are produced in the $F_2$ generation.

1. First the number of offspring expected (E) for each phenotype (out of a total of 160) is worked out using this equation:

   E = total no. of offspring ÷ ratio total × predicted ratio

   A 3 : 1 phenotypic ratio of normal : vestigial wings is expected, so the ratio total is 3 + 1 = 4. Here are the expected results:

| Phenotype | Ratio | Expected result (E) |
|---|---|---|
| Normal wings | 3 | 160 ÷ 4 × 3 = 120 |
| Vestigial wings | 1 | 160 ÷ 4 × 1 = 40 |

2. Then the actual number of offspring observed with each phenotype (out of the 160 offspring) is recorded, e.g. 111 with normal wings:

| Phenotype | Ratio | Expected result (E) | Observed result (O) |
|---|---|---|---|
| Normal wings | 3 | 120 | 111 |
| Vestigial wings | 1 | 40 | 49 |

3. The results are used to work out $\chi^2$. Taking it one step at a time:

   a. O – E is calculated for each phenotype (the expected result is subtracted from the observed result).

| Phenotype | Ratio | Expected result (E) | Observed result (O) | O – E |
|---|---|---|---|---|
| Normal wings | 3 | 120 | 111 | 111 – 120 = –9 |
| Vestigial wings | 1 | 40 | 49 | 49 – 40 = 9 |

   b. Then the resulting numbers are squared:

| Phenotype | Ratio | Expected result (E) | Observed result (O) | O – E | $(O-E)^2$ |
|---|---|---|---|---|---|
| Normal wings | 3 | 120 | 111 | –9 | $-9^2 = 81$ |
| Vestigial wings | 1 | 40 | 49 | 9 | $9^2 = 81$ |

   c. These figures are divided by the expected results:

| Phenotype | Ratio | Expected result (E) | Observed result (O) | O – E | $(O-E)^2$ | $\frac{(O-E)^2}{E}$ |
|---|---|---|---|---|---|---|
| Normal wings | 3 | 120 | 111 | –9 | 81 | 81 ÷ 120 = 0.675 |
| Vestigial wings | 1 | 40 | 49 | 9 | 81 | 81 ÷ 40 = 2.025 |

   d. Finally, the numbers are added together to get $\chi^2$.

| Phenotype | Ratio | Expected result (E) | Observed result (O) | O – E | $(O-E)^2$ | $\frac{(O-E)^2}{E}$ |
|---|---|---|---|---|---|---|
| Normal wings | 3 | 120 | 111 | –9 | 81 | 0.675 |
| Vestigial wings | 1 | 40 | 49 | 9 | 81 | 2.025 |
| | | | | | $\sum\frac{(O-E)^2}{E}$ = 0.675 + 2.025 = | 2.7 |

**Tip:** Don't forget — if you multiply a negative number by a negative number you get a positive number. So $-9^2$ $(-9 \times -9)$ is 81 and not –81.

# The critical value

In your exam, you could be given a $\chi^2$ value and be asked to determine whether there is a significant difference between the observed and expected results from an experiment. To do this you need to compare the $\chi^2$ value to a critical value. The critical value is the value of $\chi^2$ that corresponds to a 0.05 (5%) level of probability that the difference between the observed and expected results is due to chance.

**Tip:** There's more on P values on page 9.

## Finding the critical value

In the exam you might be given the critical value or asked to work it out from a table.

**Example — Maths Skills**

Figure 2 below is a chi-squared table — this shows a range of probabilities that correspond to different critical values for different **degrees of freedom** (explained below). Biologists normally use a **probability level** (P value) of 0.05 (5%), so you only need to look in that column.

| *degrees of freedom* | *no. of classes* | *Critical values* | | | | | |
|---|---|---|---|---|---|---|---|
| *1* | *2* | *0.46* | *1.64* | *2.71* | *3.84* | *6.64* | *10.83* |
| *2* | *3* | *1.39* | *3.22* | *4.61* | *5.99* | *9.21* | *13.82* |
| *3* | *4* | *2.37* | *4.64* | *6.25* | *7.82* | *11.34* | *16.27* |
| *4* | *5* | *3.36* | *5.99* | *7.78* | *9.49* | *13.28* | *18.47* |
| *probability that result is due to chance only* | | *0.50 (50%)* | *0.20 (20%)* | *0.10 (10%)* | *0.05 (5%)* | *0.01 (1%)* | *0.001 (0.1%)* |

***Figure 2:*** *A chi-squared table.*



**Exam Tip**
The table of critical values you get given in the exam might look a bit different to this, but don't panic. It'll still contain all the information you need to answer the question.

In order to find the critical value for the wing length experiment:

- First, the degrees of freedom for the experiment are worked out — this is the number of classes (number of phenotypes) minus one. There were two phenotypes, so the degrees of freedom = 2 – 1 = 1.
- Next, the critical value corresponding to the degrees of freedom (1 in this case) and a probability level of 0.05 is found in the table. By following the arrows in Figure 2 you can see that the critical value is **3.84**.

**Tip:** The two phenotypes for the wing length experiment are normal wings and vestigial wings.

**Tip:** Some other statistical tests also use degrees of freedom (e.g. Student's t-test). They're worked out differently for different tests.

## Comparing the $\chi^2$ value to the critical value

If your $\chi^2$ value is larger than (or equal to) the critical value, then there is a significant difference between the observed and expected results — i.e. something other than chance is causing the difference. This means the null hypothesis can be rejected. If your $\chi^2$ value is smaller than the critical value, then there is no significant difference between the observed and expected results — the null hypothesis can't be rejected. This is summarised in Figure 3.

$\chi^2$ value ≥ critical value = reject the null hypothesis
$\chi^2$ value < critical value = fail to reject the null hypothesis

***Figure 3:*** *Possible outcomes of a chi-squared test.*

**Tip:** In this kind of statistical test, you can never prove that the null hypothesis is true — you can only 'fail to reject it'. This just means that the evidence doesn't give you a reason to think the null hypothesis is wrong.

**Example — Maths Skills**

The chi-squared value of 2.7 is smaller than the critical value of 3.84. This means that there's no significant difference between the observed and expected results. We've failed to reject the null hypothesis — so the theory that wing length in fruit flies is controlled by monohybrid inheritance is supported.

**Tip:** If the $\chi^2$ value had been bigger than 3.84 then something else must have been affecting wing length — like epistasis or sex linkage.

## Practice Questions — Application

Q1 The critical value for a chi-squared test is 5.99. Explain whether or not the difference between the observed and expected results would be significant if the calculated chi-squared value was:

a) 6.20,

b) 4.85.

For the following questions, you may need to use the $\chi^2$ table below:

| Degrees of freedom | Probability (p) | | | | | |
|---|---|---|---|---|---|---|
| | 0.50 | 0.20 | 0.10 | 0.05 | 0.01 | 0.001 |
| 1 | 0.46 | 1.64 | 2.71 | 3.84 | 6.64 | 10.83 |
| 2 | 1.39 | 3.22 | 4.61 | 5.99 | 9.21 | 13.82 |
| 3 | 2.37 | 4.64 | 6.25 | 7.82 | 11.34 | 16.27 |
| 4 | 3.36 | 5.99 | 7.78 | 9.49 | 13.28 | 18.47 |

*probability levels* (arrow to the row of probabilities); *critical values* (bracket beside the rows of values)

Abridged from Statistical Tables for Biological Agricultural and Medical Research (6th ed.)
© 1963 R.A Fisher and F. Yates. Reprinted with permission of Pearson Education Limited.

**Tip:** Remember, the degrees of freedom here are just the number of classes minus one (n –1).

Q2 A student is looking at the inheritance of pea shape (round vs. wrinkled) and pea colour (green vs. yellow) in pea plants. His theory is that this is a simple case of dihybrid inheritance with no linkage or epistasis involved. He predicts that if this is the case, when two heterozygous plants are crossed, there will be a 9 : 3 : 3 : 1 ratio in the offspring. To test his theory, the student carries out this cross and looks at the phenotypes of the 128 offspring produced. Some of his results are shown in the table below. His null hypothesis is that there is no significant difference between the observed and expected results.

a) Copy and complete the table to calculate $\chi^2$ for this experiment:

| Phenotype | Ratio | Expected result (E) | Observed result (O) | O – E | $(O - E)^2$ | $\frac{(O - E)^2}{E}$ |
|---|---|---|---|---|---|---|
| Round, green | 9 | | 74 | | | |
| Round, yellow | 3 | | 21 | | | |
| Wrinkled, green | 3 | | | | | |
| Wrinkled, yellow | 1 | | 7 | | | |

$$\chi^2 = \Sigma \frac{(O - E)^2}{E} = \square$$

b) Find the critical value for this experiment and explain whether the null hypothesis can be rejected or not.

Q3 A flower can have red, white or pink flowers. If this is an example of codominance and two heterozygous plants were crossed, you would expect a 1 : 2 : 1 ratio of red : pink : white flowers in the offspring. In order to test this, a null hypothesis was made and the cross was performed. Of the 160 offspring produced, 92 had pink flowers, 24 had red flowers and 44 had white flowers. From these figures, a chi-squared test result of $\chi^2 = 8.6$ was obtained.

a) What should the null hypothesis be for this test?

b) Is this cross likely to be an example of codominance? Explain your answer.

## Section Summary

Make sure you know...

- That there can be one or more versions of the same gene and that these are called alleles.
- That genotype is what alleles an organism has and that phenotype is how these alleles show themselves.
- That alleles whose characteristic is always shown in the phenotype are called dominant, that those only shown in the phenotype if you have two copies are called recessive, and that codominant alleles both show in the phenotype.
- That if a diploid organism has two different alleles at the same locus it's heterozygous, but if it has two copies of the same allele at the same locus it's homozygous.
- How to use genetic diagrams showing monohybrid crosses involving dominant, recessive and codominant alleles to make predictions about offspring.
- That the phenotypic ratio is the ratio of phenotypes in the offspring.
- That the typical phenotypic ratio for a monohybrid cross between two heterozygous parents is 3 : 1 of dominant : recessive characteristic and the typical phenotypic ratio for a cross between two heterozygous parents involving codominant alleles is 1 : 2 : 1 of homozygous for one allele : heterozygous : homozygous for the other allele.
- How to use genetic diagrams showing crosses involving multiple alleles and dihybrid crosses to make predictions about offspring.
- That a typical phenotypic ratio for a dihybrid cross between two heterozygous parents is 9 : 3 : 3 : 1 (dominant both : dominant first, recessive second : recessive first, dominant second : recessive both).
- How to use genetic diagrams to show the inheritance of sex-linked characteristics (the alleles that code for them are located on sex chromosomes) and recognise that sex linkage alters expected phenotypic ratios in the offspring of crosses.
- How to use genetic diagrams to identify linked genes on autosomes and recognise that autosomal linkage alters expected phenotypic ratios in the offspring of crosses.
- That epistasis is when the allele of one gene masks the expression of the alleles of other genes.
- What recessive epistasis is and that when the epistatic allele is recessive, crossing a homozygous recessive parent with a homozygous dominant parent will produce a 9 : 3 : 4 phenotypic ratio of dominant both : dominant epistatic, recessive other : recessive epistatic in the $F_2$ generation.
- What dominant epistasis is and that when the epistatic allele is dominant, crossing a homozygous recessive parent with a homozygous dominant parent will produce a 12 : 3 : 1 phenotypic ratio of dominant epistatic : recessive epistatic, dominant other : recessive both in the $F_2$ generation.
- When a chi-squared test is used and what a null hypothesis is.
- How to find the critical value from a chi-squared table and how to use these values to determine whether the difference between observed and expected results is significant or not, and whether or not to reject the null hypothesis.

# Exam-style Questions

1 In mice, the allele for wild-type speckled coat colour, agouti (A), is dominant to the allele for solid coloured fur (a).

1.1 Several pairs of heterozygous agouti mice are crossed, producing 256 offspring.

Assuming this is a normal case of monohybrid inheritance, with no linkage involved, how many of the offspring would you expect to have the agouti coat colour?

*(1 mark)*

1.2 The alleles for coat colour (A and a), are actually controlled by another gene (P). If a mouse is homozygous recessive for this gene, it is unable to produce any pigmentation and so will be albino.

Give the possible genotype(s) that will produce the albino phenotype.

*(1 mark)*

1.3 A student produces a genetic diagram to show the phenotypic ratio produced in the $F_2$ generation if a homozygous dominant mouse (PPAA) breeds with a homozygous recessive mouse (ppaa). His results are shown in **Figure 1** below.

**Figure 1**

| | **PA** | **pA** | **Pa** | **pa** |
|---|---|---|---|---|
| **PA** | PPAA | PpAA | PPAa | PpAa |
| **pA** | PpAA | ppAA | PpAa | ppAa |
| **Pa** | PPAa | PpAa | PPaa | Ppaa |
| **pa** | PpAa | ppAa | Ppaa | ppaa |

The student concludes that this cross produces a phenotypic ratio of 9 : 3 : 3 : 1. This is incorrect. Give the phenotypic ratio that would be expected from this cross and explain why the student's conclusion is wrong.

*(3 marks)*

2 Yeast cells can convert substance 1 to substance 3 via the enzyme pathway shown in **Figure 2**. Two different gene loci control the pathway and each has two alleles. Having the dominant versions of alleles A and B means that the yeast cell will produce enzymes A and B as shown in **Figure 2**.

**Figure 2**

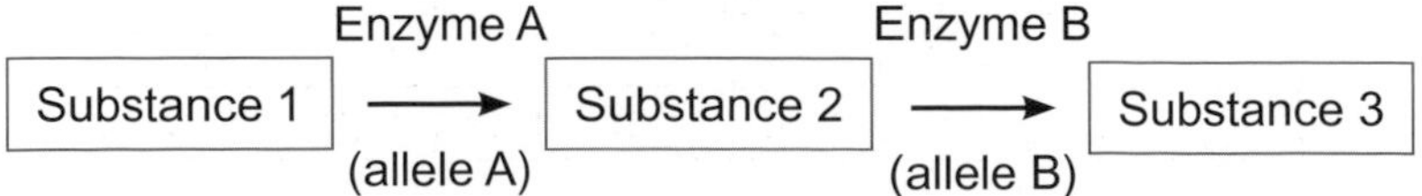


Yeast cells that lack either enzyme A or enzyme B cannot convert substance 1 to substance 3 and so cannot grow in media containing substance 1.

**2.1** Complete the table by putting a tick (✓) or a cross (✗) in the correct boxes below to show whether or not yeast cells with the following genotypes could grow on substance 1. The first one has been done for you

| Genotype | Growth on substance 1 |
|---|---|
| AaBb | ✓ |
| aaBb | |
| AAbb | |
| AABb | |

*(1 mark)*

**2.2** Some of the cells that could not grow on substance 1 will grow if supplied with substance 2. Explain why, with reference to their genotype.

*(3 marks)*

**3** Haemophilia is a sex-linked genetic disorder. It is caused by a faulty allele on the X-chromosome. The faulty allele ($X^h$) is recessive to the normal allele ($X^H$). A study was carried out into the inheritance of haemophilia. The phenotypes of children in families where the mother was a carrier of the disease (genotype $X^HX^h$) and the father was a haemophiliac (genotype $X^hY$) were recorded.

**3.1** Draw a genetic diagram to show why a 1 : 1 : 1 : 1 phenotypic ratio of haemophiliac male : haemophiliac female : carrier female : normal male was expected in the results of this study.

*(3 marks)*

Of the 272 children in this study, 130 were boys and 142 were girls. 61 of the boys and 70 of the girls had haemophilia. A chi-squared test was used to analyse the results. The results are shown in **Figure 3**. A table of critical values for chi-squared is shown in **Figure 4**.

**Figure 3**

| **Phenotype** | **Ratio** | **Expected result (E)** | **Observed result (O)** | $\frac{(O-E)^2}{E}$ |
|---|---|---|---|---|
| Carrier female | 1 | 68 | 72 | 0.24 |
| Haemophilic female | 1 | 68 | 70 | 0.06 |
| Normal male | 1 | 68 | 69 | 0.02 |
| Haemophilic male | 1 | 68 | 61 | 0.72 |
| | | | Chi-squared = | 1.04 |

**Figure 4***

| Degrees of freedom | Probability (P) | | | | | |
|---|---|---|---|---|---|---|
| | 0.50 | 0.20 | 0.10 | 0.05 | 0.01 | 0.001 |
| 1 | 0.46 | 1.64 | 2.71 | 3.84 | 6.64 | 10.83 |
| 2 | 1.39 | 3.22 | 4.61 | 5.99 | 9.21 | 13.82 |
| 3 | 2.37 | 4.64 | 6.25 | 7.82 | 11.34 | 16.27 |

**3.2** Use **Figure 3** and **Figure 4** to determine whether or not the difference between the observed and expected results is significant. Explain your answer.

*(2 marks)*

*Abridged from Statistical Tables for Biological Agricultural and Medical Research (6th ed.)

**Learning Objectives:**

- Know that species exist as one or more populations.
- Know that a population is a group of organisms of the same species occupying a particular space at a particular time that can potentially interbreed.
- Understand the concepts of gene pool and allele frequency.
- Understand that the Hardy-Weinberg principle provides a mathematical model, which predicts that allele frequencies will not change from generation to generation.
- Know the conditions under which the Hardy-Weinberg principle applies.
- Be able to calculate allele, genotype and phenotype frequencies from appropriate data using the Hardy-Weinberg equation: $p^2 + 2pq + q^2 = 1$, where $p$ is the frequency of one (usually the dominant) allele and $q$ is the frequency of the other (usually recessive) allele of the gene.

**Specification Reference 3.7.2**

# 1. The Hardy-Weinberg Principle

*A little bit of maths now... but I promise it's not too bad. Basically, you can use two fairly simple equations to work out allele, genotype and phenotype frequencies for a whole population — which is more useful than it sounds.*

## Gene pools and other terms

You need to get to grips with some key terms before you start playing around with equations and numbers:

- A **species** is defined as a group of similar organisms that can reproduce to give fertile offspring.
- A **population** is a group of organisms of the same species living in a particular area at a particular time — so they have the potential to interbreed. Species can exist as one or more populations, e.g. there are populations of the American black bear (*Ursus americanus*) in parts of America and in parts of Canada.
- The **gene pool** is the complete range of alleles present in a population. How often an allele occurs in a population is called the **allele frequency**. It's usually given as a percentage of the total population, e.g. 35%, or a decimal, e.g. 0.35.

## What is the Hardy-Weinberg principle?

The Hardy-Weinberg principle is a mathematical model that predicts the frequencies of alleles in a population won't change from one generation to the next. But this prediction is only true under certain conditions:

- It has to be a large population where there's no immigration, emigration, mutations or natural selection (see page 163).
- There needs to be random mating — all possible genotypes can breed with all others.

The Hardy-Weinberg equations (see next page) are based on this principle. They can be used to estimate the frequency of particular alleles, genotypes and phenotypes within populations.

The Hardy-Weinberg equations can also be used to test whether or not the Hardy-Weinberg principle applies to particular alleles in particular populations, i.e. to test whether selection or any other factors are influencing allele frequencies. If frequencies do change between generations in a large population then there's an influence of some kind (see pages 161-162).

## The Hardy-Weinberg equations

There are two Hardy-Weinberg equations you need to be able to use — one is used for working out allele frequency and the other one is usually used when you're dealing with genotype (and phenotype) frequencies. Both were designed to be used in situations where a gene has two alleles.

## Allele frequency

The total frequency of all possible alleles for a characteristic in a certain population is 1.0 (100%). So the frequencies of the individual alleles (e.g. the dominant one and the recessive one) must add up to 1. Here's that idea in an equation:

| $p + q = 1$ | Where...<br>$p$ = the frequency of one allele (usually the dominant one)<br>$q$ = the frequency of the other allele (usually the recessive one) |
|---|---|

**Tip:** If the frequencies for two alleles add up to more than one, they're not alleles for the same gene (characteristic). If they come to less than one, there are more than two alleles for that gene.

## Genotype frequency

The total frequency of all possible genotypes for one characteristic in a certain population is 1.0. So the frequencies of the individual genotypes must add up to 1.0. But remember there are three genotypes — homozygous recessive, homozygous dominant and heterozygous. Here's the second equation:

| $p^2 + 2pq + q^2 = 1$ | Assuming $p$ is dominant, and $q$ is recessive, then:<br>$p^2$ = frequency of homozygous dominant genotype<br>$2pq$ = frequency of heterozygous genotype<br>$q^2$ = frequency of homozygous recessive genotype |
|---|---|

**Tip:** Remember, homozygous dominant means two copies of the dominant allele (e.g. BB), homozygous recessive means two copies of the recessive allele (e.g. bb) and heterozygous means one copy of each allele (e.g. Bb).

These genotype frequencies can then be used to work out phenotype frequencies if you know how genotype relates to phenotype. Remember, genotype is the alleles an organism has (e.g. a plant could have the genotype Rr, where R codes for red flowers, and is dominant over r) and phenotype is the expression of this genotype in the environment (e.g. red flowers).

The Hardy-Weinberg equations also work if the two alleles are codominant (see page 137), or if you don't know which allele is recessive and which is dominant. In these situations, you can just make $p$ represent one allele and $q$ represent the other — it doesn't matter which is which, as long as you're consistent with how you use each letter, your calculations will work out fine.

**Tip:** There are two ways of making the genotype $pq$ — you could get the $p$ allele from the father and the $q$ allele from the mother, or you could get the $q$ allele from the father and the $p$ allele from the mother. So the frequency of the heterozygous genotype is $pq$ plus $pq$, which simplifies to $2pq$. If you get the $p$ allele from both mum and dad you'll get the genotype $p \times p = p^2$. The same is true for the $q$ allele.

# Uses of the Hardy-Weinberg principle

The best way to understand how to use the principle and the equations is to follow through some examples.

## Predicting allele frequency

You can figure out the frequency of one allele if you know the frequency of the other:

**Example — Maths Skills**

- A species of plant has either red or white flowers. Allele R (red) is dominant and allele r (white) is recessive. If the frequency of R is 0.4 in Population W, what is the frequency of r?

You know the frequency of one allele and just need to find the frequency of the other using $p + q = 1$ (where $p$ = dominant allele, R, and $q$ = recessive allele, r). So: $p + q = 1$

$$R + r = 1$$
$$0.4 + r = 1$$
$$r = 1 - 0.4 = 0.6$$

So the frequency of the r allele in Population W is **0.6**.

**Exam Tip**
Make sure you learn both equations and when to use them — you won't be given the equations in your exam.

You can also figure out allele frequencies if you're given information about genotype (or phenotype) frequencies:

**Tip:** It's a good idea to write down which letter represents which allele so you don't get confused halfway though your calculation.

**Exam Tip**
You may be given allele or genotype frequencies as percentages in the exam. To turn a percentage into a decimal just divide it by 100. For example, 90% as a decimal is $90 \div 100 = 0.9$.

**Example — Maths Skills**

- There are two alleles for flower colour (R and r), so there are three possible genotypes — RR, Rr and rr. If the frequency of genotype RR is 0.56 in Population X, what is the allele frequency of r?
- You know that RR is the homozygous dominant genotype, so RR = $p^2$. You also know that the allele frequency for R = $p$,
  so: $p^2 = 0.56$
  $p = \sqrt{0.56} = 0.75$, so R = 0.75

You also know that $p + q = 1$, where $p$ = the dominant allele, R, and $q$ = the recessive allele, r. So: $p + q = 1$

R + r = 1

0.75 + r = 1

r = 1 – 0.75 = 0.25

So the frequency of the r allele (white) in Population X is **0.25**.

## Predicting genotype frequency

Here you're after genotype, so it's $p^2$, $q^2$ or $2pq$ you need to find:

**Exam Tip**
It's easier than it might seem to decide which equation to use.
If you're given one allele frequency and asked to find the other it's the simple equation.
If you know two out of the three genotype or phenotype frequencies, you can find the other frequency using the big equation. For anything else you'll probably need to use a combination of equations.

**Example — Maths Skills**

- If there are two alleles for flower colour (R and r), there are three possible genotypes — RR, Rr and rr. In Population Y, the frequency of genotype RR is 0.34 and the frequency of genotype Rr is 0.27. Find the frequency of rr in Population Y.
- $p^2 + 2pq + q^2 = 1$, where $p^2$ = homozygous dominant genotype, RR, $2pq$ = heterozygous genotype, Rr, and $q^2$ = homozygous recessive genotype, rr. So: $p^2 + 2pq + q^2 = 1$

RR + Rr + rr = 1

0.34 + 0.27 + rr = 1

rr = 1 – 0.34 – 0.27 = 0.39

So the frequency of the rr genotype in Population Y is **0.39**.

## Predicting phenotype frequency

You need to think about how phenotypes relate to genotypes here:

**Example — Maths Skills**

- If R is dominant and r is recessive, then a plant with a red flower phenotype could have the genotype RR or the genotype Rr. Plants with the genotype rr will have a white flower phenotype.
  In population Z, the frequency of the genotype Rr is 0.23 and the frequency of the genotype rr is 0.42. Find the frequency of the red flower phenotype in population Z.
- The frequency of plants with red flowers in Population Z is equal to the genotype frequencies of RR and Rr added together.

The frequency of genotype RR = $p^2$, the frequency of genotype Rr = $2pq$ and the frequency of the genotype rr = $q^2$. The only flowers with a white phenotype in the population have the genotype rr (as r is recessive), so the frequency of the phenotype red flowers is given by:

$$p^2 + 2pq$$
$$= \text{RR} + \text{Rr}$$
$$\text{RR} + \text{Rr} + \text{rr} = 1$$
$$\text{RR} + \text{Rr} = 1 - \text{rr}$$
$$\text{RR} + \text{Rr} = 1 - 0.42 = 0.58$$

So the frequency of red flowers in Population Z is **0.58**.

**Tip:** The more examples you practise, the more confident you'll be at working out allele, genotype and phenotype frequencies when it comes to your exam.

## Predicting the percentage of a population that has a certain genotype

You're looking at genotype again, so it's ultimately something to do with $p^2$, $q^2$ or $2pq$. But you might have to use a combination of equations to get there.

**Example — Maths Skills**

- The frequency of cystic fibrosis (genotype ff) in the UK is currently approximately 1 birth in 2500. Use this information to estimate the percentage of people in the UK that are cystic fibrosis carriers (Ff).
- To do this you need to find the frequency of the heterozygous genotype Ff, i.e. $2pq$, using both equations. (You can't just use the big one as you only know one of the three genotypes — $q^2$.)

**First calculate $q$:**

Frequency of cystic fibrosis (homozygous recessive, ff) is 1 in 2500

$$\text{ff} = q^2 = \frac{1}{2500} = 0.0004. \text{ So } q = \sqrt{0.0004} = 0.02$$

**Next calculate $p$:**

Use $p + q = 1$, rearranged: $p = 1 - q = 1 - 0.02 = 0.98$

**Then calculate $2pq$:**

$2pq = 2 \times p \times q = 2 \times 0.98 \times 0.02 = 0.039$

The frequency of genotype Ff is 0.039, so the percentage of the UK population that are carriers is 0.039 × 100 = **3.9%**.

## Showing if any external factors are affecting allele frequency

The Hardy-Weinberg principle predicts that the frequencies of alleles in a population won't change from one generation to the next as long as the population is large, there's no immigration, emigration, mutations or natural selection, and mating is totally random.

So if you use the Hardy-Weinberg equations to discover that allele frequency has changed from one generation to the next, then the Hardy-Weinberg principle doesn't apply to that population. This means that one (or more) of the factors listed above must be affecting allele frequency. For example, immigration might have occurred.

**Tip:** The effect of natural selection on allele frequency is covered in more depth on pages 163-165.

**Example — Maths Skills**

- If the frequency of cystic fibrosis is measured 50 years later it might be found to be 1 birth in 4500. Use this information to decide if the Hardy-Weinberg principle applies to this population.

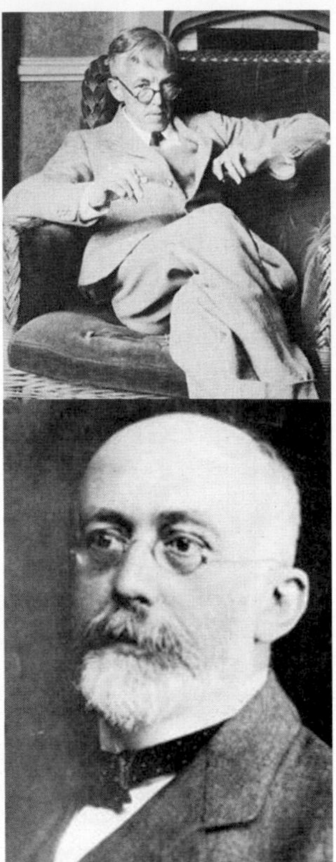

***Figure 1:*** *G H Hardy (top) and Wilhelm Weinberg (bottom) actually came up with the ideas behind the Hardy-Weinberg principle independently from one another.*

**Tip:** You don't always need to use all of the equation. You can just use the parts you want to find out, e.g. you know $p$ and $q$ and need to find the frequency of the heterozygous genotype, so just do $2pq$.

- Start by estimating the frequency of the recessive allele (f) in the population, i.e. $q$.

  **To calculate $q$:**

  Frequency of cystic fibrosis (homozygous recessive, ff) is 1 in 4500

  $$ff = q^2 = \frac{1}{4500} = 0.00022$$

  $$\text{So, } q = \sqrt{0.00022} = 0.01$$

The frequency of the recessive allele is now 0.01, compared to 0.02 currently (see previous page). As the frequency of the allele has changed between generations the Hardy-Weinberg principle doesn't apply.

## Practice Questions — Application

Q1 In a human population, the allele frequency for the recessive albino allele is measured over generations as shown in the bar chart below.

a) Calculate the frequency of the pigmented (non-albino) allele in generation 1.

b) Calculate the frequency of the heterozygous genotype in generation 1.

c) Does the Hardy-Weinberg principle apply to this population? Explain your answer.

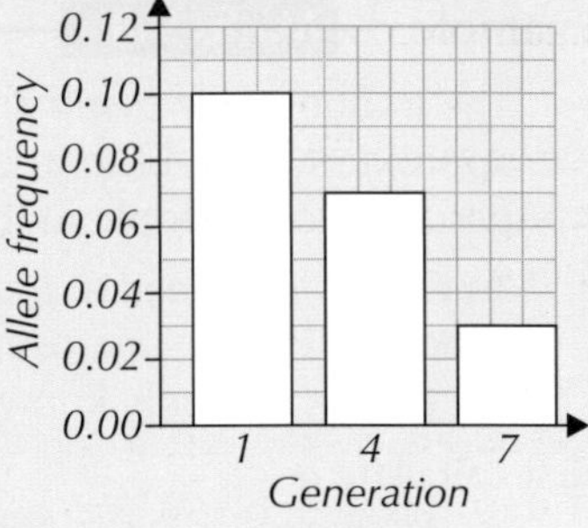


Q2 Sickle cell anaemia is caused by a mutation to a single gene. People with sickle cell anaemia are homozygous for the sickle-cell allele, $H^S$. The sickle cell allele is codominant with the normal allele, $H^N$. Heterozygotes are said to have sickle cell trait. If the frequency of sickle cell anaemia in a population is approximately 1 birth in 500, what is the frequency of sickle cell trait?

Q3 ADA deficiency is an inherited metabolic disorder caused by a recessive allele. The recessive allele frequency in a population is 0.16. What is the frequency of the homozygous dominant genotype in the same population?

Q4 Seed texture in pea plants is controlled by two alleles, the dominant round allele and the recessive wrinkled allele. 31% of a population have wrinkled seeds. What percentage of the population have a heterozygous genotype?

## Practice Questions — Fact Recall

Q1 Define the term population.

Q2 Explain what is meant by the term gene pool.

Q3 Define the term allele frequency.

Q4 Describe the Hardy-Weinberg principle and the conditions under which it is true.

Q5 Write down the two Hardy-Weinberg equations and describe what each component represents.

# 2. Variation and Selection

*The Hardy-Weinberg principle holds true if no external factors affect allele frequency. But that's not always the case in the real world...*

## Variation

Variation is the differences that exist between individuals. Variation within a species (also called 'intraspecific variation') means that individuals in a population can show a wide range of different phenotypes. Variation can be caused by genetic and/or environmental factors.

Although individuals of the same species have the same genes, they have different alleles (versions of genes) — this causes genetic variation within a species. The main source of this genetic variation is mutation, e.g. when changes in the DNA base sequence lead to the production of new alleles — see page 201. But genetic variation is also introduced during meiosis (through the crossing over of chromatids and the independent segregation of chromosomes) and because of the random fertilisation of gametes during sexual reproduction.

Variation within a species can also be caused by differences in the environment, like food, climate, or lifestyle. Most variation within a species is caused by a combination of genetic and environmental factors, but only genetic variation results in evolution.

## Evolution

The frequency of an allele in a population changes over time — this is evolution. Evolution can occur by **genetic drift** (see page 168) or by **natural selection**.

### Natural selection

Organisms face many pressures that affect their chances of surviving, such as predation, disease and competition. These are called **selection pressures**. Selection pressures create a struggle for survival. Because members of the same species have different alleles, there is variation between individuals, meaning that some are better adapted to the selection pressures than others. This means there are differential levels of survival and reproductive success in a population.

Individuals with a phenotype that increases their chance of survival are more likely to survive, reproduce and pass on their genes (including the beneficial alleles that determine their phenotype), than individuals with a different phenotype. This means that a greater proportion of the next generation inherit the beneficial alleles. They, in turn, are more likely to survive, reproduce and pass on their genes. So the frequency of the beneficial alleles in the gene pool increases from generation to generation.

## Types of natural selection

The effect of natural selection on allele frequencies depends on the selection pressures acting on the population. There are three types of natural selection — **stabilising selection**, **directional selection** and **disruptive selection**.

### Stabilising selection

This is where individuals with alleles for characteristics towards the middle of the range are more likely to survive and reproduce. It occurs when the environment isn't changing, and it reduces the range of possible phenotypes.

**Learning Objectives:**

- Know that individuals within a population of a species may show a wide range of variation in phenotype, and be able to explain why in terms of genetic and environmental factors.
- Know that the primary source of genetic variation is mutation, and that meiosis and the random fertilisation of gametes during sexual reproduction produce further genetic variation.
- Understand evolution as a change in allele frequencies within a population.
- Know that predation, disease and competition for the means of survival result in differential survival and reproduction, i.e. natural selection.
- Understand that those organisms with phenotypes providing selective advantages are likely to produce more offspring and pass on their favourable alleles to the next generation.
- Understand the effect of this differential reproductive success on allele frequencies within a gene pool.
- Know the effects of stabilising, directional and disruptive selection.

**Specification Reference 3.7.3**

**Tip:** You learnt about natural selection in Year 1 of your course.

**Tip:** How well-adapted an organism is to survive and reproduce successfully in its environment can be called its 'fitness' — so any alleles that enhance fitness are likely to increase in frequency via natural selection.

**Tip:** The breeding population is just the animals that are surviving, reproducing and passing on their alleles.

**Exam Tip**
Here the data shows phenotype, but in the exam you could get genotype or allele-specific data — the idea is still the same.

**Example**

In any mammal population there's a range of fur length. In a stable climate, having fur at the extremes of this range reduces the chances of surviving as it's harder to maintain the right body temperature, so mammals with very short or very long fur have a selective disadvantage. Mammals with alleles for average fur length are the most likely to survive, reproduce and pass on their alleles. These mammals have a selective advantage, so these alleles for average fur length increase in frequency.

Over time, the proportion of the population with average fur length increases and the range of fur lengths decreases — as shown in Figure 1. In the offspring graph the range of fur lengths has decreased, which results in a narrower graph. The proportion with average length fur has increased, resulting in a taller graph in the average fur length region.

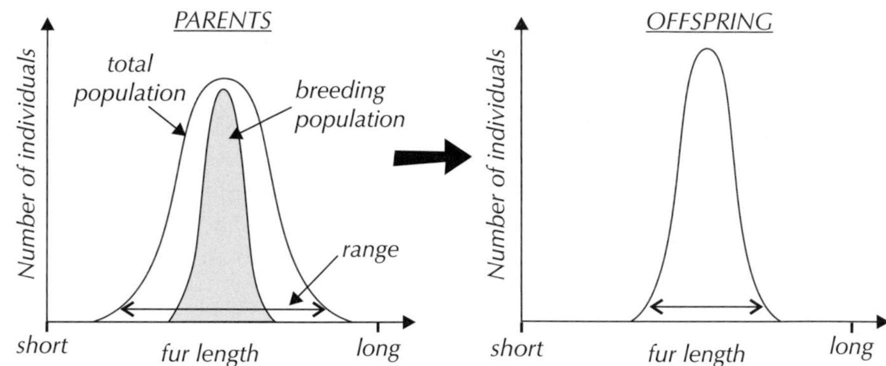


***Figure 1:*** *Graphs that show stabilising selection across generations.*

## Directional selection

This is where individuals with alleles for a single extreme phenotype are more likely to survive and reproduce. This could be in response to an environmental change.

**Tip:** With data that shows stabilising selection, the mean stays in the middle. With data that shows directional selection, the mean moves in one direction or the other.

**Exam Tip**
Here the data is shown as a graph, but you could be given a table of data in your exam.

**Example**

Cheetahs are the fastest animals on land. It's likely that this characteristic was developed through directional selection, as individuals that have alleles for increased speed are more likely to catch prey than slower individuals, meaning they're more likely to survive, reproduce and pass on their alleles.

Over time, the frequency of alleles for high speed increases and the population becomes faster — as shown in Figure 2. In the offspring graph, the average speed (dotted line) has moved towards the extreme, faster end.

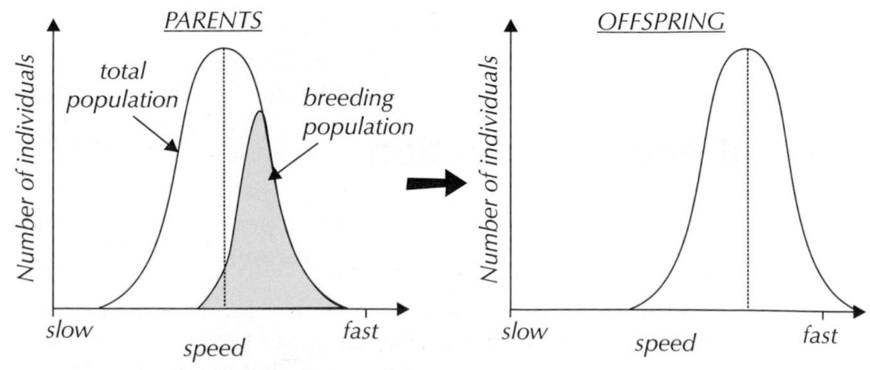


***Figure 2:*** *Graphs that show directional selection across generations.*

## Disruptive selection

This is where individuals with alleles for extreme phenotypes are more likely to survive and reproduce. It's the opposite of stabilising selection because characteristics towards the middle of the range are lost. It occurs when the environment favours more than one phenotype.

**Example**

In bird populations there's a range of beak sizes. Birds with large beaks are specialised to eat large seeds and birds with small beaks are specialised to eat small seeds. In an environment where the majority of seeds are large or small and very few (if any) are medium-sized, birds with medium-sized beaks may have a reduced chance of survival. This is because they are unable to eat either large or small seeds effectively. Birds with large or small beaks are more likely than birds with medium-sized beaks to survive, reproduce and pass on their alleles.

Over time, the alleles for a large beak and a small beak increase in frequency, but the alleles for a medium-sized beak decrease in frequency. The proportion of the population that have either small or large beaks increases — as shown in Figure 3.

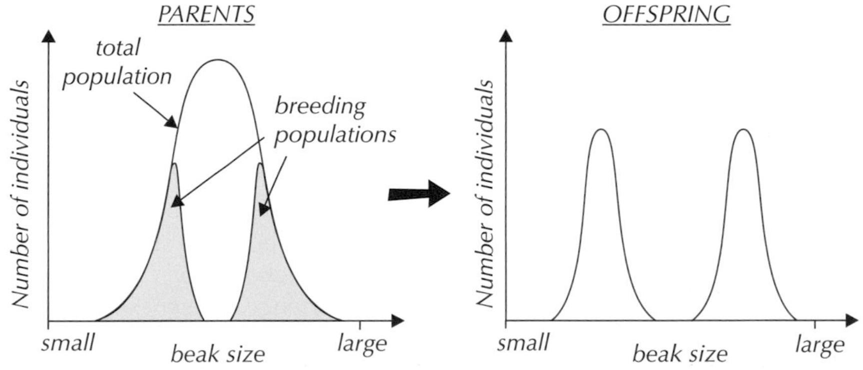


***Figure 3:*** *Graphs that show disruptive selection across generations.*

**Exam Tip**
Make sure you know the differences between the three types of selection. You could be asked to interpret data that shows one of the types of selection and explain why the change has come about.

**Exam Tip**
If you're asked to explain any of the three types of selection, you need to make sure you get in the phrase 'more likely to survive, reproduce and pass on their alleles'.

**Tip:** The mating shown here is assortative (non-random) — the birds with small beaks are more likely to mate with other birds with small beaks than they are with large-beaked birds (and vice versa). That's why you end up with two breeding populations.

## Practice Question — Application

Q1 The graph shows the fur length for a herd of caribou in 1850 and again 100 years later. In 1850 the population were moved from an area in the Arctic to an area much further south.

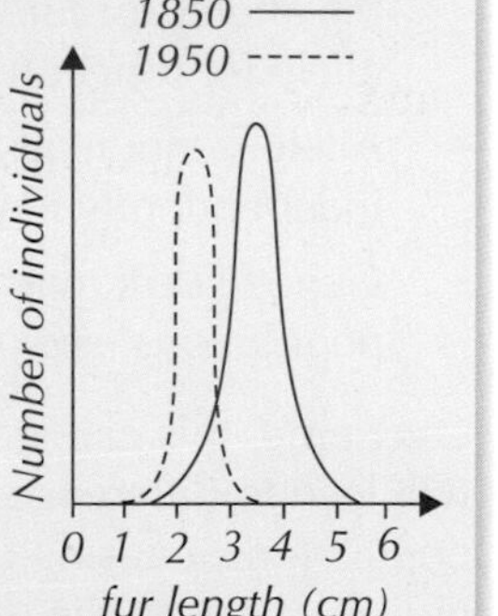


a) Calculate the range of fur lengths for 1950.

b) What kind of selection does the graph show? Explain your answer.

c) Use your knowledge of selection to explain the results.

**Tip:** To help you answer Q1 c), remember the caribou were moved to an area further <u>south</u> than the cold Arctic.

## Practice Questions — Fact Recall

Q1 Give three ways in which genetic variation is caused.

Q2 Explain how competition, predation and disease can alter allele frequencies within a gene pool over time.

Q3 Explain the differences between stabilising and disruptive selection.

# 3. Speciation and Genetic Drift

*Natural selection drives evolution, allowing species to change over time, and new species to evolve. For speciation to occur though, certain conditions need to be met. Populations can also change over time without selection acting at all, via the process of genetic drift.*

**Learning Objectives:**

- Know that reproductive separation of two populations can result in the accumulation of difference in their gene pools.
- Understand that when these genetic differences lead to an inability of members of the populations to interbreed and produce fertile offspring, new species arise from the existing species.
- Understand what is meant by allopatric and sympatric speciation.
- Be able to explain how natural selection and isolation may result in change in the allele and phenotype frequency and lead to the formation of a new species.
- Know that genetic drift causes changes in allele frequency in small populations and be able to explain why genetic drift is important only in small populations.
- Be able to explain how evolutionary change over a long period of time has resulted in a great diversity of species.

**Specification Reference 3.7.3**

## What is speciation?

Speciation is the development of a new species from an existing species. It occurs when populations of the same species become **reproductively isolated** — changes in allele frequency cause changes in phenotype, which mean they can no longer interbreed to produce fertile offspring (see page 158).

Reproductive isolation can occur when a physical barrier, e.g. a flood or an earthquake, divides a population of a species, causing some individuals to become separated from the main population. This is known as geographical isolation. There is no gene flow (transfer of genes) between the two populations, which can lead to **allopatric speciation** (see below).

Alternatively, speciation can also occur when a population becomes reproductively isolated without any physical separation. This is known as **sympatric speciation** (see next page).

**Tip:** A species is a group of individual organisms that can breed together to produce fertile offspring.

## Allopatric speciation

Populations that are geographically separated will experience slightly different conditions. For example, there might be a different climate on each side of the physical barrier. The populations will experience different selection pressures and so different changes in allele frequencies could occur:

- Different alleles will be more advantageous in the different populations, so natural selection occurs. For example, if geographical separation places one population in a colder climate than before, longer fur length will be beneficial. Directional selection (see page 164) will then act on the alleles for fur length in this population, increasing the frequency of the allele for longer fur length.
- Allele frequencies will also change as mutations (see p. 201) will occur independently in each population.
- Genetic drift may also affect the allele frequencies in one or both populations (see page 168).

Over time, this can lead to speciation. The changes in allele frequency will lead to differences accumulating in the gene pools of the separated populations, causing changes in phenotype frequencies. Eventually, individuals from the different populations will have changed so much that they won't be able to breed with one another to produce fertile offspring — they'll have become reproductively isolated. The two groups will have become separate species (see Figure 1 on the next page).

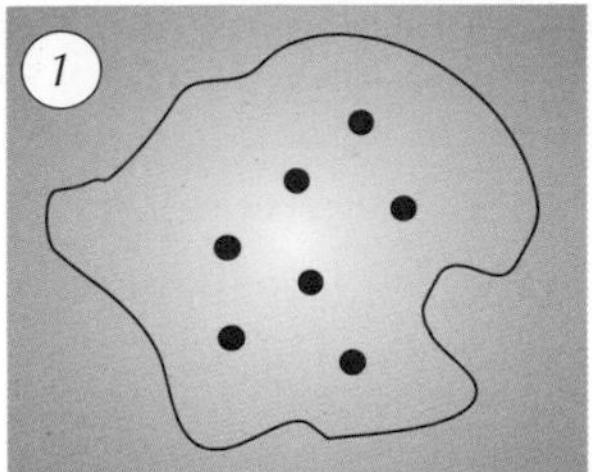


*Population of individuals*
*• = individual organism*

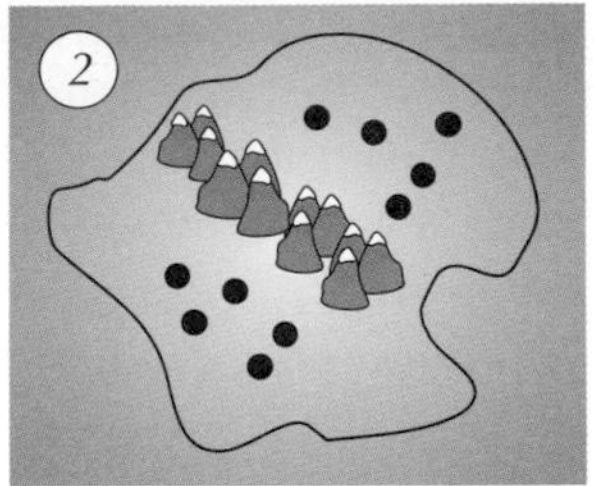


*Physical barriers stop interbreeding between populations.*

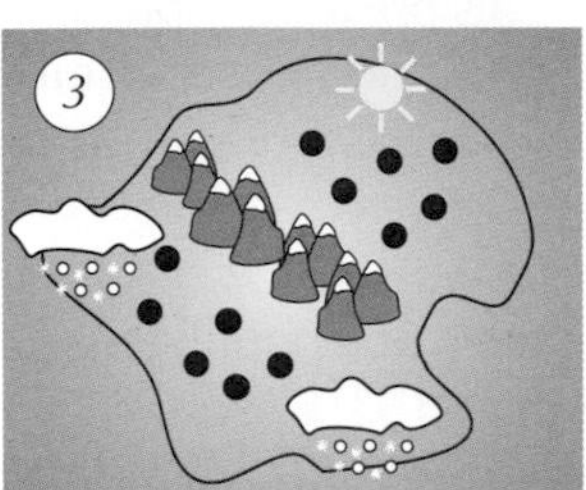


*Populations adapt to new environments.*

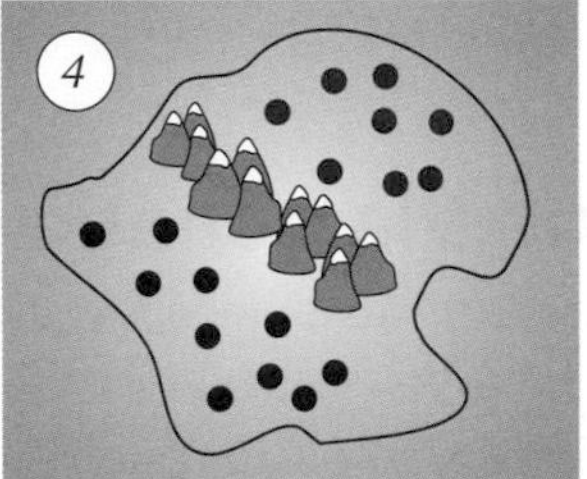


*Differences accumulate in the gene pool leading to development of new species.*

***Figure 1:*** *Diagram showing allopatric speciation.*

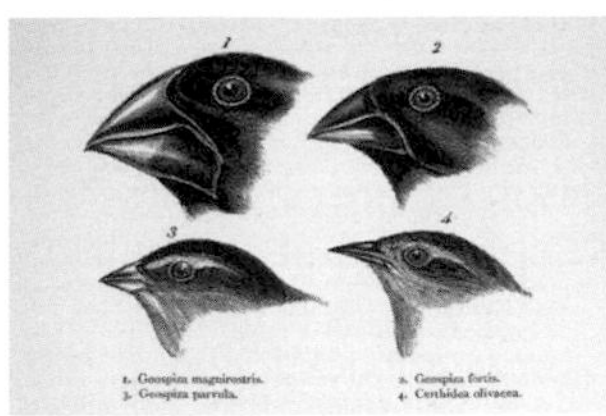

***Figure 2:*** *A drawing by Charles Darwin of four species of finch found in the Galapagos Islands. 'Darwin's finches' are often seen as a classical example of speciation.*

## Sympatric speciation

Sympatric speciation can occur when random mutations within a population prevent individuals that carry the mutation from breeding with other members of the population that don't carry the mutation. It doesn't involve geographical isolation.

It's generally thought that sympatric speciation is pretty rare, as it's difficult for a section of a population to become completely reproductively isolated from the rest of the population without being geographically isolated too (as is the case with allopatric speciation).

**Example**

Most eukaryotic organisms are diploid — they have two sets of homologous (matched) chromosomes in their cells. Sometimes, mutations can occur that increase the number of chromosomes. This is known as polyploidy. Individuals with different numbers of chromosomes can't reproduce sexually to give fertile offspring — so if a polyploid organism emerges in a diploid population, the polyploid organism will be reproductively isolated from the diploid organisms. If the polyploid organism then reproduces asexually, a new species could develop. Polyploidy can only lead to speciation if it doesn't prove fatal to the organism and more polyploid organisms can be produced. It's more common in plants than animals.

**Exam Tip**
Make sure you're clear on the difference between sympatric and allopatric speciation, and can remember which is which. If it helps, you could think of **S**ympatric speciation happening in the **S**ame place, and **A**llopatric speciation occurring in populations that are **A**way from each other.

**Tip:** Polyploidy can be a mechanism of reproductive isolation.

## Mechanisms of reproductive isolation

Reproductive isolation occurs because changes in alleles, genotypes, and phenotypes prevent individuals with these changes from successfully breeding with individuals without them. These changes include:

**Tip:** Reproductive isolation is necessary for sympatric or allopatric speciation to take place.

- Seasonal changes — individuals develop different flowering or mating seasons, or become sexually active at different times of the year. This means that they can't breed together, as they aren't reproductively active at the same time.
- Mechanical changes — changes in the size, shape or function of genitalia can prevent successful mating, preventing individuals from breeding.
- Behavioural changes — a group of individuals may, for example, develop courtship rituals that aren't attractive to the rest of the species, such as a change in song for birds. This prevents individuals from breeding with each other, even if they could do so successfully.

**Tip:** Don't confuse geographical isolation with reproductive isolation. Populations that are geographically isolated are physically separated, but may still be able to reproduce if brought back together. Geographical isolation can lead to reproductive isolation if natural selection significantly changes the allele frequencies in the two separated populations.

**Tip:** All sorts of behavioural changes can cause reproductive isolation — e.g. different groups may develop different preferences about where they breed, which could prevent them from breeding with each other.

## Evolution via genetic drift

Selection pressures can change the allele frequencies of a population over time. This is evolution by natural selection (see page 163).

Evolution also occurs due to genetic drift — this just means that instead of environmental factors affecting which individuals survive, breed and pass on their alleles, chance dictates which alleles are passed on. For this reason, genetic drift is sometimes called random drift.

Here's how it works:

- Individuals within a population show variation in their genotypes (e.g. A and B, see Figure 3).
- By chance, the allele for one genotype (B) is passed on to more offspring than the others. So the number of individuals with the allele increases.
- If by chance the same allele is passed on more often again and again, it can lead to evolution as the allele becomes more common in the population.

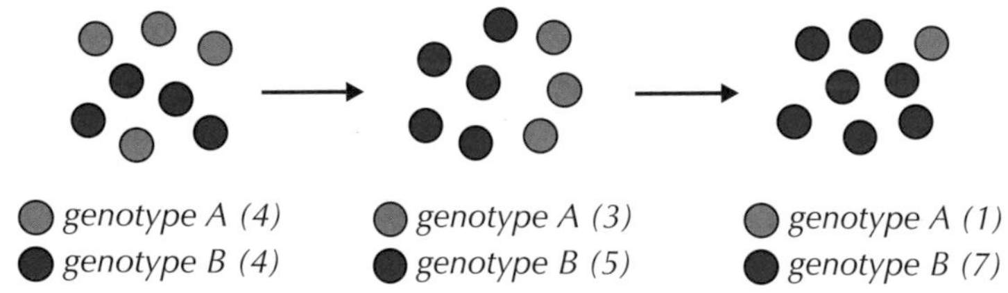


***Figure 3:*** *Diagram to show genetic drift in a population.*

**Exam Tip**
Make sure you know the difference between genetic drift and natural selection. In natural selection, characteristics become more common if they increase an organism's likelihood of survival. In genetic drift, they become more common by chance.

Genetic drift can lead to differences in allele frequency between two isolated populations. If enough differences in allele frequency build up over time, this could eventually lead to reproductive isolation and speciation.

### Genetic drift and population size

Natural selection and genetic drift work alongside each other to drive evolution, but one process can drive evolution more than the other depending on the population size. Evolution by genetic drift usually has a greater effect in smaller populations where chance has a greater influence. In larger populations any chance factors tend to even out across the whole population.

**Tip:** Genetic drift tends to cause the genetic diversity of a population to decrease. Lack of genetic diversity may make species less able to adapt to future changes in their environment, so genetic drift can be a problem for small populations.

**Example — The evolution of human blood groups**

Different Native American tribes show different blood group frequencies. For example, Blackfoot Indians are mainly group A, but Navajos are mainly group O.

Blood group doesn't affect survival or reproduction, so the differences aren't due to evolution by natural selection. In the past, human populations were much smaller and were often found in isolated groups. The blood group differences were due to evolution by genetic drift — by chance the allele for blood group O was passed on more often in the Navajo tribe, so over time this allele and blood group became more common.

**Tip:** The fact that genetic drift has affected these populations doesn't mean that speciation is taking place — blood group doesn't affect survival or cause reproductive isolation.

**Tip:** The Hardy-Weinberg principle doesn't tend to apply to populations affected by genetic drift. This is because genetic drift only really affects small populations and the Hardy-Weinberg principle only applies to large populations (see page 158).

## Speciation and diversity

The diversity of life on Earth today is the result of speciation and evolutionary change over millions of years.

To start with there was one population of organisms. The population was divided and the new populations evolved into separate species. The new species were then divided again and the new populations evolved into more separate species. This process has been repeated over a long period of time to create millions of new species (see Figure 4).

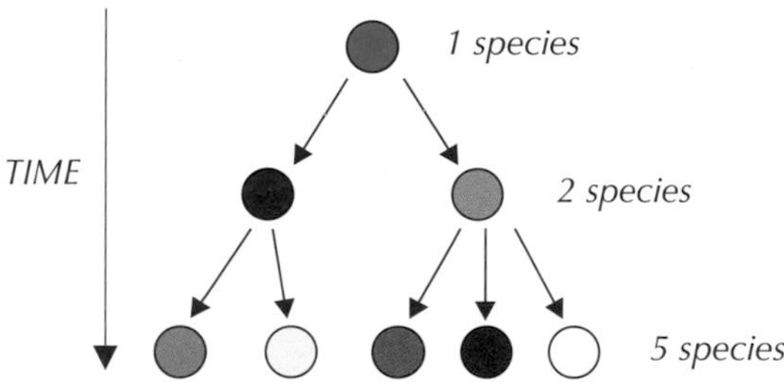


*Figure 4: Over time, new species have evolved from existing ones to give the diversity of life we see on Earth today. This process can be shown in diagrams as an 'evolutionary tree'.*

*Figure 5: One of the earliest forms of life is thought to be a kind of bacteria that creates underwater towers of rock. These kinds of bacteria still exist today.*

### Practice Questions — Application

Q1 Darwin observed 14 different species of finch on the Galapagos Islands in the Pacific Ocean. Each species of finch is unique to a single island and each island has a unique food source on it. Although the finches are all similar, the size and shapes of their beaks differ. Use your knowledge of selection and speciation to explain how these different species came about.

Q2 The Mauritian pink pigeon is an endangered species. In the mid-1980s its numbers fell to less than 20, and a captive breeding programme was initiated. Why might the scientists running the programme have been concerned about the effects of genetic drift?

**Tip:** In a captive breeding program, organisms living in a safe environment, such as a zoo, are paired up and allowed to breed. The young may then be released back into the wild to increase the population size.

Q3 In the year 1990, a valley was flooded to create a reservoir. This also created an island, on which a small population of a rodent species was trapped. Unlike on the mainland, the rodent population on the island had no mammalian predators.
A group of scientists studied the island population in comparison to a larger population of the species on the mainland nearby. Every five years they collected data on the rodents' eye colour, size and behaviour.

a) The rodent species has two eye colour phenotypes: black and pink, which are not thought to affect their probability of survival or chances of breeding. The scientists' observations of eye colour in the two populations are shown below:

| year | frequency of pink eyes in the population | |
|---|---|---|
| | island | mainland |
| 1990 | 0.15 | 0.15 |
| 1995 | 0.08 | 0.16 |
| 2000 | 0.02 | 0.15 |
| 2005 | 0.00 | 0.14 |
| 2010 | 0.00 | 0.15 |

Suggest an explanation for the observations shown in the table.

b) The scientists found that by the end of 2010, the male rodents on the island were significantly larger than male rodents on the mainland. They observed that larger males were more likely to win in territorial fights with other males, and were more easily seen in the undergrowth.
Suggest why this change in male body size happened on the island but not on the mainland.

c) Over the course of the study, the scientists also observed numerous behavioural changes in the rodents on the island. The scientists have suggested that these behavioural changes may have led to speciation. Describe how they could test whether speciation has occurred.

**Tip:** Take your time looking at any data you're given — make sure you really understand what the table in Q3 is showing you before you attempt to answer the questions.

## Practice Questions — Fact Recall

Q1 What is speciation?

Q2 Give two types of speciation and briefly describe each one.

Q3 Explain how behavioural changes may result in reproductive isolation.

Q4 Explain how evolution has led to the diversity of life on Earth.

## Section Summary

Make sure you know...

- That a species is a group of organisms that can breed together to produce fertile offspring.
- That a population is a group of organisms of the same species occupying a particular space at a particular time that can potentially interbreed.
- That species exist as one or more populations and that the full range of alleles in a population is its gene pool.
- That how often an allele occurs in a population is called allele frequency, which can be given as a percentage or as a decimal.
- That the Hardy-Weinberg principle is a mathematical model that predicts that allele frequencies will not change from generation to generation, so long as it's a large population where there's no immigration, emigration, mutations or natural selection, and mating is totally random.
- The Hardy-Weinberg equations $p + q = 1$ and $p^2 + 2pq + q^2 = 1$, where $p$ is the frequency of one (usually dominant) allele, $q$ is the frequency of the other (usually recessive) allele, $p^2$ and $q^2$ are the frequencies of the two homozygous genotypes and $2pq$ is the frequency of the heterozygous genotype.
- How to use the Hardy-Weinberg equations and any data you are given to calculate allele, genotype and phenotype frequencies.
- That individuals within a population of a species show variation in phenotype due to genetic and environmental factors.
- That the main source of genetic variation is mutation, and that meiosis and the random fertilisation of gametes during sexual reproduction produce further genetic variation.
- That evolution is a change in allele frequencies in a population over time.
- That predation, disease, and competition create a struggle for survival, which results in differential survival and reproduction within populations due to natural selection — i.e. individuals with phenotypes that make them more likely to survive and reproduce are more likely to pass on their beneficial alleles to the next generation.
- That this differential reproductive success can cause a change in allele frequency within a gene pool (i.e. the frequency of beneficial alleles increases).
- That stabilising selection is where individuals in a population with alleles for characteristics towards the middle of the range are more likely to survive, reproduce and pass on their alleles.
- That directional selection is where individuals in a population with alleles for a phenotype at one extreme of the range are more likely to survive, reproduce and pass on their alleles.
- That disruptive selection is where individuals in a population with alleles for extreme phenotypes at either end of the range are more likely to survive, reproduce and pass on their alleles than individuals with alleles for phenotypes in the middle of the range.
- That speciation occurs when changes in allele frequencies in different populations of a species cause changes in phenotype that mean they can no longer interbreed to produce fertile offspring, and that this is called reproductive isolation.
- That allopatric speciation occurs when populations of the same species are geographically isolated and differences in the gene pools develop that can eventually lead to reproductive isolation.
- That sympatric speciation occurs when a random mutation causes reproductive isolation without geographic isolation.
- That genetic drift occurs when chance (rather than natural selection) leads to a change in allele frequencies in a population over time.
- That genetic drift is likely to have a greater affect in small populations rather than large populations because in large populations chance factors tend to even out across the whole population.
- That evolution and speciation over millions of years has led to the diversity of species on Earth today.

# Exam-style Questions

**1** Read the following passage:

Lake Apoyo in Nicaragua, Central America, is home to populations of many different species, including *Amphilophus citrinellus* and *Amphilophus zaliosus* — two species of fish. *A. zaliosus* is adapted to live in open water columns in the lake, whereas *A. citrinellus* lives on the lake bed. In each species, there is some variation in the phenotypes of individuals.

Lake Apoyo is an isolated lake, and is the only place in the world where *A. zaliosus* is found. It is thought that the *A. zaliosus* species evolved from the *A. citrinellus* population that originally inhabited the lake, and it has been suggested that disruptive selection may have contributed to the speciation. The two species are reproductively isolated and only tend to mate with fish of the same species.

Use the information above and your own scientific knowledge to answer these questions:

**1.1** Define the term population (line 1).

*(1 mark)*

**1.2** There is some variation in the phenotypes of individuals within both the *A. citrinellus* and the *A. zaliosus* species (lines 4-5). Other than the effect of environmental factors, explain how this variation in phenotypes could be caused.

*(4 marks)*

**1.3** *A. zaliosus* and *A. citrinellus* are reproductively isolated (line 9). Explain what this means and give **one** suggestion of how this may have occurred.

*(3 marks)*

**1.4** It is thought that *A. zaliosus* evolved from *A. citrinellus* (line 7). Name the type of speciation that is likely to have occurred. Explain your answer.

*(2 marks)*

**1.5** It has been suggested that disruptive selection may have contributed to speciation in Lake Apoyo (lines 8-9). Suggest the reasoning behind this.

*(5 marks)*

**2** The Amish population of North America descended from a small group of migrants. They live isolated from the surrounding population, and it is rare for people to migrate into the Amish community. The Amish population has an unusually high incidence of genetic disorders, including a rare form of dwarfism called Ellis van Creveld syndrome, which can lead to health problems and death in childhood.

**2.1** Ellis van Creveld syndrome is caused by a recessive allele (e). In some Amish communities, the frequency of Ellis van Creveld syndrome may be as high as 5 births in every 1000. Use the Hardy-Weinberg equation to calculate the percentage of these communities that are **carriers** of Ellis van Creveld syndrome (genotype Ee). Show your working. Give your answer to **two decimal places**.

*(2 marks)*

**2.2** The frequency of the Ellis van Creveld allele is much higher in some Amish communities than in the general population. What process is likely to have led to the high frequency of this allele? Give a reason for your answer.

*(2 marks)*

# Topic 7 C: Populations in Ecosystems

## 1. Ecosystems

*All living things are found in places where they can cope with the local conditions, like the temperature and the availability of food. It's a fairly simple concept, but you need to be able to use some fancy words to describe it...*

**Learning Objectives:**

- Know that a community and the non-living components of its environment together form an ecosystem.
- Understand that ecosystems can range in size from the very small to the very large.
- Understand that, within a habitat, a species occupies a niche governed by adaptation to both biotic and abiotic conditions.

**Specification Reference 3.7.4**

### What is an ecosystem?

An **ecosystem** is all the organisms living in a **community** (see page 176), plus all the non-living (abiotic) conditions in the area in which they live. Ecosystems include both biotic and abiotic conditions:

- Biotic conditions are the living features of an ecosystem, for example, the presence of predators or food.
- Abiotic conditions are the non-living features of an ecosystem, such as the temperature and soil.

**Example**

In a freshwater ecosystem such as a lake, the biotic conditions would include the fish and the abiotic conditions would include the temperature of the water.

Ecosystems vary in size — they can be small, e.g. a pond, or large, e.g. an entire ocean. The place where an organism lives within an ecosystem is known as its **habitat** — for example, an area of reeds at the edge of a pond. Within a habitat each species has its own niche.

### What is a niche?

A **niche** is the role of a species within its habitat, for example, what it eats, and where and when it feeds. The niche a species occupies includes:

- Its biotic interactions — e.g. the organisms it eats, and those it's eaten by.
- Its abiotic interactions — e.g. the temperature range an organism can live in, the time of day when an organism is active.

Every species has its own unique niche — a niche can only be occupied by one species. It may look like two species are filling the same niche (e.g. they're both eaten by the same species), but there'll be slight differences (e.g. variations in what they eat).

**Tip:** You may know the expression "find your own niche", i.e. find the things you're good at. A species' niche is similar — it's the things a species does better than any other species.

**Example**

- **Common pipistrelle bat**
  This bat lives throughout Britain on farmland, open woodland, hedgerows and urban areas. It feeds by flying and catching insects using echolocation (high-pitched sounds) at a frequency of around 45 kHz.
- **Soprano pipistrelle bat**
  This bat lives in Britain in woodland areas, close to lakes or rivers. It feeds by flying and catching insects using echolocation, at a frequency of 55 kHz.

It may look like both species are filling the same niche (e.g. they both eat insects), but there are slight differences (e.g. they use different frequencies for their echolocation).

***Figure 1:*** *The common (top) and soprano (bottom) bats are similar species but occupy different niches.*

Tip: For more on competition take a look at pages 176-177.

If two species try to occupy the same niche, they will compete with each other. One species will be more successful than the other, until only one of the species is left.

## Adaptations

An **adaptation** is a feature that members of a species have that increases their chance of survival and reproduction. These features can be physiological (processes inside their body), behavioural (the way an organism acts) or anatomical (structural features of their body). For example, giraffes have long necks to help them reach vegetation that's high up. This increases their chance of survival when food is scarce. Organisms with better adaptations are more likely to survive, reproduce and pass on the advantageous alleles that determine these adaptations. This increases the frequency of these alleles in the population, which means the adaptations become more common. This is called **natural selection**.

**Exam Tip**
In questions where you're asked about the effect of natural selection on an adaptation, make sure you mention how survival or reproductive success of the species is affected.

Every species is adapted to use an ecosystem in a way that no other species can — it has its own unique niche. For example, only giant anteaters can break into ant nests and reach the ants. They have claws to rip open the nest, and a long, sticky tongue which can move rapidly in and out of its mouth to pick up the ants. Organisms are adapted to both the abiotic conditions (e.g. how much water is available) and the biotic conditions (e.g. what predators there are) in their ecosystem.

*Figure 2: The webbed paw of a North American river otter is an adaptation to abiotic conditions.*

### Examples

**Adaptations to abiotic conditions**

- Otters have webbed paws (see Figure 2) — this means they can both walk on land and swim effectively. This increases their chance of survival because they can live and hunt both on land and in water.
- Seals have a thick layer of blubber (fat) — this helps to keep them warm in the coldest seas. This increases their chance of survival because they can live in places where food is plentiful.
- Hedgehogs hibernate — they lower their rate of metabolism over winter. This increases their chance of survival because they can conserve energy during the coldest months.

Tip: Metabolism is all the chemical reactions taking place inside an organism.

**Adaptations to biotic conditions**

- Chimpanzees use twigs to fish termites out of termite mounds (see Figure 3). This increases their chance of survival because it gives them access to another source of food.
- Male frogs produce mating calls to attract females — this makes sure they attract a mate of the same species. This increases their chance of reproduction by making successful mating more likely.
- Some bacteria produce antibiotics — these kill other species of bacteria in the same area. This increases their chance of survival because there's less competition for resources.

*Figure 3: The use of twigs by chimpanzees to get termites out of termite holes is an adaptation to biotic conditions.*

### Practice Questions — Application

Q1 The kangaroo rat is found in deserts. Its kidneys produce extremely concentrated urine.

a) Is the production of concentrated urine an adaptation to biotic or abiotic conditions?

b) Suggest how this adaptation helps the kangaroo rat to survive.

Q2 The length of probosci was studied in bees in a mountain habitat in Colorado. The bees were found to be dominated by three species: one with a long proboscis, one with a medium-sized proboscis and one with a short proboscis. The bees use their probosci to get nectar from the corolla of flowers. One such flower is shown below.

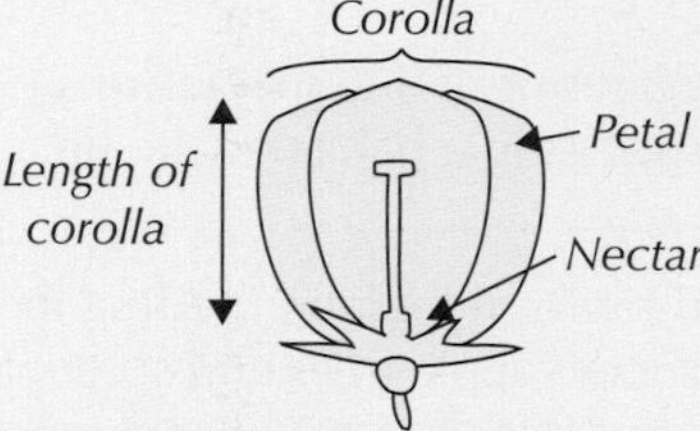


Flowers with a variety of corolla lengths were observed on the mountain.

a) Give one adaptation of the bees to a biotic condition in their habitat.

b) Suggest what would happen if another species of bee with a long proboscis was introduced to the mountain habitat.

Q3 An investigation looked at the length of beaks in two closely related species of bird living in the same habitat. The birds eat seeds of similar plant species. The results are shown below.

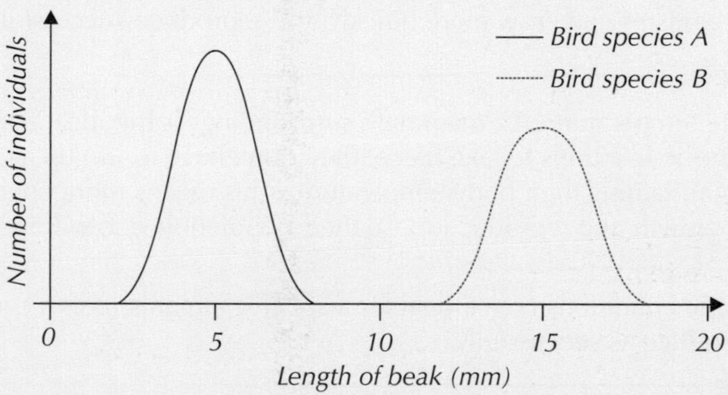


a) Describe the data shown by the graph.

b) Suggest why the two bird species are able to share the same habitat.

**Tip:** Proboscі is the plural of proboscis — a long, straw-like sucking mouth part.

**Tip:** All the petals of a flower form a corolla.

## Practice Questions — Fact Recall

Q1 What is an ecosystem?

Q2 What is a habitat?

Q3 What is a niche?

Q4 Give two examples of:

a) the biotic interactions of a species within its niche,

b) the abiotic interactions of a species within its niche.

Q5 What is an adaptation?

Q6 a) Describe the process in which adaptations become more common in a population.

b) What is the name given to this process?

# 2. Variation in Population Size

**Learning Objectives:**

- Know that populations of different species form a community.
- Know that an ecosystem supports a certain size of population of a species, called the carrying capacity.
- Know that this population size can vary as a result of:
  - the effect of abiotic factors,
  - interactions between organisms: interspecific and intraspecific competition and predation.

**Specification Reference 3.7.4**

*Population sizes change all the time for lots of different reasons. To understand why this happens, first you need to know exactly what a population is...*

## Populations

A **population** is all the organisms of one species in a habitat. Populations of different species in a habitat make up a **community**.

**Example**

All the foxes in a wood form a population. All of the species in the wood, like the foxes, squirrels, crab apple trees and so on, form a community.

**Population size** is the total number of organisms of one species in a habitat. This number changes over time because of the effect of various factors.

The maximum stable population size of a species that an ecosystem can support is called the **carrying capacity**. Carrying capacity varies as a result of both abiotic and biotic factors.

**Exam Tip**
Make sure you know what the terms 'population', 'community' and 'population size' mean.

## Abiotic factors and population size

The population size of any species varies due to abiotic factors, e.g. the amount of light, water or space available, or the temperature or the chemical composition of their surroundings. When abiotic conditions are ideal for a species, organisms can grow more quickly and reproduce successfully.

**Example**

When the temperature of a mammal's surroundings is the ideal temperature for metabolic reactions to take place, they don't have to use up as much energy maintaining their body temperature. This means more energy can be used for growth and reproduction, so their population size will increase.

When abiotic conditions aren't ideal for a species, organisms can't grow as fast or reproduce as successfully.

**Example**

When the temperature of a mammal's surroundings is significantly lower or higher than their optimum body temperature, they have to use a lot of energy to maintain the right body temperature. This means less energy will be available for growth and reproduction, so their population size decreases.

**Tip:** Remember — abiotic factors are the non-living features of the ecosystem.

## Biotic factors and population size

Population size can also vary because of biotic factors. These factors include interspecific competition, intraspecific competition and predation.

**Tip:** Remember — biotic factors are the living features of the ecosystem.

### 1. Interspecific competition

Interspecific competition is when organisms of different species compete with each other for the same resources. This can mean that the resources available to both populations are reduced, e.g. if they share the same source of food, there will be less available to both of them. This means both populations will be limited by a lower amount of food. They'll have less energy for growth and reproduction, so the population sizes will be lower for both species. If two species are competing but one is better adapted to its surroundings than the other, the less well adapted species is likely to be out-competed — it won't be able to exist alongside the better adapted species.

**Example**

Grey squirrels were introduced to the UK. They now compete with the native red squirrels for the same food sources and habitats. As they share the same source of food, there is less available to both of them. So in areas where both red and grey squirrels live, both populations are smaller than they would be if there was only one species there.

Since the introduction of the grey squirrel to the UK, the native red squirrel has disappeared from large areas. The grey squirrel has a better chance of survival because it's larger and can store more fat over winter. It can also eat a wider range of food than the red squirrel.

### 2. Intraspecific competition

Intraspecific competition is when organisms of the same species compete with each other for the same resources. It can cause a cyclical change in population size around the ecosystem's carrying capacity — where the population grows, shrinks, grows again and so on (see Figure 1). This is because the population of a species increases when resources are plentiful. As the population increases, there'll be more organisms competing for the same amount of space and food. Eventually, these resources become limiting. If the population grows beyond the carrying capacity, there won't be enough resources for all the organisms and the population will begin to decline. A smaller population then means that there's less competition for space and food, which is better for growth and reproduction — so the population starts to grow again. This cyclical pattern then continues...

**Tip:** Don't get inter- and intra-specific competition mixed up. If you're struggling, just remember — int**er** means diff**er**ent species, whereas intr**a** means the s**a**me species.

**Example**

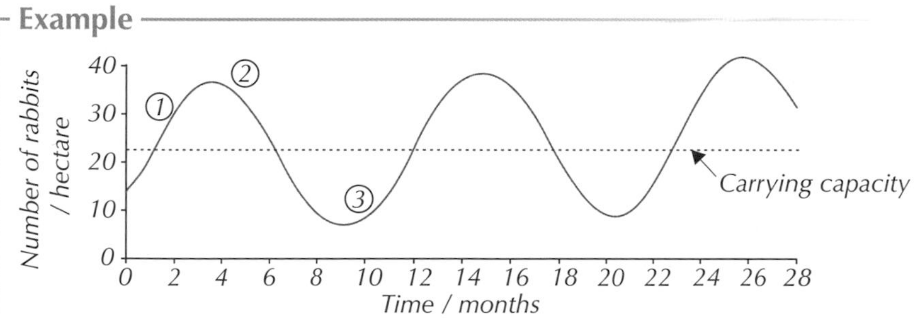

***Figure 1**: Intraspecific competition in a rabbit population.*

1. There were lots of resources available so the population of rabbits grew.
2. The population grew so large that the resources became limiting — the carrying capacity of the ecosystem was exceeded. As there weren't enough resources, the rabbit population fell.
3. A smaller population of rabbits (below the carrying capacity) meant there was less competition, so the population of rabbits began to grow again.

**Tip:** Populations don't always overshoot their carrying capacities like this — a population can grow up to its carrying capacity and remain at a fairly stable size.

### 3. Predation

Predation is where an organism (the predator) kills and eats another organism (the prey), e.g. lions kill and eat (predate on) buffalo. The population sizes of predators and prey are interlinked — as the population of one changes, it causes the other population to change (see Figure 3 on the next page).

As the prey population increases, there's more food for predators, so the predator population grows. As the predator population increases, more prey is eaten so the prey population then begins to fall. This means there's less food for the predators, so their population decreases, and so on.

*Figure 2: Predation of snowshoe hares by the lynx causes the populations of both species to fluctuate over time.*

**Example**

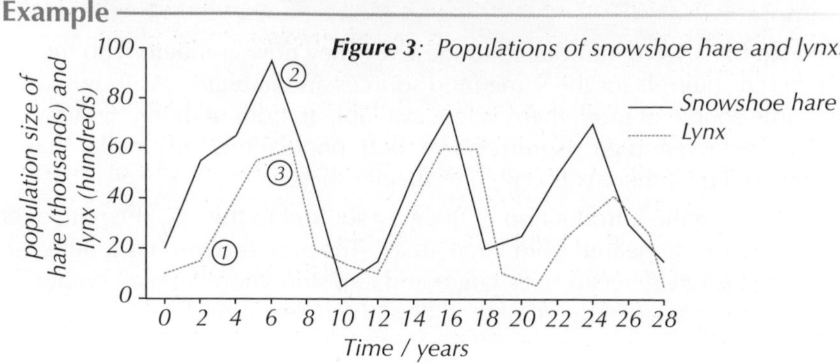


***Figure 3**: Populations of snowshoe hare and lynx.*

1. The lynx population grew after the snowshoe hare population increased. This is because there was more food available for the lynx.
2. Greater numbers of lynx ate lots of snowshoe hares, so the population of hares fell.
3. Reduced snowshoe hare numbers meant there was less food for the lynx, so the population of lynx fell.

Predator-prey relationships are usually more complicated than this though because there are other factors involved, like availability of food for the prey. E.g. it's thought that the population of snowshoe hare initially begins to decline because there's too many of them for the amount of food available. This is then accelerated by predation from the lynx.

## Investigating population growth of bacteria

With enough food and space, the size of a population of microorganisms, e.g. bacteria, will grow at a steady rate. This can be investigated experimentally by growing bacteria in a liquid broth — a liquid containing the nutrients the bacteria need to grow. A liquid broth containing bacteria can be called a **broth culture**.

**Tip:** A broth culture containing lots of bacteria will appear cloudy (turbid) — see Figure 4.

When light is passed through a sample of broth culture, some of it is scattered because bacteria are present — this reduces the amount of light passing through the culture. A machine called a spectrophotometer can measure the amount of light passing through a sample of the culture and produce an **absorbance value**. The more bacteria present in a culture, the less light will pass through to be detected by the spectrophometer, producing a higher absorbance value (see Figure 4). So a broth culture sample with a high absorbance has a high number of bacteria present and vice versa.

**Tip:** Spectrophotometers can also output a value for the percentage of light transmitted. E.g. a sample of clear liquid will have a very high percentage transmission because most of the light will pass through it.

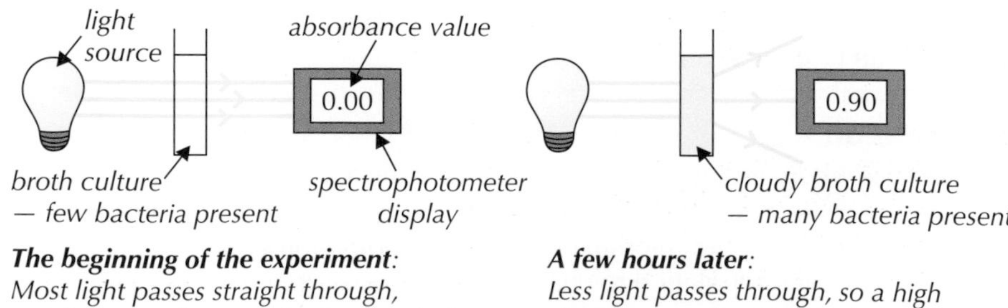


***The beginning of the experiment**: Most light passes straight through, so a low absorbance value is recorded.*

***A few hours later**: Less light passes through, so a high absorbance value is recorded.*

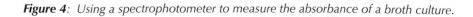

***Figure 4**: Using a spectrophotometer to measure the absorbance of a broth culture.*

If you plot a graph of absorbance against time, you'll get a graph with a shape like the one in Figure 5. This is called an **exponential graph** — it shows the bacteria doubling in number at regular intervals.

As the absorbance is proportional to the number of bacteria in a sample, you can convert the figures and draw a graph showing how the population of bacteria changes over time. However, the number of bacteria present will increase hugely over time, making it hard to draw a scale on your *y*-axis that can cover all the values you measure.

To get round this problem, you can take the **logarithm** of the number of bacteria at each point. These log values will be much smaller than the number of bacteria so they'll be easier to draw a scale for. If you plot the log of the number of bacteria against time, you'll get a straight line (Figure 6). You can use a graph like the one shown in Figure 6 to find the bacterial population at any given time on the *x*-axis.

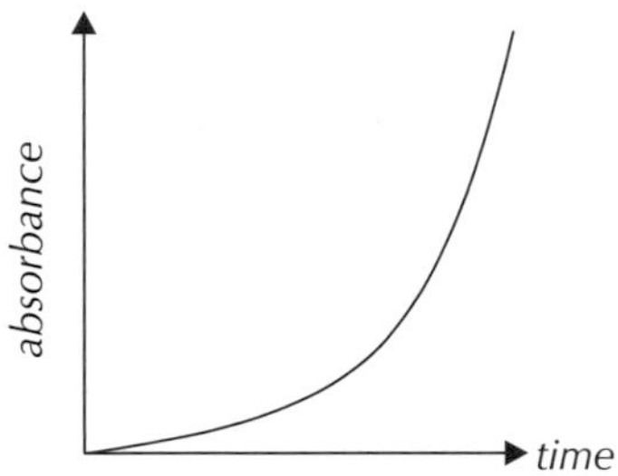


***Figure 5**: An exponential graph showing how absorbance increases with time.*

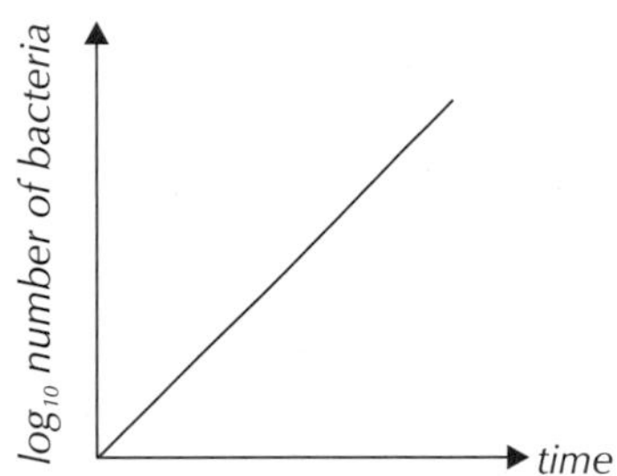


***Figure 6**: A graph showing how a population of bacteria changes over time using a log scale.*

**Tip:** When bacteria are growing exponentially, you can work out how many bacteria are present in a population using the formula: number of cells = initial number of cells $\times 2^n$, where 'n' is the number of divisions. E.g. if 300 bacteria grow exponentially for 7 divisions, you will end up with: $300 \times 2^7$ = 38400 cells (or $3.84 \times 10^4$ cells).

**Tip:** If the experiment continues for long enough, the number of bacteria eventually levels off, then declines as the bacteria used up all the nutrients in the culture.

## Interpreting data values from a logarithmic scale

If you see microbial growth data plotted on a graph with the $\log_{10}$ number of bacteria on the *y*-axis, it's possible to work out how many cells are present in the culture at a given time by finding the antilog (also known as the reverse or inverse log). To do this you need to use the $10^x$ button on your calculator. Simply press this, then enter the $\log_{10}$ value at your chosen time. When you press equals, you'll get the number of cells.

**Example — Maths Skills**

The graph shows part of a growth curve for a bacterial culture.

**Estimate how many bacterial cells are present after 4 hours.**

- You can see from the graph that at 4 hours, the log number of bacterial cells is 4.7.
- To get the actual number of bacterial cells, you need to calculate the antilog using your calculator:

  $10^{4.7}$ = **50118 cells** present at 4 hours.

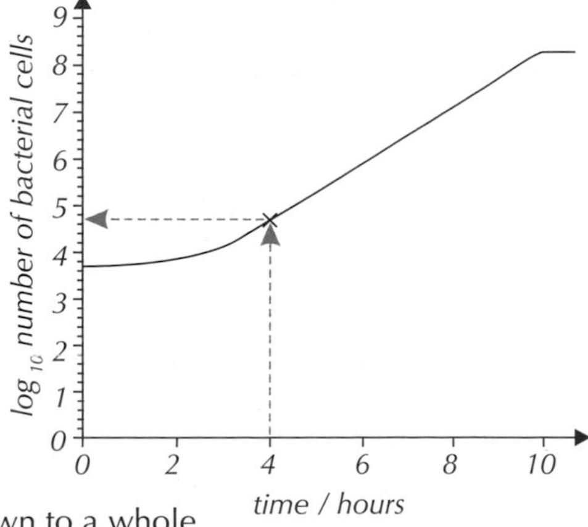


(You should round estimations down to a whole number, because you can't get parts of cells.)

**Tip:** Take a look back at p. 113 for more about log values. Remember, $\log_{10}$ of 10 000 just means 'how many 10s need to be multiplied together to get 10 000?'. The answer is 4 because 10 x 10 x 10 x 10 = 10 000. There's a button for calculating log values on every scientific calculator. Spreadsheets can be used to calculate log values too.

**Tip:** $10^x$ is usually found written above the log button on a calculator (it's a second function of log). But different calculators work differently so make sure you know how to use yours.

Tip: Logarithmic graph paper has one axis with a logarithmic scale — the first 10 divisions on the paper gradually get closer together, until the 10th division when everything resets again. The pattern repeats every 10 divisions:

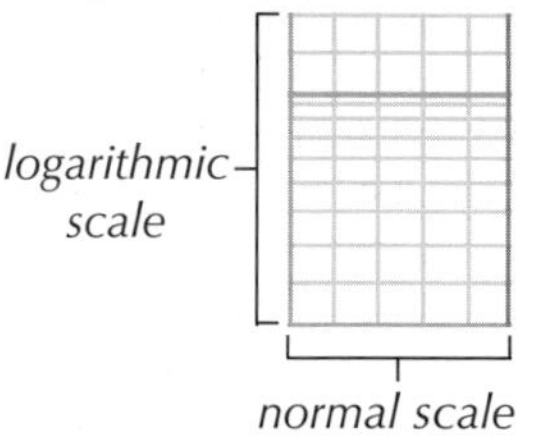


Tip: If you work out the number of cells present at two time points on a growth curve, you can use them to work out the rate of growth during that time period. See p. 11 for more on working out rates from graphs.

Tip: In the exam, if you're given a graph with two y-axes like the one on the right, make sure you read the key carefully so you know which line relates to which axis.

Tip: With 'suggest' questions, like in Q2 on the right, you probably won't have learned the exact answer — you need to use the information you're given and apply your own knowledge to answer the question.

Logarithmic graph paper can also be used to plot microbial data on a logarithmic scale. The paper allows you to plot the actual number of bacteria rather than the $\log_{10}$ values. This means you can read the number of bacteria present in the culture directly off the y-axis. Be careful though — the increments on the y-axis are not evenly spaced.

**Example — Maths Skills**

The graph below shows the growth of a bacterial culture over six hours. **Estimate how many bacteria per cm³ were in the culture after four hours.**

Draw a line up from 4 hours and across to the y-axis. The large square between 100 and 1000 is divided into nine sections, so the scale must be going up by 100 bacteria for each of those sections.

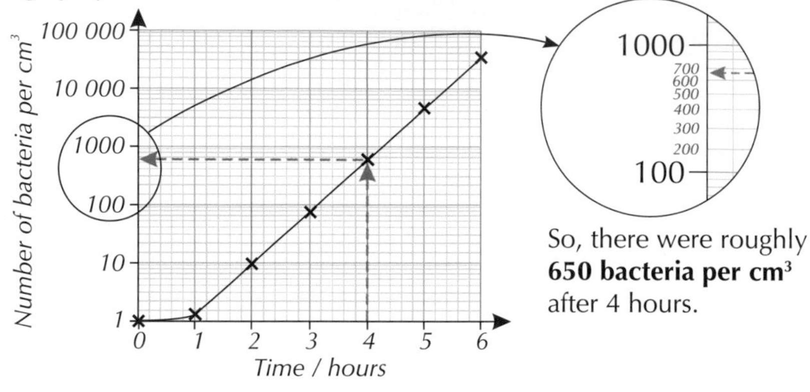


So, there were roughly **650 bacteria per cm³** after 4 hours.

## Practice Questions — Application

A team investigated changes in the size of a population of owls and a population of mice over twenty years. They also monitored changes in temperature. Their results are shown on the graph below.

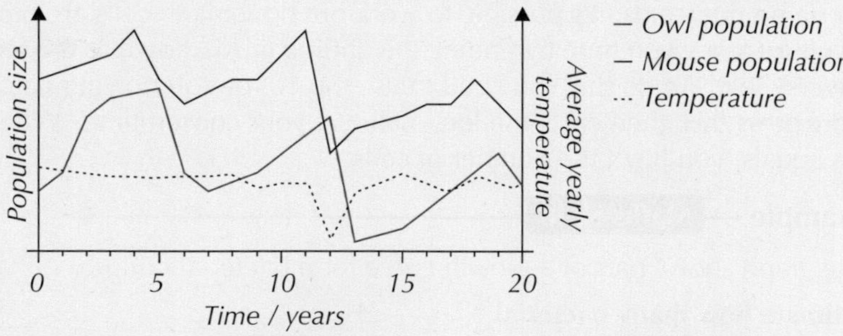


Q1 Give one factor affecting the population of owls which is biotic.

Q2 Describe how the fall in temperature between years 11 and 12 may have affected the mouse population size, and suggest a reason for the change in population size.

Q3 Explain how variation in the mouse population size over the twenty year period could have caused changes in the owl population size.

## Practice Questions — Fact Recall

Q1 What is: a) a population? b) a community?

Q2 Define carrying capacity.

Q3 Define interspecific competition and intraspecific competition.

# 3. Investigating Populations

*There are lots of ways of investigating populations. Whichever method you use, you need to make sure your samples are random, you've carried out a risk assessment and you've thought about the ethics involved.*

**Learning Objectives:**

- Know that the size of a population can be estimated using:
  - randomly placed quadrats, or quadrats along a belt transect, for slow-moving or non-motile organisms,
  - the mark-release-recapture method for motile organisms and know the assumptions made when using the mark-release-recapture method.
- Be able to use given data to calculate the size of a population estimated using the mark-release-recapture method.
- Be able to investigate the effect of a named environmental factor on the distribution of a given species (Required Practical 12).

**Specification Reference 3.7.4**

## Abundance and distribution

Investigating populations of organisms involves looking at the abundance and distribution of species in a particular area.

### Abundance

Abundance is the number of individuals of one species in a particular area (i.e. population size). Abundance can be estimated by simply counting the number of individuals in samples taken. There are other measures of abundance that can be used too:

- Frequency — the number of samples a species is recorded in, e.g. 70% of samples.
- Percentage cover (non-motile or slow-moving species only) — how much of the area you're investigating is covered by a species (see next page).

### Distribution

Distribution is where a particular species is within the area you're investigating.

## Random sampling

Most of the time it would be too time-consuming to measure the abundance (population size) and the distribution of each species present in the entire area you're investigating, so instead you take samples:

1. Choose an area to sample — a small area within the area being investigated.
2. Samples should be random to avoid bias. You can use a random number generator to ensure your samples are random (see below).
3. Use an appropriate technique to take a sample of the population (see pages 182-183).
4. Repeat the process, taking as many samples as possible. This will reduce the likelihood that your results are down to chance (see page 3).
5. The number of individuals for the whole area can then be estimated by taking the mean of the data collected in each sample and multiplying it by the size of the whole area. The percentage cover for the whole area can be estimated by taking the mean of all the samples.

### Random number generators

If you were investigating populations in a field, you could pick random sample sites by dividing the field into a grid and using a random number generator and a random letter generator to select coordinates. This will give you coordinates at random, e.g. B7, E5, etc (see Figure 1). Then you just take your samples from these coordinates.

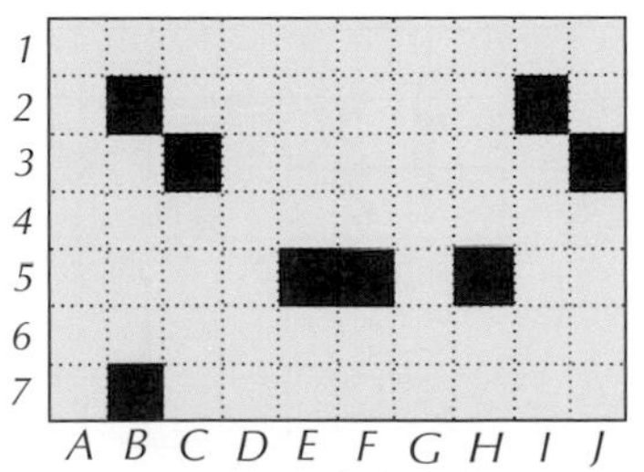


***Figure 1**: Randomly selected squares in a field.*

**Exam Tip**
Make sure you know that the distribution of a species describes how individuals are spread out within an area.

**Tip:** Using tables of random numbers is another way of generating random numbers.

Tip: The point at which the running mean stabilises will be different in each area you study.

## Running means

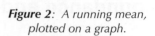

It's important that you take enough samples to give a good estimate. One way of doing this is to take a running mean — this is where you work out the mean of all the data each time you collect a new sample. Once the mean no longer changes by a large amount, you should have data that gives a realistic estimate for the whole area.

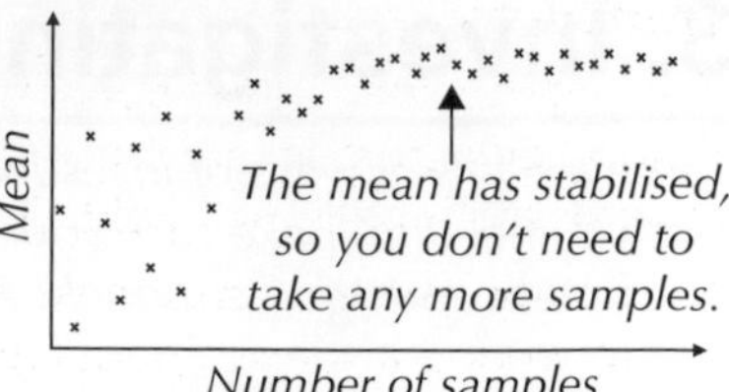
Mean
The mean has stabilised, so you don't need to take any more samples.
Number of samples

***Figure 2**: A running mean, plotted on a graph.*

# Methods for investigating populations

There are lots of different methods for studying populations of organisms, but you need to choose the most suitable one to use — this depends on the type of organism and its habitat. **Quadrats** and **transects** can be used for studying non-motile organisms, e.g. plants and corals, or slow-moving organisms like limpets. On the other hand, if you're studying more motile organisms, like insects, nets and traps are more appropriate.

Tip: Non-motile organisms don't move around — they're fixed to a surface. Non-motile organisms can also be called sessile organisms. Motile organisms are able to move around freely, but they might move really slowly.

## Quadrats

A quadrat is a square frame, which is usually divided into a grid of 100 smaller squares by strings attached across the frame — see Figure 3.

***Figure 3**: A 0.25 m² quadrat.*

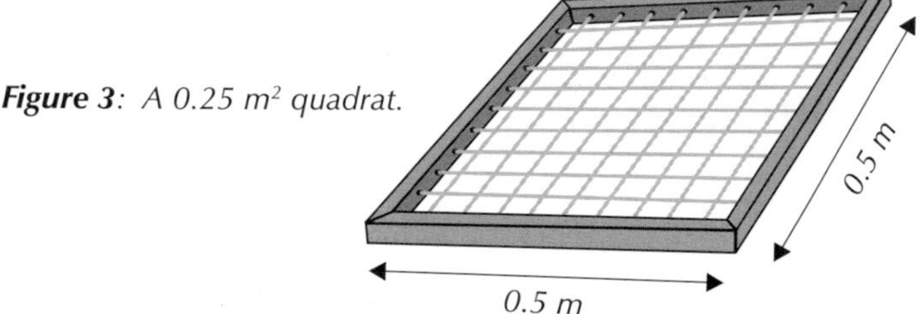
0.5 m
0.5 m

Tip: Putting your quadrat down where you happen to be standing, or even chucking it over your shoulder, doesn't count as taking a random sample. You're best off using a random number generator to select the coordinates to take your samples from (see previous page).

Quadrats are placed on the ground at different points within the area you're investigating. The species frequency (how often a species is found) or the number of individuals of each species is recorded in each quadrat.

The percentage cover of a species can also be measured by counting how much of the quadrat is covered by the species — you count a square if it's more than half-covered (see Figure 5). Percentage cover is a quick way to investigate populations and you don't have to count all the individual organisms.

***Figure 4**: Quadrats can be used to measure the abundance of plant species in a field.*

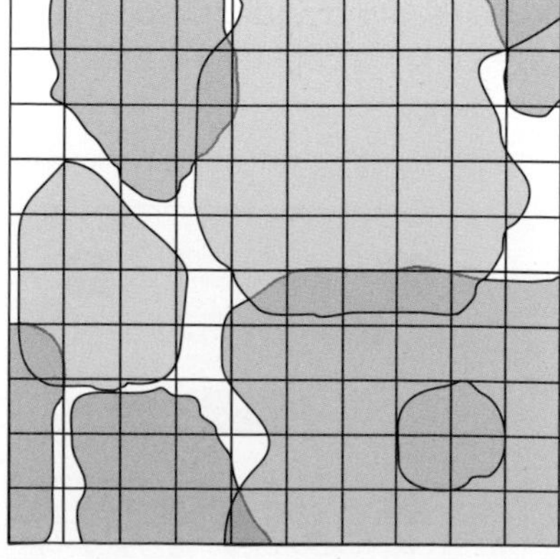

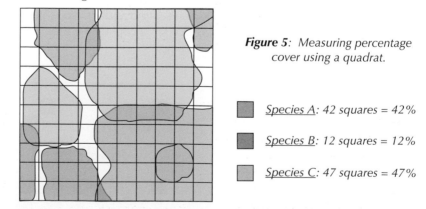

***Figure 5**: Measuring percentage cover using a quadrat.*

*Species A: 42 squares = 42%*

*Species B: 12 squares = 12%*

*Species C: 47 squares = 47%*

Quadrats are useful for quickly investigating areas with plant species that fit within a small quadrat — areas with larger plants and trees need very large quadrats.

## Transects

You can use lines called transects to help find out how organisms are distributed across an area, e.g. how plant species change from a hedge towards the middle of a field. You need to know about:

1. **Belt transects** — quadrats are placed next to each other along the transect to work out species frequency and percentage cover along the transect.
2. **Interrupted belt transects** — instead of investigating the whole transect you can take measurements using a quadrat placed at regular intervals, e.g. every 2 metres. This can make it easier to cover a large distance.

**Tip:** Interrupted belt transects are quicker to carry out than belt transects but give you less information. Which one it's best to do will depend on how much time you have and how long your transect is.

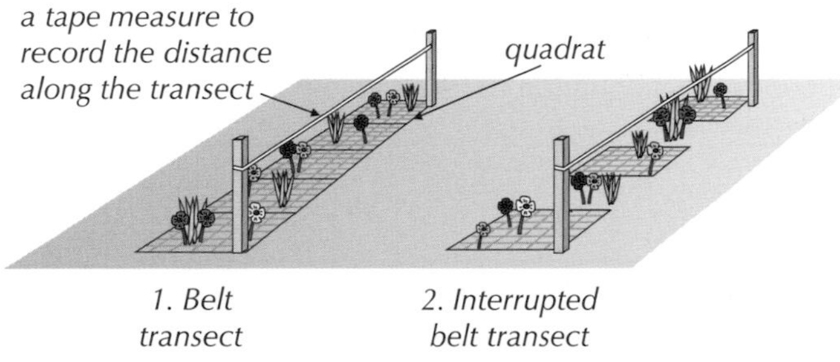


***Figure 6**: Diagram to show two different types of transect.*

**Tip:** Transects can be used in any ecosystem, not just fields. For example, along a beach.

## Capturing motile organisms

If you're investigating motile organisms, you might need to use equipment to capture them. The best method of capturing organisms will depend on what you're studying.

**Examples**

For flying insects, you'd use a sweep net (a net on a pole).

For aquatic animals you'd use a net.

For ground insects you'd use a pitfall trap (a steep-sided container that's sunk into the ground, see Figure 7).

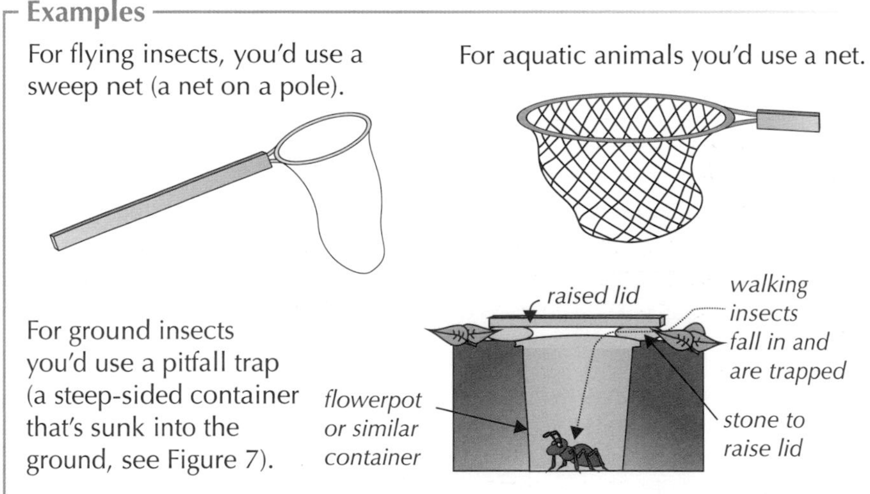


**Tip:** When using equipment to take a sample of organisms in an area, it's important to use the same method each time. For example, with a sweep net you could sweep three times at shoulder height in each area you sample.

***Figure 7**: A pitfall trap with a cover to protect insects from rain and predators.*

## Practice Questions — Application

Q1 A student is investigating the abundance of daisies in a field.

a) She decides to use a quadrat to measure the percentage cover of daisies in the field. Describe how she could do this.

b) Describe how the student could take random samples using a quadrat.

Q2 A scientist is investigating how the abundance of limpets on a rocky shore changes with distance from the sea. Describe a suitable method he could use to investigate this at low tide.

# Mark-release-recapture

Mark-release-recapture is a method used to measure the abundance of more mobile species. Here's how it's done:

1. Capture a sample of a species using an appropriate technique (see previous page) and count them.
2. Mark them in a harmless way, e.g. by putting a spot of paint on them (see Figure 8) or by using an identification tag (see Figure 9).
3. Release them back into their habitat.
4. Wait a week, then take a second sample from the same population.
5. Count how many of the second sample are marked.
6. You can then use this equation to estimate the total population size:

*Figure 8: A turtle being marked with a spot of yellow paint before being released.*

**Exam Tip**
Make sure you know the equation for estimating the total population size — don't rely on being given it in the exam.

$$\text{Total population size} = \frac{\text{Number caught in 1st sample} \times \text{Number caught in 2nd sample}}{\text{Number marked in 2nd sample}}$$

**Example** — Maths Skills

A pitfall trap was used to capture a sample of woodlice in a garden. The first sample contained 15 woodlice. The woodlice were marked and then released. A week later, a second sample of woodlice was collected from the same pitfall trap. There were 23 woodlice in the second sample, and 9 of them were marked.

$$\text{Total population size} = \frac{\text{Number caught in 1st sample} \times \text{Number caught in 2nd sample}}{\text{Number marked in 2nd sample}} = \frac{15 \times 23}{9} = 38.3$$

So the mark-release-recapture method gives an estimated total population size of 38 woodlice.

**Tip:** The answer is rounded down to 38... so that you don't end up with a third of a woodlouse.

The accuracy of the mark-release-recapture method depends on a few assumptions:

- The marked sample has had enough time and opportunity to mix back in with the population.
- The marking hasn't affected the individuals' chances of survival (e.g. by making them more visible to predators), and the marking itself is still visible (e.g. it hasn't rubbed off).
- There are no changes in population size due to births, deaths and migration during the period of the study.

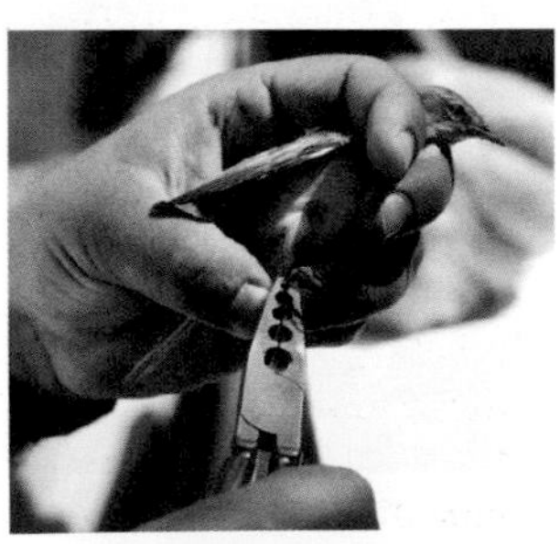

*Figure 9: Birds that are caught can be marked by attaching a metal ring around one of their legs. These rings each have a code on them to identify individual birds. Capture may cause stress to some birds, which can raise ethical issues.*

Some people think that capturing animals for study is unethical as it might cause them unnecessary stress. Also, if animals are put under too much stress during capture it could reduce their chances of survival after release, or influence them to avoid the trap in future. These would interfere with the accuracy of any estimates of population size made using the mark-release-recapture method. To minimise stress investigations should be planned so that organisms are treated carefully, and are kept and handled as little as possible.

## Practice Question — Application

Q1 The mark-release-recapture method was used to estimate the size of a black beetle population in two different locations. On day one, the beetles were marked using white paint and then released. A second sample was captured the following day. The results are shown in the table below.

| Location | Size of first sample | Size of second sample | Number of marked beetles in second sample |
|---|---|---|---|
| A | 19 | 14 | 3 |
| B | 17 | 21 | 6 |

a) Use the data in the table to estimate the total population size of beetles at:

i) location A,

ii) location B.

b) Are the estimates for these locations accurate? Explain your answer.

**Tip:** Remember, the method used to investigate the population of a particular organism depends on the organism itself. For example, using quadrats wouldn't be suitable for assessing bird populations.

# Investigating the effect of an environmental factor on the distribution of a species

The distribution of species often changes within a particular area. For example, you might find more shade-loving plants at the edge of a field where they're sheltered by a tree, than in the centre where they're exposed to full sunlight. To find the effect of an environmental (abiotic) factor on the distribution of a species, you need to carry out a carefully planned investigation.

*Figure 10: Marram grass is commonly found growing on sand dunes near the sea.*

**Example**

You could investigate the effect of soil pH on marram grass in a coastal ecosystem. Here's how you could do it:

REQUIRED PRACTICAL 12

### Method

1. Place a tape measure in a straight line from the shore, heading inland. This will be your transect.
2. Take a 1 m$^2$ quadrat divided into 100 squares (10 by 10).
3. Starting from the shore, place the quadrat next to the tape measure. It doesn't matter where you position the quadrat relative to the tape measure, but you should do it the same way each time.
4. Count the squares containing marram grass and record the result in a table as percentage cover (as shown on the next page). If you have time, take two repeat quadrat samples next to your initial quadrat and take a mean of your results. Alternatively, you could take a mean of the data from your whole class.
5. At each sample point, you should also measure the pH (see next page) and record the results in the table.
6. Repeat the observations every 10 m along the transect.

**Tip:** Always carry out a full risk assessment before doing any practical work. Have a look at the next page for some examples of safety issues that you need to think about before doing this Required Practical.

**Tip:** This is an example of an interrupted belt transect.

Tip: Being 'in the field' is when you're outside in the area which you're sampling. The term can be used for all sorts of locations, not just fields.

Tip: Label your samples carefully so you don't get them mixed up.

Tip: You can use this sort of method to investigate how the distribution of any non-motile species changes as the environmental (abiotic) conditions change.

## Measuring pH

If you have one, you can use a digital pH probe to take pH readings of sand or soil in the field. If you don't have one, you can take a sample of sand/soil to test back at school. When you get back to school, you'll need to sieve it to remove any debris, like twigs and leaves, and place it in a test tube. Add some barium sulfate, distilled water and pH indicator. Shake thoroughly and then leave to it settle. Check the colour against a pH chart and record the result.

## Results

Your results might look like this:

| *Distance from shoreline / m* | *% cover* | *pH* |
|---|---|---|
| *0* | *0* | *8.5* |
| *10* | *11* | *8.4* |
| *20* | *27* | *8.0* |
| *30* | *40* | *7.6* |
| *40* | *58* | *7.5* |
| *50* | *55* | *7.5* |
| *60* | *21* | *7.1* |
| *70* | *15* | *7.0* |
| *80* | *8* | *6.8* |
| *90* | *7* | *6.6* |
| *100* | *0* | *6.5* |

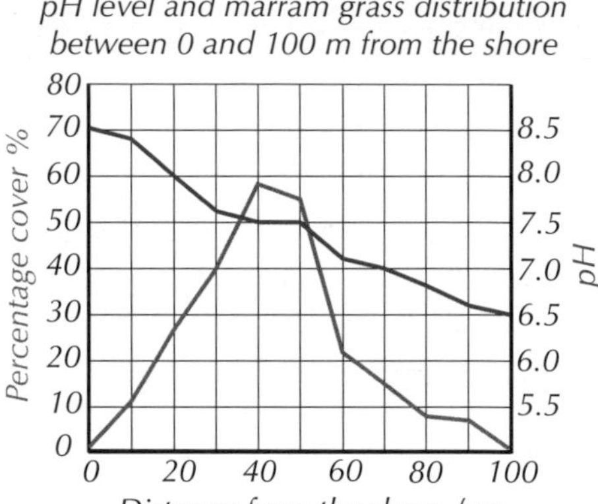


***Figure 11**: Example results showing how soil pH and abundance of marram grass might change with distance from the shore.*

- pH (the blue line on the graph above) decreases as you move inland. This is because near the shore the sand/soil contains lots of shell fragments which are made of calcium carbonate, an alkaline compound. Further inland, the rotting vegetation adds organic matter to the soil, which is more acidic.
- At first, as pH decreases from 8.5 to 7.5, the percentage cover of marram grass (the orange line on the graph above) increases. After pH 7.5, marram grass percentage cover decreases as pH continues to decrease. You can't say pH caused these trends in marram grass cover though — there could be other factors affecting it, including soil moisture content, salinity, and competition from other species.

## Ethical issues

All fieldwork affects the environment where it's carried out, e.g. lots of people walking around may cause soil erosion and marram grass can be killed by people trampling all over it. Investigations should be planned to have the smallest impact possible, e.g. people should restrict where they walk to the area being studied and try to avoid treading on the plants themselves.

## Safety issues

When you're carrying out fieldwork you expose yourself to risks. You need to think about what risks you'll be exposed to, so you can plan ways to reduce the chance of them happening — this is called a risk assessment. For example, in this investigation you should use tide timetables, so you know what the local tide times are — low tide is the best time to work on a beach. Make sure you also wash your hands before eating, especially after handling soil.

Here are some examples of other fieldwork risks and ways to reduce them:

| | |
|---|---|
| Falls and slips | Wear suitable footwear for the terrain, e.g. wellies on wet or boggy ground and sturdy shoes on rough terrain to help stop you slipping. Make sure the study area isn't near any cliffs or on steep ground. |
| Weather | Check the weather forecast beforehand and take precautions, e.g. wear warm or waterproof clothing on cold or wet days and on hot days wear a sun hat and apply sun cream. If the weather is too severe, do the fieldwork another day. |
| Stings and bites | Wear insect repellent or, if you have an allergy, take medication with you. |

***Figure 12:*** *You can minimise the risk of slipping on boggy ground, e.g. by wearing appropriate footwear.*

## Practice Questions — Application

A scientist has been investigating the effect of salt spray from a road adjacent to an inland field. Her results are shown below.

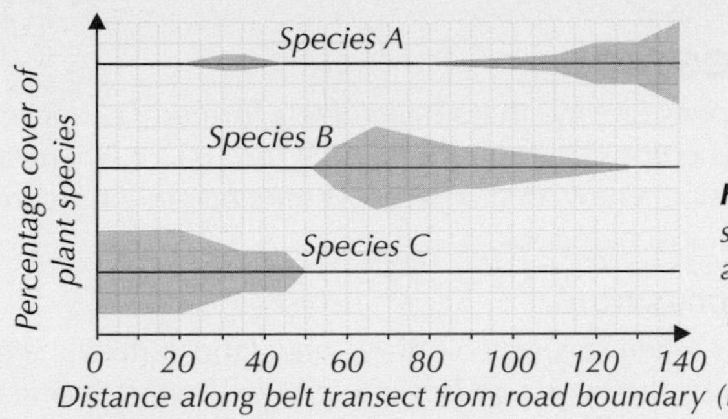


***Figure 13:*** *Kite diagram showing the distribution and abundance of three plant species in a field.*

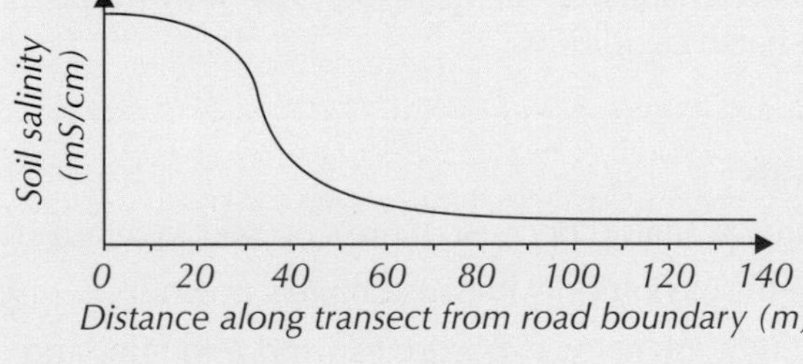


***Figure 14:*** *Graph showing the change in soil salinity in a field.*

Q1 Describe the data shown in the kite diagram and the graph.

Q2 One of the plant species is normally found in coastal areas. Which species is this likely to be, A, B or C? Explain your answer.

Q3 The scientist is unable to prove that salt spray from the road is responsible for the absence of species B between 0 and 20 m from the road using the data shown above. Explain why.

**Tip:** A kite diagram shows the distribution and abundance of organisms along a transect. The thickness of the kite shape shows the abundance — the thicker the kite shape, the more organisms there are.

## Practice Questions — Fact Recall

Q1 What is meant by the terms: a) abundance, b) distribution?

Q2 Name and describe two measures of abundance.

Q3 What is: a) a quadrat, b) a belt transect?

Q4 Give the equation for estimating total population size using data collected by the mark-release-recapture method.

**Learning Objectives:**

- Know that ecosystems are dynamic systems.
- Understand the process of primary succession, from colonisation by pioneer species to climax community.
- Understand that, at each stage in succession, certain species may be recognised which change the environment so that it becomes more suitable for other species with different adaptations.
- Understand that the new species which colonise an environment may change the environment in such a way that it becomes less suitable for the previous species.
- Understand that the changes that organisms produce in their abiotic environment can result in a less hostile environment and change biodiversity.

**Specification Reference 3.7.4**

# 4. Succession

*The plants and animals in an environment gradually change over long periods of time — and the environment itself changes too. This is due to a natural process called succession.*

## What is succession?

Ecosystems are **dynamic** — they're constantly changing. **Succession** is the process by which an ecosystem (see page 173) changes over time. Succession happens in a series of stages. At each stage, the plant and animal communities in an area slowly change the environmental conditions (for example, by making the soil more fertile), making the conditions more suitable for other species with different adaptations. This means that the **biotic conditions** change as the **abiotic conditions** change, causing one community of organisms to be succeeded (replaced) by another. There are two main types of succession — primary succession (see below) and secondary succession (see page 190).

## Primary succession

Primary succession happens on land that's been newly formed or exposed, e.g. where a volcano has erupted to form a new rock surface, or where sea level has dropped, exposing a new area of land. There's no soil or organic material to start with, i.e. just bare rock.

### Pioneer stage of succession

Primary succession starts when species colonise a new land surface. Seeds and spores are blown in by the wind and begin to grow. The first species to colonise the area are called **pioneer species**. The abiotic conditions are hostile (harsh) and only pioneer species can grow because they're specially adapted to cope with the harsh conditions.

**Examples**

**Hostile abiotic conditions**

- There is limited water available because there's no soil to retain water.
- There are few minerals or nutrients because there's no soil.
- There may be high light intensity, exposure to wind and rain, and fluctuating temperatures because the area is directly exposed to the Sun and the elements.

**Pioneer species**

- Marram grass (see p. 185) can grow on sand dunes near the sea because it has deep roots to get water and can tolerate the salty environment.
- Lichens (see Figure 1, next page) are organisms usually made up of a fungus and an alga. They're able to survive in rocky conditions because the fungus secretes acids which erode the rock, releasing minerals.
- Shrubs of the *Calligonum* genus are pioneer species that can grow in areas that experience periodic drought.

Pioneer species change the abiotic conditions — they die and microorganisms decompose the dead organic material (humus), which forms a basic soil. This makes conditions less hostile, e.g. the basic soil helps to retain water, so new organisms with different adaptations can move in and grow.

**Tip:** Remember, biotic conditions are the living features of an ecosystem, e.g. the plant and animal communities. Abiotic conditions are the non-living features, such as light, $CO_2$ and water availability.

The new organisms then die and are decomposed, adding more organic material, making the soil deeper and richer in minerals such as nitrates. Nitrogen-fixing bacteria turn nitrogen from the atmosphere into ammonia, which can then be used by plants (see page 61). This means larger plants like shrubs can start to grow in the deeper soil, which retains even more water and contains more nutrients.

Some new species may change the environment so that it becomes less suitable for the previous species. For example, sand sedge stabilises the sand through the growth of rhizomes (underground stems). This makes the conditions less suitable for marram grass, which needs constant reburial by sand in order to grow healthily.

**Tip:** You learnt about biodiversity in the first year of your course — it's the variety of living organisms in an area.

## Later stages of succession

At each stage, different plants and animals that are better adapted for the improved conditions move in, out-compete the plants and animals that are already there, and become the dominant species in the ecosystem. The dominant species are the ones which cause the most change to the abiotic environment, making it more suitable for other species.

As succession goes on, the ecosystem becomes more complex. New species move in alongside existing species, which means that biodiversity increases. Plants create more habitats for animals, the abiotic conditions become less hostile and the amount of biomass increases.

Eventually these changes result in a **climax community** — the ecosystem is supporting the largest and most complex community of plants and animals it can. It won't change much more — it's in a steady state.

**Tip:** Biomass is the mass of living material in an ecosystem.

**Tip:** A community is all the populations of different species found in a habitat — see page 176.

### Example

1. Bare rock lacks soil, is exposed to strong winds and has periods of drought. Lichens (the pioneer species) are able to survive because they can grow in cracks to avoid the wind, break down rock to release minerals and are adapted to survive periods of drought.

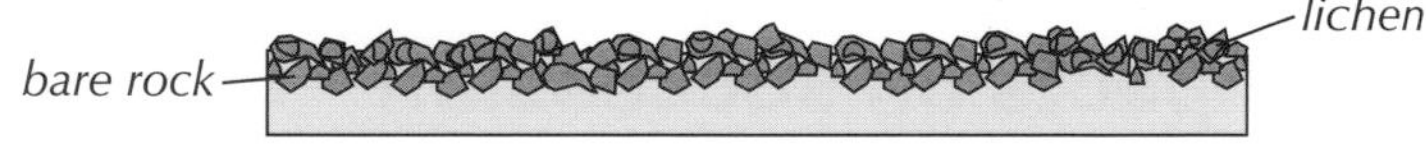


2. The lichens die and are decomposed helping to form a thin soil, which thickens as more organic material is formed. This means other species such as mosses can grow.

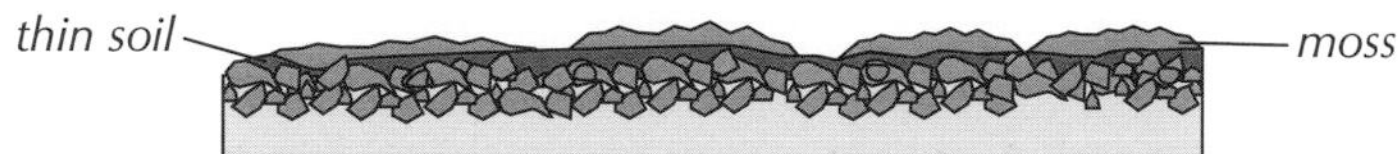


3. Larger plants that need more water can move in as the soil deepens, e.g. grasses and small flowering plants. The soil continues to deepen as the larger plants die and are decomposed.

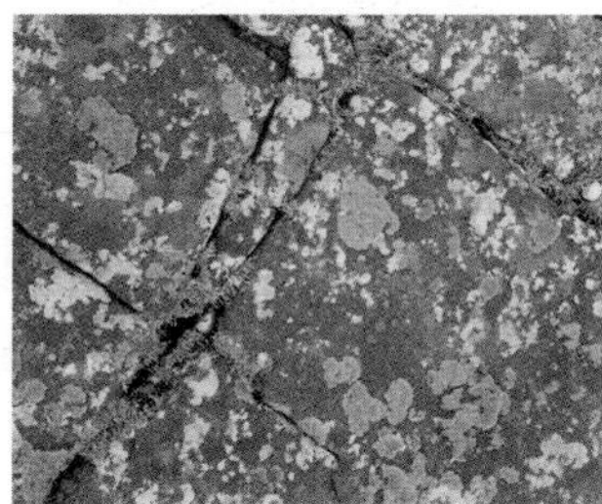

*Figure 1: Lichens (orange and white) have adaptations that allow them to live on bare rock.*

**Tip:** Primary succession also happens on sand dunes, salt marshes and even in lakes.

**Exam Tip**
You don't need to learn the exact details of this example for the exam, but you do need to understand what's going on and why.

**Tip:** Tall plants can reduce the light available to shorter plants and can help stabilise fluctuating temperatures. For example, trees increase air humidity, provide shade and reduce wind, which moderates local temperatures.

4. Shrubs, ferns and small trees begin to grow, out-competing the grasses and smaller plants to become the dominant species. Diversity increases.

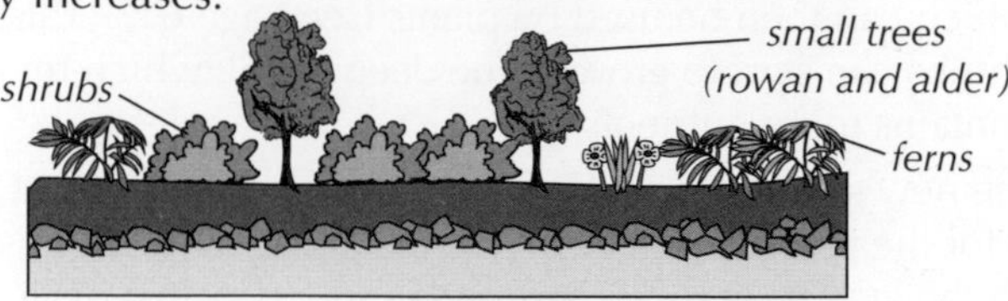


5. Finally, the soil is deep and rich enough in nutrients to support large trees. These become the dominant species, and the climax community is formed.

**Tip:** The main difference between the two types of succession is that soil is present at the start of secondary succession but not in primary succession. Secondary succession therefore tends to reach the climax community more quickly as a result.

## Secondary succession

Secondary succession happens on land that's been cleared of all the plants, but where the soil remains, e.g. after a forest fire or where a forest has been cut down by humans. The established community of species is usually destroyed, but without too much disturbance to the soil. It can occur during any stage (including the climax community) after the pioneer stage.

The process of secondary succession is similar to primary succession, but because there's already a soil layer, secondary succession starts at a later stage — and the pioneer species are larger plants, e.g. shrubs.

## Human impacts on succession

Human activities can prevent succession, stopping a climax community from developing. When succession is stopped artificially like this the climax community is called a plagioclimax.

**Example**

A regularly mown grassy field won't develop shrubs and trees (woody plants), even if the climate of the ecosystem could support them. The growing points of the woody plants are cut off by the lawnmower, so larger plants can't establish themselves.

The longer the interval between mowing, the further succession can progress and the more diversity increases. But with more frequent mowing, succession can't progress and diversity will be lower — only the grasses can survive being mowed. Mowing doesn't just affect plants, it can affect the wider biodiversity of the area. For example, removing the woody plants destroys habitats for insects, decreasing the number of insect species.

**Tip:** Allowing animals to graze on land has a similar impact to mowing on succession — see page 193.

## Climatic climax communities

Which species make up the climax community depends on what the climate's like in an ecosystem. The climax community for a particular climate is called its **climatic climax**.

**Examples**

- In a temperate climate, e.g. the UK, there's plenty of available water, mild temperatures and not much change between the seasons. The climatic climax will contain large trees because they can grow in these conditions once deep soils have developed (see Figure 2).
- In a polar climate there's not much available water, temperatures are low and there are massive changes between the seasons. Large trees won't ever be able to grow in these conditions, so the climatic climax contains only herbs or shrubs, but it's still the climax community.

***Figure 2**: The climax community in many parts of Britain is deciduous woodland.*

### Practice Questions — Application

A team analysed data on ecological changes in part of a national park. Their results are shown in the graph below.

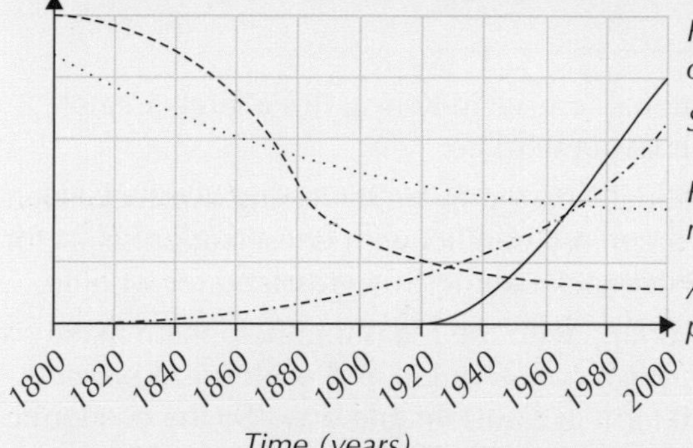


Q1 What type of succession is shown on the graph? Explain your answer.

Q2 Describe the characteristics of the dominant plant community between 1800 and 1860.

Q3 Describe and suggest an explanation for the change shown in the average length of time dominant plant seeds remain viable for.

Q4 During what time period would you expect to see a high percentage of plants whose seeds require high light intensity for germination? Explain your answer.

Q5 Describe and suggest an explanation for the change in the soil moisture content shown on the graph.

**Tip:** 'Remains viable for' means how long the plant seeds are capable of germinating (sprouting).

### Practice Questions — Fact Recall

Q1 Why are ecosystems described as 'dynamic'?

Q2 What is succession?

Q3 Which type of succession happens in areas with no soil?

Q4 Give an example of a pioneer species.

Q5 What is a climax community?

**Exam Tip**
You need to be able to use the correct ecological terms (like primary succession, climax community, etc.) in your exam — and spell them correctly too.

# 5. Conservation

*Lots of things humans do endanger species and cause the loss of habitats. Happily, all is not lost — there are things we can do to protect them.*

**Learning Objectives:**
- Be able to show an understanding of the need to manage the conflict between human needs and conservation in order to maintain the sustainability of natural resources.
- Understand that conservation of habitats frequently involves management of succession.

**Specification Reference 3.7.4**

## What is conservation?

Conservation is the protection and management of species and habitats (ecosystems) in a sustainable way. Sustainable means that enough resources are taken to meet the needs of people today, without reducing the ability of people in the future to meet their own needs.

Conservation is a dynamic process as conservation methods need to be adapted to the constant changes (caused naturally and by humans) that occur within ecosystems.

### Conflicts in conservation

Not everyone agrees with every conservation measure though — there's often **conflict** between human needs and conservation. Careful management is needed to find a balance between the two and maintain the sustainability of natural resources.

**Tip:** Remember, an ecosystem is all the organisms living in a community, plus all the abiotic conditions in the area in which they live (see page 173).

**Example**
- The Maasai Mara is a national reserve in Kenya. It's a large area of grassland (savannah) with lots of wildlife.
- The Maasai people traditionally earn a living by raising livestock, such as cattle. This can bring them into conflict with conservationists — for example, overgrazing by livestock can destroy grassland for wildlife.
- Conservation trusts are working with the Maasai to help them make money from their land through conservation and ecotourism projects, as well as farming, and to farm in a sustainable way. So the economic needs of the Maasai are met, while still allowing the area and its wildlife to be conserved.

## Conservation methods

Different species and habitats need to be conserved in different ways. Here are some examples of the different conservation methods that can be used.

**Tip:** The method used to manage succession always depends on the environment, e.g. clearing winter scrub (grasses and low shrubs) that would otherwise build up and dry out the land is useful to prevent wetland becoming woodland.

### 1. Management of succession

Human activities can interrupt the process of succession (see page 190). Conservation frequently involves preventing succession in order to preserve an ecosystem in its current stage of succession.

**Tip:** There are lots of ways of managing succession to aid conservation, some of which involve altering the abiotic conditions. For example, ditches and sluices can be used to control the water content of the soil.

**Example**

There are large areas of moorland in Scotland that provide habitats for many species of plants and animals. If the moorland was left to natural processes, succession would lead to a climax community of spruce forest. This would mean the loss of the moorland habitat and could lead to the loss of some of the plants and animals that currently live there. Preventing succession keeps the moorland ecosystem intact. There are a couple of ways to manage succession to conserve the moorland ecosystem:

- Animals are allowed to graze on the land. This is similar to mowing — the animals eat the growing points of the shrubs and trees, which stops them from establishing themselves and helps to keep vegetation low.
- Managed fires are lit. After the fires, secondary succession will occur on the moorland — the plant species that grow back first (pioneer species) are the species that are being conserved, e.g. heather. Larger plant species will take longer to grow back and will be removed again the next time the moor's burnt.

***Figure 1**: Grazing sheep (top) and managed fires (bottom) have been used to halt succession and conserve Scottish moorland.*

### 2. Seed banks

A seed bank is a store of seeds from lots of different plant species. Seed banks act as a backup for the conservation of plant species in the wild — for example, if a plant species becomes extinct or is lost from a particular habitat, stored seeds can be used to reintroduce the species.

Seed banks are a good way of conserving plant species — large numbers of species can be conserved in a fairly small space as most seeds are quite small. Seeds can also be stored anywhere in the world and for long periods of time, as long as it's cool and dry. However, the seeds have to be regularly tested to see if they're still viable (whether they can grow into a plant), which can be expensive and time-consuming.

### 3. Captive breeding

Captive breeding programmes involve breeding animals in controlled environments. Species that are endangered, or already extinct in the wild, can be bred in captivity to help increase their numbers. However, there are some problems with captive breeding programmes, e.g. animals like pandas can have problems breeding outside their natural habitat, which can be hard to recreate in a zoo.

Animals bred in captivity can be reintroduced to the wild. This increases their numbers in the wild, which can help to conserve their numbers or bring them back from the brink of extinction. Reintroducing animals into the wild can cause problems though, e.g. reintroduced animals could bring new diseases to habitats, harming other species living there.

### 4. Fishing quotas

Fishing quotas are limits to the amount of certain fish species that fishermen are allowed to catch. Fishing quotas help to conserve fish species by reducing the numbers that are caught and killed — they aim to prevent a situation where fish populations reach such low levels that they are threatened with extinction.

However, fishing quotas can be unpopular with fishermen as they limit their potential income. There can also be problems with 'discards' — ships catching more fish than they are allowed to, then throwing back some fish (which are often dead already) so they don't exceed their quota. This is wasteful and doesn't contribute to the conservation of fish populations. In areas where there are fishing vessels from more than one country, international cooperation is needed for quotas to be fully effective.

**Tip:** Fishing is a good example of an area where there is a conflict between human needs (our need for food and the need of fishermen to earn a living) and conservation needs. To protect fish populations for the future, we need to find ways to make fishing sustainable.

### 5. Protected areas

Protected areas, like national parks and nature reserves, protect habitats and the species in them by restricting urban development, industrial development and farming. Habitats in protected areas can be managed to conserve them.

**Exam Tip**
The only conservation method you need to know about is managing succession. However, it's a good idea to be aware of other methods because you could be given data about them in the exam.

**Example**

Some woodlands are managed by coppicing — cutting down trees in a way that lets them grow back, so they don't need to be replanted. This helps to conserve the woodland, but allows some wood to be harvested.

Protected areas also have problems. For example, national parks are also used as tourist destinations (many are funded by revenue from tourists). This means there's conflict between the need to conserve the habitats and the need to allow people to visit and use them.

## Practice Questions — Application

Succession in an area of steppe (grassland) can result in a forest. A nature reserve wishes to conserve the steppe landscape by managing succession. Grazing, mowing and fire were used on three areas that were then left for a set amount of time. The results were compared to a control area which was left undisturbed for the same length of time. The data is shown on the bar chart below.

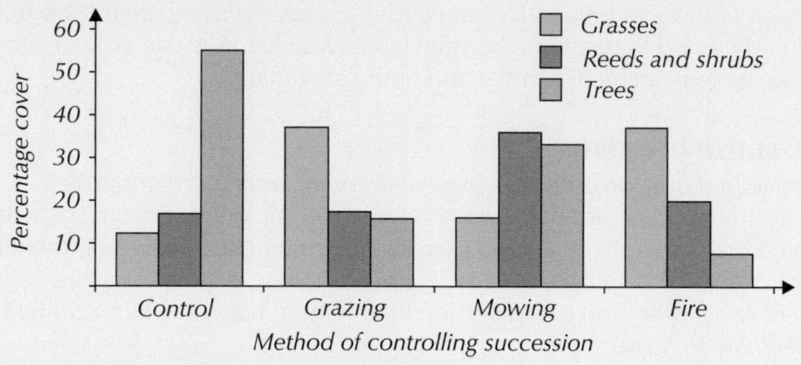


**Tip:** To answer these questions, you might need to take a look back at pages 188-190 to remind yourself about how succession works.

Q1 a) Describe what the results show about the effectiveness of the three methods of managing succession.

b) Suggest two advantages of controlling succession by grazing rather than by fire.

Q2 The saiga antelope is an endangered species living in this area. A major cause of the population decline of the saiga has been hunting by local people for meat and also for its horns, which are sold for use in traditional medicine.
Suggest why education programs and developing alternative livelihoods for local people could be a useful part of the effort to conserve the saiga antelope.

**Exam Tip**
You always need to read exam questions carefully, but that's especially true when you're given data on a topic you know really well. It's dead easy to give a general answer based on what you know when actually the question wants you to use the data you're given.

**Tip:** When a question says 'suggest' you're not expected to know the exact answer — you're expected to use your knowledge to come up with a sensible answer.

## Practice Questions — Fact Recall

Q1 What is conservation?

Q2 Give one reason why people don't always agree with conservation measures.

Q3 Describe how a managed fire can be used to prevent succession, in order to preserve an ecosystem in its current stage.

Q4 Give an example of a method of conservation other than the management of succession.

# 6. Conservation Evidence and Data

*You need to be able to evaluate data on conservation. Sometimes though, it can be a bit tricky — especially when data sets show conflicting trends...*

**Learning Objective:**

- Be able to evaluate evidence and data concerning issues relating to the conservation of species and habitats and consider conflicting evidence.

**Specification Reference 3.7.4**

## Evaluating evidence on conservation

You need to be able to evaluate any evidence or data about conservation projects and research that the examiners throw at you — so here's an example I made earlier...

**Example**

In recent years, native British bluebells have become less common in woodland areas. It's thought that this is due to the presence of non-native Spanish bluebells, which compete with the native species for a similar niche and are capable of breeding with the native species to produce a hybrid.

An experiment was carried out to see if removing the invasive Spanish species would help to conserve the native species. Each year for 15 years the percentage cover of native species was estimated in a 50 m by 50 m area of woodland using random sampling and 250, 1 $m^2$ quadrats. After five years, all the Spanish bluebells were removed. A similar sized control woodland in which the Spanish bluebells remained untouched was also studied. The results are shown below.

**Tip:** A niche is the role of a species within its habitat (see page 173). If you need a reminder about using quadrats, take a look at page 182.

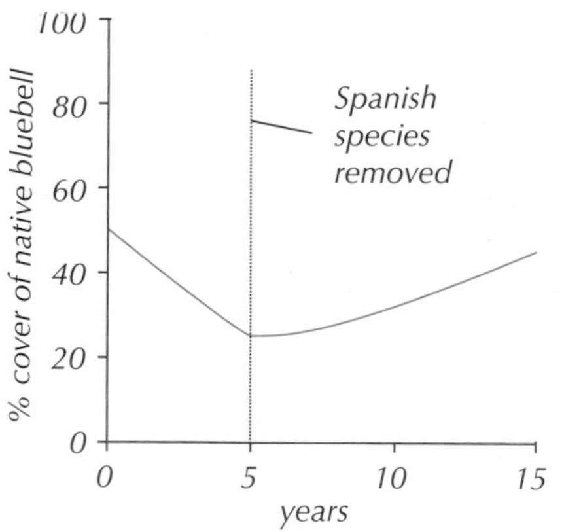


***Figure 1**: Percentage cover of native British bluebells in a woodland.*

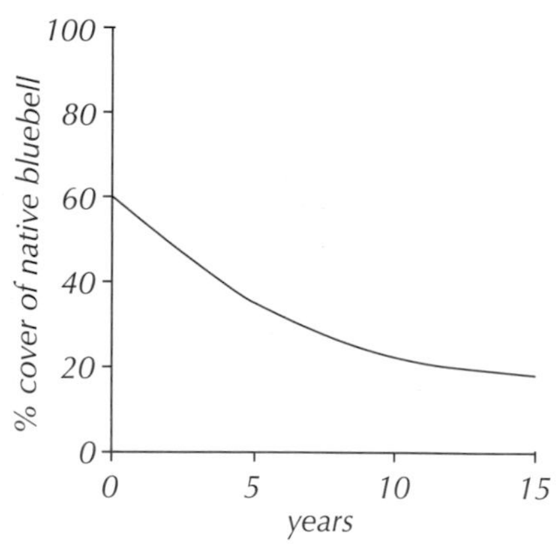


***Figure 2**: Control experiment.*

You might be asked to:

**Describe the data**

- For the first five years, the percentage cover of native bluebells fell from 50% to around 25%. After the Spanish species was removed, it increased from around 25% to around 45% in ten years.
- The control experiment shows a fairly steady drop in native bluebell percentage cover from 60% to 20% over the 15 years.

**Draw conclusions**

The removal of Spanish bluebells resulted in an increase in the percentage cover of native bluebells over a ten year period. This suggests that the recent decrease in native British bluebells is due to competition with the Spanish bluebells.

***Figure 3**: Some attempts to conserve British bluebells (top) have involved removing Spanish bluebells (bottom).*

**Evaluate the method**

- The effects of some other variables (e.g. changing weather) were removed by the control experiment, where the percentage cover of native bluebells continued to fall throughout the 15 year study. This makes the test more valid.
- The study area and sample size were quite large, giving more accurate data.
- Random sampling removed bias — the data's more likely to be an accurate estimate of the whole area.

## Conflicting evidence

There's more about interpreting data and evaluating experiments on pages 13-16.

The evidence from one study alone wouldn't usually be enough to conclude that there's a link between decreasing percentage cover of native bluebells, and the presence of Spanish bluebells. Similar studies would be carried out to investigate the link.

If these studies came to the same conclusion, the conclusion would become increasingly accepted. Sometimes studies come up with conflicting evidence though — evidence that leads to a different conclusion than other studies.

**Tip:** Ecosystems are such complicated things that studies can sometimes throw up conflicting data — which can be both really interesting and a bit of pain if the data for both studies looks precise. But the first thing you should always do when you get conflicting data is look at the methodology — chances are something in the method has caused the conflict.

**Example**

Another study was carried out to investigate the effect on native bluebells of removing Spanish bluebells.

It was similar to the study on the previous page except a 20 m by 20 m area was sampled using a random sample of 20 quadrats, and no control woodland was used.

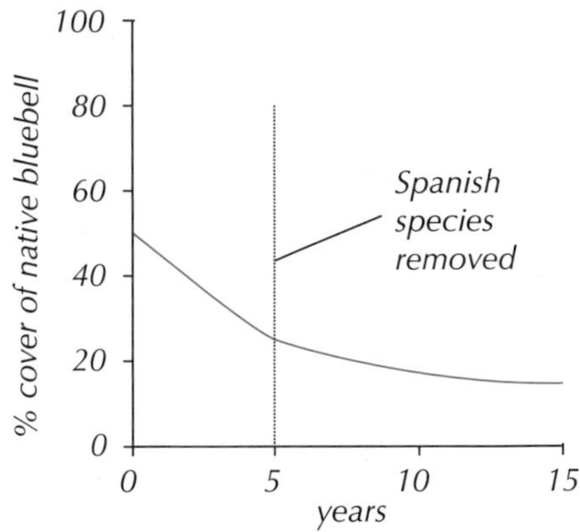


***Figure 4**: Percentage cover of native British bluebells in a woodland.*

You might be asked to:

**Describe the data**

In the first five years, the percentage cover of native bluebells fell from 50% to around 25%. After the Spanish species was removed, it kept decreasing to around 15% after the full 15 years.

**Draw conclusions**

The removal of the Spanish bluebells had no effect on the decreasing percentage cover of native bluebells — which conflicts with the study on the previous page.

**Evaluate the method**

- There wasn't a control woodland, so the continuing decrease in native bluebell cover after the removal of the Spanish bluebells could be due to another factor, e.g. cold weather in years 5-10.
- The study area and sample size were quite small, giving a less accurate total percentage cover.

## Practice Questions — Application

The diversity of native plants on certain areas of grassland has been reduced by the invasion of non-native species. A team wishing to conserve the native species investigated two methods. The first involved harrowing the soil and dispersing native seeds, and the second involved continual grazing by sheep. These methods were each conducted on 14 fields, and their effects were compared to a control field (which was left untouched). The fields were left for four years. The results were averaged and are shown below.

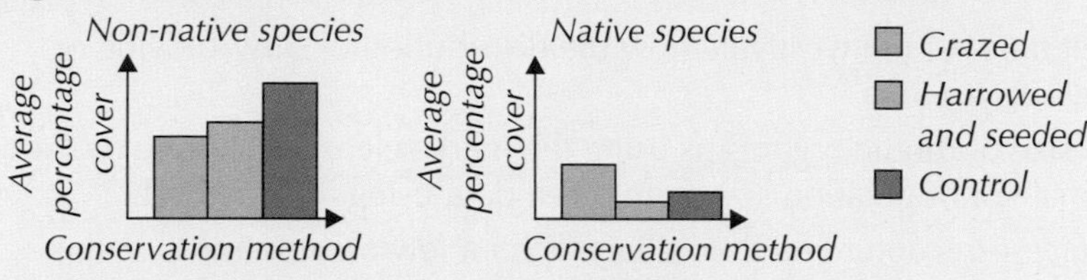


Q1 Describe the results shown in the graph.

Q2 a) Which method of conservation was most successful? Give a reason for your answer.

b) Suggest why the method you named in part a) worked and why the other did not.

Q3 A second team conducted an investigation using the same methods. Each method was used on a single field and the fields were left for six years.

a) A different number of fields were used in the investigations carried out by the two teams. Explain what effect this would have on the validity of the results produced.

b) Did the first investigation use a positive or negative control? Explain your answer.

**Tip:** Harrowing is where the surface of the soil is broken up and smoothed over. This makes the soil better for seed growth.

**Tip:** If you need a reminder about the different types of control see page 2.

## Section Summary

Make sure you know:

- That an ecosystem is all the organisms living in a community, plus all the abiotic conditions in the area in which they live.
- That ecosystems vary in size and can be very small, e.g. a pond, or very large, e.g. an entire ocean.
- That the place where an organism lives is known as its habitat.
- That a niche is the role of a species within its habitat and includes its biotic and abiotic interactions. Every species occupies its own unique niche.
- That species have adaptations that increase their chance of survival and reproduction, and that they are adapted to both the abiotic and biotic conditions in their niche.
- That a population is all the organisms of one species in a habitat and that the populations of different species in a habitat form a community.
- That the carrying capacity is the maximum stable population size of a species that an ecosystem can support.
- That population size can vary due to abiotic factors, e.g. the amount of light or space available.
- That population size can also vary because of biotic factors including interspecific competition, intraspecific competition and predation.

- That interspecific competition is when organisms of different species compete with each other for the same resources, and that it results in the less well-adapted species being out-competed.
- That intraspecific competition is when organisms of the same species compete with each other for the same resources, and results in a cyclical change in population size around an ecosystem's carrying capacity.
- That predation is when an organism (the predator) kills and eats another organism (the prey), and that this results in the population sizes of the predators and prey being interlinked.
- How to estimate the size of a population of slow-moving or non-motile organisms using randomly placed quadrats.
- How to use quadrats along a belt transect to investigate how the distribution of slow-moving or non-motile organisms changes across an area.
- How to estimate the population size of motile organisms using the mark-release-recapture method, and be able to calculate an estimate of population size from given data using this method.
- That the accuracy of the mark-release-recapture method depends on a few assumptions. These include that the marked sample has had enough time and opportunity to remix with the population, that marking doesn't affect the chances of survival of marked organisms, and that there are no changes in population size during the period of the study.
- How to investigate the effect of an environmental factor on the distribution of a species, e.g. the effect of soil pH on marram grass (Required Practical 12).
- That ecosystems are dynamic systems, which means they are constantly changing. The process by which this change occurs is called succession.
- That primary succession starts with pioneer species colonising a new land surface — pioneer species are so called because they are the first species to colonise an area.
- That succession is made up of stages. At each stage different plant and animal communities develop. Certain species can affect the environment (i.e. the abiotic and biotic conditions) so that it becomes more suitable for other species with different adaptations. As new species colonise an environment they may change it in a way that makes it less suitable for previous species. So as the process of succession takes place, communities of organisms are succeeded (replaced) by other communities.
- That during succession, organisms change their abiotic environment in ways that make the environment less hostile. This means that new species move in alongside existing species, which increases biodiversity.
- That a climax community is the largest and most complex community of plants and animals that an ecosystem can support. At this stage the ecosystem is in a steady state and won't change much.
- That humans can interrupt succession and stop a climax community from developing, e.g. by mowing, grazing or controlled burning — this keeps an ecosystem at a particular stage of succession.
- That conservation aims to manage species and habitats in a sustainable way in order to preserve natural resources, but this can create conflict with human needs. Conflicts require careful management in order to maintain the sustainability of natural resources.
- That the conservation of habitats frequently involves the management of succession by humans, e.g. allowing animals to graze on land. This is a method of conservation that preserves the ecosystem in its current stage of succession.
- That there are other methods to conserve species and habitats, which include the use of seed banks, captive breeding, fishing quotas and protected areas.
- How to evaluate evidence and data about conservation projects, including data from studies which give conflicting evidence.

# Exam-style Questions

**1** A team of scientists is investigating the distribution of marsh marigolds across a field that is directly next to a stream.

**1.1** Suggest and describe a method the scientists could use to investigate the distribution of marsh marigolds.

*(2 marks)*

**1.2** The team decide they want to record the percentage cover of marsh marigolds. Describe how they could measure the percentage cover and give an advantage of measuring species abundance this way.

*(3 marks)*

**1.3** Abiotic factors were investigated at each place where data on marsh marigolds was recorded. Explain what is meant by the term 'abiotic conditions'.

*(1 mark)*

The results of the investigation are recorded in **Figure 1** and **Figure 2**.

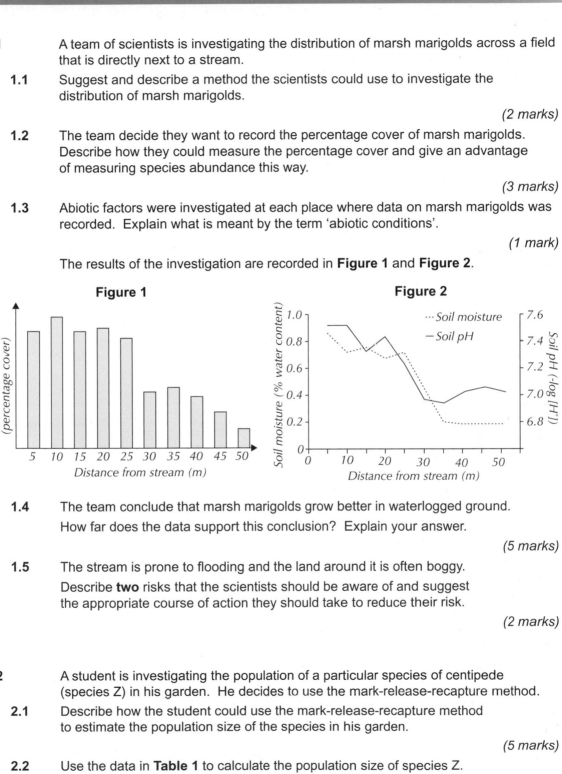

**Figure 1**

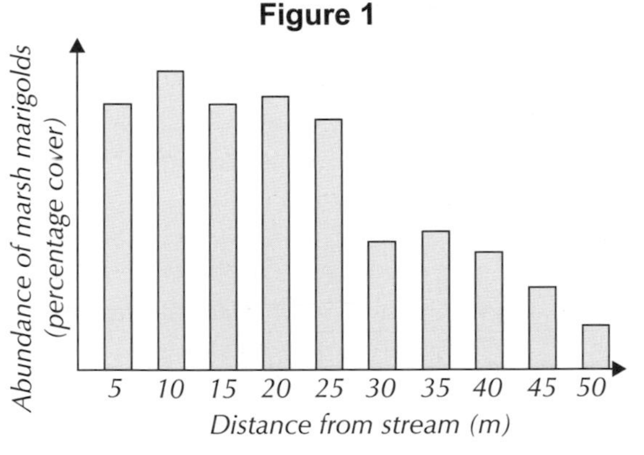


**Figure 2**

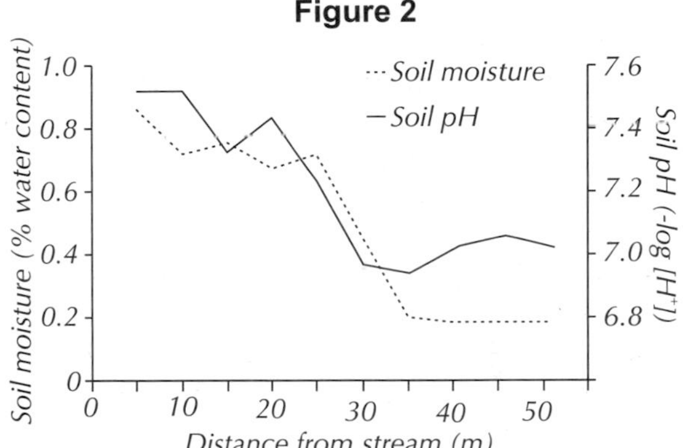


**1.4** The team conclude that marsh marigolds grow better in waterlogged ground. How far does the data support this conclusion? Explain your answer.

*(5 marks)*

**1.5** The stream is prone to flooding and the land around it is often boggy. Describe **two** risks that the scientists should be aware of and suggest the appropriate course of action they should take to reduce their risk.

*(2 marks)*

**2** A student is investigating the population of a particular species of centipede (species Z) in his garden. He decides to use the mark-release-recapture method.

**2.1** Describe how the student could use the mark-release-recapture method to estimate the population size of the species in his garden.

*(5 marks)*

**2.2** Use the data in **Table 1** to calculate the population size of species Z.

**Table 1**

| Individuals of species Z | Number of individuals in trap | |
|---|---|---|
| | First sample | Second sample |
| Total caught | 10 | 15 |
| Total marked caught | - | 8 |

*(1 mark)*

**3** An area of heathland in a national park is home to an endangered plant species which needs high light intensity and acidic soils to grow successfully. The park managers have decided to halt succession on the heath and are exploring ways in which to do this. They are considering burning the heathland every fifty years.

**3.1** Suggest **two** reasons why burning the heathland every fifty years might not help to conserve the endangered plant species.

*(2 marks)*

The managers have found data from another heathland which halted succession by burning every 20 years. The data is shown in **Figure 3**.

**Figure 3**

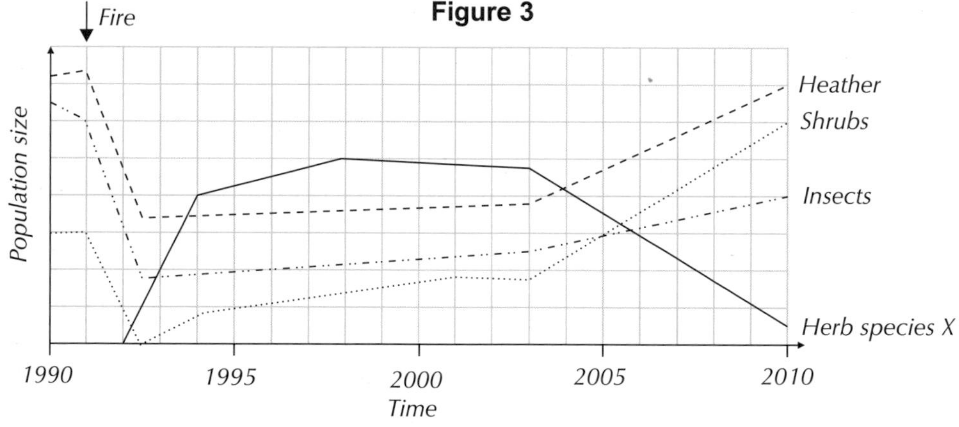


**3.2** Describe and explain the changes in the population sizes of heather, shrubs and insects between 1991 and 2000.

*(3 marks)*

**3.3** Herb species X is a pioneer species.

Explain what is meant by the term 'pioneer species'.

*(1 mark)*

**3.4** Describe the changes in the population size of herb species X shown in **Figure 3** over the twenty year period. Suggest explanations for the changes seen.

*(3 marks)*

**3.5** The managers have met opposition against the use of fire to halt succession. Some campaigners against the use of fire have used the data shown above to argue that insect populations do not recover following heathland fires.

Suggest and explain **two** reasons why the data doesn't support this conclusion.

*(2 marks)*

**3.6** Explain an alternative way in which the plant species could be conserved.

*(3 marks)*

## Topic 8 A: Mutations and Gene Expression

# 1. Mutations

*Genes are pretty awesome. However, their base sequences can sometimes be mutated, changing the protein that gets produced. You met mutations in Topic 4, but you need to know a bit more about them here.*

## What are mutations?

Any change to the base (nucleotide) sequence of DNA is called a **mutation**. Mutations can be caused by errors during DNA replication. The rate of mutation can be increased by **mutagenic agents** (see page 204). The types of mutations that can occur include:

- **Substitution** — one or more bases are swapped for another, e.g. ATGCCT becomes ATTCCT (G is swapped for T).
- **Deletion** — one or more bases are removed, e.g. ATGCCT becomes ATCCT (G is removed).
- **Addition** — one or more bases are added, e.g. ATGCCT becomes ATGACCT (A is added).
- **Duplication** — one or more bases are repeated, e.g. ATGCCT becomes ATGCCCCT (CC is repeated).
- **Inversion** — a sequence of bases is reversed, e.g. ATGCCT becomes ATCCGT (GCC is reversed to CCG).
- **Translocation** — a sequence of bases is moved from one location in the genome to another. This could be movement within the same chromosome or movement to a different chromosome.

The order of DNA bases in a gene determines the sequence of amino acids in a particular polypeptide. If a mutation occurs in a gene, the sequence of amino acids in the polypeptide that it codes for could be changed.

**Example**

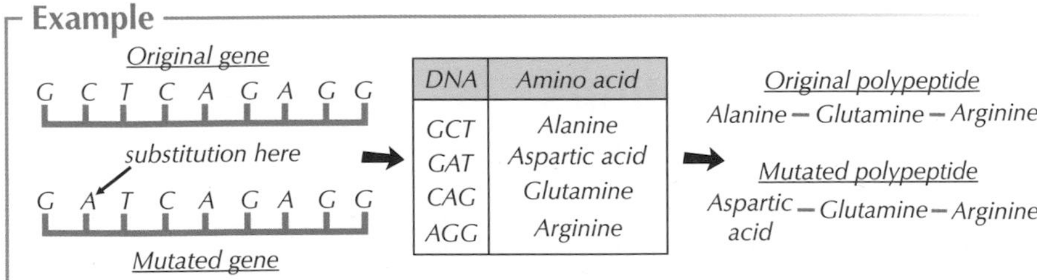


Polypeptides make up proteins. A change in the amino acid sequence of a polypeptide may change the final 3D shape of the protein, which could mean that it doesn't work properly.

**Example**

A mutation in a polypeptide that makes up an enzyme may change the shape of the enzyme's active site. This may stop substrates from being able to bind to the active site, leaving the enzyme unable to catalyse the reaction.

Some mutations can increase the likelihood of developing certain cancers, e.g. mutations of the gene BRCA1 can increase the chances of developing breast cancer.

**Learning Objectives:**

- Know that gene mutations might arise during DNA replication and that they can include substitution, deletion, addition, duplication, inversion and translocation of bases.
- Know that mutations can result in a different amino acid sequence in the encoded polypeptide.
- Know that some gene mutations change only one triplet code and that, due to the degenerate nature of the genetic code, not all such mutations result in a change to the encoded amino acid.
- Understand that some gene mutations change the nature of all base triplets downstream from the mutation — they result in a frameshift.
- Be able to relate the nature of a gene mutation to its effect on the encoded polypeptide.

**Specification Reference 3.8.1**

**Tip:** Remember, when more than two amino acids join together, they form a polypeptide chain. The sequence of amino acids in the chain forms the primary structure of a protein and the final folding of the chain forms the tertiary structure.

Some mutations can cause **genetic disorders** — inherited disorders caused by abnormal genes or chromosomes, e.g. cystic fibrosis.

If a gamete (sex cell) containing a mutation for a type of cancer or a genetic disorder is fertilised, the mutation will be present in the new fetus formed — these are called **hereditary mutations** because they are passed on to the offspring.

**Tip:** Cystic fibrosis is a genetic disorder of the cell membranes. It results in the body producing a lot of thick sticky mucus in the air passages and in the pancreas.

**Tip:** Not all hereditary mutations are harmful — beneficial hereditary mutations drive evolution (see p. 163).

## Mutations and proteins

Not all mutations affect the order of amino acids in a protein. The degenerate nature of the genetic code means that some amino acids are coded for by more than one DNA triplet (e.g. tyrosine can be coded for by TAT or TAC in DNA). This means that not all types of mutation will always result in a change to the amino acid sequence of the polypeptide.

**Examples**

Some substitutions will still code for the same amino acid. In this example, the mutated polypeptide is the same as the original polypeptide, despite the base substitution.

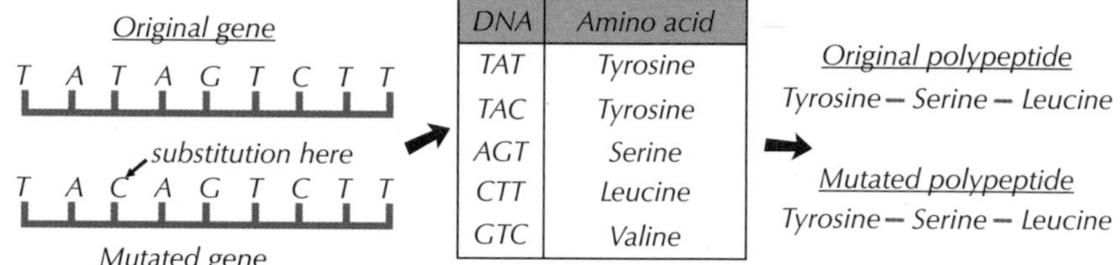


**Tip:** If a mutation doesn't cause a change in the amino acid order, it's called a 'silent mutation'.

Sometimes, inversion mutations don't cause a change in the amino acid sequence either. In this example, the mutated polypeptide is the same as the original polypeptide, despite the reversal of the bases.

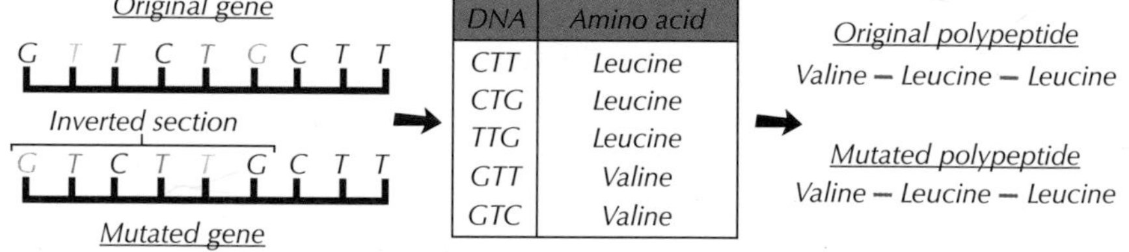


## Frameshift mutations

Some mutations have a huge effect on the base sequence of a gene. Additions, duplications and deletions within a gene will almost always change the amino acid sequence of a polypeptide. That's because these mutations all change the number of bases in the DNA code. This causes a shift (called a **frameshift**) in the base triplets that follow, so that the triplet code is read in a different way.

**Exam Tip**
You could be asked to predict how much a mutation will affect a protein's structure. Just remember that a frameshift mutation affects more amino acids than a substitution mutation, so it will have a bigger overall effect on the protein's structure.

**Examples**

Here's how an addition can cause a frameshift and change the amino acid order:

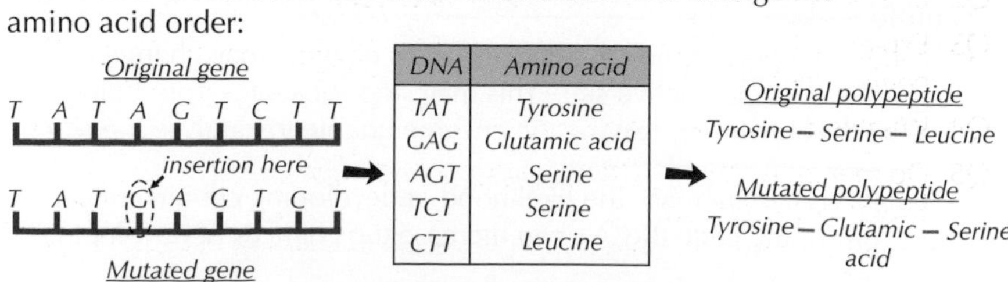

Here's how a deletion can cause a frameshift and change the amino acid order:

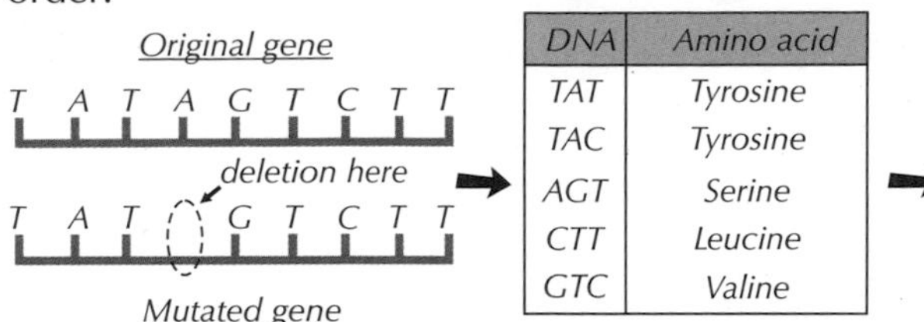


| DNA | Amino acid |
|---|---|
| TAT | Tyrosine |
| TAC | Tyrosine |
| AGT | Serine |
| CTT | Leucine |
| GTC | Valine |

*Original polypeptide*

*Tyrosine — Serine — Leucine*

*Mutated polypeptide*

*Tyrosine — Valine*

**Tip:** The base triplets that follow on from the mutation are said to be 'downstream' of the mutation.

## Practice Questions — Application

The table below shows some amino acids and the base triplets that code for them.

| Base Triplet(s) | Amino Acid |
|---|---|
| GAT | Asp |
| CAT | His |
| ATA | Ile |
| CTT/CTC | Leu |
| ATG | Met |
| ACA | Thr |
| TAT | Tyr |

The following letters represent part of the DNA base sequence of a gene:

CTTCATGATACA

Look at the four mutated base sequences below.

Mutation A: CTCCATGATACA

Mutation B: CTTCATCATACA

Mutation C: CTTATGATACA

Mutation D: CTTCTTCATGATACA

Q1 For each of the base sequences:

a) State the type of mutation that has taken place.

b) Give the amino acid sequence coded for by the mutated gene.

Q2 Explain which mutation is likely to have:

a) the least serious effect on the structure of the protein produced,

b) the most serious effect on the structure of the protein produced.

**Tip:** 'Asp', 'His', 'Ile', etc are just abbreviated names of amino acids, e.g. 'Asp' is short for aspartic acid.

**Exam Tip**

If you're asked how a mutation affects protein structure in the exam, don't fall into the trap of only writing about how the mutation will change the base sequence. Make sure you make it clear how the altered base sequence will affect both the amino acid sequence and the protein's structure.

## Practice Questions — Fact Recall

Q1 What is a mutation?

Q2 Briefly describe what happens in a translocation mutation.

Q3 Explain why a mutation in a polypeptide that makes up an enzyme could affect the enzyme's function.

Q4 What is a hereditary mutation?

Q5 Do mutations always affect the protein coded for by a gene? Explain your answer.

**Learning Objective:**

- Understand that gene mutations occur spontaneously and that the mutation rate is increased by mutagenic agents.

**Specification Reference 3.8.1**

# 2. Mutagenic Agents

*Mutations just happen, but there are certain things that can make them happen more often...*

## What are mutagenic agents?

Mutations occur spontaneously, e.g. when DNA is misread during replication. But some things can increase the rate of mutations — these are called **mutagenic agents**. Ultraviolet radiation, ionising radiation, some chemicals and some viruses are examples of mutagenic agents. They can increase the rate of mutations in different ways.

**Tip:** Remember, DNA replicates itself every time a cell divides.

### 1. Acting as a base

Chemicals called base analogs can substitute for a base during DNA replication, changing the base sequence in the new DNA.

**Example**

5-bromouracil is a base analog that can substitute for thymine. It can pair with guanine (instead of adenine), causing a substitution mutation in the new DNA.

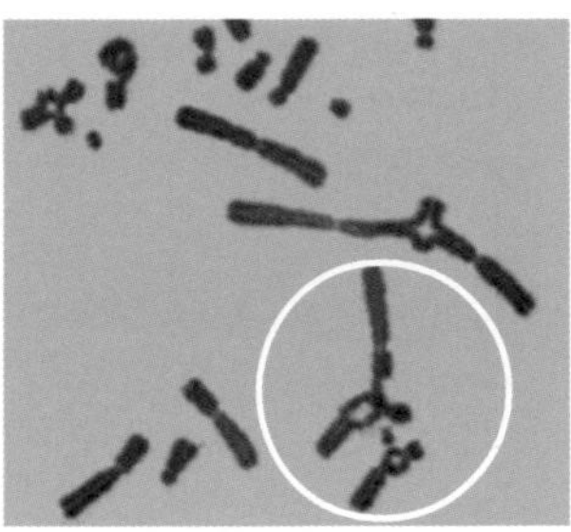

***Figure 1:*** *The circled chromosomes have been damaged by exposure to an alkylating agent.*

### 2. Altering bases

Some chemicals can delete or alter bases.

**Example**

Alkylating agents can add an alkyl group to guanine, which changes the structure so that it pairs with thymine (instead of cytosine).

### 3. Changing the structure of DNA

Some types of radiation can change the structure of DNA, which causes problems during DNA replication.

**Example**

UV radiation can cause adjacent thymine bases to pair up together.

**Practice Questions — Application**

Q1 2-aminopurine is a base analog that can substitute for both adenine and guanine during DNA replication.
Explain why 2-aminopurine is a mutagenic agent.

Q2 Mustard gas is an alkylating agent, sometimes used in chemical warfare. Exposure to it results in severe burns and blisters.
Explain how exposure to mustard gas may affect the sequence of amino acids in a particular polypeptide.

**Practice Questions — Fact Recall**

Q1 When might a mutation occur spontaneously?

Q2 What is a mutagenic agent?

Q3 Give an example of a mutagenic agent.

# 3. Cancer

*If a mutation occurs in a gene that controls cell division it can cause cancer. This is because the genes that control cell division don't behave as they should, which can result in uncontrolled cell growth.*

## Cell division and cancer

Mutations that occur in individual cells after fertilisation (e.g. in adulthood) are called **acquired mutations**. If these mutations occur in the genes that control the rate of cell division (by mitosis), it can cause uncontrolled cell division. If a cell divides uncontrollably the result is a **tumour** — a mass of abnormal cells. Tumours that invade and destroy surrounding tissue are called **cancers** (see next page).

There are two types of gene that control cell division — **tumour suppressor genes** and **proto-oncogenes**. Mutations in these genes can cause cancer.

### Tumour suppressor genes

When functioning normally, tumour suppressor genes slow cell division by producing proteins that stop cells dividing or cause them to self-destruct (apoptosis) — see Figure 1.

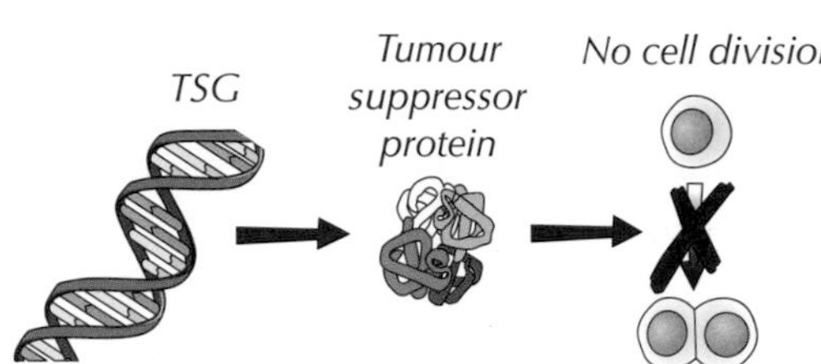


**Figure 1:** *Action of a normal tumour suppressor gene (TSG).*

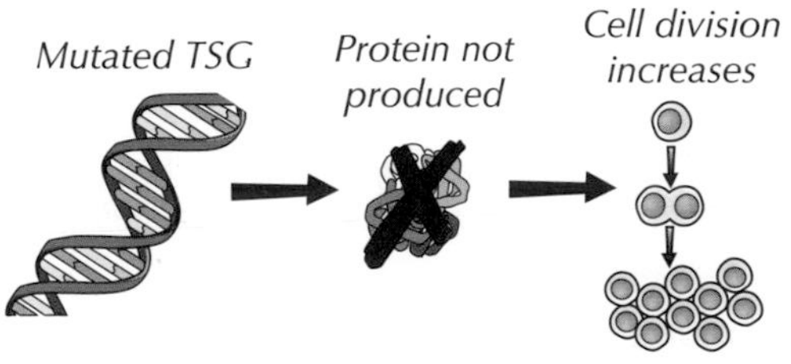


**Figure 2:** *A mutated tumour suppressor gene (TSG) results in uncontrolled cell division.*

If a mutation occurs in a tumour suppressor gene, the gene will be inactivated. The protein it codes for isn't produced and the cells divide uncontrollably (the rate of division increases) resulting in a tumour — see Figure 2.

### Proto-oncogenes

When functioning normally, proto-oncogenes stimulate cell division by producing proteins that make cells divide — see Figure 3.

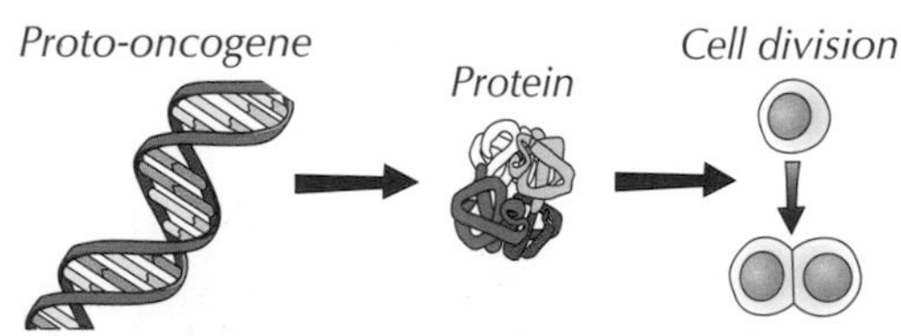


**Figure 3:** *Action of a normal proto-oncogene.*

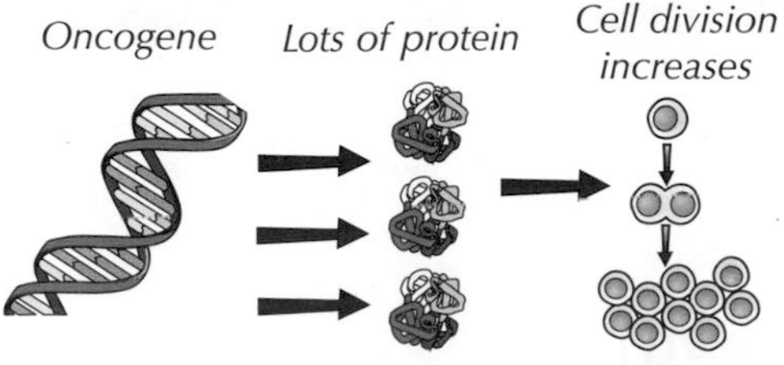


**Figure 4:** *A mutated proto-oncogene stimulates uncontrolled cell division.*

If a mutation occurs in a proto-oncogene, the gene can become overactive. This stimulates the cells to divide uncontrollably (the rate of division increases) resulting in a tumour — see Figure 4. A mutated proto-oncogene is called an **oncogene**.

**Learning Objectives:**

- Understand the role of tumour suppressor genes and oncogenes in the development of tumours.
- Know the main characteristics of benign and malignant tumours.
- Understand the role of abnormal methylation of tumour suppressor genes and oncogenes in the development of tumours.
- Understand the role of increased oestrogen concentrations in the development of some breast cancers.

**Specification Reference 3.8.2.3**

**Tip:** Apoptosis is a type of programmed cell death. It's where cells that are infected, damaged or have reached the end of their functional life are destroyed.

**Tip:** Mutations in tumour suppressor genes and proto-oncogenes are often acquired but some are inherited.

**Tip:** If you're struggling to remember which gene does what, the clue is in the name. Tumour suppressor genes suppress the growth of tumours — so they're the ones that slow down cell division.

## Tumours and cancers

Tumours can develop for years without any obvious symptoms and can be quite large by the time they're discovered. Not all tumours are cancerous — there are two different types:

### 1. Malignant tumours

Malignant tumours are cancers. They usually grow rapidly and invade and destroy surrounding tissues. Cells can break off the tumours and spread to other parts of the body in the bloodstream or lymphatic system.

### 2. Benign tumours

Benign tumours are not cancerous. They usually grow slower than malignant tumours and are often covered in fibrous tissue that stops cells invading other tissues. Benign tumours are often harmless, but they can cause blockages and put pressure on organs. Some benign tumours can become malignant.

**Tip:** You met the lymphatic system in Topic 3. It's a network of tubes which transports excess tissue fluid back into the circulatory system.

**Tip:** You need to understand the difference between benign and malignant. You should never say benign cancers — there's no such thing. Only malignant tumours are cancerous.

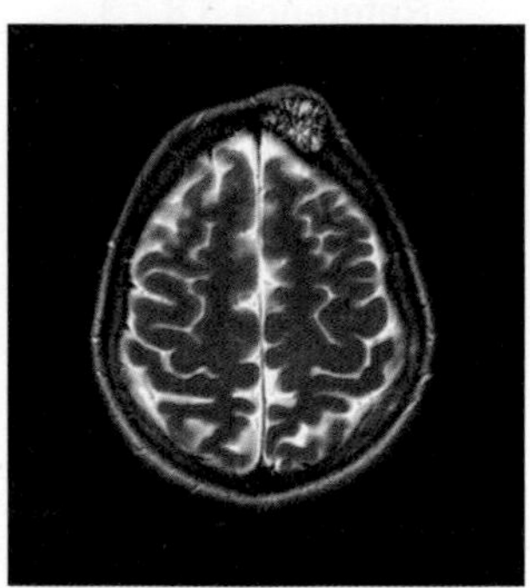

***Figure 5:*** *MRI scan showing a benign brain tumour (top right).*

## Tumour cells

Tumour cells can differ from normal cells in many different ways:

- The nucleus is larger and darker than in normal cells. Sometimes the cells have more than one nucleus.
- They have an irregular shape.
- They don't produce all the proteins needed to function correctly.
- They have different antigens on their surface.
- They don't respond to growth regulating processes.
- They divide (by mitosis) more frequently than normal cells.

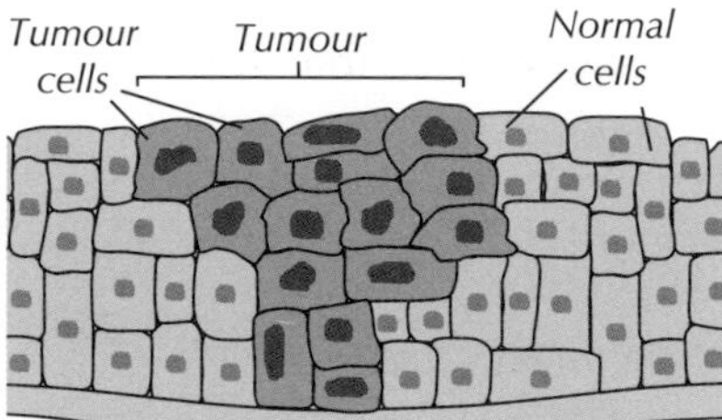


***Figure 6:*** *The appearance of tumour cells in comparison to normal cells.*

**Example**

Figure 7 below shows a light micrograph of a culture of normal cells. Figure 8 shows the same cells following exposure to a cancer-causing chemical. The cells in Figure 8 are a lot denser, are a lot darker and have a more irregular structure.

***Figure 7:*** *Light micrograph of a culture of normal cells.*

***Figure 8:*** *Light micrograph of cells shown in Figure 7, following exposure to a cancer-causing chemical.*

## Causes of tumour growth

There are a number of different factors that are thought to lead to the growth of tumours. These include abnormal methylation of DNA and increased exposure to oestrogen.

## Abnormal methylation

Methylation means adding a methyl ($-CH_3$) group onto something. Methylation of DNA is an important method of regulating gene expression — it can control whether or not a gene is **transcribed** (copied into mRNA) and **translated** (turned into a protein). When methylation is happening normally, it plays a key role in many processes in the body.

It's only when it happens too much (**hypermethylation**) or too little (**hypomethylation**) that it becomes a problem. The growth of tumours can be caused by abnormal methylation of certain cancer-related genes.

**Tip:** You should remember transcription and translation from Topic 4. The regulation of these processes is covered in more detail on pages 219-221.

**Tip:** You can read more about methylation on page 224.

**Examples**

- When tumour suppressor genes are hypermethylated, the genes are not transcribed — so the proteins they produce to slow cell division aren't made. This means that cells are able to divide uncontrollably by mitosis and tumours can develop.

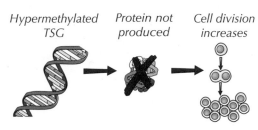

*Figure 9: The result of hypermethylation of a tumour suppressor gene (TSG).*

- Hypomethylation of proto-oncogenes causes them to act as oncogenes — increasing the production of the proteins that encourage cell division. This stimulates cells to divide uncontrollably, which causes the formation of tumours.

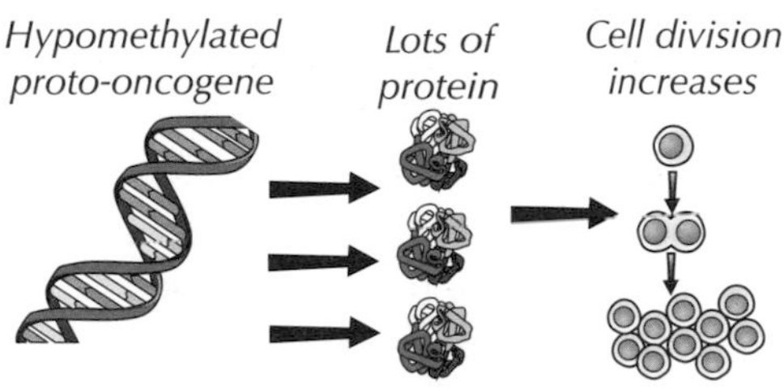


*Figure 10: The result of hypomethylation of a proto-oncogene.*

**Tip:** Make sure that you don't get 'hypermethylation' and 'hypomethylation' mixed up. Remember — 'hyp<u>o</u>' means l<u>o</u>w.

## Role of oestrogen in breast cancer

Some women may be exposed to more oestrogen than others. Increased exposure to oestrogen may be the result of starting menstruation earlier than usual, starting the menopause later than usual, or taking oestrogen-containing drugs, such as HRT.

Increased exposure to oestrogen over an extended period of time is thought to increase a woman's risk of developing breast cancer. The exact reasons behind this aren't fully understood, but there are a few theories as to how oestrogen can contribute to the development of some breast cancers:

- Oestrogen can stimulate certain breast cells to divide and replicate. The fact that more cell divisions are taking place naturally increases the chance of mutations occurring, and so increases the chance of cells becoming cancerous.
- Oestrogen's ability to stimulate division could also mean that if cells do become cancerous, their rapid replication could be further assisted by oestrogen, helping tumours to form quickly.
- Other research suggests that oestrogen is actually able to introduce mutations directly into the DNA of certain breast cells, again increasing the chance of these cells becoming cancerous.

**Tip:** HRT stands for hormone replacement therapy. It is used to increase oestrogen (and usually also progesterone) levels in some women in order to treat symptoms experienced during the menopause (the end of menstruation).

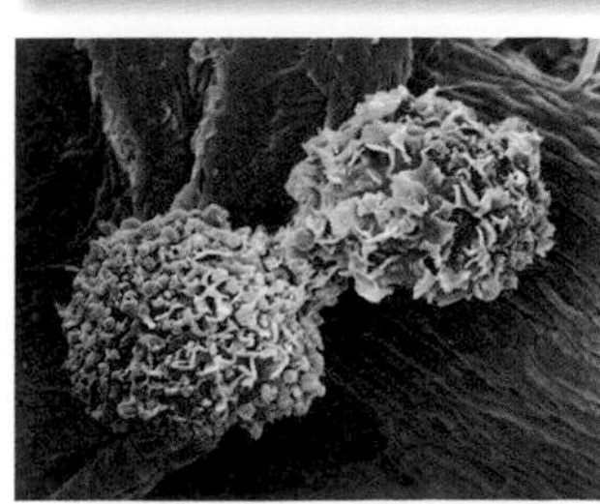

*Figure 11: Micrograph of dividing breast cancer cells. Oestrogen is thought to stimulate this division, increasing the rate of tumour formation.*

**Exam Tip**
If you're given a light micrograph to look at in the exam, don't panic — it's just a way of getting you to apply your knowledge. Read the question carefully to work out what it is that you're looking at. Then have a think about which part of your course it's testing and do a short mental recap of it — that should help you answer the question.

## Practice Questions — Application

Q1 Cervical intraepithelial neoplasia is a condition in which cells on the surface of the cervix grow abnormally. If untreated, these changes can lead to cancer of the cervix. One of the light micrographs below shows healthy cervical tissue. The other light micrograph shows tissue with cervical intraepithelial neoplasia.

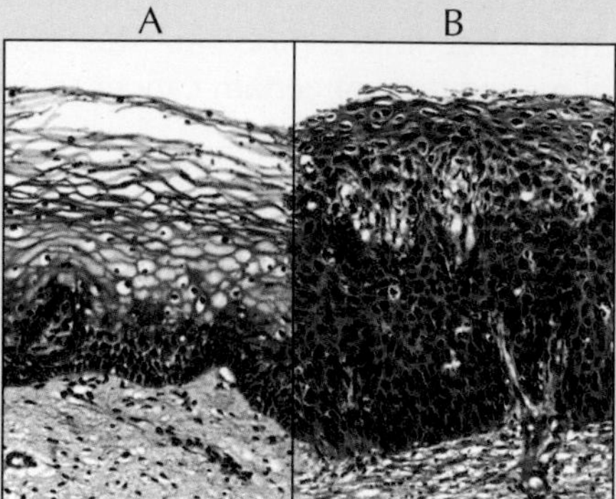


Which of the light micrographs (A or B) do you think shows tissue with cervical intraepithelial neoplasia? Explain your answer.

Q2 p53 is a tumour suppressor gene. Mutations in p53 are found in over half of all cancers.

a) Suggest how p53 normally functions.

b) Suggest how mutations in p53 could lead to cancer.

Q3 A woman has found a lump in her breast. After tests, her doctor tells her that she has breast cancer and that it has spread to her liver. The woman is 49 years old and is having oestrogen-containing HRT to treat symptoms of the menopause.

a) What type of tumour does she have? Explain your answer.

b) Explain why taking HRT may have contributed to the woman developing breast cancer.

Q4 Dichloroacetic acid is a carcinogen (cancer-causing chemical). Research has shown that dichloroacetic acid causes hypomethylation of c-*myc* (a proto-oncogene).

Explain why dichloroacetic acid is a carcinogen.

## Practice Questions — Fact Recall

Q1 What is an acquired mutation?

Q2 What is a mass of cells resulting from uncontrolled cell division known as?

Q3 Describe the role of proto-oncogenes.

Q4 What is an oncogene?

Q5 Give a difference between a benign tumour and a malignant tumour.

Q6 Explain how hypermethylation of tumour suppressor genes can cause a tumour to develop.

Q7 Give one way in which increased exposure to oestrogen over a period of time is thought to contribute to the development of some breast cancers.

# 4. Interpreting Data on Cancer

*As you've probably gathered from reading the papers, there's lots of things that could 'give you cancer'. You need to be able to evaluate evidence of genetic and environmental risk factors for cancer...*

**Learning Objectives:**

- Be able to evaluate evidence showing correlations between genetic and environmental factors and various forms of cancer.
- Be able to interpret information relating to the way in which an understanding of the roles of oncogenes and tumour suppressor genes could be used in the prevention, treatment and cure of cancer.

**Specification Reference 3.8.2.3**

## Risk factors for cancer

There's no single cause for cancer but scientists have identified lots of different 'risk factors' — things that increase a person's chance of getting cancer. Risk factors can be either genetic or environmental.

### Genetic factors

Some cancers are linked with specific inherited **alleles** (an allele is a version of a gene). If you inherit that allele you're more likely to get that type of cancer (but it doesn't mean you'll definitely get that type of cancer).

**Example**

Hereditary mutations of the gene BRCA1 can greatly increase the chance of a woman developing breast cancer in her lifetime.

**Tip:** A hereditary mutation in the BRCA1 gene might significantly increase your chances of developing breast cancer — but it doesn't mean you definitely will develop breast cancer.

### Environmental factors

Exposure to radiation, lifestyle choices such as smoking, increased alcohol consumption, and a high-fat diet have all been linked to an increased chance of developing some cancers.

## Interpreting the data on risk factors

Data on variation (the differences that exist between individuals) can be very tricky to interpret because some characteristics can be affected by many different genes (they're polygenic) and many environmental factors. It's difficult to know which factors (genes or environment) are having the greatest effect. This makes it hard to draw conclusions about the causes of variation.

**Tip:** You can read more about variation on page 163.

**Example**

Take a look at Figure 1:

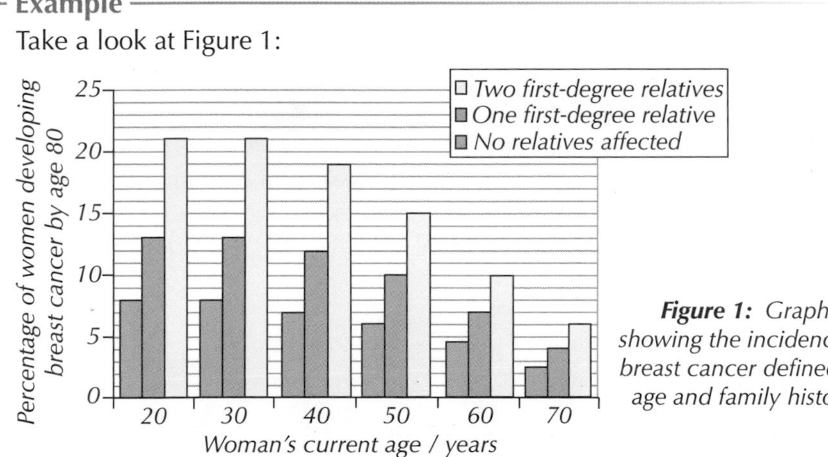


***Figure 1:*** *Graph showing the incidence of breast cancer defined by age and family history.*

**Tip:** First-degree relatives in this case include mothers, sisters and daughters.

This graph shows how the incidence of breast cancer is affected by both age and family history. There's a **positive correlation** between incidence of breast cancer in women and the number of their first-degree relatives who have also had breast cancer.

The effect of family history decreases with age, but the incidence of breast cancer is always higher in women with a close family history of the disease. A woman is more likely to develop breast cancer if members of her family have had breast cancer, which suggests a **genetic link**.

**Tip:** A positive correlation means that as one variable increases so does the other. Have a look at page 13 for more on correlations.

Now look at Figure 2:

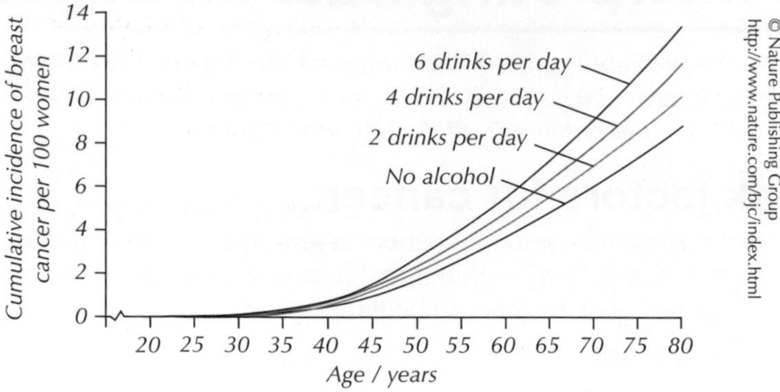


***Figure 2:*** *Graph showing the estimated incidence of breast cancer per 100 women according to the number of alcoholic drinks consumed each day.*

This graph shows that the incidence of breast cancer is linked to both age and alcohol consumption. The graph shows that the incidence of breast cancer in women increases with age — i.e. there's a positive correlation between incidence of breast cancer and age.

There's also a positive correlation between the number of alcoholic drinks consumed each day and incidence of breast cancer. Alcohol consumption is an environmental factor.

Drawing conclusions from the evidence...

If you only saw one of these graphs you may think only genetics and age, or only alcohol consumption and age, affect your risk of developing breast cancer.

When you look at both sets of data you can see that all these things affect the risk. It's difficult to tell which factor (genes or alcohol) has the largest effect. Also, there are other environmental factors that are thought to be involved in increasing the risk of developing breast cancer (e.g. diet, exercise, etc.) that aren't considered here.

**Tip:** Look carefully at titles, labels and scales on graphs. They're all there to help you understand the data.

**Exam Tip**
In the exam you might have to evaluate evidence showing correlations between genetic and environmental factors and cancer. Just remember that there are usually several factors at work and that correlation doesn't always mean cause.

## Practice Question — Application

Q1 A study was carried out to determine if smoking is linked to an increased risk of breast cancer. 116 544 women without breast cancer in California were sent questionnaires to establish their smoking history and other personal information. The women were then followed for 5 years. The results on the right show the relative risk of breast cancer, adjusted for other factors such as age and alcohol consumption, for women with different smoking histories.

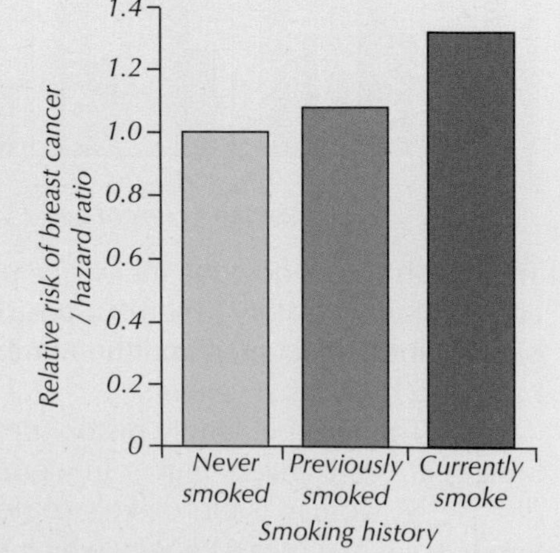


a) Describe the results shown in the graph.

b) Can you conclude from this data that smoking causes breast cancer? Explain your answer.

# Preventing, treating and curing cancer

Cancer is caused by mutations in proto-oncogenes and tumour suppressor genes (see page 205). Understanding the role that these genes play in causing cancer, and knowing exactly how they work, can be really helpful for coming up with ways to prevent, treat and cure cancer.

## Preventing cancer

If a specific cancer-causing mutation is known, then it is possible to **screen** for (look for) the mutation in a person's DNA.

**Example**

It's possible to screen for the mutated allele of BRCA1 (the tumour suppressor gene, which greatly increases a woman's risk of developing breast cancer in her lifetime).

Knowing about this increased risk means that preventative steps can be taken to reduce it.

**Example**

A woman with the BRCA1 mutation may choose to have a mastectomy (removal of one or both breasts) to significantly reduce the risk of breast cancer developing. Women with this mutation may also be screened for signs of breast cancer more often than the rest of the population, as early diagnosis increases the chances of recovery.

**Tip:** It's very rare that such an extreme measure (like removing a breast) is taken, but a mutation in BRAC1 gives an extremely high (50-65%) chance of breast cancer developing.

Knowing about specific mutations also means that more sensitive tests can be developed, which can lead to earlier and more accurate diagnoses.

**Examples**

- There's a mutation in the RAS proto-oncogene in around half of all bowel cancers. Bowel cancer can be detected early by looking for RAS mutations in the DNA of bowel cells.
- People with a mutated APC tumour suppressor gene have frequent colonoscopies to diagnose hereditary colon cancer earlier.

**Tip:** A colonoscopy involves attaching a camera onto a long tube and passing it through the colon.

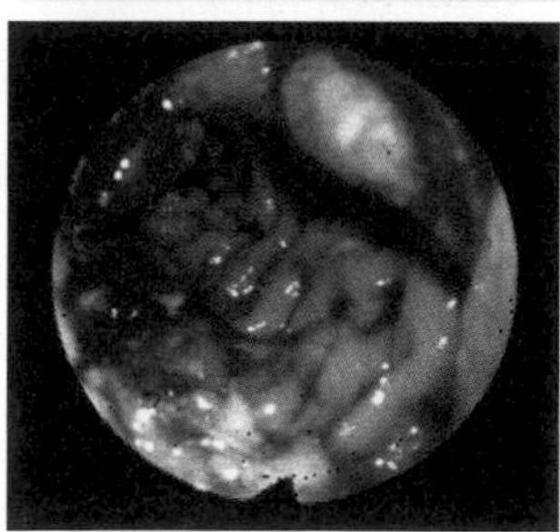

*Figure 3: Colonoscopic view of a human colon with colon cancer. Tumours appear bright red.*

## Treating and curing cancer

The treatment for cancer can be different for different mutations, so knowing how specific mutations actually cause cancer can be very useful for developing drugs to effectively target them.

**Examples**

- Skin cancer caused by a mutation of the B-RAF proto-oncogene can be treated with the drug ZELBORAF™. ZELBORAF™ inhibits the mutated B-RAF enzyme — this stops cells that express the mutation from growing. Skin cancers caused by other mutations can't be treated this way.
- Breast cancer caused by a mutation of the HER2 proto-oncogene can be treated with a drug called Herceptin®. This drug binds specifically to the altered HER2 protein receptor and suppresses cell division and tumour growth. Breast cancer caused by other mutations is not treated with this drug as it doesn't work.
- Research is being conducted into a treatment for breast, pancreatic and cervical cancers caused by a faulty BRCA tumour suppressor gene. This involves using small molecules which block an enzyme involved in repairing DNA. The molecules may be able to prevent the DNA repair in cancerous cells containing a faulty BRCA gene.

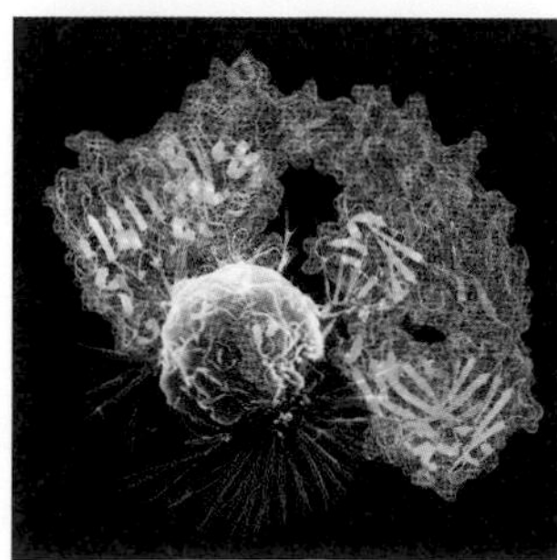

*Figure 4: Molecular model of Herceptin® (green) and a breast cancer cell (pink).*

This kills the cancer cells and so could provide a targeted treatment for cancers caused by BRCA mutations.

Some cancer-causing mutations require more aggressive treatment than others, so understanding how the mutation that causes them works can help produce the best treatment plan.

**Example**

If a mutation is known to cause an aggressive (fast-growing) cancer, it may be treated with higher doses of radiotherapy or by removing larger areas of the tumour and surrounding tissue during surgery.

**Tip:** Radiotherapy involves using radiation in an attempt to shrink a tumour. The radiation damages the DNA of the tumour cells, causing them to die and the tumour to shrink.

**Gene therapy** (where faulty alleles in a person's cells are replaced by working versions of those alleles — see page 245) may also be able to treat cancer caused by some mutations.

**Example**

If you know that the cancer is being caused by inactivated tumour suppressor genes, it's hoped that gene therapy could be used in the future to provide working versions of the genes.

Currently, gene therapy has only been used to treat cancer in clinical trials.

## Practice Questions — Application

Q1 Retinoblastoma is a rare form of childhood cancer, characterised by tumours in one or both eyes. It is caused by a mutation in the RB1 tumour suppressor gene, which codes for the pRB protein.

a) The RB1 gene has two alleles. A mutation has to occur in both RB1 alleles for retinoblastoma to develop. Suggest why this is the case.

b) Some children with retinoblastoma inherit a mutation in one of their RB1 alleles. These children are more likely to develop further tumours than children who acquire a mutation in early childhood.
Explain how screening to determine whether a child has inherited an RB1 mutation may be beneficial.

Q2 Imatinib is an anti-cancer drug that inhibits the function of CD117, a receptor protein produced by the KIT oncogene.

a) The KIT oncogene is responsible for some gastrointestinal tumours. Suggest why a doctor will biopsy one of these tumours and test it for the presence of CD117 before deciding on a course of treatment.

b) There are many anti-cancer drugs available that target oncogenes. They work by inhibiting the function of the oncogene protein. Developing a drug against mutated tumour suppressor genes can be more difficult. Suggest why this might be the case.

**Tip:** Remember, an acquired mutation is a mutation that occurs in individual cells after fertilisation (e.g. in adulthood). Hereditary mutations are mutations passed from a parent to their offspring via their gametes.

**Tip:** You need to know how tumour suppressor genes and proto-oncogenes work to answer Q2. Take a look back at p. 205 if you get stuck.

**Tip:** When doctors biopsy a tumour they take a small sample of cells from it to test and examine under a microscope.

# 5. Stem Cells

*All multicellular organisms stem from, err, stem cells. Every cell in your body was produced from a stem cell. So was every cell in every other multicellular organism's body. So they're pretty important.*

**Learning Objectives:**

- Know that totipotent cells are cells that can mature into any type of body cell and that they occur only for a limited time in mammalian embryos.
- Know that pluripotent cells are cells that can mature into any type of body cell (except placental cells) and that they occur in mammalian embryos.
- Know that multipotent and unipotent cells are found in mature mammals and that they can divide to form a limited number of different cell types.
- Understand that during development, totipotent cells translate only part of their DNA, resulting in cell specialisation.
- Know about unipotent cells, exemplified by the formation of cardiomyocytes.

**Specification Reference 3.8.2.1**

## What are stem cells?

Multicellular organisms are made up from many different cell types that are specialised for their function, e.g. liver cells, muscle cells, white blood cells. All these specialised cell types originally came from stem cells. Stem cells are unspecialised cells that can develop into other types of cell. Stem cells divide to become new cells, which then become specialised.

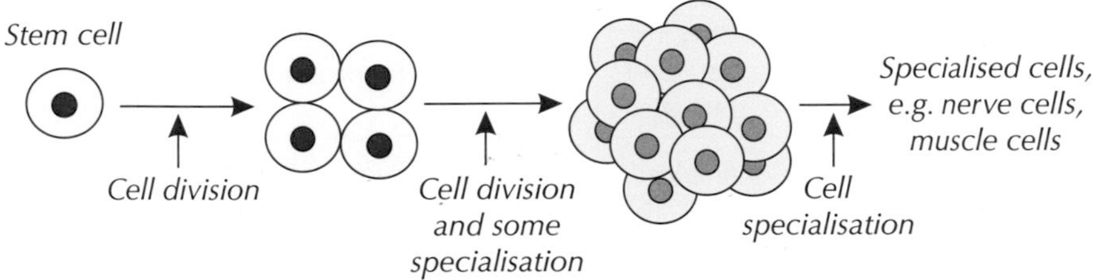


***Figure 1:*** *Diagram showing stem cell division.*

## Where are stem cells found?

All multicellular organisms have some form of stem cell. Stem cells are found in the embryo (where they become all the specialised cells needed to form a fetus) and in some adult tissues (where they become specialised cells that need to be replaced, e.g. stem cells in the intestines constantly replace intestinal epithelial cells).

Stem cells that can mature (develop) into any type of body cell in an organism, (including the cells that make up the placenta in mammals) are called **totipotent** cells. Totipotent stem cells are only present in mammals in the first few cell divisions of an embryo. After this point the embryonic stem cells become **pluripotent**. They can still specialise into any cell in the body, but lose the ability to become the cells that make up the placenta.

The stem cells present in adult mammals are either **multipotent** or **unipotent**. Multipotent stem cells are able to differentiate into a few different types of cell.

**Example**

Both red and white blood cells can be formed from multipotent stem cells found in bone marrow.

***Figure 2:*** *A cluster of human embryonic stem cells.*

Unipotent stem cells can only differentiate into one type of cell.

**Example**

There's a type of unipotent stem cell that can only divide to produce epidermal skin cells, which make up the outer layer of your skin.

## Becoming specialised

Stem cells become specialised because during their development they only transcribe and translate part of their DNA. Stem cells all contain the same genes — but during development not all of them are transcribed and translated (expressed). Under one set of conditions, certain genes are expressed and others are switched off. Under different conditions, different genes are expressed and others are switched off.

**Tip:** Remember: transcription is when DNA is copied into mRNA. Translation is when proteins are produced using the code in mRNA.

Tip: The process of cells becoming specialised is known as differentiation.

Tip: It's a mix of some genes being switched on and other genes being switched off that causes specialisation.

Genes that are expressed get transcribed into mRNA, which is then translated into proteins. These proteins modify the cell — they determine the cell structure and control cell processes (including the expression of more genes, which produces more proteins).

Changes to the cell produced by these proteins cause the cell to become specialised. These changes are difficult to reverse, so once a cell has specialised it stays specialised. This is summarised in Figure 3.

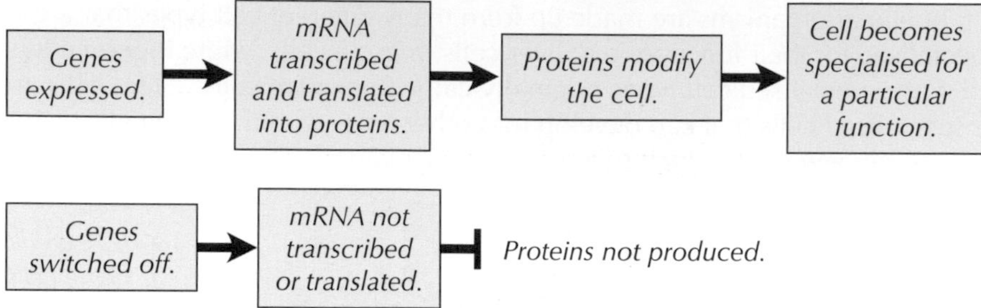


***Figure 3:** Summary of how cells become specialised through gene expression.*

**Example 1 — red blood cells**

Red blood cells are produced from a type of stem cell in the bone marrow. They contain lots of haemoglobin and have no nucleus (to make room for more haemoglobin). The stem cell produces a new cell in which the genes for haemoglobin production are expressed. Other genes, such as those involved in removing the nucleus, are expressed too. Many other genes are not expressed (switched off), resulting in a specialised red blood cell.

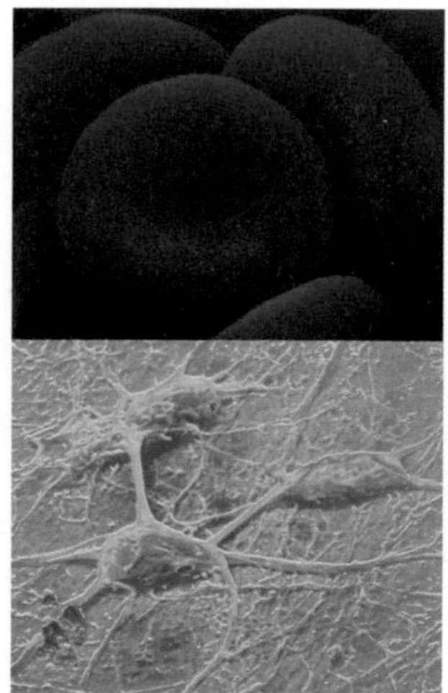

***Figure 4:** Red blood cells (top) and nerve cells (bottom) are both types of specialised cell.*

**Example 2 — nerve cells**

Nerve cells have long axons and dendrites (branches), which connect them to other nerve cells. They're produced from stem cells in the neural tube. The stem cells produce new cells in which the genes that direct the axon to extend outwards are expressed. Genes that direct the dendrites to form are also expressed. Many other genes are switched off.

## Cardiomyocytes

Cardiomyocytes (see Figure 5) are heart muscle cells that make up a lot of the tissue in our hearts. In mature mammals, it's thought that they can't divide to replicate themselves. This meant that for ages, everyone thought that we weren't able to regenerate our own heart cells at all. This is a major problem if the heart becomes damaged, e.g. by a heart attack, or the cells became worn out through age.

Recent research however, has suggested that our hearts do have some regenerative capability. Some scientists now think that old or damaged cardiomyocytes can be replaced by new cardiomyocytes derived from a small supply of unipotent stem cells in the heart.

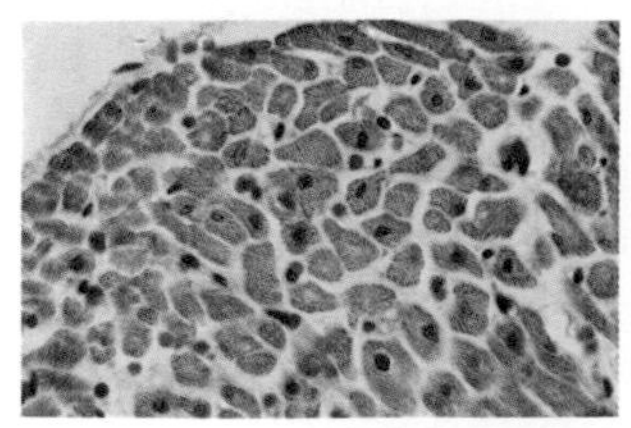

***Figure 5:** Light micrograph showing cardiomyocytes.*

Some researchers think that this process could be constantly occurring, but haven't yet agreed on how quickly it happens. Some believe that it's a really slow process and that it's possible that some cardiomyocytes are never replaced throughout a person's entire lifetime. Others think that it's occurring more quickly, so that every cardiomyocyte in the heart is replaced several times in a lifetime.

## Practice Questions — Application

Q1 Spermatogonial stem cells are a type of stem cell found in the testes. These cells can only differentiate into sperm cells.

What type of stem cell are spermatogonial stem cells?

Q2 The stem cells shown in the electron micrograph below can differentiate into any type of cell, except the cells that make up the placenta.

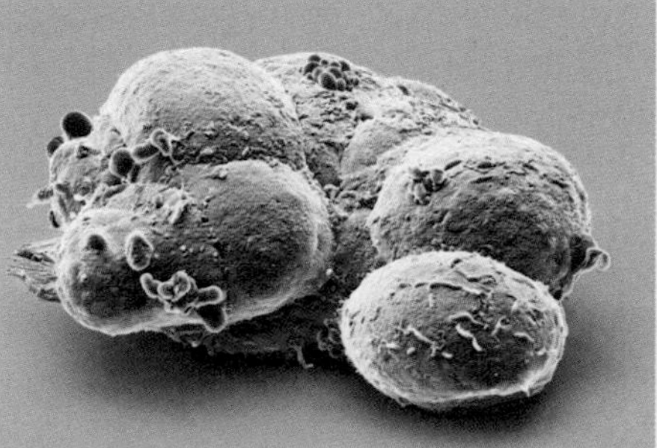

a) What type of stem cells are they?

b) Where would you find this type of stem cell?

c) If these cells could also differentiate into placental cells what type of stem cells would they be?

## Practice Questions — Fact Recall

Q1 What are stem cells?

Q2 Where are stem cells found in mammals?

Q3 Explain the difference between totipotent, multipotent and unipotent stem cells.

Q4 Describe how stem cells become specialised.

Q5 a) What is a cardiomyocyte?

b) What type of stem cell do some scientists think that new cardiomyocytes can be derived from?

**Tip:** The different types of stem cell have similar names so they're easy to get confused — make sure you take the time to learn which one is which.

# 6. Stem Cells in Medicine

*Stem cells can be used in medicine to treat or cure various diseases. Some stem cell therapies are already being used, others are still being developed.*

**Learning Objectives:**

- Understand that pluripotent stem cells can divide in unlimited numbers and can be used in treating human disorders.
- Know that induced pluripotent stem cells (iPS cells) can be produced from adult cells using appropriate protein transcription factors.
- Be able to evaluate the use of stem cells in treating human disorders.

**Specification Reference 3.8.2.1**

## Stem cell therapies in existence

Since stem cells can divide into a range of specialised cell types, doctors and scientists think they could be used to replace cells damaged by illness or injury. Some stem cell therapies already exist for some diseases affecting the blood and immune system.

### Bone marrow transplants

Bone marrow contains stem cells that can become specialised to form any type of blood cell. Bone marrow transplants can be used to replace the faulty bone marrow in patients that produce abnormal blood cells. The stem cells in the transplanted bone marrow divide and specialise to produce healthy blood cells.

This technique has been used successfully to treat leukaemia (a cancer of the blood or bone marrow) and lymphoma (a cancer of the lymphatic system). It has also been used to treat some genetic disorders, such as sickle-cell anaemia and severe combined immunodeficiency (SCID).

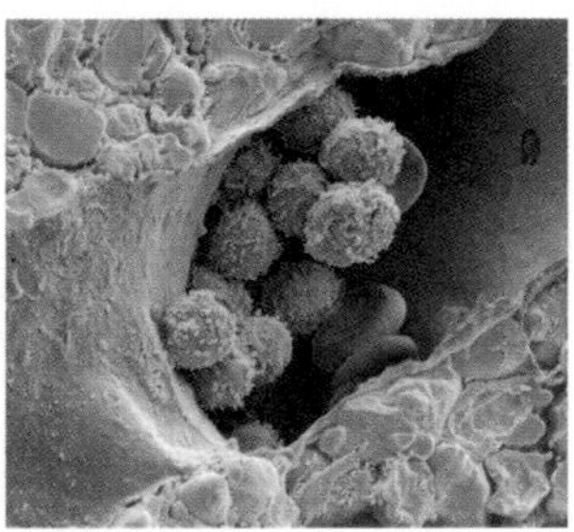

***Figure 1:** Bone marrow with developing white blood cells (blue).*

**Example — SCID**

Severe combined immunodeficiency (SCID) is a genetic disorder that affects the immune system. People with SCID have a poorly functioning immune system as their white blood cells (made in the bone marrow from stem cells) are defective. This means they can't defend the body against infections by identifying and destroying microorganisms. So SCID sufferers are extremely susceptible to infections.

Treatment with a bone marrow transplant replaces the faulty bone marrow with donor bone marrow that contains stem cells without the faulty genes that cause SCID. These then differentiate to produce functional white blood cells. These cells can identify and destroy invading pathogens, so the immune system functions properly.

## Stem cell therapies of the future

As stem cells can divide into specialised cell types, scientists think they could be used to replace damaged tissues in a range of diseases. Scientists are researching the use of stem cells as treatment for lots of conditions, including:

- Spinal cord injuries — stem cells could be used to replace damaged nerve tissue.
- Heart disease and damage caused by heart attacks — stem cells could be used to replace damaged heart tissue.
- Bladder conditions — stem cells could be used to grow whole bladders, which are then implanted in patients to replace diseased ones.
- Respiratory diseases — donated windpipes can be stripped down to their simple collagen structure and then covered with tissue generated by stem cells. This can then be transplanted into patients.
- Organ transplants — organs could be grown from stem cells to provide new organs for people on donor waiting lists.

**Tip:** These treatments aren't available yet, although some of them are at the clinical trial stage of testing.

## Sources of stem cells

To use stem cells scientists have to get them from somewhere. There are three main potential sources of human stem cells:

### 1. Adult stem cells

These are obtained from the body tissues of an adult. For example, adult stem cells are found in bone marrow. They can be obtained in a relatively simple operation — with very little risk involved, but quite a lot of discomfort. Adult stem cells aren't as flexible as embryonic stem cells (see below) — they can only specialise into a limited range of cells, not all body cell types (they're multipotent). Although scientists are trying to find ways to make adult stem cells specialise into any cell type.

### 2. Embryonic stem cells

These are obtained from embryos at an early stage of development. Embryos are created in a laboratory using *in vitro* fertilisation (IVF) — egg cells are fertilised by sperm outside the womb. Once the embryos are approximately 4 to 5 days old, stem cells are removed from them and the rest of the embryo is destroyed. Embryonic stem cells can divide an unlimited number of times and develop into all types of body cells (they're pluripotent).

**Tip:** Embryos in the normal sense are made when a sperm fertilises an egg. But it is possible to create an embryo by artificially stimulating an unfertilised egg cell to divide.

### 3. Induced pluripotent stem cells (iPS cells)

iPS cells are created by scientists in the lab. The process involves 'reprogramming' specialised adult body cells so that they become pluripotent. The adult cells are made to express a series of **transcription factors** that are normally associated with pluripotent stem cells. The transcription factors cause the adult body cells to express genes that are associated with pluripotency.

**Tip:** Transcription factors are proteins that control whether or not genes are transcribed — see page 219 for more.

One of the ways that these transcription factors can be introduced to the adult cells is by infecting them with a specially-modified virus. The virus has the genes coding for the transcription factors within its DNA. When the virus infects the adult cell, these genes are passed into the adult cell's DNA, meaning that the cell is able to produce the transcription factors.

Induced pluripotent stem cells could become really useful in research and medicine in the future — see next page. At the moment though, more research into how similar they actually are to true pluripotent embryonic stem cells is needed before they can be properly utilised.

## Ethical considerations

Obtaining stem cells from embryos created by IVF raises ethical issues because the procedure results in the destruction of an embryo that could become a fetus if placed in a womb. Some people believe that at the moment of fertilisation an individual is formed that has the right to life — so they believe that it's wrong to destroy embryos.

Some people have fewer objections to stem cells being obtained from egg cells that haven't been fertilised by sperm, but have been artificially activated to start dividing. This is because the cells couldn't survive past a few days and wouldn't produce a fetus if placed in a womb.

Some people think that scientists should only use adult stem cells because their production doesn't destroy an embryo. But adult stem cells can't develop into all the specialised cell types that embryonic stem cells can.

This is where induced pluripotent stem cells could prove really useful. They have the potential to be as flexible as embryonic stem cells, but, as

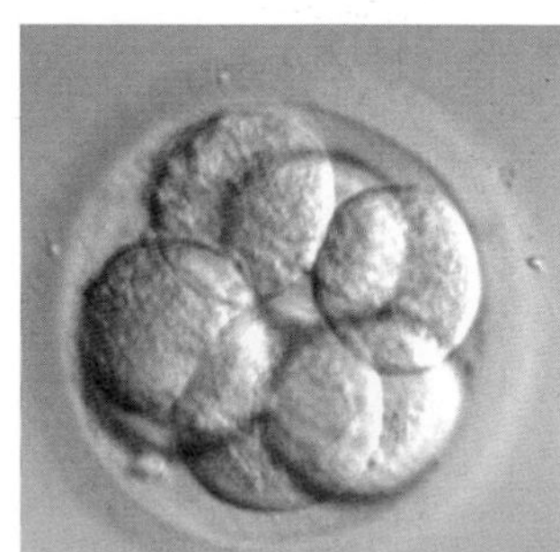

***Figure 2:*** *A pre-implantation IVF embryo.*

they're obtained from adult tissue, there aren't the same ethical issues surrounding their use. It's also possible that iPS cells could be made from a patient's own cells. These iPS cells, which would be genetically identical to the patient's cells, could then be used to grow some new tissue or an organ that the patient's body wouldn't reject (rejection of transplants occurs quite often and is caused by the patient's immune system recognising the tissue as foreign and attacking it).

The decision makers in society have to take into account everyone's views when making decisions about important scientific work like stem cell research and its use to treat human disorders.

**Exam Tip**
You might have to evaluate the use of stem cells in treating human disorders in the exam. Make sure you consider both sides of the argument and balance the benefits against the possible risks.

## Benefits of stem cell therapy

People who make decisions about the use of stem cells to treat human disorders have to consider the potential benefits of stem cell therapies:

- They could save many lives — e.g. many people waiting for organ transplants die before a donor organ becomes available. Stem cells could be used to grow organs for those people awaiting transplants.
- It might even be possible to make stem cells genetically identical to a patient's own cells. These could then be used to grow some new tissue or an organ that the patient's body wouldn't reject.
- They could improve the quality of life for many people — e.g. they could be used to replace damaged cells in the eyes of people who are blind.

**Tip:** Adult stem cells taken from the patient's own tissues are also less likely to be rejected by the patient's body as they won't be seen as foreign.

### Practice Questions — Application

Q1 Sickle cell anaemia is an inherited disorder caused by a mutation in the haemoglobin protein. The mutated protein causes red blood cells to 'sickle' (twist into a crescent shape). The sickled cells then clump together, blocking capillaries and restricting blood flow.
All blood cells are produced from multipotent cells in the bone marrow. Describe how a bone marrow transplant could be used to cure sickle cell anaemia.

Q2 The cornea is the front part of the eye. Together with the lens, it refracts light into the eye and enables us to see. Scientists have been able to restore loss of vision caused by damage to the cornea using stem cells taken from healthy corneas.

a) Suggest why stem cells are able to restore loss of vision in these circumstances.

b) Patients with loss of vision in one eye are treated with stem cells taken from their other, healthy eye. Suggest two benefits of this.

Q3 Plasmids are small loops of DNA that can be inserted into cells. Suggest how plasmids could be used to produce induced pluripotent stem cells (iPS cells).

Q4 A team of scientists is investigating the use of embryonic stem cells in spinal cord injuries. Spinal cord injuries can cause paralysis, and patients may require long-term medical care and can have a lower quality of life. The team inject patients with embryonic stem cells taken from donated embryos left over from fertility treatment that would otherwise be discarded. If this injection works it could potentially allow for more movement in the patients. There are also other treatments being developed that use iPS cells.
Discuss the use of embryonic stem cells in this investigation.

**Exam Tip**
If you're asked to discuss the use of stem cells in the exam, you need to make your answer specific to the question asked to get full marks — don't just give general advantages and disadvantages.

# 7. Regulation of Transcription and Translation

*Every cell in an organism contains the same DNA, but not all the proteins it codes for are made. This is because transcription and translation are controlled.*

**Learning Objectives:**

- Know that the transcription of target genes in eukaryotes can be stimulated or inhibited when specific transcriptional factors move from the cytoplasm into the nucleus.
- Understand the role of the steroid hormone, oestrogen, in initiating transcription.
- Know that in eukaryotes and some prokaryotes, translation of the mRNA produced from target genes can be inhibited by RNA interference (RNAi).
- Be able to interpret data from investigations into gene expression.

**Specification Reference 3.8.2.2**

## Controlling transcription

You should remember from Topic 4 that transcription is when a gene is copied from DNA into messenger RNA (mRNA). The enzyme responsible for synthesising mRNA from DNA is called RNA polymerase.

All the cells in an organism carry the same genes (DNA) but the structure and function of different cells varies. This is because not all the genes in a cell are expressed (transcribed and used to make a protein). Because different genes are expressed, different proteins are made and these proteins modify the cell — they determine the cell structure and control cell processes (including the expression of more genes, which produce more proteins). The transcription of genes is controlled by protein molecules called **transcription factors**.

### The role of transcription factors

In eukaryotes, transcription factors move from the cytoplasm to the nucleus. In the nucleus they bind to specific DNA sites called **promoters**, which are found near the start of their target genes — the genes they control the expression of. Transcription factors control expression by controlling the rate of transcription.

Some transcription factors, called **activators**, stimulate or increase the rate of transcription — e.g. they help RNA polymerase bind to the start of the target gene and activate transcription. Other transcription factors, called **repressors**, inhibit or decrease the rate of transcription — e.g. they bind to the start of the target gene, preventing RNA polymerase from binding, stopping transcription. Figure 1 shows activators and repressors at work.

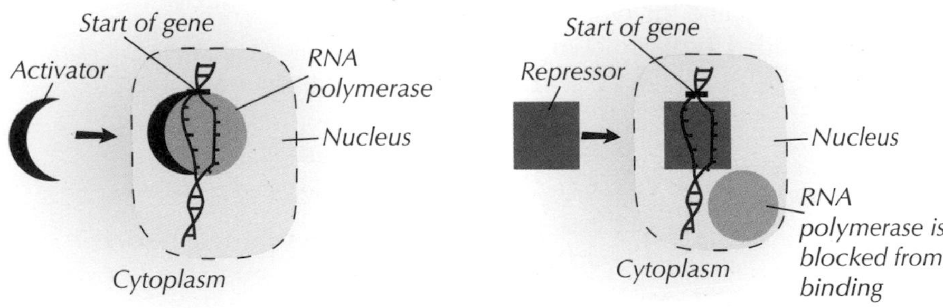


***Figure 1:*** *An activator (left) and a repressor (right) can control the rate of transcription by affecting RNA polymerase.*

## Oestrogen

The expression of genes can also be affected by other molecules in the cell, e.g. oestrogen. Oestrogen is a steroid hormone that can affect transcription by binding to a transcription factor called an oestrogen receptor, forming an oestrogen-oestrogen receptor complex (see Figure 2 on the next page).

**Tip:** Not all cell types have oestrogen receptors — so not all cells are affected by oestrogen.

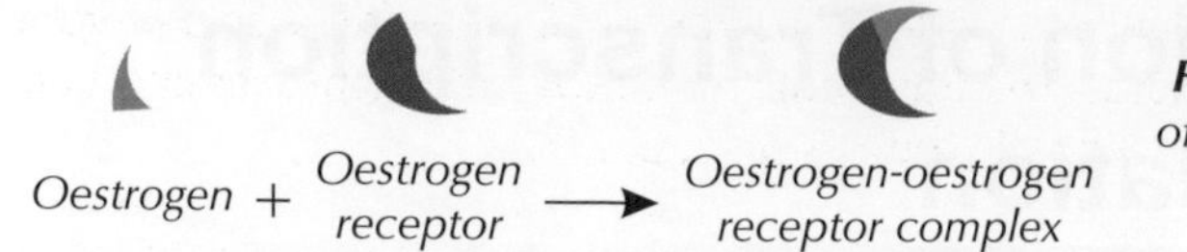


***Figure 2:** The formation of an oestrogen-oestrogen receptor complex.*

The complex moves from the cytoplasm into the nucleus where it binds to specific DNA sites near the start of the target gene. The complex can act as an activator of transcription, e.g. helping RNA polymerase bind to the start of the target gene (see Figure 3).

**Tip:** In some cells, the oestrogen-oestrogen receptor complex can act as a repressor of transcription instead of an activator. It depends on the type of cell and the target gene.

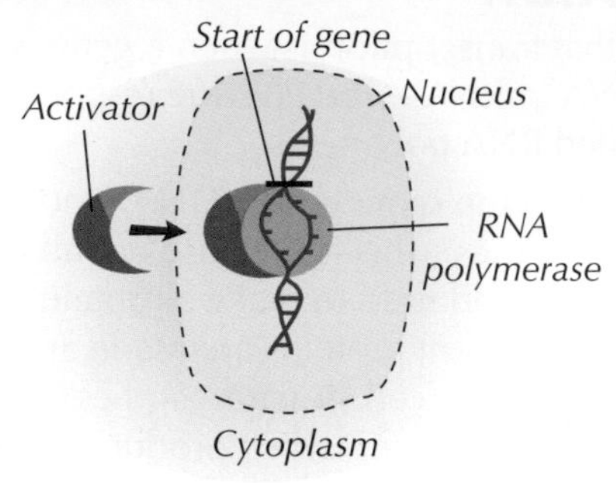


***Figure 3:** An oestrogen-oestrogen receptor complex activating transcription.*

## RNAi

In eukaryotes, gene expression is also affected by RNA interference (RNAi). RNAi is where small, double-stranded RNA molecules stop mRNA from target genes being translated into proteins. A similar process to RNAi can also occur in prokaryotes. The molecules involved in RNAi are called siRNA (small interfering RNA) and miRNA (microRNA). Here's how RNAi works:

**Tip:** RNAi molecules are small lengths of non-coding RNA (they don't code for proteins).

### siRNA (and miRNA in plants)

Once mRNA has been transcribed, it leaves the nucleus for the cytoplasm (see Figure 4). In the cytoplasm, double-stranded siRNA associates with several proteins and unwinds. One of the resulting single strands of siRNA is selected and the other strand is degraded (broken down) — see Figure 5.

**Tip:** Unlike mRNA and tRNA, siRNA is double-stranded.

**Tip:** Double-stranded siRNA is unwound into two single-stranded siRNA molecules by an enzyme.

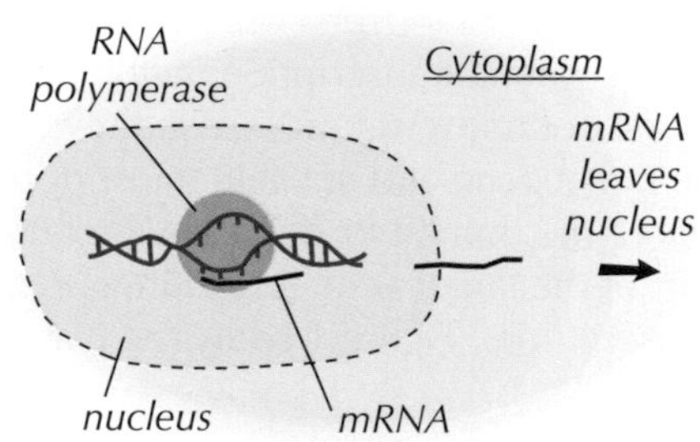

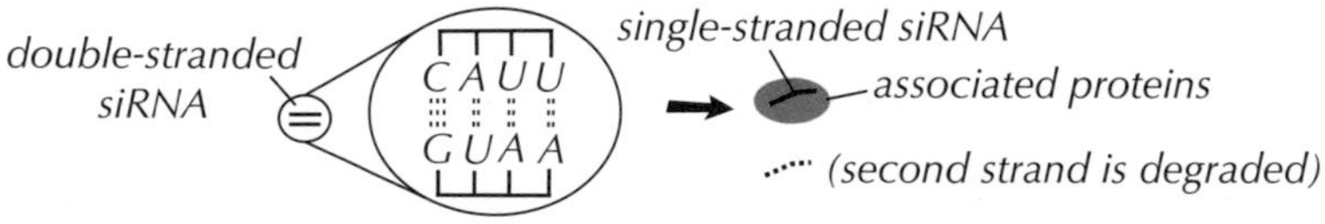

***Figure 4:** mRNA leaves the nucleus after transcription.*



***Figure 5:** siRNA associates with proteins in the cytoplasm.*

**Tip:** siRNA is actually about 20-25 nucleotides long (this diagram just shows a short section).

The single strand of siRNA then binds to the target mRNA. The base sequence of the siRNA is complementary to the base sequence in sections of the target mRNA (see Figure 6).

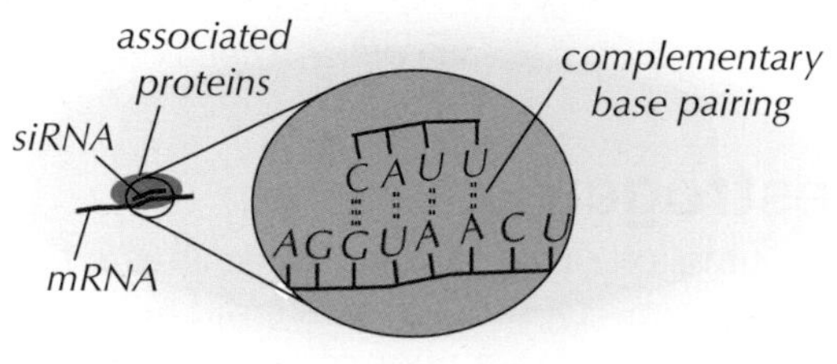


***Figure 6:** siRNA binds to the target mRNA.*

The proteins associated with the siRNA cut the mRNA into fragments — so it can no longer be translated. The fragments then move into a processing body, which contains 'tools' to degrade them (see Figure 7).

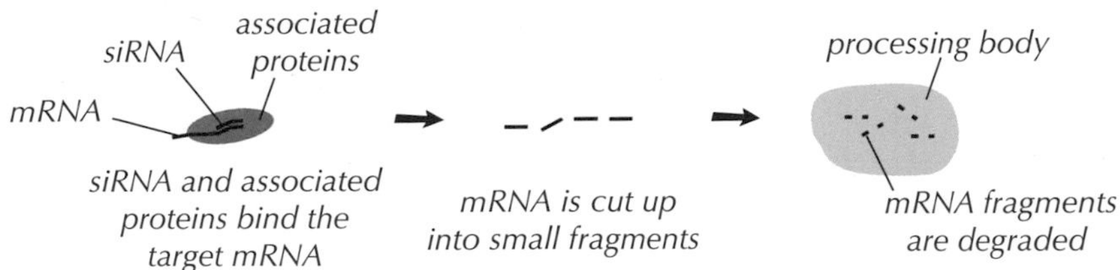


***Figure 7:** siRNA affects gene expression by directing the target mRNA to be cut up.*

A similar process happens with miRNA in plants. Like siRNA, the base sequence of plant miRNA is complementary to its target mRNA sequence and so binding results in the cutting up and degradation of the mRNA. However, its production in the cell is similar to that of mammalian miRNA — see below.

**Tip:** siRNA has a potential use in treating genetic disorders, for example stopping a known harmful gene from being expressed. siRNA molecules with a base sequence complementary to the mRNA from that gene could be inserted into the affected cells — they will bind to the mRNA and so block translation of that protein.

### miRNA in mammals

In mammals, the miRNA isn't usually fully complementary to the target mRNA. This makes it less specific than siRNA and so it may target more than one mRNA molecule.

When miRNA is first transcribed, it exists as a long, folded strand. It is processed into a double strand, and then into two single strands, by enzymes in the cytoplasm.

Like siRNA, one strand associates with proteins and binds to target mRNA in the cytoplasm. Instead of the proteins associated with miRNA cutting mRNA into fragments, the miRNA-protein complex physically blocks the translation of the target mRNA. The mRNA is then moved into a processing body, where it can either be stored or degraded. When it's stored, it can be returned and translated at another time.

**Tip:** miRNA is processed like this:

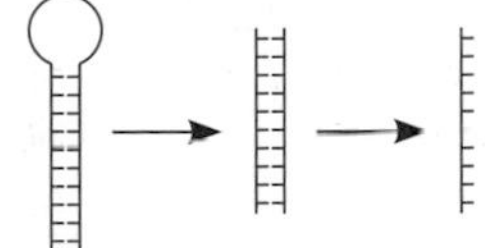

The unused single strand is degraded in the cytoplasm (like the second strand of siRNA, see previous page).

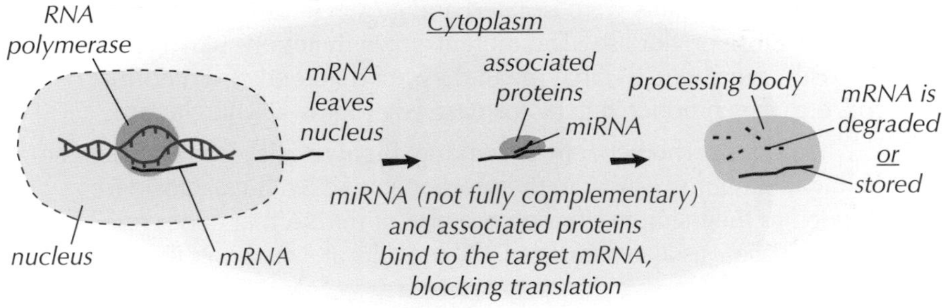


***Figure 8:** miRNA affects gene expression by blocking the translation of mRNA.*

## Practice Questions — Application

Q1 Rett syndrome is a neuro-developmental disorder caused by a mutation in the MECP2 gene. The protein produced by the gene is a transcription factor which acts as a repressor and is needed for normal functioning of nerve cells. Mutations in the gene often result in reduced production of the protein. Suggest how a mutation in the MECP2 gene causes Rett syndrome.

Q2 AMD is a medical condition which results in loss of vision because of damage to the retina. It is caused by the expression of multiple genes and by environmental factors. A treatment is being developed using siRNA. Suggest how siRNA could be used to treat AMD.

# Interpreting data on gene expression

You could get a question in the exam where you have to interpret data about gene expression. It could be on anything you've learnt on pages 219-221 (e.g. transcription factors, oestrogen or RNAi) or it could be on epigenetic control of gene expression (see pages 224-226). Below is an example of a gene expression system in bacteria and an experiment that investigates how it works.

**Exam Tip**
You don't need to learn all the information in this example for your exam, but do make sure you understand what the results of the experiment tell you about how the expression of the gene is controlled.

**Example**

**The *lac* repressor**

*E. coli* is a bacterium that respires glucose, but it can use lactose if glucose isn't available. If lactose is present, *E. coli* makes an enzyme (β-galactosidase) to digest it. But if there's no lactose, it doesn't waste energy making an enzyme it doesn't need.

The enzyme's gene is only expressed when lactose is present. The production of the enzyme is controlled by a transcription factor — the *lac* repressor. When there's no lactose, the *lac* repressor binds to the DNA at the start of the gene, stopping transcription. When lactose is present it binds to the *lac* repressor, stopping it binding to the DNA, so the gene is transcribed (see Figure 9).

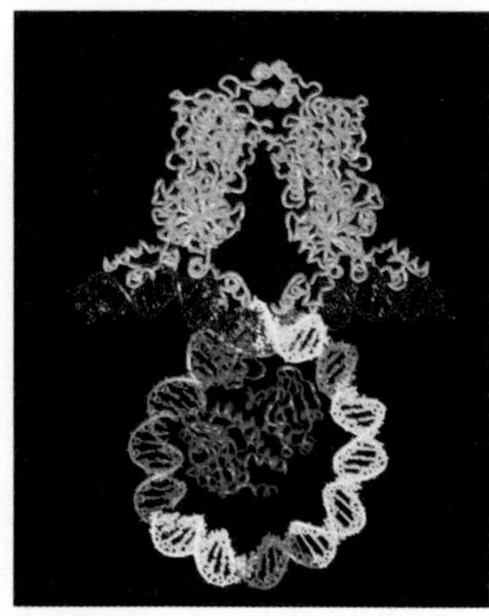

*Figure 10: Molecular model of the lac repressor (pink) binding to DNA.*

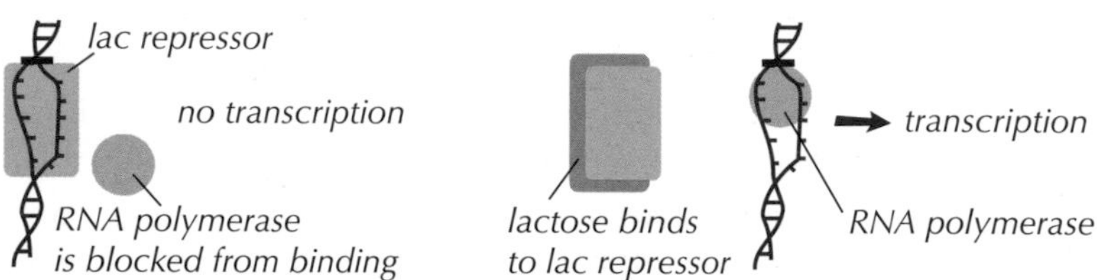


*Figure 9: Lactose can activate transcription by stopping the* lac *repressor from binding to the DNA, so that RNA polymerase can bind instead.*

**The experiment**

Different *E. coli* mutants were isolated and grown in different media, e.g. with lactose or glucose. The mutants have mutations (changes in their DNA bases, see page 201) that mean they act differently from normal *E. coli*, e.g. they produce β-galactosidase when grown with glucose.

To detect whether active (working) β-galactosidase was produced, a chemical that turns yellow in the presence of active β-galactosidase was added to the medium. The production of mRNA that codes for β-galactosidase was also measured. The results are shown in the table.

| Medium | Mutant | mRNA | Colour |
|---|---|---|---|
| Glucose | Normal | No | No yellow |
| Lactose | Normal | Yes | Yellow |
| Glucose | Mutant 1 | Yes | Yellow |
| Lactose | Mutant 1 | Yes | Yellow |
| Glucose | Mutant 2 | No | No yellow |
| Lactose | Mutant 2 | Yes | No yellow |

**Exam Tip**
The data you are given in the exam won't necessarily be a table. You could be given a bar chart, scatter graph, or even a frequency table. Make sure you're comfortable analysing data in all its forms.

In mutant 1, mRNA and active β-galactosidase were produced even when they were grown with only glucose — the gene is always being expressed. This suggests that mutant 1 has a faulty *lac* repressor, e.g. in the absence of lactose the repressor isn't able to bind DNA, so transcription can occur and mRNA and active β-galactosidase are produced.

In mutant 2, mRNA is produced but active β-galactosidase isn't when lactose is present — the gene is being transcribed but it isn't producing active β-galactosidase. This suggests mutant 2 is producing faulty β-galactosidase, e.g. because a mutation has affected its active site.

## Practice Questions — Application

The production of tryptophan in bacteria is controlled by a repressor. When tryptophan is present in the bacterial cell it binds to the repressor, allowing it to bind to promoters near its target genes.

A team of scientists have studied the activity of normal bacteria and bacteria that have a mutation in the tryptophan repressor gene, by measuring the amount of tryptophan mRNA present in the bacteria. Their results are shown in the table below.

| Starter culture | Target mRNA (arbitrary units) |
|---|---|
| Normal bacteria in the presence of tryptophan. | 0.13 |
| Normal bacteria without tryptophan present. | 9.30 |
| Mutant bacteria in the presence of tryptophan. | 9.28 |
| Mutant bacteria without tryptophan present. | 9.33 |

Q1 Suggest three factors that should be controlled in this experiment.

Q2 In normal bacteria, the presence of tryptophan prevents the production of more tryptophan.

a) Use evidence from the table to explain how the presence of tryptophan prevents the production of more tryptophan in normal bacteria.

b) Suggest why it is beneficial for bacteria to be able to control their tryptophan production.

Q3 Describe the results for the mutant bacteria, and suggest an explanation.

**Exam Tip**
Tryptophan is just a type of amino acid — but you don't actually need to know this to answer the question. If something unfamiliar like this comes up in the exam, don't let it throw you. Just apply what you do know to the information you're given and you should be able to get all the marks.

**Tip:** You don't need to know the exact details of an experiment to be able to work out the kind of controls it should include.

**Tip:** Questions like this on repressors can start to become a bit confusing if you're not careful... so take your time and work through the questions carefully. A quick sketch might help, for example:

repressor gene → ↓transcription

~~repressor gene~~ (mutant) → ↑transcription

## Practice Questions — Fact Recall

Q1 What are transcription factors?

Q2 What is:

a) an activator? b) a repressor?

Q3 Explain why not all cells are affected by oestrogen.

Q4 Describe the process by which oestrogen activates the transcription of a gene.

Q5 What is RNAi and how does it work? (Use siRNA as an example.)

Q6 Why might a mammalian miRNA molecule target a greater range of mRNA molecules than siRNA?

# 8. Epigenetic Control of Gene Expression

*Gene expression isn't just controlled by transcription factors. Epigenetic changes also play a part in whether a gene is expressed or not.*

**Learning Objectives:**

- Recall the process of epigenetic control of gene expression in eukaryotes.
- Know that epigenetics involves heritable changes in gene function, without changes to the base sequence of DNA.
- Understand that epigenetic changes are caused by changes in the environment that inhibit transcription by:
  - increased methylation of the DNA or
  - decreased acetylation of associated histones.
- Understand the relevance of epigenetics on the development and treatment of disease, especially cancer.

**Specification Reference 3.8.2.2**

## How does epigenetic control work?

In eukaryotes, epigenetic control can determine whether a gene is switched on or off — i.e. whether the gene is expressed (transcribed and translated) or not. It works through the attachment or removal of chemical groups (known as epigenetic marks) to or from DNA or histone proteins (see below and next page). These epigenetic marks don't alter the base sequence of DNA. Instead, they alter how easy it is for the enzymes and other proteins needed for transcription to interact with and transcribe the DNA.

Epigenetic changes to gene expression play a role in lots of normal cellular processes and can also occur in response to changes in the environment — e.g. pollution and availability of food.

## Inheriting epigenetic changes

Organisms inherit their DNA base sequence from their parents. Most epigenetic marks on the DNA are removed between generations, but some escape the removal process and are passed on to offspring. This means that the expression of some genes in the offspring can be affected by environmental changes that affected their parents or grandparents.

**Example**

Epigenetic changes in some plants in response to drought have been shown to be passed on to later generations.

**Tip:** Epigenetic marks are important for cell specialisation. Most epigenetic marks are removed between generations because cells from the fertilised egg need to be able to become any type of cell (i.e. they need to be totipotent — see p. 213).

## Controlling gene expression

There are several epigenetic mechanisms used to control gene expression. You need to know about methylation of DNA and the acetylation of histones.

### Increased methylation of DNA

Methylation is when a methyl group (an example of an epigenetic mark) is attached to the DNA coding for a gene.

The group always attaches at a CpG site, which is where a cytosine and guanine base are next to each other in the DNA (linked by a phosphodiester bond). Increased methylation changes the DNA structure so that the transcriptional machinery (enzymes, etc.) can't interact with the gene — so the gene is not expressed (i.e. it's switched off).

**Tip:** A methyl group is a $-CH_3$ group.

**Tip:** The methyl group is attached to cytosine by enzymes called DNA methyltransferases.

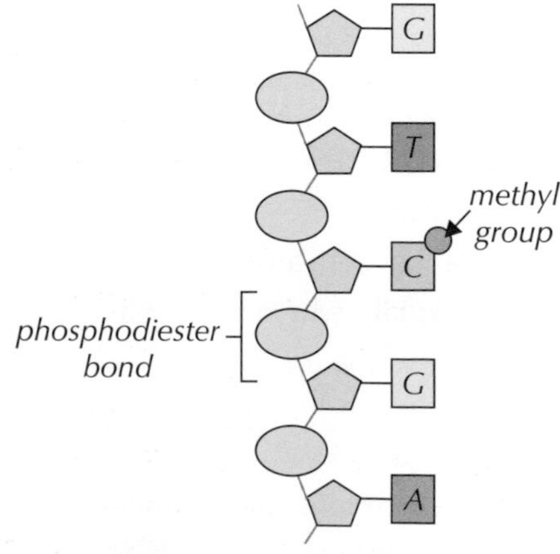


***Figure 1:*** *DNA strand with a methyl group attached.*

### Decreased acetylation of histones

**Histones** are proteins that DNA wraps around to form chromatin, which makes up chromosomes. Chromatin can be highly condensed or less condensed. How condensed it is affects the accessibility of the DNA and whether or not it can be transcribed.

Histones can be epigenetically modified by the addition or removal of **acetyl groups** (which are another example of an epigenetic mark). When histones are acetylated, the chromatin is less condensed. This means that the transcriptional machinery can access the DNA, allowing genes to be transcribed. When acetyl groups are removed from the histones, the chromatin becomes highly condensed and genes in the DNA can't be transcribed because the transcriptional machinery can't physically access them. Histone deacetylase (HDAC) enzymes are responsible for removing the acetyl groups.

**Tip:** An acetyl group is a $-COCH_3$ group.

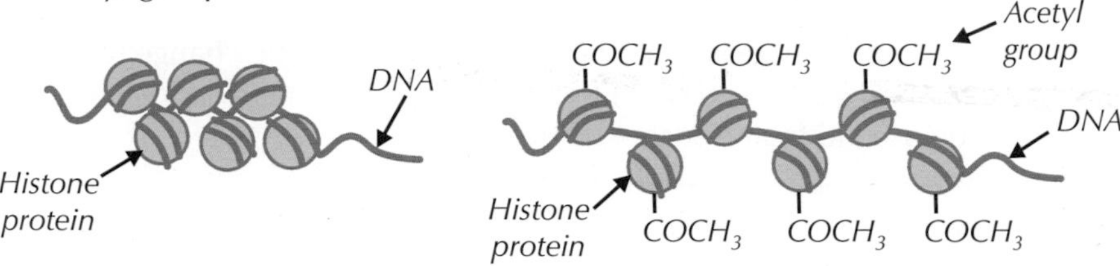


***Figure 2:*** *Highly condensed chromatin (left) and less condensed chromatin (right).*

## Development of disease

You've already seen on page 207 how epigenetics can play a role in the development of disease, with the fact that abnormal methylation of tumour suppressor genes and oncogenes can cause cancer. However, the role of epigenetics in disease doesn't stop there. It can play a role in the development of many other diseases, including Fragile-X syndrome, Angelman syndrome and Prader-Willi syndrome.

**Example — Fragile-X syndrome**

Fragile-X syndrome is a genetic disorder that can cause symptoms such as learning and behavioural difficulties, as well as characteristic physical features. It's caused by a heritable duplication mutation (see page 201) in a gene on the X chromosome, called FMR1. The mutation results in the short DNA sequence CGG being repeated many more times than usual.

These repeats mean that there are lots more CpG sites (see previous page) in the gene than usual. More CpG sites result in increased methylation of the gene, which switches it off. Because the gene is switched off, the protein that it codes for isn't produced. It's the lack of this protein that causes the symptoms of the disease.

**Tip:** The FMR1 CGG sequence is normally repeated between 5 and 40 times, but in the mutated gene it's repeated over 200 times.

**Example — Angelman syndrome**

Angelman syndrome is a genetic disorder that affects the nervous system and causes symptoms such as delayed development and motor problems. It's caused by a mutation or deletion of a region of chromosome 15. In most cases, the maternal allele in the affected region of chromosome 15 is missing. The paternal allele is present in the cell, but it is switched off by methylation and so the gene is not transcribed. Like for fragile-X syndrome this means that a protein is not produced, which leads to the symptoms of the disorder.

**Exam Tip**
You don't need to remember these specific examples for your exam, but you do need to understand how epigenetics can cause disorders.

**Example — Prader-Willi syndrome**

Prader-Willi syndrome is a genetic disorder characterised by developmental issues and excessive hunger. Most cases of Prader-Willi syndrome are caused by the loss of function of genes from the same region of chromosome 15 as Angelman syndrome. However, in this case it is the paternal allele that's usually transcribed and so the syndrome results when the deletion occurs on the paternal chromosome. The maternal gene is silenced by methylation and so is unable to compensate. The lack of the protein encoded by this gene leads to the disorder.

## Treating disease

**Tip:** Epigenetic changes are a lot easier to treat than DNA sequence mutations (due to their reversibility).

Epigenetic changes are reversible, which makes them good targets for new drugs to combat diseases they cause. These drugs are designed to counteract the epigenetic changes that cause the diseases.

For example, increased methylation is an epigenetic change that can lead to a gene being switched off. Drugs that stop DNA methylation can sometimes be used to treat diseases caused in this way.

**Example**

The drug azacitidine is used in chemotherapy for types of cancer that are caused by increased methylation of tumour suppressor genes. Tumour suppressor genes usually slow cell division, so if they are switched off by methylation, cells are able to divide uncontrollably and can form a tumour. Azacitidine inhibits the methylation of these genes by physically blocking the enzymes involved in the process.

**Tip:** There's more about the function of tumour suppressor genes on page 205.

Decreased acetylation of histones can also lead to genes being switched off. HDAC inhibitor drugs, e.g. romidepsin, can be used to treat diseases that are caused in this way — including some types of cancer. These drugs work by inhibiting the activity of histone deacetylase (HDAC) enzymes, which are responsible for removing the acetyl groups from the histones. Without the activity of HDAC enzymes, the genes remain acetylated and the proteins they code for can be transcribed.

The problem with developing drugs to counteract epigenetic changes is that these changes take place normally in a lot of cells, so it's important to make sure the drugs are as specific as possible. E.g. drugs used in cancer therapies can be designed to only target dividing cells to avoid damaging normal body cells.

**Tip:** If these drugs that counteract epigenetic changes also activate transcription in normal cells, the cells could become cancerous, creating the very problem that the drugs are supposed to be treating.

### Practice Questions — Application

A single genotype of plant was subjected to nutrient deprivation and was left to produce a second generation of plants. Most plants of the second generation were found to have an increased number of methylated genes.

Q1 What would be the effect of methylation on the affected genes?

Q2 Suggest why a single genotype of parental plant was used.

Q3 A small number of individuals in the second generation did not show the methylation changes. Explain why.

### Practice Questions — Fact Recall

Q1 Give two examples of epigenetic marks.

Q2 How can histone acetylation affect gene expression?

# 9. Evaluating Data on Phenotypes

*Both genetic and environmental factors influence the phenotype of an organism. You need to be able to evaluate data on their relative influences — this may just pop up in your exam...*

**Learning Objective:**

- Be able to evaluate appropriate data for the relative influences of genetic and environmental factors on phenotype.

**Specification Reference 3.8.2.2**

## Evaluating data about influences on phenotypes

The **phenotype** (characteristics) of an organism is the result of the organism's **genotype** and the interaction of its genotype with the environment (see page 136). It's not always clear how much a phenotype is influenced by genes and how much it's influenced by the environment — have a look at these two examples:

**Example 1 — Overeating**

Overeating was thought to be caused only by environmental factors, like an increased availability of food in developed countries. It was later discovered that food consumption increases brain dopamine levels in animals. Once enough dopamine was released, people would stop eating.

Researchers discovered that people with one particular allele had 30% fewer dopamine receptors. They found that people with this particular allele were more likely to overeat — they wouldn't stop eating when dopamine levels increased. Based on this evidence, scientists now think that overeating has both genetic and environmental causes.

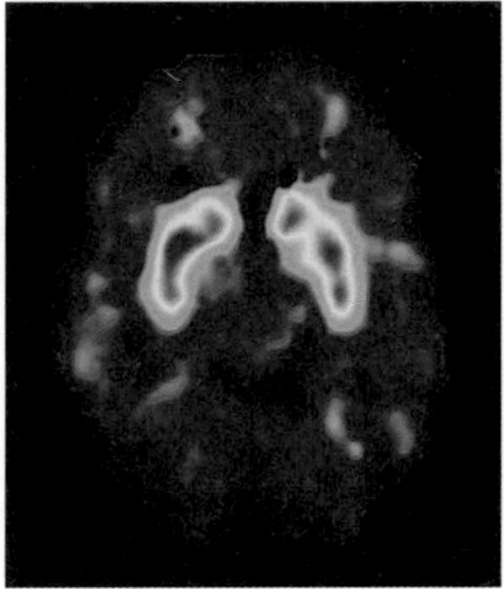

***Figure 1:*** *A coloured PET scan showing a slice through the brain. Brighter areas show high dopamine activity.*

**Example 2 — Antioxidants**

Many foods in our diet contain antioxidants — compounds that are thought to play a role in preventing chronic diseases. Foods such as berries contain high levels of antioxidants. Scientists thought that the berries produced by different species of plant contained different levels of antioxidants because of genetic factors.

But experiments that were carried out to see if environmental conditions affected antioxidant levels found that environmental conditions caused a great deal of variation. Scientists now believe that antioxidant levels in berries are due to both genetic and environmental factors.

## Twin studies

In the exam, you might have to evaluate data on the relative influences of genes and the environment on phenotype. This data may come from twin studies.

Studies of identical twins are extremely useful when trying to determine what's due to environmental factors and what's due to genetic factors. These twins are genetically identical, so any differences in phenotype must be entirely due to environmental factors. If a characteristic is very similar in identical twins, genetics probably plays a more important role. But if a characteristic is different between the twins, the environment must have a larger influence.

**Tip:** Identical twins have very similar epigenetic marks when they are born and in the first years of their life. Different epigenetic changes occur in each twin as they get older. Environmental factors that can affect the epigenome (the epigenetic marks that have been added to the entire genome) include diet, physical exercise and stress.

**Example**

Studies of identical twins can be useful for determining the importance of genetic and environmental factors in the development of certain diseases. Comparisons between the prevalence of Alzheimer's disease in identical twins and non-identical twins have shown that the disease has a genetic risk. However, the disease is not always found in both identical twins, which suggests that environmental factors also play a part. In fact, it's thought that genetics account for about 80% of the risk.

Data that comes from twin studies involving a large sample size (i.e. lots of pairs of twins) is better for drawing valid conclusions than data based on a small sample size. That's because a large sample size is more representative of the population.

**Tip:** It's not always clear what the main cause of differences in phenotype is, so you need to be careful when drawing any conclusions about these differences.

## Practice Question — Application

Q1 A twin study was performed to determine whether head circumference is influenced mainly by environmental factors or by genetic factors. 25 pairs of identical twins were selected for the study and the mean difference in the head circumference of each pair was calculated. The same was done for 25 pairs of non-identical siblings and 25 pairs of unrelated individuals. The results are shown on the right.

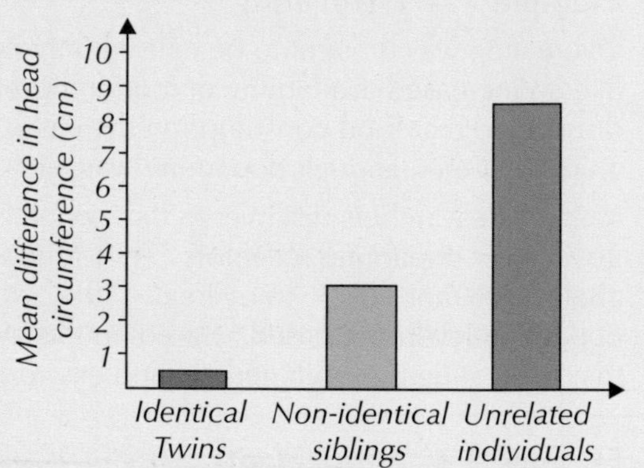


a) Describe the data.

b) Do you think that genetic or environmental factors have a larger effect on head circumference? Explain your answer.

A similar study was performed on adults to determine the effects of genetic and environmental factors on activity levels. Pairs of identical twins, pairs of non-identical siblings and pairs of unrelated individuals were asked to wear a pedometer and the mean difference in steps taken per day was recorded. The results are shown on the right.

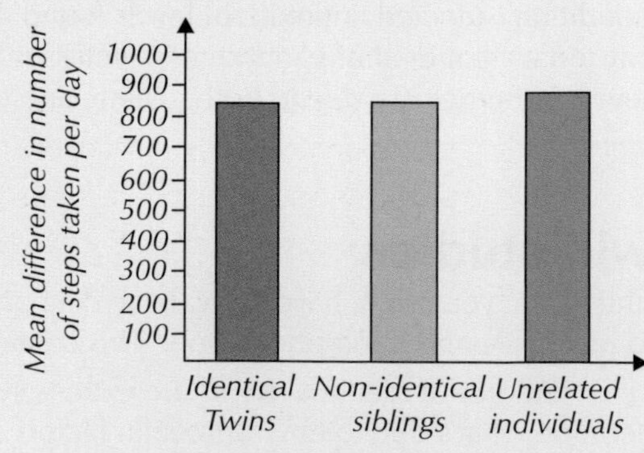


c) Explain what the results show about the role of genetics in determining activity levels.

## Practice Question — Fact Recall

Q1 Why are studies using identical twins useful for determining the effect of both environmental and genetic factors on a phenotype?

## Section Summary

Make sure you know...

- That mutations are changes to the base sequence of DNA that can occur during DNA replication.
- That mutations can include substitution, deletion, addition, duplication, inversion and translocation of bases.
- That some mutations can affect polypeptide function by altering the amino acid sequence.
- That some mutations only change one triplet code and not all of these mutations change the amino acid because the genetic code is degenerate.
- That some mutations result in a frameshift (all base triplets downstream of the mutation are changed).
- How the type of mutation relates to its effect on the encoded polypeptide.
- That mutations can occur spontaneously, e.g. if mistakes are made during DNA replication, and the rate of mutations is increased by mutagenic agents (e.g. UV radiation, ionising radiation).
- That tumour suppressor genes slow down cell division and proto-oncogenes stimulate cell division.
- That mutated tumour suppressor genes can be inactivated and fail to stop cell division. This allows cells to divide uncontrollably, leading to the formation of a tumour.
- That mutated proto-oncogenes (called oncogenes) stimulate cells to divide uncontrollably leading to the formation of a tumour.
- That malignant tumours are cancerous, grow rapidly and invade (and destroy) surrounding tissues, while benign tumours are not cancerous, grow slowly and are covered in fibrous tissue.
- That abnormal methylation of tumour suppressor genes and proto-oncogenes leads to changes in those cells that promote the development of tumours.
- That increased exposure to oestrogen over a long period of time is thought to increase the risk of breast cancer and the theories behind why this is.
- How to evaluate evidence of correlations between genetic and environmental factors, and cancer.
- How to interpret information about proto-oncogenes and tumour suppressor genes in relation to the prevention, treatment and cure of cancers.
- That totipotent stem cells can mature (develop) into any type of body cell and that they occur only for the first few cell divisions in mammalian embryos, and that pluripotent stem cells occur in mammalian embryos and that they can mature into any type of body cell (except placental cells).
- That multipotent and unipotent stem cells are found in mature mammals and can only form a limited number of cell types.
- That stem cells become specialised during their development by only translating some of their DNA.
- That cardiomyocytes (heart muscle cells) can be produced by unipotent stem cells in the heart.
- That pluripotent stem cells can be used for treating human disorders because they can divide an unlimited number of times and divide into a range of specialised cell types.
- How induced pluripotent stem cells can be produced from adult cells by using transcription factors.
- That there are many benefits to stem cell therapy, but that there are also ethical issues to consider.
- How transcription and translation are regulated by transcription factors.
- That oestrogen can affect translation by binding to a transcription factor.
- How translation is regulated by RNA interference (RNAi).
- How to interpret data from investigations into gene expression.
- That the process of epigenetic control in eukaryotes involves epigenetic changes that determine whether a gene is switched on or off.
- That epigenetic changes are heritable changes in gene function that don't change the DNA sequence.
- That epigenetic changes are caused by changes in the environment, leading to increased methylation of DNA or decreased acetylation of histones.
- How epigenetic changes can cause disease and how these diseases could be treated.
- How to evaluate data on the effect of environmental and genetic factors on phenotypes.

# Exam-style Questions

1 A genus of bacteria that produce many important antibiotics is being investigated. One species produces a blue-coloured antibiotic. Production of the antibiotic is controlled by a transcription factor that binds to the start region of the antibiotic gene. **Figure 1** shows part of the DNA sequence for the transcription factor gene and the same part of the DNA sequence from a mutant strain of the bacteria.

**Figure 1**

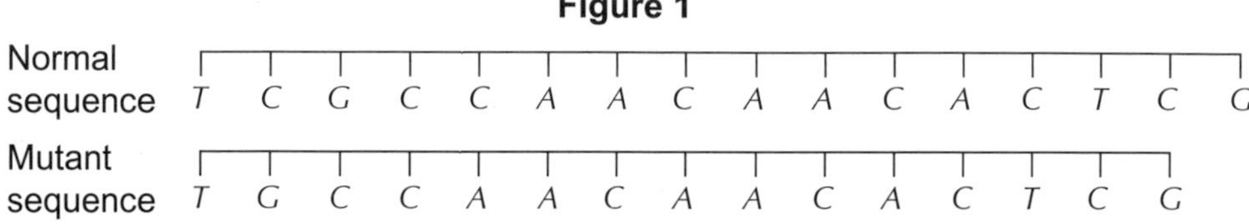


**1.1** Name the type of mutation in the sequence above.

*(1 mark)*

**1.2** Using the information provided in **Table 1**, give the mRNA and amino acid sequences for the mutant DNA sequence.

*(2 marks)*

**Table 1**

| mRNA codon | Amino acid |
|---|---|
| GAA | Glutamic acid |
| GUG | Valine |
| GUU | Valine |
| GCG | Alanine |
| AGC | Serine |
| ACG | Threonine |
| UCG | Serine |
| UUG | Leucine |

**1.3** Scientists investigated how the amounts of the transcription factor protein, antibiotic mRNA and the antibiotic itself were affected in the mutant. Their results are shown in **Table 2** and **Figure 2**.

**Table 2**

| Bacteria | Transcription factor protein (arbitrary units) | Antibiotic mRNA (arbitrary units) |
|---|---|---|
| Normal | 7.9 | 8.2 |
| Mutant | 7.7 | 0.9 |

**Figure 2**

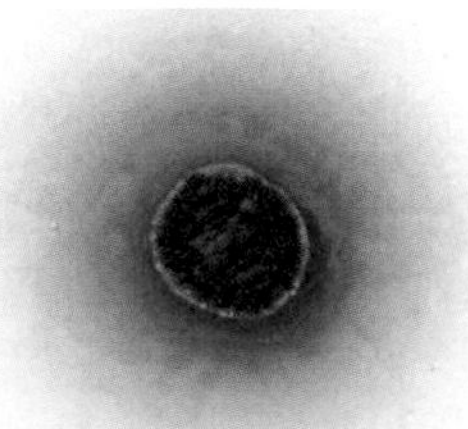

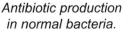

*Antibiotic production in normal bacteria.*

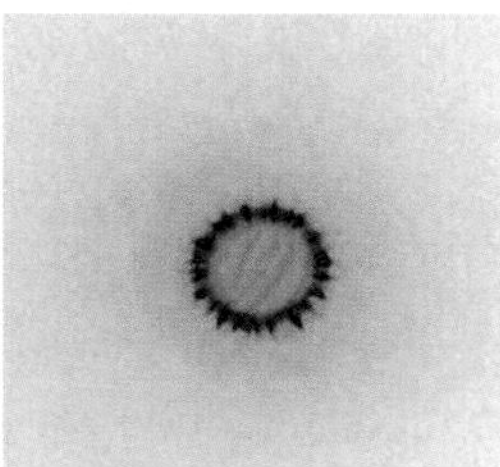

*Antibiotic production in mutant bacteria.*

Is the transcription factor an activator or a repressor?
Use the evidence provided above to explain your answer.

*(4 marks)*

**2** A mutation in the APC gene is found in the majority of colon cancers. A smaller number have a mutation in the gene which codes for β-catenin. The APC protein helps to mark β-catenin for destruction in the cytoplasm. This prevents β-catenin from moving to the nucleus and activating the transcription of genes needed for cell division. Mutations in the APC gene prevent the protein produced from carrying out its function.

**2.1** Of the two genes described above, which is a tumour suppressor gene and which is a proto-oncogene? Explain your answer.

*(2 marks)*

**2.2** Suggest how a mutation in each of these genes could lead to cancer.

*(2 marks)*

**2.3** Mutations that result in a non-functioning APC protein are usually caused by base deletions. Explain how a deletion of one or more bases could result in a non-functioning APC protein.

*(3 marks)*

**2.4** People with a hereditary mutation in the APC gene have a condition called FAP. FAP sufferers will almost certainly develop colon cancer by the age of forty if preventative measures are not taken.

Suggest one way in which knowing you have a hereditary APC mutation could help in the prevention, diagnosis or treatment of colon cancer.

*(1 mark)*

**3** Plant stem cells are totipotent. Plant cells and tissues can be grown artificially from plant stem cells — this is called tissue culture. Alkaloids are useful chemicals produced by plants. They can be harvested from plants grown by tissue culture. An investigation was carried out into the best time to harvest alkaloids produced via tissue culture. Alkaloids were collected from five different cultures of the same plant species. The cells in each tissue culture were at a different stage of specialisation. The results are shown in **Figure 3**.

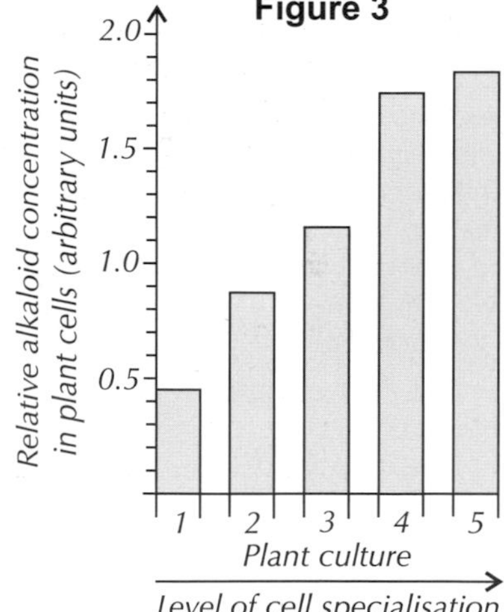


**3.1** Describe the results shown in the graph.

*(1 mark)*

**3.2** Calculate the percentage change in alkaloid concentration between culture 1 and culture 5.

*(1 mark)*

**3.3** Auxins promote cell growth and division, but high concentrations of auxins can reduce cell specialisation. When plants are grown via tissue culture for alkaloid production, auxins are often added to the growth medium during the early stages, but removed later on. Suggest why this is the case.

*(2 marks)*

**3.4** Auxins can affect whether or not certain genes are expressed. Describe and explain how this could affect cell specialisation.

*(5 marks)*

# 1. Genome Projects

**Learning Objectives:**

- Know that sequencing projects have read the genomes of a wide range of organisms, including humans.
- Know that determining the genome of simpler organisms allows the sequences of the proteins that derive from the genetic code (the proteome) of the organism to be determined and that this may have many applications, including the identification of potential antigens for use in vaccine production.
- Know that in more complex organisms, the presence of non-coding DNA and of regulatory genes means that knowledge of the genome cannot easily be translated into the proteome.
- Know that sequencing methods are continuously updated and have become automated.

**Specification Reference 3.8.3**

*A genome is the entire set of DNA, including all the genes, in an organism. In genome projects, scientists work to determine the complete genome sequence of an organism. Their success depends on the complexity of the organism and the technology that is available.*

## Sequencing genomes

Improvements in technology have allowed us to sequence the genomes of a variety of organisms, from bacteria to humans. Gene sequencing methods only work on fragments of DNA, so if you want to sequence the entire genome of an organism, you need to chop it up into smaller pieces first. The smaller pieces are sequenced and then put back in order to give the sequence of the whole genome.

**Example**

The Human Genome Project, which was completed in 2003, mapped the entire sequence of the human genome for the first time. In 1990, scientists round the world joined together to attempt to sequence all 3 billion base pairs in the human genome. The aim was to improve our understanding of the genetic factors in human disease, so that new ways to diagnose and treat illness could be developed. Now that we have the complete sequence of the human genome, genes causing inherited diseases can be found in days rather than the years it took previously.

## Sequencing proteomes

The proteome of an organism is all the proteins that are made by it. You might remember from Topic 4 that while some parts of the genome code for specific proteins, some parts don't code for anything at all (the DNA is non-coding).

### Simple organisms

Simple organisms, such as bacteria, don't have much non-coding DNA. This means it is relatively easy to determine their proteome from the DNA sequence of their genome. This can be useful in medical research and development. For example, identifying the protein antigens on the surface of disease-causing bacteria and viruses can help in the development of vaccines to prevent the disease.

**Example**

*N. meningitidis* group B bacteria cause meningitis B. Sequencing the genome of these bacteria helped researchers identify antigens for use in developing a vaccine against the disease.

Being able to determine the proteomes of disease-causing bacteria and viruses also allows pathogens to be monitored during outbreaks of disease, which can lead to better management of the spread of infection, and can help to identify antibiotic resistance factors (e.g. mechanisms of antibiotic resistance).

**Tip:** Remember, vaccines contain antigens that cause your body to produce memory cells. If you're later infected by a pathogen with the same antigens, your memory cells will quickly recognise it and divide to produce antibodies against it.

### Complex organisms

More complex organisms contain large sections of non-coding DNA. They also contain complex regulatory genes, which determine when the genes that code for particular proteins should be switched on and off. This makes it more difficult to translate their genome into their proteome, because it's hard to find the bits that code for proteins among the non-coding and regulatory DNA. However, work is being done on the human proteome. The codes for more than 30 000 human proteins have been identified so far.

## Developing new sequencing methods

In the past, many sequencing methods were labour-intensive, expensive and could only be done on a small scale.

**Example**

During the 1970s, Frederick Sanger developed a technique in which a sample of DNA was tagged with radioactive bases, separated into four lanes on a gel and allowed to migrate. The result was photographed by X-ray. As each lane represented one of the four bases, the sequence of the DNA could be worked out by combining the results in each lane. This was a time-consuming process as only one sample could be run at a time and X-ray photographs had to be taken manually.

**Tip:** Sanger had to split the DNA sample into four and replicate each portion with a different radioactive base to produce the sample for each lane.

Now these techniques are often automated, more cost-effective and can be done on a large scale.

**Example**

Pyrosequencing is a recently developed technique that can sequence around 400 million bases in a ten hour period (which is super fast compared to older techniques).

***Figure 1:*** *Automated DNA sequencer used for the Human Genome Project.*

With newer, faster techniques such as pyrosequencing available, scientists can now sequence whole genomes much more quickly.

### Practice Questions — Fact Recall

Q1 What is the main aim of a genome project?

Q2 a) What is the proteome of an organism?

b) Give one example of why determining the proteome of an organism is useful for medical research and development.

Q3 Why is it more difficult to determine the proteome of a more complex organism than a simple organism?

Q4 In what ways have sequencing methods been improved since they were first introduced?

# 2. Making DNA Fragments

*Recombinant DNA technology allows us to combine genetic material from different sources. The first step in recombinant DNA technology is often making a DNA fragment — a bit of DNA containing a gene.*

**Learning Objectives:**

- Know that recombinant DNA technology involves the transfer of fragments of DNA from one organism, or species, to another and that since the genetic code is universal, as are transcription and translation mechanisms, the transferred DNA can be translated within cells of the recipient (transgenic) organism.
- Know that fragments of DNA can be produced by conversion of mRNA to complementary DNA (cDNA), using reverse transcriptase.
- Know that fragments of DNA can be produced using restriction enzymes to cut a fragment containing the desired gene from DNA.
- Know that fragments of DNA can be produced by creating the gene in a 'gene machine'.

**Specification Reference 3.8.4.1**

## Recombinant DNA technology

Recombinant DNA technology involves transferring a fragment of DNA from one organism to another. Because the genetic code is universal (the same DNA base triplets code for the same amino acids in all living things), and because transcription and translation mechanisms are pretty similar too, the transferred DNA can be used to produce a protein in the cells of the recipient organism. The recipient and donor organisms don't even have to be from the same species. This can be pretty useful — see page 243. Organisms that contain transferred DNA are known as transgenic organisms.

## Methods for making DNA fragments

In order to transfer a gene from one organism to another, you first need to get a DNA fragment containing the gene you're interested in (the target gene). There are three ways that DNA fragments can be produced:

### Method 1 — using reverse transcriptase

Most cells only contain two copies of each gene, making it difficult to obtain a DNA fragment containing the target gene. But cells that produce the protein coded for by the target gene will contain many mRNA molecules that are complementary to the gene — so mRNA is often easier to obtain. The mRNA molecules can be used as templates to make lots of DNA. The enzyme, **reverse transcriptase**, makes DNA from an RNA template. The DNA produced is called **complementary DNA** (cDNA).

**Example**

Pancreatic cells produce the protein insulin. They have loads of mRNA molecules complementary to the insulin gene, but only two copies of the gene itself. So reverse transcriptase could be used to make cDNA from the insulin mRNA.

**Tip:** Remember that DNA is copied into mRNA during transcription.

To make cDNA, mRNA is first isolated from cells. Then it's mixed with free DNA nucleotides and reverse transcriptase. The reverse transcriptase uses the mRNA as a template to synthesise new strands of cDNA — see Figure 1.

**Tip:** The cDNA is a complementary copy of the mRNA because of specific base pairing.

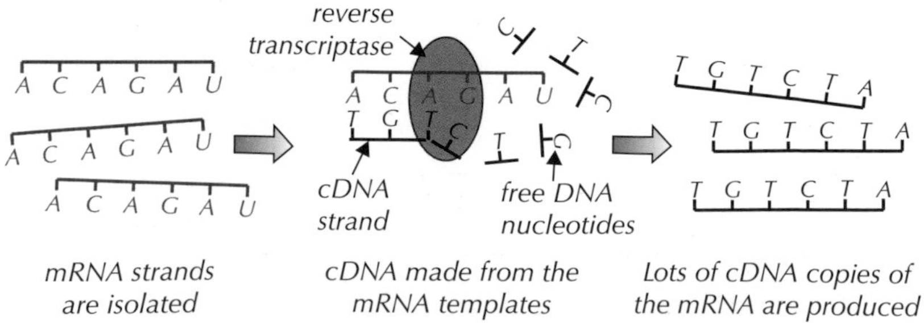


***Figure 1:*** *cDNA synthesis using reverse transcriptase.*

## Method 2 — using restriction endonuclease enzymes

Some sections of DNA have **palindromic sequences** of nucleotides. These sequences consist of antiparallel base pairs (base pairs that read the same in opposite directions) — see Figure 2.

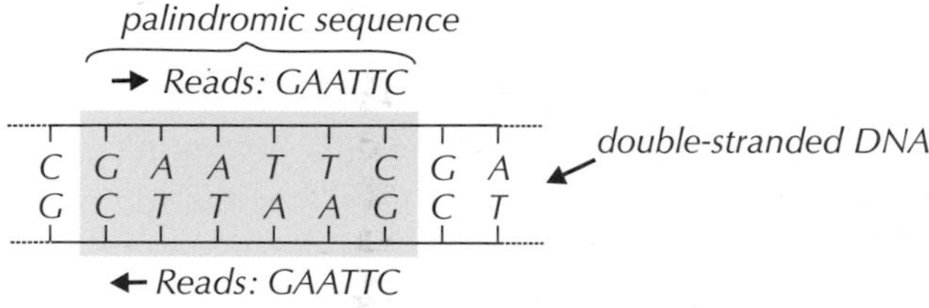

***Figure 2:*** *A palindromic DNA sequence.*

**Restriction endonucleases** are enzymes that recognise specific palindromic sequences (known as recognition sequences) and cut (digest) the DNA at these places. Different restriction endonucleases cut at different specific recognition sequences, because the shape of the recognition sequence is complementary to the enzyme's active site.

**Examples**

- The restriction endonuclease *Eco*RI cuts at GAATTC.
- The restriction endonuclease *Hind*III cuts at AAGCTT.

If recognition sequences are present at either side of the DNA fragment you want, you can use restriction endonucleases to separate it from the rest of the DNA — see Figure 3. The DNA sample is incubated with the specific restriction endonuclease, which cuts the DNA fragment out via a hydrolysis reaction. Sometimes the cut leaves **sticky ends** — small tails of unpaired bases at each end of the fragment. Sticky ends can be used to bind (anneal) the DNA fragment to another piece of DNA that has sticky ends with complementary sequences (there's more about this on p. 237).

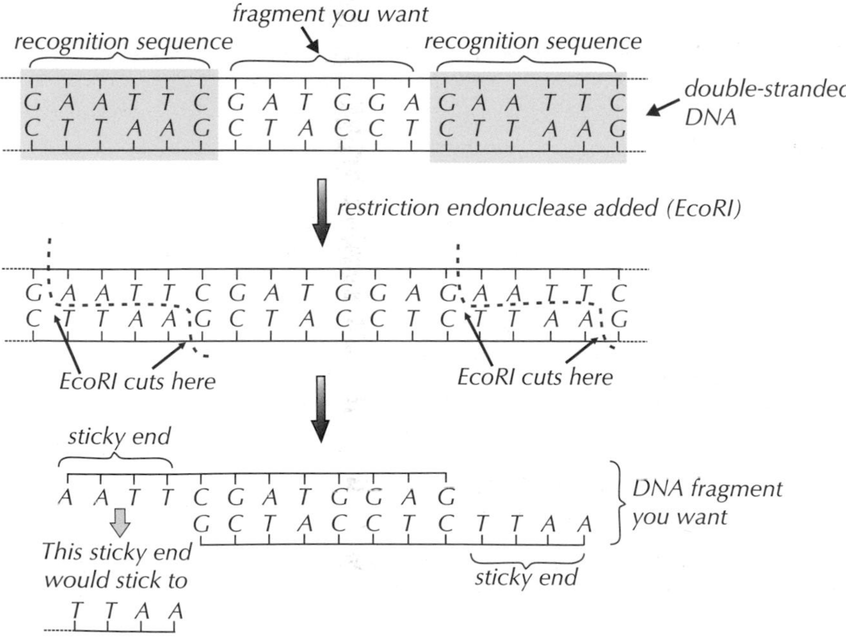


***Figure 3:*** *Using a restriction endonuclease enzyme to cut DNA.*

**Tip:** You should remember from Topic 4 that genes contain both coding regions (exons) and non-coding regions (introns). Introns are removed from pre-mRNA to produce mRNA. Method 2 produces fragments of the whole bit of DNA you want, including the introns. But method 1 uses mRNA to make DNA, so you only get the exons.

**Tip:** Remember, the active site is where an enzyme's substrate binds. In this case, the recognition sequence is the substrate molecule.

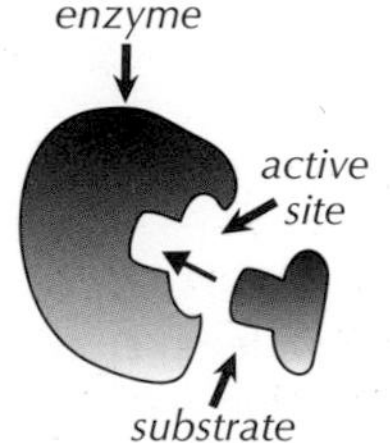


**Exam Tip**

Make sure you use the right words to describe these processes in the exam, e.g. complementary shape not 'the same shape'.

**Tip:** You won't always find the same restriction enzyme site either side of the fragment you want. E.g. you might get an *Eco*RI site on one side and a *Hind*III on the other, so you'd have to incubate the DNA sample with both enzymes to cut the piece you're after.

### Method 3 — using a gene machine

More recently, technology has been developed so that fragments of DNA can be synthesised from scratch, without the need for a pre-existing DNA template. Instead, a database contains the necessary information to produce the DNA fragment. This means that the DNA sequence does not have to exist naturally — any sequence can be made.

Here's how it's done:

1. The sequence that is required is designed (if one doesn't already exist).
2. The first nucleotide in the sequence is fixed to some sort of support, e.g. a bead.
3. Nucleotides are added step by step in the correct order, in a cycle of processes that includes adding protecting groups. Protecting groups make sure that the nucleotides are joined at the right points, to prevent unwanted branching.
4. Short sections of DNA called oligonucleotides, roughly 20 nucleotides long, are produced. Once these are complete, they are broken off from the support and all the protecting groups are removed. The oligonucleotides can then be joined together to make longer DNA fragments.

## Practice Questions — Application

Q1 A scientist wants to produce DNA copies of a gene using some mRNA as a starting template. What enzyme will she need to do this?

Q2 Using information from the table below, describe and explain how restriction endonucleases could be used to cut this DNA sequence:

CAGGATCCTCCTTACATAGTGAATTCATGC

| *Restriction endonuclease* | *Recognition sequence* |
|---|---|
| *BamHI* | *GGATCC* |
| *HindIII* | *AAGCTT* |
| *EcoRI* | *GAATTC* |

**Tip:** Restriction endonuclease enzymes are used a lot in gene technology to cut DNA fragments, so make sure you can answer Q2 — they'll pop up again, I promise.

**Exam Tip**
You could easily get asked about a restriction endonuclease you haven't heard of before — but don't panic. They all work in the same basic way, so just apply what you know to the question.

## Practice Questions — Fact Recall

Q1 What is recombinant DNA technology?

Q2 Why is it possible to transfer DNA to a recipient organism of a different species?

Q3 a) What is cDNA?

b) Describe how cDNA can be made from mRNA.

c) Give one reason why cDNA is made in this way.

Q4 Explain what is meant by the term 'palindromic sequence'.

Q5 What are sticky ends? Why are they useful?

Q6 Describe how a gene machine can be used to synthesise a DNA fragment from scratch.

# 3. Amplifying DNA Fragments

*Once you've got a fragment of DNA (using one of the methods on p. 234-236), you'll probably want to make more copies of it. This is done using gene cloning.*

**Learning Objectives:**

- Know that fragments of DNA can be amplified by *in vitro* and *in vivo* techniques.
- Know that *in vivo* cloning amplifies DNA fragments using a culture of transformed host cells.
- Understand that *in vivo* cloning involves the use of restriction endonucleases and ligases to insert fragments of DNA into vectors, which are then used to transform host cells.
- Understand that in *in vivo* cloning, marker genes are used to detect genetically modified (GM) cells or organisms.
- Understand that *in vivo* cloning involves the addition of promoter and terminator regions to the fragments of DNA.
- Understand the principles of the polymerase chain reaction (PCR) as an *in vitro* method to amplify DNA fragments.

**Specification Reference 3.8.4.1**

## *In vivo* and *in vitro* gene cloning

Gene cloning is all about making loads of identical copies of a gene. This can be done using two different techniques:

- *In vivo* cloning — where the gene copies are made within a living organism. As the organism grows and divides, it replicates the DNA, creating multiple copies of the gene (see below).
- *In vitro* cloning — where the gene copies are made outside of a living organism using the polymerase chain reaction (PCR) (see pages 239-240).

## *In vivo* cloning

Once you've got the DNA fragment containing the target gene you can use it for *in vivo* cloning:

### Part 1 — Making recombinant DNA

The first step in *in vivo* cloning is to insert the DNA fragment into a **vector's DNA** — a vector is something that's used to transfer DNA into a cell. Vectors can be plasmids (small, circular molecules of DNA in bacteria) or bacteriophages (viruses that infect bacteria). The vector DNA is isolated and then restriction endonucleases and DNA **ligase** (an enzyme) are used to stick the DNA fragment and vector DNA together — see Figure 1.

Here's how it works:

**Step 1**

The vector DNA is isolated.

**Step 2**

The vector DNA is cut open using the same restriction endonuclease that was used to isolate the DNA fragment containing the target gene (see p. 235). This means that the sticky ends of the vector DNA are complementary to the sticky ends of the DNA fragment containing the gene.

**Step 3**

The vector DNA and DNA fragment are mixed together with DNA ligase. DNA ligase joins the sticky ends of the DNA fragment to the sticky ends of the vector DNA. This process is called **ligation**.

**Step 4**

The new combination of bases in the DNA (vector DNA + DNA fragment) is called **recombinant DNA**.

① ATCGAATTCGAT / TAGCTTAAGCTA — Vector DNA

restriction endonuclease

② ATCG / TAGCTTAA — sticky end; AATTCGAT / GCTA — sticky end

③ + sticky end AATTCGATG / GCTACTTAA sticky end — DNA fragment containing gene

DNA ligase

④ ATCGAATTCGATGAATTCGAT / TAGCTTAAGCTACTTAAGCTA — Recombinant DNA

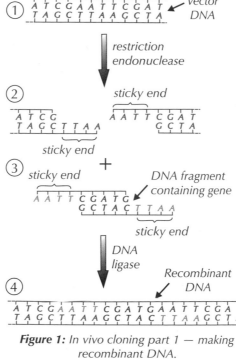

*Figure 1: In vivo cloning part 1 — making recombinant DNA.*

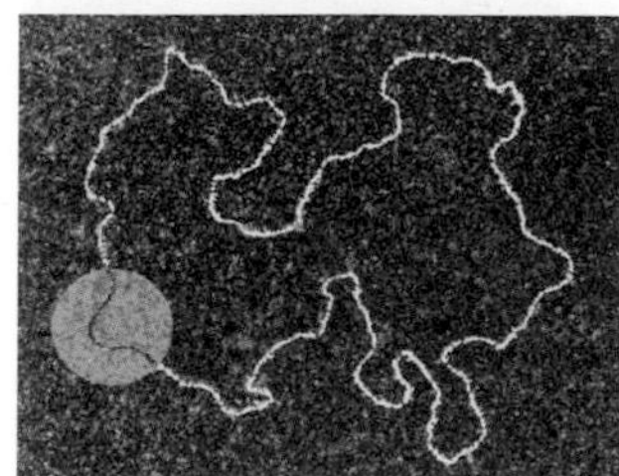

***Figure 2:** Recombinant plasmid DNA. The DNA fragment containing the target gene is highlighted red.*

**Tip:** Bacteria can also be encouraged to take up DNA by electroporation — the bacteria are given a very short electric shock that's thought to create holes in the cell though which DNA can pass.

## Part 2 — Transforming cells

The vector with the recombinant DNA is used to transfer the gene into cells (called **host cells**). Host cells that take up the vectors containing the gene of interest are said to be **transformed**. If a plasmid vector is used, host cells have to be persuaded to take in the plasmid vector and its DNA.

**Example**

Host bacterial cells are placed into ice-cold calcium chloride solution to make their cell walls more permeable. The plasmids are added and the mixture is heat-shocked (heated to around 42 °C for 1-2 minutes), which encourages the cells to take in the plasmids.

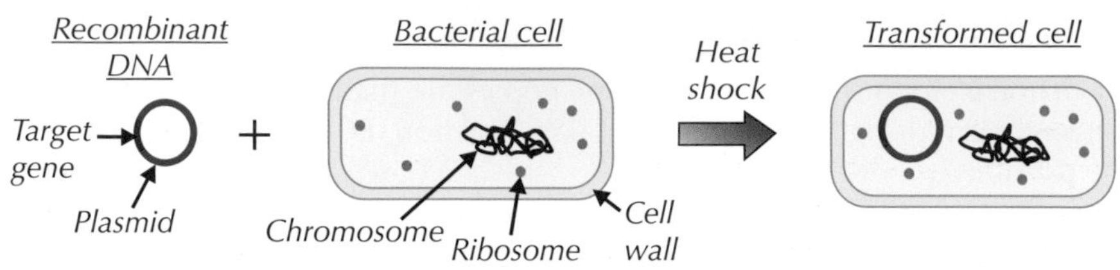


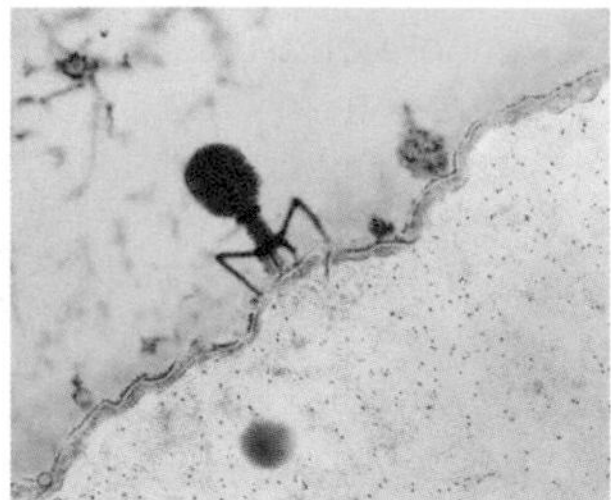

*Figure 3: This isn't an alien spaceship — it's actually a bacteriophage (orange) injecting its viral DNA into an E. coli bacterium (blue).*

With a bacteriophage vector, the bacteriophage will infect the host bacterium by injecting its DNA into it — see Figure 3. The phage DNA (with the target gene in it) then integrates into the bacterial DNA.

## Part 3 — Identifying transformed cells

Only around 5% of host cells will take up the vector and its DNA, so it's important to be able to identify which cells have been transformed. **Marker genes** can be used to identify the transformed cells (see Figure 5):

**Tip:** Scientists will often use vector DNA that already contains a marker gene in it, then they don't have to add it in.

### Step 1

Marker genes can be inserted into vectors at the same time as the gene to be cloned. This means any transformed host cells will contain the gene to be cloned and the marker gene.

### Step 2

Host cells are grown on agar plates and each cell divides and replicates its DNA, creating a colony of cloned cells. Transformed cells will produce colonies where all the cells contain the cloned gene and the marker gene.

The marker gene can code for antibiotic resistance — host cells are grown on agar plates containing the specific antibiotic, so only transformed cells that have the marker gene will survive and grow. Or the marker gene can code for fluorescence — when the agar plate is placed under a UV light only transformed cells will fluoresce.

### Step 3

Identified transformed cells are allowed to grow more, producing lots and lots of copies of the cloned gene.

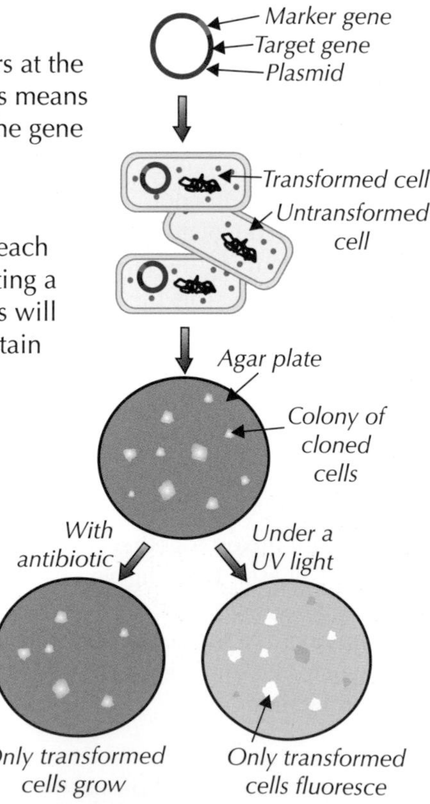


*Figure 5: In vivo cloning part 3 — identifying transformed cells.*

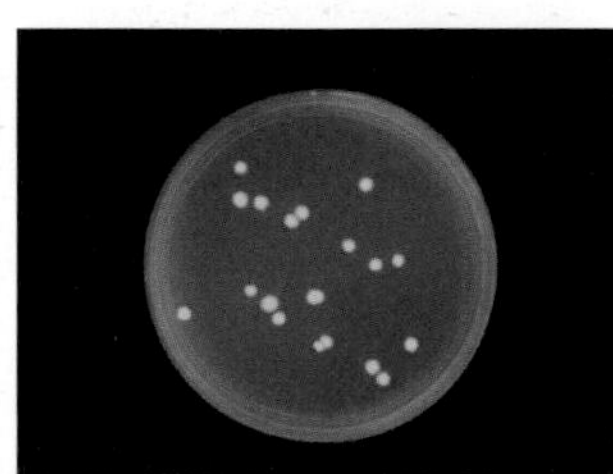

*Figure 4: Fluorescing transformed bacteria colonies containing the commonly used marker gene for GFP (green fluorescent protein).*

## Producing proteins

If you want the transformed host cells to produce the protein coded for by the DNA fragment, you need to make sure that the vector contains specific promoter and terminator regions. Promoter regions are DNA sequences that tell the enzyme RNA polymerase where to start producing mRNA. Terminator regions tell it where to stop. Without the right promoter region, the DNA fragment won't be transcribed by the host cell and a protein won't be made. Promoter and terminator regions may be present in the vector DNA or they may have to be added in along with the fragment.

# *In vitro* cloning

DNA fragments can also be amplified using *in vitro* cloning — this is where copies of the DNA fragments are made outside of a living organism using the **polymerase chain reaction** (**PCR**). PCR can be used to make millions of copies of a fragment of DNA in just a few hours. PCR has several stages and is repeated over and over to make lots of copies — see Figure 6.

### Step 1

A reaction mixture is set up that contains the DNA sample, free nucleotides, **primers** and **DNA polymerase**. Primers are short pieces of DNA that are complementary to the bases at the start of the fragment you want. DNA polymerase is an enzyme that creates new DNA strands.

### Step 2

The DNA mixture is heated to 95 °C to break the hydrogen bonds between the two strands of DNA. The mixture is then cooled to between 50 and 65 °C so that the primers can bind (anneal) to the strands.

### Step 3

The reaction mixture is heated to 72 °C, so DNA polymerase can work. The DNA polymerase lines up free DNA nucleotides alongside each template strand. Specific base pairing means new complementary strands are formed.

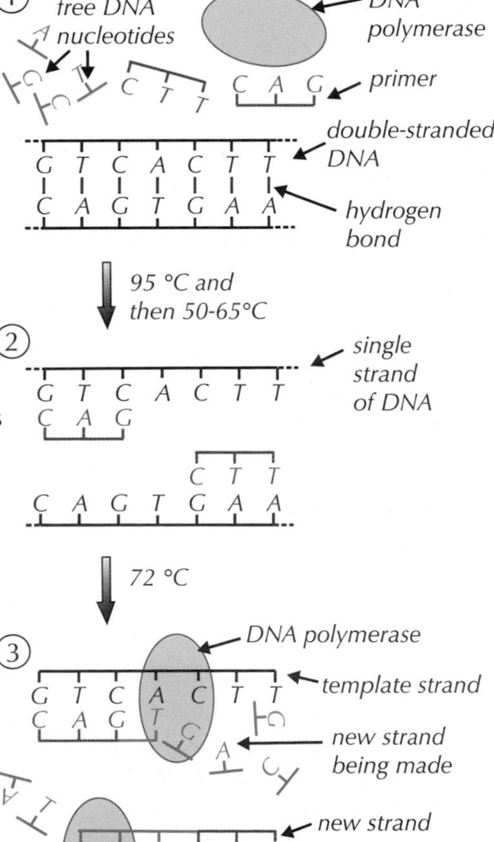


***Figure 6:*** *First three steps of the polymerase chain reaction (PCR).*

**Tip:** We've only shown very small pieces of DNA to make the diagrams easier to follow, but real genes are much longer. (Real primers are longer too but not as big as genes.)

**Tip:** The DNA polymerase used in PCR is usually *Taq* polymerase. It comes from bacteria that live in hot springs, so it is able to withstand high temperatures without denaturing. Most enzymes would denature well below 95 °C.

**Tip:** When PCR was first developed it took a lot of time and patience as the scientist had to use multiple water baths and manually time and move the tubes from bath to bath. Nowadays the process is automated — you can buy programmable PCR machines that do almost all of the work for you.

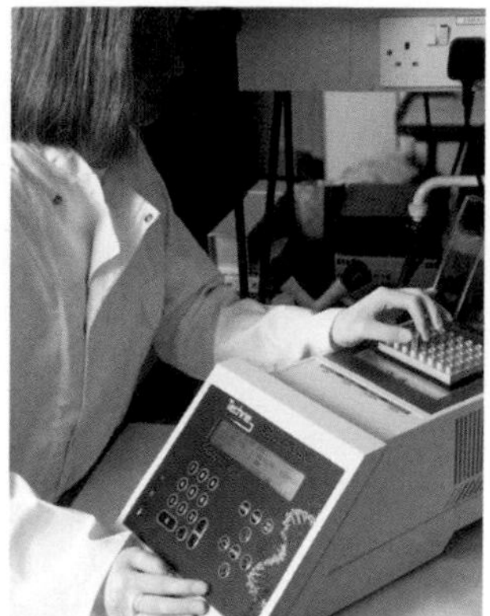
**Figure 8:** *Scientist using a programmable PCR machine.*

### Step 4

Two new copies of the fragment of DNA are formed and one cycle of PCR is complete. The cycle starts again — the mixture is heated to 95 °C and this time all four strands (two original and two new) are used as templates.

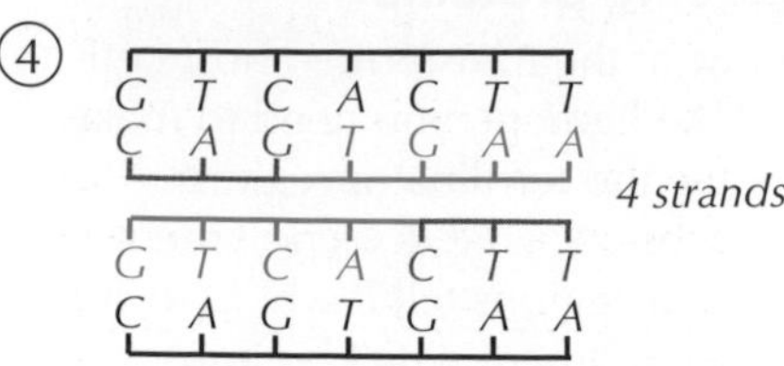


**Figure 7:** *The final step of one cycle of the polymerase chain reaction (PCR).*

As shown below, each PCR cycle doubles the amount of DNA, e.g. 1st cycle = 2 × 2 = 4 DNA fragments, 2nd cycle = 4 × 2 = 8 DNA fragments, 3rd cycle = 8 × 2 = 16 DNA fragments, and so on.

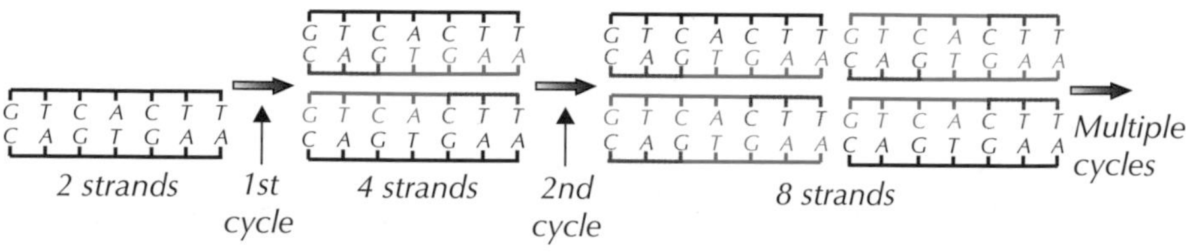


**Figure 9:** *DNA doubling during each cycle of PCR.*

## Practice Questions — Application

Q1 A scientist is studying the role of a protein in cancer progression. He used *in vivo* cloning to transform some *E. coli* cells with recombinant DNA containing the gene that codes for the protein. He then grew the cells on an agar plate containing penicillin.

a) A DNA fragment containing the target gene is made using restriction endonucleases. Describe and explain how the recombinant DNA is produced using this fragment.

b) Explain why you think the cells have been grown on an agar plate containing penicillin.

Q2 The following DNA fragment is being copied using PCR. The arrows mark the start of each DNA strand.

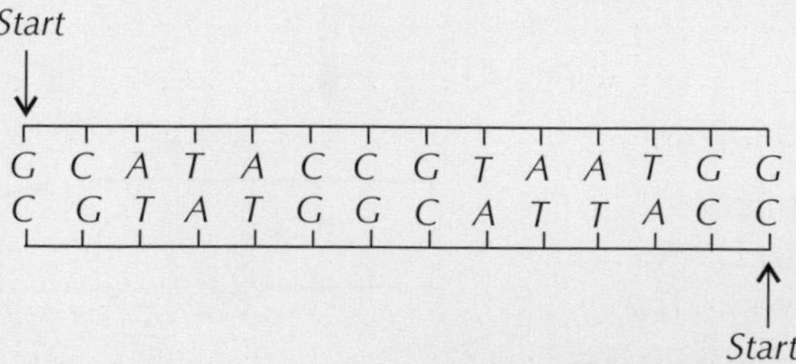


a) The scientist carrying out the PCR uses primers that are four bases long. Give the sequences of the primers he will need to use to copy the DNA fragment.

b) The scientist carries out six cycles of PCR. How many single strands of DNA will he have once the six cycles are complete?

Q3 Read the passage below and answer the questions that follow.

The LacZ gene is found in *E.coli*. It codes for an enzyme called β-galactosidase. β-galactosidase breaks down the colourless substance X-gal into a blue pigment.

LacZα and LacZΩ are mutated versions of the LacZ gene. Each one codes for a protein that forms part of the β-galactosidase enzyme. When the two proteins are produced in the same cell, they assemble to form a fully-functional β-galactosidase enzyme. Neither protein works as the enzyme by itself.

LacZα and LacZΩ can be used as marker genes to test whether *E.coli* have taken up recombinant DNA. The target gene is inserted into the middle of a LacZα gene on bacterial plasmids (see diagram on the right). The plasmids also contain a gene for ampicillin-resistance.

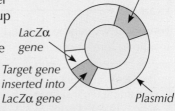

*Ampicillin-resistance gene*
*LacZα gene*
*Target gene inserted into LacZα gene*
*Plasmid*

The plasmids are taken up by *E.coli* containing a copy of the LacZΩ gene. The *E.coli* are then cultured on agar plates containing X-gal and ampicillin.

a) What is the role of the bacterial plasmids?

b) Explain why the plasmids contain an ampicillin-resistance gene.

c) *E.coli* that have taken up plasmids containing the target gene will be white. *E.coli* containing plasmids without the target gene will be blue. Explain why this is the case.

**Exam Tip**
Make sure you read any information you get given in the exam very carefully. It's there for a reason — to help you answer the question.

**Tip:** Inserting a target gene into another gene disrupts the transcription and translation of that gene.

## Practice Questions — Fact Recall

Q1 How is *in vivo* cloning different to *in vitro* cloning?

Q2 Explain what is meant by the term 'vector'.

Q3 Give an example of a vector used in *in vivo* cloning.

Q4 Describe the role of DNA ligase in *in vivo* cloning.

Q5 In *in vivo* cloning, what is a host cell?

Q6 What does it mean when a cell is described as being 'transformed'?

Q7 Explain the importance of identifying transformed cells in *in vivo* cloning.

Q8 What are marker genes are used for?

Q9 What specific sequences might you need to add to vector DNA to ensure the transformed host cell will produce the protein that is coded for by the DNA fragment?

Q10 Name the process that *in vitro* cloning uses.

Q11 a) In *in vitro* cloning, what should the reaction mixture contain?

b) Describe the process that happens once the mixture is set up.

**Exam Tip**
Make sure you know the differences between *in vivo* and *in vitro* cloning so you don't get confused between the two processes. They may have similar names but they're actually very different.

# 4. Recombinant DNA Technology

**Learning Objectives:**

- Be able to interpret information relating to the use of recombinant DNA technology.
- Be able to evaluate the ethical, financial and social issues associated with the use and ownership of recombinant DNA technology in agriculture, in industry and in medicine.
- Be able to balance the humanitarian aspects of recombinant DNA technology with the opposition from environmentalists and anti-globalisation activists.

**Specification Reference 3.8.4.1**

*You get stories on genetically engineered crops and food popping up a lot in newspapers. Let's start with what genetic engineering really is.*

## Transformed organisms

Microorganisms, plants and animals can all be transformed using recombinant DNA technology. This is called genetic engineering. Transformed microorganisms can be made using the same technology as *in vivo* cloning (see pages 237-238).

**Example**

Foreign DNA can be inserted into microorganisms to produce the protein insulin. Here's how:

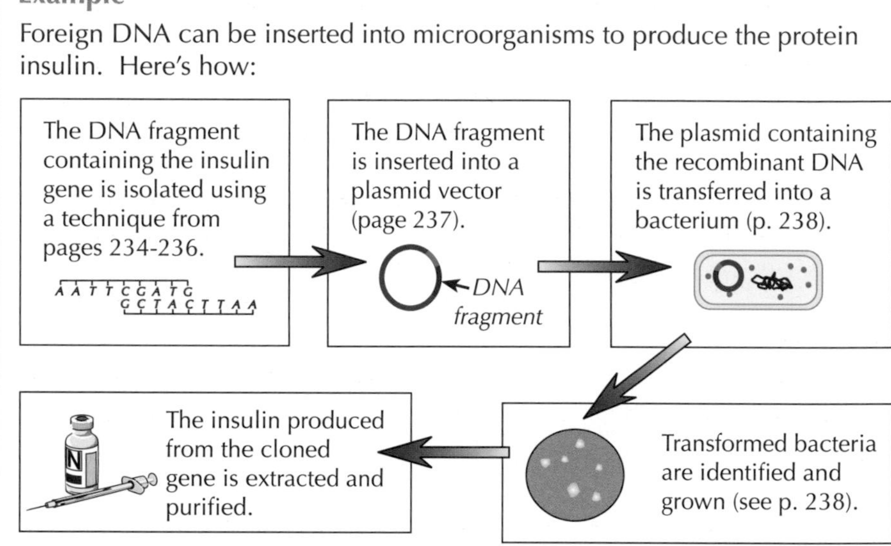

The DNA fragment containing the insulin gene is isolated using a technique from pages 234-236.
AATTCGATG
GCTACTTAA
The DNA fragment is inserted into a plasmid vector (page 237).
DNA fragment
The plasmid containing the recombinant DNA is transferred into a bacterium (p. 238).
Transformed bacteria are identified and grown (see p. 238).
The insulin produced from the cloned gene is extracted and purified.
N


**Tip:** Transformed organisms are also known as genetically engineered or genetically modified (GM) organisms.

Transformed plants can also be produced — a gene that codes for a desirable protein is inserted into a plasmid. The plasmid is added to a bacterium and the bacterium is used as a vector to get the gene into the plant cells. If the right promoter region has been added along with the gene (see p. 239), the transformed cells will be able to produce the desired protein.

Transformed animals can be produced too — a gene that codes for a desirable protein can be inserted into an early animal embryo or into the egg cells of a female. If the gene is inserted into a very early embryo, all the body cells of the resulting transformed animal will end up containing the gene. Inserting it into the egg cells means that when the female reproduces, all the cells of her offspring will contain the gene.

***Figure 1:** Genetically engineered mice. The jellyfish gene that codes for green fluorescent protein has been inserted into the mice so they fluoresce.*

Promoter regions that are only activated in specific cell types can be used to control exactly which of an animal's body cells the protein is produced in. If the protein is only produced in certain cells, it can be harvested more easily. Producing the protein in the wrong cells could also damage the organism.

## The recombinant DNA technology debate

Some people have concerns about transformed organisms (see pages 243-244). But producing transformed organisms can benefit humans in lots of ways. You need to understand both sides of the recombinant DNA technology debate — then you can balance the humanitarian benefits with opposing views from environmentalists and anti-globalisation activists.

# The benefits of transformed organisms

Humanitarians believe that using recombinant technology will benefit people in lots of different ways:

### In agriculture

Agricultural crops can be transformed so that they give higher yields or are more nutritious. This means these plants can be used to reduce the risk of famine and malnutrition.

**Example**

Golden Rice is a variety of transformed rice. It contains one gene from maize and one gene from a soil bacterium, which together enable the rice to produce beta-carotene. The beta-carotene is used by our bodies to produce vitamin A. Golden Rice is being developed to reduce vitamin A deficiency in areas where there's a shortage of dietary vitamin A, e.g. south Asia, Africa. Vitamin A deficiency is a big problem in these areas (up to 500 000 children per year worldwide go blind due to vitamin A deficiency).

Crops can also be transformed to have resistance to pests or droughts. Pest-resistant crops need fewer pesticides, which reduces costs and any environmental problems associated with using the chemicals. Drought-resistant crops can survive in drought-prone areas with little water.

### In industry

Industrial processes often use enzymes (biological catalysts). These enzymes can be produced from transformed organisms, so they can be produced in large quantities for less money, reducing costs.

**Example**

Chymosin (or rennin) is an enzyme used in cheese-making. It used to be made from rennet (a substance produced in the stomach of cows), but it can now be produced by transformed organisms. This means it can be made in large quantities, relatively cheaply and without killing any cows, making some cheese suitable for vegetarians.

### In medicine

Many drugs and vaccines are produced by transformed organisms using recombinant DNA technology.

**Example**

Insulin is used to treat Type 1 diabetes and used to come from animal (cow, horse or pig) pancreases. This insulin wasn't human insulin though, so it didn't work quite as well. Human insulin is now made from transformed microorganisms, using a cloned human insulin gene (see previous page).

Drugs made using recombinant DNA technology can be produced quickly, cheaply and in large quantities. This could make them more affordable and so available to more people.

# The concerns about transformed organisms

Some people have ethical, financial and social concerns about the use of recombinant DNA technology. These people include anti-globalisation activists (who oppose globalisation, e.g. the growth of large multinational companies at the expense of smaller ones). Some environmentalists also have concerns about the possible environmental effects of the technology.

**Exam Tip**
Transformed organisms (microorganisms, plants and animals) can be used in a variety of ways. You need to be able to interpret information about how they are used.

*Figure 2: Genetically engineered (transformed) Golden Rice (right) compared to normal white rice (left).*

**Tip:** Recombinant DNA technology has the potential to be used in gene therapy to treat human diseases (see page 245).

**Tip:** Transformed crops could be used to make vaccines in areas where refrigeration isn't available (vaccines usually need to be stored in fridges). This would make the vaccines available to more people.

Tip: Biodiversity describes the variety of living organisms in an area. Monoculture reduces biodiversity by reducing the number of plant species in an area. This in turn reduces the number of other species, e.g. insects, that the area can support.

### In agriculture

Farmers might plant only one type of transformed crop (this is called monoculture). This could make the whole crop vulnerable to the same disease because the plants are genetically identical. Environmentalists are also concerned about monocultures reducing biodiversity, as this could damage the environment.

Some people are concerned about the possibility of 'superweeds' — weeds that are resistant to herbicides. These could occur if transformed crops interbreed with wild plants. There could then be an uncontrolled spread of recombinant DNA, with unknown consequences.

Organic farmers can have their crops contaminated by wind-blown seeds from nearby genetically modified crops. This means they can't sell their crop as organic and may lose their income.

### In industry

Without proper labelling, some people think they won't have a choice about whether to consume food made using genetically engineered organisms. Some people are worried that the process used to purify proteins (from genetically engineered organisms) could lead to the introduction of toxins into the food industry.

A few, large biotechnology companies control some forms of genetic engineering. As the use of this technology increases, these companies get bigger and more powerful. This may force smaller companies out of business, e.g. by making it harder for them to compete. Anti-globalisation activists are against this.

**Exam Tip**
It can't be said enough — if you're asked about issues involved in recombinant DNA technology, make sure you think about both sides of the debate. That means talking about the pros and cons, pluses and negatives, benefits and concerns.

### In medicine

Companies who own genetic engineering technologies may limit the use of technologies that could be saving lives. Also, some people worry that this technology could be used unethically, e.g. to make designer babies (babies that have characteristics chosen by their parents). This is currently illegal though.

Recombinant DNA technology also creates ownership issues.

**Examples**

- There is some debate about who owns genetic material from humans once it has been removed from the body — the donor or the researcher. Some people argue that the individual holds the right to their own genetic information. However, others argue that value is created by the researcher who uses it to develop a medicine or in diagnosis.
- A small number of large corporations own patents to particular seeds. They can charge high prices, sometimes including a 'technology fee', and can require farmers to repurchase seeds each year. If non-GM crops are contaminated by GM crops, farmers can be sued for breaching the patent law.

## Practice Questions — Application

A large agricultural company's research and development department have created transformed soybean plants that are resistant to a certain herbicide. The resistance gene was isolated from bacteria.

Q1 Explain how the transformed soybean plant could have been created.

Q2 Suggest how the transformed soybean plant may benefit humans.

Q3 Why might some people oppose the use of this transformed plant?

# 5. Gene Therapy

*Recombinant DNA technology could also be used to treat human diseases. This is known as gene therapy.*

**Learning Objective:**
- Be able to relate recombinant DNA technology to gene therapy.

**Specification Reference 3.8.4.1**

## How does gene therapy work?

Gene therapy involves altering the defective genes (mutated alleles) inside cells to treat genetic disorders and cancer. How you do this depends on whether the disorder is caused by a mutated dominant allele or two mutated recessive alleles.

- If it's caused by two mutated recessive alleles you can add a working dominant allele to make up for them — you 'supplement' the faulty ones.
- If it's caused by a mutated dominant allele you can 'silence' the dominant allele (e.g. by sticking a bit of DNA in the middle of the allele so it doesn't work any more).

Both of these processes involve inserting a DNA fragment into the person's original DNA. Just like in recombinant DNA technology, you need a vector to get the DNA into the cell (see page 237). A range of different vectors can be used, e.g. altered viruses, plasmids or liposomes (spheres made of lipid).

**Tip:** If you can't remember the difference between dominant and recessive alleles, check out page 137.

## The two types of gene therapy

There are two types of gene therapy:

### Somatic therapy

This involves altering the alleles in body cells, particularly the cells that are most affected by the disorder.

**Example**

Cystic fibrosis (CF) is a genetic disorder that's very damaging to the respiratory system, so somatic therapy for CF targets the epithelial cells lining the lungs.

Somatic therapy doesn't affect the individual's sex cells (sperm or eggs) though, so any offspring could still inherit the disease.

### Germ line therapy

This involves altering the alleles in the sex cells. This means that every cell of any offspring produced from these cells will be affected by the gene therapy and they won't suffer from the disease. Germ line therapy in humans is currently illegal though.

**Tip:** Gene therapy isn't being used widely yet, but there is a form of somatic gene therapy available to treat some people with a genetic disease called LPLD. Treatments for other dieases, such as cystic fibrosis, are undergoing clinical trials.

**Tip:** Sex cells are the gametes — eggs and sperm. Body cells are all the rest, e.g. skin cells, liver cells, heart cells, etc.

## Ethical issues surrounding gene therapy

There are also many ethical issues associated with gene therapy. For example, some people are worried that the technology could be used in ways other than for medical treatment, such as for treating the cosmetic effects of aging. Other people worry that there's the potential to do more harm than good by using the technology (e.g. risk of overexpression of genes — gene produces too much of the missing protein).

**Practice Questions — Fact Recall**

Q1 What does gene therapy involve?

Q2 What is the difference between somatic and germ line therapy?

**Learning Objectives:**
- Understand the use of labelled DNA probes and DNA hybridisation to locate specific alleles of genes.
- Understand the use of labelled DNA probes that can be used to screen patients for heritable conditions, drug responses or health risks.
- Understand the use of screening information in genetic counselling and personalised medicine.
- Be able to evaluate information relating to screening individuals for genetically determined conditions and drug responses.

**Specification Reference 3.8.4.2**

# 6. Gene Probes and Medical Diagnosis

*To produce a DNA probe, you first need to sequence the allele that you want to screen for (see page 232). You then use PCR (see p. 239) to produce multiple complementary copies of part of the allele — these are the probes.*

## Locating alleles using DNA probes

DNA probes can be used to locate specific alleles of genes (e.g. on chromosomes) or to see if a person's DNA contains a mutated allele that causes a genetic disorder. DNA probes are short strands of DNA — see Figure 1. They have a specific base sequence that's complementary to the base sequence of part of a target allele (the allele you're looking for, e.g. an allele that causes a genetic disorder). This means a DNA probe will bind (hybridise) to the target allele if it's present in a sample of DNA.

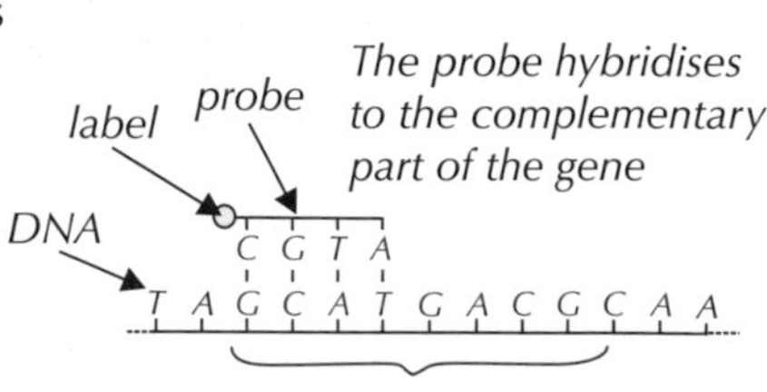


***Figure 1:*** *A DNA probe.*

A DNA probe also has a label attached, so that it can be detected. The two most common labels are a radioactive label (detected using X-ray film) or a fluorescent label (detected using UV light). Figure 2 and the text below explain how fluorescently labelled probes are used:

### Step 1

A sample of DNA is digested into fragments using restriction enzymes (see page 235) and separated using electrophoresis (see page 250).

### Step 2

The separated DNA fragments are then transferred to a nylon membrane and incubated with a fluorescently labelled DNA probe. If the allele is present, the DNA probe will bind (hybridise) to it.

### Step 3

The membrane is then exposed to UV light and if the gene is present there will be a fluorescent band. E.g. in this case, the DNA in fragment X contains the target allele.

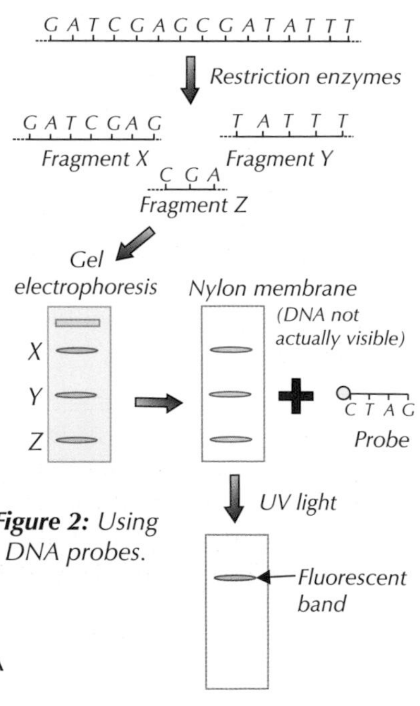


***Figure 2:*** *Using DNA probes.*

**Tip:** If a radioactively labelled probe is used, the fragments are transferred to X-ray film. If the gene and probe are present, a shadow will form on the film.

***Figure 3:*** *Human chromosomes (red) with DNA probes (yellow) hybridised to complementary base sequences.*

## Screening for multiple genes

The probe can be used as part of a DNA **microarray**, which can screen for lots of different genes at the same time. A DNA microarray is a glass slide (see Figures 4 and 5 on the next page) with microscopic spots of different DNA probes attached to it in rows.

A sample of fluorescently labelled human DNA is washed over the array. If the labelled human DNA contains any DNA sequences that match any of the probes, it will stick to the array. So this means you can screen the DNA for lots of different mutated genes at the same time. The array is washed, to remove any fluorescently labelled DNA that hasn't stuck to it, and then visualised under UV light. Any labelled DNA attached to a probe will show up (fluoresce) — see Figure 4. Any spot that fluoresces means that the person's DNA contains that specific allele. E.g. if the probe is for a mutated allele that causes a genetic disorder, this person has the allele.

> **Tip:** Microarrays aren't just used to diagnose genetic diseases. Researchers can use them to analyse other DNA samples, or even to analyse mRNA samples.

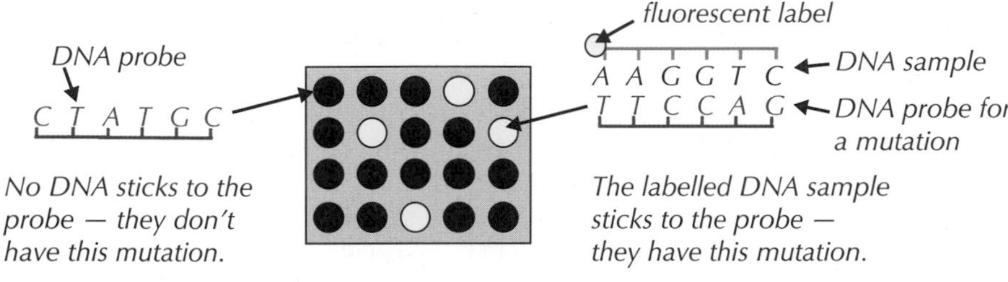


***Figure 4:*** *Diagram of a DNA microarray.*

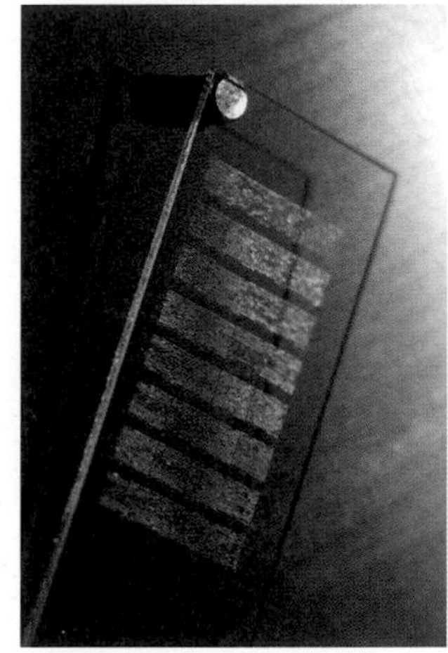

***Figure 5:*** *A DNA microarray.*

## Uses of screening with DNA probes

Screening using DNA probes has lots of uses. For example:

- It can be used to help identify inherited conditions.

**Examples**

- Huntington's disease is an inherited condition that affects the nervous system and does not usually start to display symptoms until a person is aged between 30 and 50. People with a family history of the disease may choose to be screened for the mutated allele to find out if they have inherited it.
- The NHS offers to screen all newborn babies for the inherited disorder cystic fibrosis (which can cause breathing and digestive difficulties) so that treatment for the condition can begin as soon as possible.

> **Tip:** You need to be able to evaluate information about screening for inherited conditions and people's responses to drugs.

- It can be used to help determine how a patient will respond to specific drugs.

**Example**

Breast cancer can be caused by a mutation in the HER2 proto-oncogene and treated with the drug Herceptin® (see page 211). Herceptin® is only effective against this type of breast cancer because it targets a specific receptor. Screening for this particular mutation helps determine whether Herceptin® will be a useful treatment or not.

- It can also be used to help identify health risks.

**Example**

Inheriting particular mutated alleles increases your risk of developing certain types of cancer (although it doesn't make it certain that you'll develop cancer). If a person knows they have these alleles, it might help them make choices that could reduce the risk of the disease developing (see next page).

However, some people are concerned that genetic screening may lead to discrimination by insurance companies and employers if people are known to have a high risk of developing a condition.

## Genetic counselling

The results of screening can be used for genetic counselling. Genetic counselling is advising patients and their relatives about the risks of genetic disorders. It involves advising people about screening (e.g. looking for mutated alleles if there's a family history of cancer) and explaining the results of a screening. Screening can help to identify if someone is the carrier of a mutated allele, the type of mutated allele they're carrying (indicating the type of genetic disorder or cancer) and the most effective treatment. If the results of a screening are positive (an individual has the mutation) then genetic counselling is used to advise the patient on the options of prevention or treatment available.

**Example 1**

A woman with a family history of breast cancer may have genetic counselling to help her decide whether or not to be screened for known mutations that can lead to breast cancer, e.g. a mutation in the BRCA1 tumour suppressor gene (see page 211). If she is screened and the result is positive, genetic counsellors might explain to the woman what her lifetime chance of developing breast cancer is (a woman with the mutated BRCA1 gene has around a 50 to 85% chance of developing breast cancer in her lifetime). Counselling could also help the woman to decide if, for example, she wants to take surgical steps to reduce the risk of breast cancer developing (by having a mastectomy).

**Tip:** A carrier is a person with an allele that is not expressed in their phenotype but that can be passed on to offspring — see p. 144.

**Example 2**

Sickle-cell anaemia is a recessive genetic disorder caused by a mutation in the haemoglobin gene. A couple who are both carriers of the sickle-cell allele may like to have kids. They may undergo genetic counselling to help them understand their chances of having a child with sickle-cell anaemia (one in four). Genetic counselling also provides unbiased advice on the possibility of having IVF and screening their embryos for the allele, so embryos without the mutation are implanted in the womb. It could also provide information on the help and drugs available if they have a child with sickle-cell anaemia.

## Personalised medicine

The results of screening can also be used in personalised medicine. Your genes determine how your body responds to certain drugs. Different people respond to the same drug in different ways — which makes certain drugs more effective for some people than others. This is where personalised medicines come in. Personalised medicines are medicines that are tailored to an individual's DNA. The theory is that if doctors have your genetic information, they can use it to predict how you will respond to different drugs and only prescribe the ones that will be most effective for you.

### Practice Questions — Application

A couple's first child has been born showing symptoms associated with a variety of genetic disorders. Scientists decide to screen the child to determine which specific genetic mutation his DNA contains.

Q1 Describe the process that should be used to screen the child.

Q2 The child is eventually diagnosed with a rare recessive genetic disorder. Explain why the couple might have genetic counselling.

# 7. Genetic Fingerprinting

*As well as actual fingerprints, forensic scientists can now use genetic fingerprinting to identify people by their DNA.*

## The principles of genetic fingerprinting

Not all of an organism's genome (all the genetic material in an organism) codes for proteins. Some of the genome consists of variable number tandem repeats (VNTRs) — base sequences that don't code for proteins and repeat next to each other over and over (sometimes thousands of times), e.g. CATGCATGCATG is a repeat of the non-coding base sequence CATG.

The number of times these sequences are repeated differs from person to person, so the length of these sequences in nucleotides differs too. E.g. a four nucleotide sequence might be repeated 12 times in one person giving 48 nucleotides (12 × 4), but repeated 16 times in another person giving 64 nucleotides (16 × 4).

The repeated sequences occur in lots of places in the genome. The number of times a sequence is repeated (and so the number of nucleotides) at different places in the genome can be compared between individuals — this is called **genetic fingerprinting**. The probability of two individuals having the same genetic fingerprint is very low because the chance of two individuals having the same number of VNTRs at each place they're found in DNA is very low.

## Producing genetic fingerprints

So genetic fingerprints can be compared between different individuals. Now you need to know how one is made.

### Step 1 — PCR is used to make DNA fragments

A sample of DNA is obtained, e.g. from a person's blood, saliva, etc. PCR (see page 239) is used to make many copies of the areas of DNA that contain the VNTRs — see Figure 1. Primers are used that bind to either side of these repeats and so the whole repeat is amplified (copied many times). Different primers are used for each position under investigation. You end up with DNA fragments where the length (in nucleotides) corresponds to the number of repeats the person has at each specific position, e.g. one person may have 80 nucleotides, another person 120. A fluorescent tag is added to all the DNA fragments (usually to the primers) so they can be viewed under UV light (see next page).

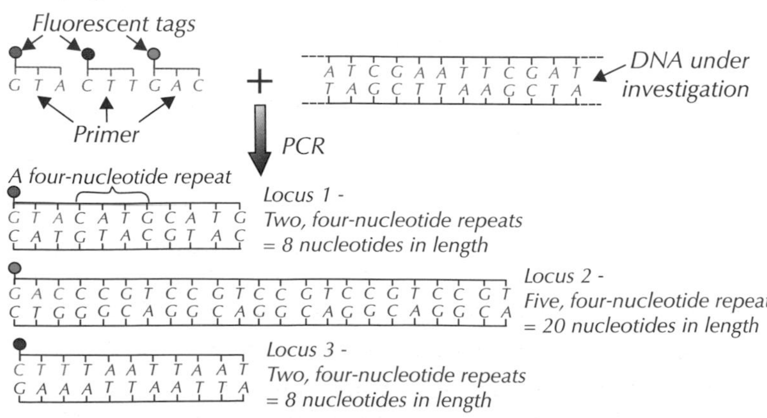


***Figure 1:*** *DNA fragments are made for fingerprint analysis by PCR.*

**Learning Objectives:**

- Know that an organism's genome contains many variable number tandem repeats (VNTRs).
- Know that the probability of two individuals having the same VNTRs is very low.
- Understand the technique of genetic fingerprinting in analysing DNA fragments that have been cloned by PCR, and its use in determining genetic relationships and in determining the genetic variability within a population.
- Be able to explain the biological principles that underpin genetic fingerprinting techniques.
- Be able to interpret data showing the results of gel electrophoresis to separate DNA fragments.
- Be able to explain why scientists might use genetic fingerprinting in the fields of forensic science, medical diagnosis and animal and plant breeding.

**Specification Reference 3.8.4.3**

**Tip:** A locus (plural, loci) is the fixed position of a gene on a chromosome (see page 136).

**Tip:** Fragments move through the gel in order of length, so longer fragments stay towards the top (-ve) end and shorter fragments move further down (towards the +ve end).

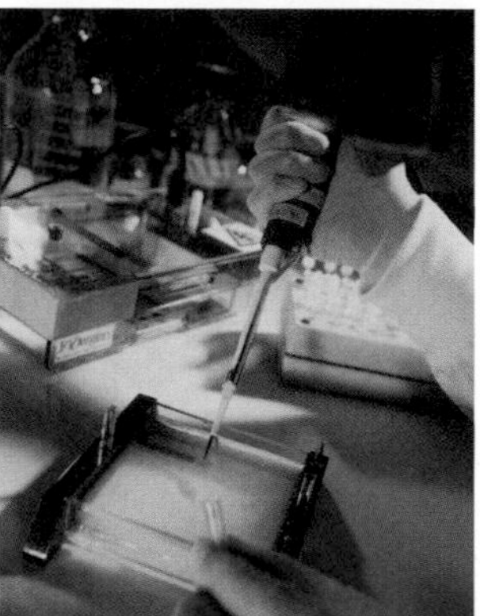

***Figure 2:*** *A scientist loading a DNA sample into a gel.*

**Tip:** The positive electrode is called the anode and the negative electrode is called the cathode.

**Tip:** Gels are also used to separate RNA by length or proteins according to size. (And they can be run vertically in slightly different equipment too.)

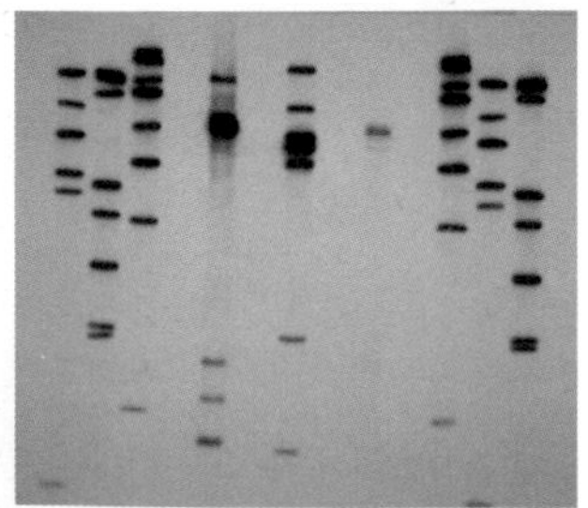

***Figure 4:*** *A genetic fingerprint.*

## Step 2 — Separation of the DNA fragments by gel electrophoresis

To separate out DNA fragments, the DNA mixture is placed into a well in a slab of gel and covered in a buffer solution that conducts electricity — see Figure 2 (Side view). An electrical current is passed through the gel — DNA fragments are negatively charged, so they move towards the positive electrode at the far end of the gel. Shorter DNA fragments move faster and travel further through the gel, so the DNA fragments separate according to length. This produces a pattern of bands — see Figure 3 (View of gel from above).

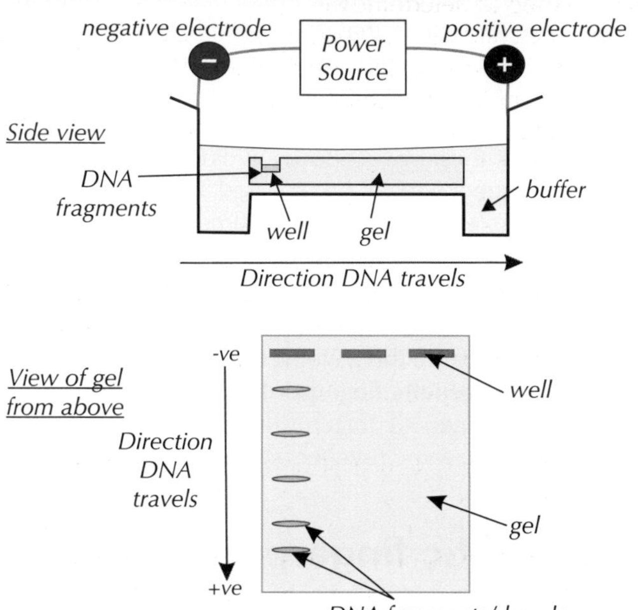


***Figure 3:*** *DNA fragments are separated by gel electrophoresis.*

## Step 3 — Analysis of the genetic fingerprints

After the gel has been running long enough, the equipment is turned off and the gel is placed under a UV light. Under the UV light the DNA fragments can be seen as bands. These bands make up the genetic fingerprint — see Figure 5. A DNA ladder may have been added to one well — this is a mixture of DNA fragments of known length that allows you to work out the length of the other bands on the gel. Two genetic fingerprints can be compared, e.g. if both fingerprints have a band at the same location on the gel it means they have the same number of nucleotides and so the same number of VNTRs at that place — it's a match.

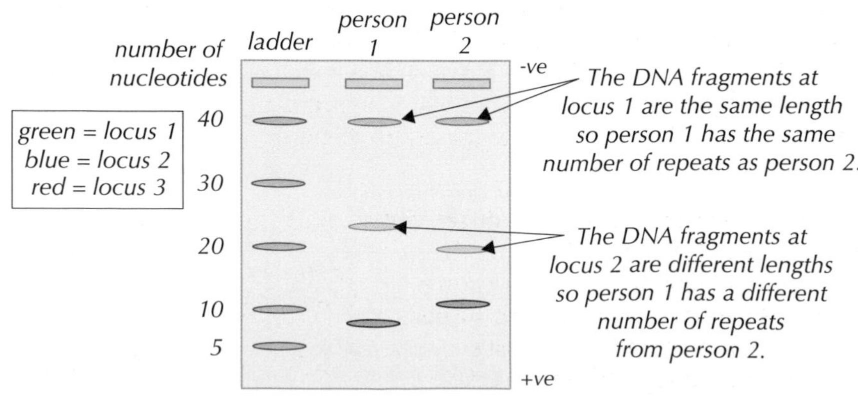


***Figure 5:*** *Diagram showing a genetic fingerprint.*

# Uses of genetic fingerprinting

## 1. Determining genetic relationships

We inherit VNTR base sequences from our parents. Roughly half of the sequences come from each parent. This means the more bands on a genetic fingerprint that match, the more closely related (genetically similar) two people are.

**Tip:** Roughly half the bands will match in a paternity test as we inherit half our DNA from our mum and half from our dad.

**Example**

Paternity tests are used to determine the biological father of a child by comparing genetic fingerprints. If lots of bands match, then that person is most probably the child's father. The higher the number of places in the genome compared, the more accurate the test result. The gel on the right shows that Adult 2 is most likely the father, as six out of ten bands match.

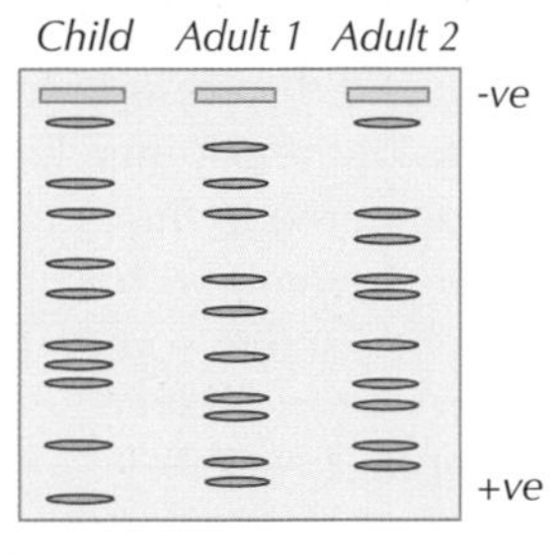


Genetic fingerprinting can also be used to look at much wider ranging genetic relationships, e.g. to see if a population of black bears found in Virginia is descended from a population in Canada or Alaska. The idea is still the same — the more bands the populations have in common, the more closely related they are.

Sometimes you might be interested in tracing only the male or female line of descent. To look at the female line of descent you need to look at DNA in mitochondria. This is because in humans and most other organisms, mitochondrial DNA (mtDNA) is only inherited from your mum. If you're after the male side, you need to look at Y chromosome DNA, as only men have a Y chromosome.

**Tip:** Comparing mtDNA to see how closely related species are is used a lot in phylogenetics (the study of the evolution of organisms).

## 2. Determining genetic variability within a population

The greater the number of bands that don't match on a genetic fingerprint, the more genetically different individuals are. This means you can compare the number of repeats at several places in the genome for a population to find out how genetically varied that population is. E.g. the more the number of repeats varies at several places, the greater the genetic variability within a population.

## 3. In forensic science

Forensic scientists use genetic fingerprinting to compare samples of DNA collected from crime scenes (e.g. DNA from blood, semen, skin cells, saliva, hair etc.) to samples of DNA from possible suspects, which could link them to crime scenes. The DNA is isolated from all the collected samples (from the crime scene and from the suspects). Each sample is replicated using PCR (see p. 239). The PCR products are run on an electrophoresis gel and the genetic fingerprints produced are compared to see if any match. If the samples match, it links a person to the crime scene.

**Tip:** PCR is used to amplify the areas of DNA that contain the repeated sequences, so enough is produced for them to be seen on the gel.

**Example**

This gel shows that the genetic fingerprint from suspect C matches that from the crime scene, linking them to the crime scene. All four bands match, so suspect C has the same number of repeats (nucleotides) at four different places.

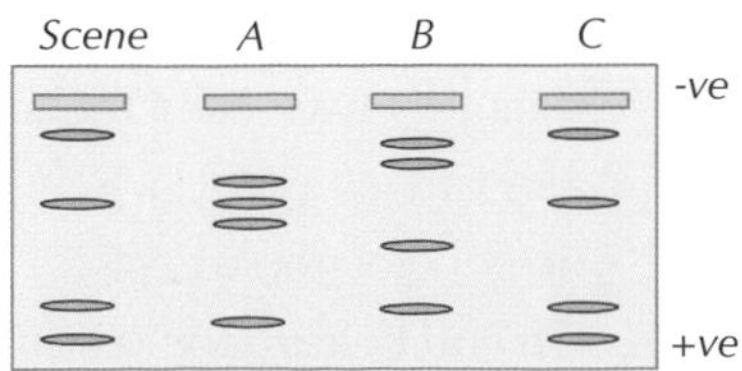


**Tip:** In fingerprint analysis in the UK, the results from ten different loci (plural for locus) are analysed. The chances of two fingerprints matching by chance is at least 1 in 1000 million.

Tip: The type of genetic fingerprinting used in medical diagnosis is slightly different to the one described on pages 249-250, but don't worry — you just need to know why genetic fingerprinting is important for medical diagnosis.

Tip: Genetic disorders and cancer are both caused by mutations in DNA — see page 201 for more.

Tip: A specific mutation can be found using gene probes and sequencing (see p. 246-247).

### 4. For medical diagnosis

In medical diagnosis, a genetic fingerprint can refer to a unique pattern of several alleles. It can be used to diagnose genetic disorders and cancer. It's useful when the specific mutation isn't known or where several mutations could have caused the disorder, because it identifies a broader, altered genetic pattern.

**Example 1**

Preimplantation genetic haplotyping (PGH) screens embryos created by IVF for genetic disorders before they're implanted into the uterus. The faulty regions of the parents' DNA are used to produce genetic fingerprints, which are compared to the genetic fingerprint of the embryo. If the fingerprints match, the embryo has inherited the disorder and so it is not implanted. It can be used to screen for cystic fibrosis, Huntington's disease, etc.

**Example 2**

Genetic fingerprinting can be used to diagnose sarcomas (types of tumour). Conventional methods of identifying a tumour (e.g. biopsies) only show the physical differences between tumours. Now the genetic fingerprint of a known sarcoma (e.g. the different mutated alleles) can be compared to the genetic fingerprint of a patient's tumour. If there's a match (i.e. the mutated alleles are the same), the sarcoma can be specifically diagnosed and the treatment can be targeted to that specific type (see page 211).

### 5. In animal and plant breeding

Genetic fingerprinting can be used on animals and plants to prevent inbreeding, which decreases the gene pool (the number of different alleles in a population, see p. 158). Inbreeding can lead to an increased risk of genetic disorders, leading to health, productivity and reproductive problems. Since genetic fingerprinting can be used to identify how closely related individuals are (see previous page), it can be used to identify the least related individuals in a population so that we can breed them together.

Genetic fingerprinting can also be used by animal breeders to prove pedigree (who an animal's parents and descendents are). Animals with a good pedigree will sell for more money. E.g. the offspring of Crufts or Grand National winners can sell for a lot of money if you can prove their pedigree.

**Exam Tip**
In the exams, you could get a question about genetic fingerprinting in any of a huge range of contexts. So make sure you understand and can explain how it works, and are able to describe all its possible uses.

## Practice Questions — Application

A young woman has come forward claiming to be the long lost daughter of a wealthy diplomat. Scientists have used genetic fingerprinting to produce the gel shown below.

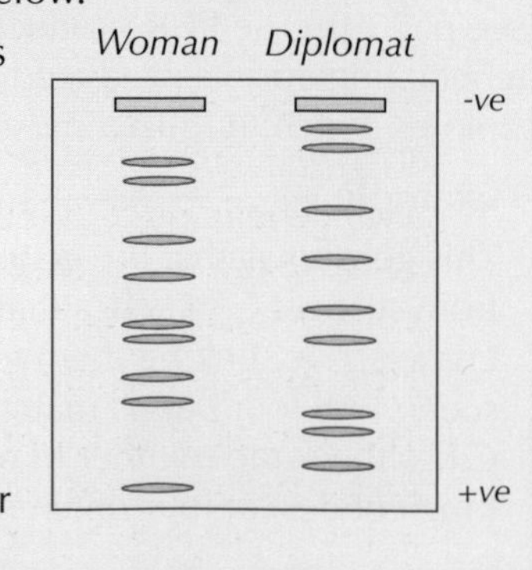


Q1 Explain how the structure of an organism's genome allows a genetic fingerprint to be made.

Q2 For what purpose during the genetic fingerprinting procedure would the scientists have used the following:
a) PCR,
b) gel electrophoresis?

Q3 Do you believe the woman is the daughter of the diplomat? Explain your answer.

## Section Summary

Make sure you know...

- That genome projects have sequenced the genomes of a wide range of organisms, including humans.
- That sequencing the genome of a simpler organism allows us to determine all the proteins that it can make (its proteome) and that this is useful in identifying antigens for creating vaccines.
- That more complex organisms have lots of non-coding DNA and complex regulatory genes, which make it difficult to translate the sequenced genomes into the proteomes.
- That sequencing methods are continually being improved and are now automated.
- That recombinant DNA technology involves the transfer of fragments of DNA from one organism to another and that the transferred DNA can be translated in the transformed organism due to the universal nature of the genetic code.
- That fragments of DNA can be made from mRNA using reverse transcriptase and that this DNA is called complementary DNA (cDNA).
- That fragments of DNA can also be isolated using restriction endonuclease enzymes. These enzymes recognise and cut DNA at different, specific palindromic sequences of nucleotides.
- That fragments of DNA can be made in a 'gene machine'.
- That *in vitro* and *in vivo* cloning can be used to amplify DNA fragments.
- That *in vivo* cloning is when copies of genes are made inside a living organism.
- That *in vivo* cloning involves creating recombinant DNA (using restriction endonucleases and ligases), producing transformed cells, and then identifying and growing those cells.
- That in *in vivo* cloning, marker genes are added so that genetically modified cells can be identified.
- That in *in vivo* cloning, you need to add promoter and terminator regions to the fragments of DNA.
- That *in vitro* cloning is when copies of genes are made outside of a living organism using the polymerase chain reaction (PCR).
- That recombinant DNA technology (genetic engineering) can be used to produce transformed organisms and the benefits of this for agriculture, industry and medicine.
- Some of the ethical, financial and social concerns about the use of recombinant DNA technology in agriculture, industry and medicine, and be able to evaluate these concerns.
- How to interpret information relating to the use of recombinant DNA technology and be able to balance the benefits of genetic engineering with the concerns and opposition from various groups.
- How recombinant DNA technology might be used in gene therapy to alter defective genes inside body cells (somatic gene therapy) or sex cells (germ line gene therapy).
- That DNA probes are short strands of labelled DNA that can be used to locate certain sequences of DNA (e.g. target alleles). A DNA probe is complementary to its target allele, so will hybridise (bind) to it.
- That DNA probes can be used to screen patients for heritable conditions, drug responses or health risks, and any information gained can be used in genetic counselling and to develop personalised medicine.
- That genomes contain variable number tandem repeats (VNTRs) that can be used in genetic fingerprinting, as the probability of two individuals having the same VNTRs is very low.
- That genetic fingerprinting involves using PCR to clone DNA fragments from a sample of DNA, running these fragments on an electrophoresis gel to separate them according to size, and then comparing the length of the fragments against other DNA samples.
- How to analyse genetic fingerprinting gels by looking at the pattern of bands produced.
- That genetic fingerprinting can be used to determine genetic relationships and the genetic variability within a population, and is also used within the fields of forensic science, medical diagnosis, and animal and plant breeding.

# Exam-style Questions

1 An agricultural company is creating a transformed wheat plant containing a gene for herbicide resistance. After announcing some early positive results, the company was approached by anti-genetic engineering activists. The company spoke with some of the activists to hear their concerns but continued production of the plant.

1.1 Suggest **two** ethical concerns that the anti-genetic engineering activists may have had with the agricultural company's work.

*(2 marks)*

Scientists at the company used a **DNA probe** to first locate the resistance gene.

1.2 What is a DNA probe?

*(1 mark)*

1.3 Describe how a DNA probe could have been used to locate the gene.

In your answer, you should make clear the sequence of the steps involved in locating the gene.

*(4 marks)*

The scientists used *in vivo* cloning techniques to introduce the gene into some host bacteria. The host bacteria were grown on standard agar plates to produce colonies and the colonies were then transferred to a second set of plates. The first and second sets of plates are shown in **Figure 1**.

**Figure 1**

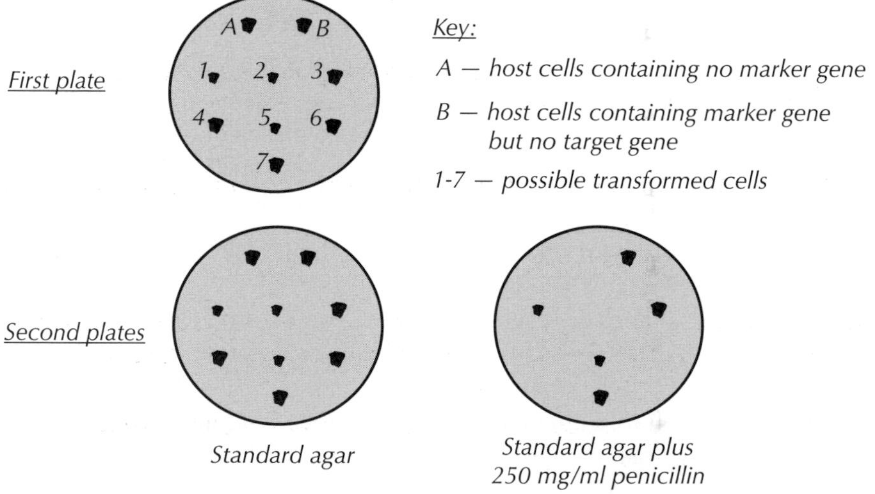

*First plate*

A B
1 2 3
4 5 6
7

*Key:*

*A — host cells containing no marker gene*

*B — host cells containing marker gene but no target gene*

*1-7 — possible transformed cells*

*Second plates*

*Standard agar*

*Standard agar plus 250 mg/ml penicillin*

1.4 Explain why the colonies of bacteria were transferred to the second set of plates.

*(3 marks)*

1.5 Explain why the bacteria in **colony A** were added to the plates.

*(1 mark)*

1.6 Suggest **one** colony for use in further experiments on the transformed wheat plant. Explain your choice.

*(1 mark)*

**2** A prize-winning race horse has been stolen from its stables. Police suspect it has been taken to a stud farm where it has previously gone to breed. The police have obtained DNA samples from four similar-looking horses at the stud farm and used them to produce genetic fingerprints to compare against a genetic fingerprint taken previously from the stolen animal. The genetic fingerprints are shown in **Figure 2**.

**Figure 2**

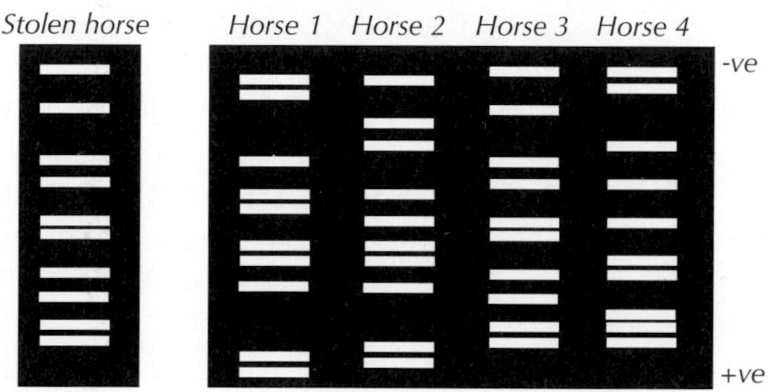


**2.1** Describe and explain how the genetic fingerprints have been produced from the DNA samples.

*(5 marks)*

**2.2** Use your understanding of the biology behind genetic fingerprint technology to explain why the chances of two genetic fingerprints matching by chance are so small.

*(3 marks)*

**2.3** Is the stolen animal at the stud farm? Explain your answer.

*(1 mark)*

**2.4** Compare the genetic fingerprints of horse 4 and the stolen horse. Suggest a reason for these results.

*(3 marks)*

**2.5** Give **one** use for genetic fingerprint technology other than in forensic science.

*(1 mark)*

**3** Scientists are cloning the gene *BtrA* so they can study the effects of the protein it codes for in a species of fish. They start by using reverse transcriptase to obtain fragments of DNA containing the gene.

**3.1** Describe **one** other method they could use to obtain a DNA fragment.

*(2 marks)*

The scientists next incubate the DNA fragments with a restriction enzyme to produce sticky ends, then use *in vivo* cloning techniques to introduce the gene into a bacterial cell along with a fluorescent marker gene.

**3.2** Explain the importance of producing sticky ends for gene cloning.

*(1 mark)*

**3.3** Describe the *in vivo* cloning techniques used after the production of the sticky ends on the DNA fragments.

*(6 marks)*

# Exam Help

## 1. The Exams

*You'll take three exams as part of A-level Biology. It seems obvious, but if you know exactly what will be covered in each of the exams, how much time you'll have to do them and how they'll be structured, you can be better prepared. So let's take a look at the ins and outs of the exams you'll be facing...*

### What's assessed in each paper?

AQA A-level Biology is examined in three papers. Papers 1 and 2 are worth 35% of the total marks and Paper 3 is worth 30% of the total marks.

| Paper | Total marks | Time | Topics assessed |
|---|---|---|---|
| 1 | 91 | 2 hours | 1, 2, 3, 4 & relevant Practical Skills |
| 2 | 91 | 2 hours | 5, 6, 7, 8 & relevant Practical Skills |
| 3 | 78 | 2 hours | 1 to 8 & relevant Practical Skills |

This book covers Topics 5 to 8 — the material from Year 2 of your course. You'll have covered Topics 1 to 4 in Year 1 of your course, so make sure you revise your Year 1 notes for the Paper 1 and Paper 3 exams.

**Exam Tip**
All three A-level papers test you on Practical Skills — take a look at the Practical and Maths Skills section at the front of this book for more.

### How are the exams structured?

- Papers 1 and 2 are mainly a mixture of short and long answer questions. Some of these questions will test you on the facts you need to know, some will test whether you can apply your knowledge to unfamiliar contexts and some will test your knowledge of Practical Skills. There'll even be a few calculation questions thrown in.
- Paper 1 also contains 15 marks' worth of extended response questions. These are questions that require you to write a longer answer with a logical structure. E.g. you could be asked to describe the steps in a particular process. These questions could involve an extended calculation too.
- Paper 2 also contains a 15 mark comprehension question. You'll be given a passage of information to read and will then need to answer the question parts that follow using both the information you've been given and your own scientific knowledge.
- Paper 3 is split into two sections. Section A has lots of questions on practical techniques and skills, with 15 marks being awarded for questions that ask you for a critical analysis of experimental data. For example, you could be given some data (e.g. in a graph or table) and asked to draw conclusions from it or you could be given a conclusion and asked to evaluate how well the data supports the conclusion. As for Papers 1 and 2, there'll also be fact recall questions, questions that test whether you can apply your knowledge, and calculation questions.
- Section B of Paper 3 consists of a 25 mark synoptic essay question. There's more on this on the next page.

**Exam Tip**
Even though you're taking an A-level in Biology, there will be some maths to do in these papers that's set in a biological context. There's lots more on the maths you could be tested on on pages 5 to 14, as well as in the Maths Skills examples throughout the book.

**Exam Tip**
Synoptic means you will need to draw together your knowledge of different areas of Biology in relation to a theme.

## Answering the essay question

You'll be given a choice of two essay titles in Section B of Paper 3 and asked to write about one of them. The titles are designed to get you to write about a range of material from both years of your A-level course. Writing an essay might seem like a daunting task, but don't panic. Here are some tips for getting top marks:

- Before you start your essay, it's a good idea to quickly scribble down a rough plan — this should help you to present your ideas in a clear, logical way. It should also stop you from repeating yourself or missing out any important bits. You should aim to write about at least five different topic areas.
- You'll need to clearly show how all the information you include is relevant to the essay title — don't just write down everything you know about a topic.
- The information you include must be detailed, scientifically correct and of A-level standard. 'Plants are green and have leaves' won't get you any marks at this level.
- You must use appropriate scientific terminology.
- Your essay should be well-written and clearly explained.
- To get the very highest marks, your answer should show evidence of wider reading (i.e. it should include things that aren't explicitly on the specification, but are still of a high standard and relevant to the question).

You'll get 2 hours in total for this paper and should aim to leave yourself about 50 minutes to plan and write your essay. This should be enough time to write about 3 sides of A4.

**Exam Tip**
Remember, you need to read the essay question carefully and answer the question you're asked — don't just rehash an old essay that you happen to have learnt off by heart.

**Exam Tip**
Making a quick plan of the topics you'll cover might help you decide which title you can write a better essay for.

**Tip:** There's an essay question for you to have a go at on the next page. It's worth timing yourself as you do it, so you get an idea of what it will be like to write the essay under exam conditions.

## Solving problems in a practical context

In the exams, you'll get plenty of questions set in a 'practical context'. As well as answering questions about the methods used or the conclusions drawn (see pages 1 to 16), you'll need to be able to apply your scientific knowledge to solve problems set in these contexts.

**Example**

1 A scientist amplified a gene by transferring a plasmid containing the target gene and a fluorescent marker gene into some bacterial cells. The cells were grown on an agar plate. The plate was then placed under UV light. The result is shown in Figure 1.

**Figure 1**

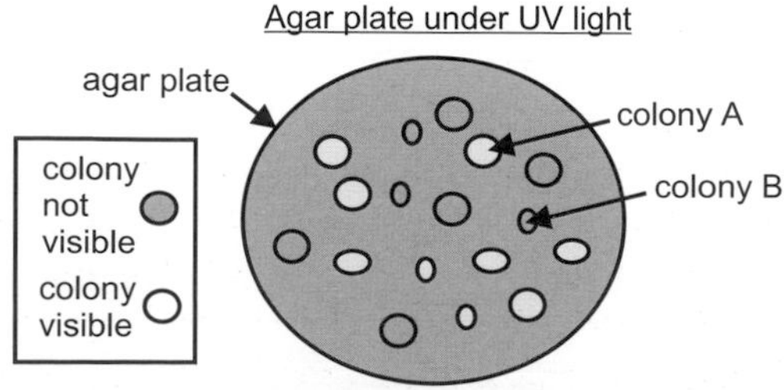


**Exam Tip**
Make sure you read all the information you're given at the start of an exam question carefully, and pay attention to what's being shown in any figures that are included too.

**Exam Tip**
Questions like this can look a bit scary, but you just have to apply what you already know about Biology to a real-life example. There are plenty of questions like this for you to have a go at in this book.

**1.1** Which colony, **A** or **B**, contains transformed host cells? Explain your answer.

*(2 marks)*

You should remember from page 238 that the fluorescent marker gene is included in the plasmid so that bacterial cells that have taken up the plasmid (transformed cells) can be identified. Cells that contain the marker gene, and therefore the plasmid, will fluoresce under UV light. Cells that don't contain the marker gene won't be visible. So colony A contains transformed host cells and colony B does not.

**Practice Question — Exam-style Question**

Q1 Write an essay about the importance of inorganic ions in living organisms.

(25 marks)

# 2. Command Words

*Command words are just the bits of a question that tell you what to do.*

**Exam Tip**
When you're reading exam questions, underline the command words. That way you'll know exactly what type of answer to give.

You'll find answering exam questions much easier if you understand exactly what they mean, so here's a brief summary table of the most common command words:

| Command word: | What to do: |
|---|---|
| Give / Name / State | Give a brief one or two word answer, or a short sentence. |
| Describe | Write about what something's like, e.g. describe the structure of fish gills. |
| Explain | Give reasons for something. |
| Suggest | Use your scientific knowledge to work out what the answer might be. |
| Compare | Give the similarities and differences between two things. |
| Contrast | Give the differences between two things. |
| Calculate | Work out the solution to a mathematical problem. |
| Evaluate | Give the arguments both for and against an issue, or the advantages and disadvantages of something. You also need to give an overall judgement. |

**Exam Tip**
If you're answering a longer 'compare' or 'evaluate' question make a mental list of the similarities and differences or pros and cons first, so you know what you want your answer to include before you start writing.

Some questions will also ask you to answer 'using the information/data provided' (e.g. a graph, table or passage of text) or 'with reference to figure X' — if so, you must refer to the information, data or figure you've been given or you won't get the marks. Make sure you quote the unit with any values taken from a graph or table too — the number alone is not enough.

Some questions may also ask you to answer 'using your calculation' — it's the same here, you need to use your answer to a particular calculation, otherwise you won't get the marks.

Not all of the questions will have command words — instead they may just ask a which / what / how type of question.

**Exam Tip**
Make sure you take a calculator (to help you with the calculation questions) and a ruler (with millimetre measurements) into all three of your exams. A pencil and a spare black pen may come in handy as well.

# 3. Time Management

*Time management is really important in your exams — it's no good writing a perfect answer to a 3 mark question if it takes you an hour.*

For Papers 1 and 2, you get just over a minute per mark in each paper. So, if you get stuck on a short question, sometimes it's worth moving on to another one and then coming back to it if you have time. Bear in mind that you might want to spend a bit longer than a minute per mark on the extended response and comprehension questions. For Paper 3, it's a similar story — you'll want to spend longer per mark on the essay question than on the shorter questions, so make sure you leave enough time for this at the end.

If you've got any time left once you've finished the paper, hold off on celebrating and have a look back through the questions. You can use the time to go back to any questions you've skipped, check your answers to calculation questions and to make sure you haven't accidentally missed any questions out.

**Exam Tip**
If the question is only worth 1 mark, don't waste time writing more than you need to. Questions worth more marks require longer answers.

# Answers

## Topic 5

### Topic 5 — A: Photosynthesis and Respiration

#### 1. Photosynthesis, Respiration and Energy

**Page 21 — Application Question**

Q1 a) 07:30 and 16:30

*Anything between 07:20 and 07:40 would be acceptable for the first compensation point. Anything between 16:20 and 16:40 would be OK for the second one.*

b) The rate of photosynthesis depends partly on the intensity of light. 07:30 is not long after the Sun has risen. The light intensity has increased to a level where the rate of photosynthesis has increased to match the rate of respiration. 16:30 is not long before the Sun completely sets. The light intensity has decreased to a level where the rate of photosynthesis has decreased to match the rate of respiration.

#### 2. Photosynthesis and the Light-dependent Reaction

**Pages 25-26 — Application Questions**

Q1 a) i) proton/hydrogen ion/$H^+$

ii) Because this forms a proton gradient across the membrane. Protons move down their concentration gradient, into the stroma, via an enzyme called ATP synthase. The energy from this movement combines ADP and inorganic phosphate ($P_i$) to form ATP.

b) PSII / photosystem II

c) D

d) ATP

*Cyclic photophosphorylation doesn't produce any reduced NADP or $O_2$ — just ATP.*

Q2 a) photosystem X = photosystem II/PSII
photosystem Y = photosystem I/PSI

b) Light energy absorbed by PSII excites electrons in chlorophyll. This causes the electrons to move to a higher energy level (i.e. they have more energy).

c) To transport protons into the thylakoid.

*In this way a proton gradient is formed across the thylakoid membrane. As the protons move down this concentration gradient, back into the stroma, ATP is formed by ATP synthase.*

d) The electrons are transferred to NADP, along with a proton from the stroma, to form reduced NADP.

**Page 26 — Fact Recall Questions**

Q1 a) Coloured substances that absorb the light energy needed for photosynthesis.

b) E.g. chlorophyll a / chlorophyll b / carotene.

Q2 hydrogen

Q3 the thylakoid membranes

Q4 Light energy excites the electrons in the chlorophyll molecule, giving them more energy, which eventually causes them to be released from the chlorophyll. The chlorophyll is left as a positively charged ion.

Q5 ATP and reduced NADP

Q6 The process of adding phosphate to a molecule using light.

Q7 A chain of proteins down which excited electrons flow.

Q8 a) protons, electrons and oxygen

b) To replace excited electrons in PSII.

Q9 This energy is used to transport protons into the thylakoid so that the thylakoid has a higher concentration of protons than the stroma. This forms a proton gradient across the membrane. Protons move down their concentration gradient, into the stroma, via an enzyme called ATP synthase. The energy from this movement combines ADP and inorganic phosphate ($P_i$) to form ATP.

Q10 a) ATP, reduced NADP and oxygen

b) ATP

#### 3. Photosynthesis and the Light-independent Reaction

**Page 29 — Application Questions**

Q1 Increasing the speed of rubisco could increase the production rate of glycerate 3-phosphate from ribulose bisphosphate and carbon dioxide, as rubisco catalyses this reaction. The increased production rate of glycerate 3-phosphate would increase the production rate of triose phosphate, which in turn could be converted into organic substances such as glucose more quickly.

Q2 The rate of the light-independent reaction would slow down, because the amount of ribulose bisphosphate that could be regenerated in the Calvin cycle would decrease.

**Page 29 — Fact Recall Questions**

Q1 a) ribulose bisphosphate (RuBP)

b) glycerate 3-phosphate (GP)

Q2 a)

2 × ATP → 2 × ADP + $P_i$; 2 × reduced NADP → 2 × NADP

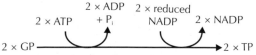

2 × GP → 2 × TP

(GP is glycerate 3-phosphate and TP is triose phosphate)

b) reduction

Q3 In the Calvin cycle ATP is needed for the reduction of glycerate 3-phosphate (GP) to triose phosphate (TP). It's also needed for the regeneration of ribulose bisphosphate (RuBP) from triose phosphate.

Q4 five

Q5 a) six

*Six turns of the Calvin cycle produces 12 molecules of triose phosphate (TP). Ten of these molecules (5 out of every 6) are used to make ribulose bisphosphate (RuBP) and two are used to make one hexose sugar.*

b) 18

*Six turns of cycle × 3 ATP molecules per turn = 18 ATP*

c) 12

*Six turns of cycle × 2 reduced NADP molecules per turn = 12 reduced NADP*

Q6 a) Two triose phosphate molecules are joined together to produce a hexose sugar. Large carbohydrates are then made by joining the hexose sugars together.

b) Lipids are made from glycerol and fatty acids. Glycerol is synthesised from triose phosphate, while fatty acids are made from glycerate 3-phosphate.

## 4. Limiting Factors in Photosynthesis

### Page 33 — Application Question

Q1 a) Increased irradiance results in an increased rate of photosynthesis, which means that more $CO_2$ is needed, so uptake increases.

b) Because the $CO_2$ concentration becomes the limiting factor for photosynthesis. As the rate of photosynthesis is no longer increasing, the rate of $CO_2$ uptake remains the same.

c) E.g. the data suggests that increasing the atmospheric $CO_2$ concentration increases $CO_2$ uptake. This suggests that the rate of photosynthesis also increases. An increased rate of photosynthesis would lead to an increase in the production of sugars/glucose for respiration and so an increase in ATP production. In turn, this could lead to an increased growth rate — but there is nothing in the data to suggest that this would improve the yield of tomatoes (e.g. the plants themselves may grow bigger, but the number of tomatoes they produce might stay the same). This data was also collected under laboratory conditions, in which the temperature was kept constant — this may be harder to do in a glasshouse and using a paraffin heater, which may mean that these results wouldn't apply in glasshouse conditions.

## 5. Photosynthesis Experiments

### Page 36 — Application Question

Q1 a) Different pigments will spend different amounts of time in the mobile phase, so they will travel different distances up the plate in the same amount of time, which separates them out.

b) $R_f \text{ value} = \dfrac{\text{distance travelled by spot}}{\text{distance travelled by solvent}}$

$= 3.47 \text{ cm} \div 9.00 \text{ cm} = \mathbf{0.386}$ (3 s.f.)

### Page 37 — Fact Recall Questions

Q1 In all chromatography, a mobile phase (e.g. a liquid solvent) moves over a stationary phase (e.g. chromatography paper or a TLC plate). The components in the mixture spend different amounts of time in the mobile phase and the stationary phase. The components that spend longer in the mobile phase travel faster or further. The time spent in the different phases is what separates out the components of the mixture.

Q2 DCPIP changes from blue to colourless when it gets reduced, indicating that a redox reaction has taken place.

Q3 E.g. the leaves could be cut up into pieces, their stalks removed, and then ground up using a pestle and mortar with some cold isolation solution. The liquid could then be filtered into a beaker through muslin cloth and transferred to centrifuge tubes. These tubes would be centrifuged at high speed, causing the chloroplasts to gather in pellets at the bottom of each tube. The liquid above the pellets could then be removed and the pellets re-suspended in fresh isolation solution to form the chloroplast extract.

## 6. Aerobic and Anaerobic Respiration

### Page 40 — Application Questions

Q1 a) It catalyses the phosphorylation of glucose to glucose phosphate, using a phosphate from ATP.

b) E.g. it may help to stop the over-production of glucose phosphate.

Q2 a) i) lactate/lactic acid

ii) pyruvate

iii) ethanol

b) i) A

ii) B

iii) A

### Page 40 — Fact Recall Questions

Q1 ATP is used to phosphorylate glucose, making triose phosphate.

Q2 In the oxidation of triose phosphate to pyruvate, NAD collects the hydrogen ions from triose phosphate, forming reduced NAD.

Q3 10

*Two molecules of pyruvate are made for every molecule of glucose that enters glycolysis.*

Q4 It is used in glycolysis (to collect the hydrogen ions lost from triose phosphate in the production of pyruvate).

Q5 lactate/lactic acid

## 7. Aerobic Respiration — The Mitochondrial Reactions

### Page 42 — Application Questions

Q1 a) oxaloacetate = 4C, citrate = 6C

b) Decarboxylation and dehydrogenation occur, producing one molecule of reduced FAD and two of reduced NAD. ATP is produced by substrate level phosphorylation.

Q2 24

*Two molecules of carbon dioxide are produced per turn of the Krebs cycle and the Krebs cycle turns twice for each molecule of glucose. So for one molecule of glucose four molecules of carbon dioxide are produced. Therefore if six molecules of glucose were respired, 24 (6 x 4) molecules of carbon dioxide would be produced in the Krebs cycle.*

Q3 Acetyl coenzyme A can enter the Krebs cycle, leading to the formation of reduced coenzymes, which are then used in oxidative phosphorylation.

### Page 45 — Application Questions

Q1 a) Carrier 1 will be in a reduced state because it has received electrons from reduced NAD but can't pass them on. Carrier 3 will be in an oxidised state because it has passed its electrons onto oxygen, but hasn't received any more from carrier 2.

*If a substance gains electrons it is reduced. If a substance loses electrons it is oxidised.*

b) Antimycin A inhibits carrier 2 and so stops electrons moving down the electron transport chain. This means no more energy will be lost from electrons moving down the chain, so H+ ions will not be transported across the inner mitochondrial membrane and the electrochemical gradient across the membrane won't be maintained. This means the synthesis of ATP by ATP synthase will stop. If a fish can't produce ATP it will die as energy from ATP is needed to fuel all biological processes.

Q2 The fact that ATP synthesis stops when DCC is added suggests that the movement of protons through the ATP synthase is essential for ATP production. This supports the chemiosmotic theory because it suggests that the proton gradient is being used to synthesise ATP.

### Page 45 — Fact Recall Questions

Q1 a) Pyruvate is decarboxylated — one carbon atom is removed from pyruvate in the form of carbon dioxide. Then NAD is reduced — it collects hydrogen from pyruvate. Pyruvate becomes oxidised and acetate is formed.

b) It combines with acetate to form acetyl coenzyme A.

c) Acetyl coenzyme A enters the Krebs cycle. Reduced NAD is used in oxidative phosphorylation. Carbon dioxide is released as a waste product.

Q2 a) Two molecules of $CO_2$ are released — one $CO_2$ is released from the conversion of citrate to a 5-carbon compound and the other $CO_2$ is released from the conversion of the 5-carbon compound to oxaloacetate.

b) one

Q3 substrate-level phosphorylation

Q4 a) It is reused in the link reaction.

b) It is regenerated for use in the next Krebs cycle.

Q5 They lose energy.

Q6 oxygen

Q7 E.g. the conversion of pyruvate to acetate in the link reaction. / The conversion of citrate to the 5-carbon compound in the Krebs cycle. / The conversion of the 5-carbon compound to oxaloacetate in the Krebs cycle.

*Every time $CO_2$ is lost in a reaction, decarboxylation is happening.*

Q8

| *Substance* | *Glycolysis* | *Link reaction* | *Krebs cycle* | *Oxidative phosphorylation* |
|---|---|---|---|---|
| *ATP* | *X* | | *X* | *X* |
| *reduced NAD* | *X* | *X* | *X* | |
| *reduced FAD* | | | *X* | |
| *$CO_2$* | | *X* | *X* | |

## 8. Respiration Experiments

### Page 47 — Application Question

Q1 a) E.g. the scientist could have set up a test tube containing a known volume and concentration of substrate (e.g. glucose) solution and a buffer solution at specific pH. She could then have added a known mass of dried yeast of species A to the tube and stirred until the yeast dissolved. Next, she could have sealed the test tube with a bung and attached it via a tube to a gas syringe in order to catch the $CO_2$ produced by the respiring yeast. At regular intervals (e.g. every minute) for a set amount of time (e.g. 10 minutes), the scientist could have recorded the volume of gas present in the gas syringe. By repeating the experiment (e.g. three times) at this pH, she could then have calculated the mean rate of $CO_2$ production at this pH. She could then have repeated the experiment at a range of pH levels by using buffer solutions of different pH levels. She could have done the same thing for species B.

b) Respiration is a series of reactions controlled by enzymes. The enzymes used in respiration by the different species of yeast may have different optimum pH levels, at which they are able to catalyse the reactions most effectively.

c) Mean rate of $CO_2$ production of species A at pH 5.5 = 1.75 $cm^3$ $min^{-1}$

*Anything between 1.7 and 1.8 $cm^3$ would be acceptable here.*

Mean rate of $CO_2$ production of species B at pH 5.5 = 3.75 $cm^3$ $min^{-1}$

*Anything between 3.7 and 3.8 $cm^3$ would be acceptable here.*

Percentage change in rate from species A to species B = ((1.75 – 3.75) ÷ 1.75) × 100 = **114% faster**

*Your final answer may differ a little depending on what you got for the mean rates of $CO_2$ production for the two species.*

d) Boiled yeast won't respire as the boiling will have killed it. Therefore, it acts as a negative control to show that the $CO_2$ production is a result of the respiring yeast and not any other reactions that may be happening in the tube.

## Page 49 — Fact Recall Questions

Q1 To stop oxygen getting into the yeast solution, forcing the yeast to respire anaerobically.

Q2 Prepare and treat a test tube in the same way as the others in the investigation, but do not put any yeast in it.

Q3 10 g

*You know the answer here is 10 g because the mass of the peas and the mass of the glass beads in the control tube have to be the same.*

## Exam-style Questions — pages 51-52

1.1 E.g. if the mitochondria can't produce proteins, they won't be able to produce the enzymes needed to make ATP (e.g. ATP synthase) ***(1 mark)***. / They won't be able to produce proteins that form part of the electron transport chain, which is needed to make ATP ***(1 mark)***.

1.2 Because glycolysis takes place in the cytoplasm of the cell ***(1 mark)***.

*Because glycolysis takes place in the cytoplasm and not the mitochondria, it doesn't matter whether you have functioning mitochondria or not — glycolysis can still happen.*

1.3 Glucose is phosphorylated using ATP to create glucose phosphate ***(1 mark)***. Glucose phosphate is phosphorylated using ATP to form hexose bisphosphate/a six carbon intermediate ***(1 mark)***, which is split to form two molecules of triose phosphate ***(1 mark)***.

1.4 In the oxidation of triose phosphate to pyruvate, NAD collects the hydrogen ions from triose phosphate ***(1 mark)***, forming reduced NAD ***(1 mark)***.

2.1 A sample of the solution could have been placed in a cuvette ***(1 mark)*** and put in a colorimeter, a machine that measures absorbance ***(1 mark)***.

2.2 As DCPIP is reduced and loses its blue colour, the absorbance of the solution will decrease ***(1 mark)***. When photosynthesis occurs at a faster rate, DCPIP will be reduced at a faster rate ***(1 mark)***, and absorbance will decrease faster as a result ***(1 mark)***.

2.3 Because the high temperature has denatured the enzymes involved in photosynthesis, meaning that photosynthesis cannot occur ***(1 mark)***. As a result, the colour of the DCPIP won't change and neither will the absorbance ***(1 mark)***.

3.1 The oxidation of triose phosphate to pyruvate produces one molecule of reduced NAD ***(1 mark)***. The conversion of pyruvate to acetate produces one molecule of reduced NAD ***(1 mark)***. The conversion of citrate to a 5-carbon compound in the Krebs cycle produces one molecule of reduced NAD ***(1 mark)***. The conversion of this 5-carbon compound to oxaloacetate produces another two molecules of reduced NAD ***(1 mark)*** and one molecule of reduced FAD ***(1 mark)***.

3.2 The electrons move down the electron transport chain, losing energy at each electron carrier ***(1 mark)***. Finally they are passed onto oxygen as it is the final electron acceptor ***(1 mark)***.

3.3 There would be no electrochemical gradient produced across the inner mitochondrial membrane ***(1 mark)***. This means there would be no movement of ions across the mitochondrial membrane to drive ATP synthase ***(1 mark)*** so no ATP would be made ***(1 mark)***. The cells would only get ATP from anaerobic respiration ***(1 mark)***.

*Even though $H^+$ ions will still be pumped across the inner mitochondrial membrane into the intermembrane space, the uncoupler will be moving them back into the matrix at the same time — so no gradient would be produced.*

4.1 The student hasn't taken into account the amount of oxygen that the plant has used for respiration ***(1 mark)***, so less oxygen will be released by the plant than it has actually produced during photosynthesis ***(1 mark)***.

4.2 The limiting factor in experiment 2 must be temperature because the graph for experiment 3 levels off at a higher point ***(1 mark)*** but experiment 3 had the same light intensity and $CO_2$ concentration as experiment 2 ***(1 mark)***.

4.3 The level of RuBP will have increased because there would have been less $CO_2$ to combine with RuBP to form GP ***(1 mark)***. The level of TP will have decreased because less GP would have been made and so less converted to TP ***(1 mark)***. As TP was made into useful organic substances this will have decreased the level of TP further ***(1 mark)***.

*If you get a question like this in the exam, make sure you think of the substances before the reactant in the cycle as well as those that come after it.*

## Topic 5 — B: Energy Transfer and Nutrient Cycles

### 1. Energy Transfer in Ecosystems

### Page 56 — Application Questions

Q1 a) He could have dried out the sample he took in an oven set at a low temperature, checking the weight every day until it became constant. At this point, all the water would have been removed and this would be the dry mass of the sample.

b) It will give him an estimate of the chemical energy stored in the wheat.

Q2 a) $N = I - (F + R)$
$N = 57\ 153 - (34\ 292 + 17\ 000)$
$N =$ **5861 kJ m$^{-2}$ yr$^{-1}$**

b) % efficiency of energy transfer =
(net productivity of trophic level ÷ net productivity of previous trophic level) × 100
(627 ÷ 5861) × 100 = **10.7%**

Q3 a) $NPP = GPP - R$. This can be rearranged to give:
$GPP = NPP + R$, so
$GPP = 31\ 023 + 15\ 604$
= **46 627 kJ m$^{-2}$ yr$^{-1}$**

b) $N = I - (F + R)$. This can be rearranged to give:
$R = I - F - N$, so
$R = 8105 - 3988 - 2073$
= **2044 kJ m$^{-2}$ yr$^{-1}$**

*Remember, N is the net productivity of the small fish, I is the amount of energy the small fish ingest from food, F is the amount of energy lost in faeces and urine, and R is the respiratory loss of the fish. You're given the numbers you need for I and F in the question — you just have to find N from the diagram, and rearrange the formula to find R. Double check your answer by plugging the values for I, F, and R back into the equation for N. If you've calculated R correctly, you should come up with N = 2073 KJ m$^{-2}$yr$^{-1}$.*

c) $N = I - (F + R)$. This can be rearranged to give:
$F = I - R - N$, so
$F = 2073 - 879 - 119$
= **1075 kJ m$^{-2}$ yr$^{-1}$**

*Again, rearrange the formula and put in the values you know. R is given in the question, N is shown on the diagram and I is also on the diagram — it's the net productivity of the small fish.*

d) Any two from: e.g. because some parts of the small fish aren't eaten so the energy isn't taken in. / Because some parts of the small fish are indigestible and so are egested as faeces. / Because some of the energy is lost to the environment through respiration or excretion of urine.

e) % efficiency of energy transfer =
(net productivity of trophic level ÷ net productivity of previous trophic level) × 100
Between plant plankton and animal plankton =
(8105 ÷ 31 023) × 100 = **26.1%**
Between animal plankton and small fish =
(2073 ÷ 8105) × 100 = **25.6%**
Between small fish and large fish =
(119 ÷ 2073) × 100 = **5.7%**

### Page 56 — Fact Recall Questions

Q1 The mass of living material in the plant. / The chemical energy stored in the plant.

Q2 The total amount of chemical energy converted from light energy by plants in a given area.

Q3 The energy lost to the environment as heat when organisms respire.

Q4 a) The energy stored in the consumers' biomass. It is also the energy available to organisms at the next trophic level.

b) $N = I - (F + R)$

### 2. Farming Practices and Production

### Page 59 — Application Question

Q1 a) $\text{rate} = \dfrac{\text{change in } y}{\text{change in } x}$
$= \dfrac{57 - 47}{22 - 18}$
= **2.5 kg week$^{-1}$**

b) Breed 1: 64 ÷ 100 x 82 = 52 kg (2 s.f.)
Breed 2: 73 ÷ 100 x 76 = 55 kg (2 s.f.)
Breed 3: 66 ÷ 100 x 57 = 38 kg (2 s.f.)
**Breed 2** would produce the most meat at 22 weeks.

c) E.g. using antibiotics may mean that the pigs use less energy fighting diseases so they can use more energy to grow, increasing their net production.

d) Any one from: e.g. keep the pigs in pens to restrict their movement. This will reduce the energy lost through respiration. / Keep the pigs indoors, so that they are kept warm. This will reduce the energy lost through generating body heat.

### Page 59 — Fact Recall Questions

Q1 Simple lines of energy transfer through an ecosystem.

Q2 Lots of overlapping food chains in an ecosystem.

Q3 Simplifying the food web gets rid of food chains that don't involve humans/involving pests. This means that less energy is transferred to the pests, increasing the efficiency of energy transfer to humans.

Q4 E.g. pesticides / insecticides / herbicides / biological agents.

## 3. Nutrient Cycles in Natural Ecosystems

### Pages 62-63 — Application Questions

Q1 a) $\frac{(31.5 + 107)}{(5.4 + 107 + 31.5 + 86)} \times 100$

= **60%** (2 s.f.)

b) $\frac{120 - 107}{120} \times 100$

= **11%** (2 s.f.)

c) E.g. more land was being cultivated in the 1990s than in 1860, so there was less uncultivated land.

d) E.g. through the manufacture of fertilisers/increased use of fertilisers.

Q2 It might decrease because waterlogged soils create anaerobic conditions. This means that denitrifying bacteria convert nitrates in the soil back into nitrogen gas, which the plants can't assimilate without nitrogen fixation.

Q3 a) Figure 2 because phosphorus is not cycled through the atmosphere, unlike nitrogen.

*Don't let the fact that both the figures show the ocean as part of the cycle throw you. You know that nitrogen is needed for plant growth and that aquatic ecosystems also involve plants.*

b) As phosphate ions dissolved in water.

c) Ammonification.

d) Phosphate ions dissolved in the oceans are assimilated by aquatic producers (such as algae).

e) Through the death and decomposition of organisms and thorough the breakdown of compounds in faeces and urine.

### Page 63 — Fact Recall Questions

Q1 a) Fungi, bacteria.

b) They secrete enzymes and digest their food externally, then absorb the nutrients they need.

Q2 a) Mycorrhizae are symbiotic relationships between fungi and the roots of plants.

b) The fungi have long thin stands called hyphae which connect to the plant's roots. The hyphae greatly increase the surface area of the plant's root system, allowing the plant to absorb more water and mineral ions.

Q3 nitrogen fixation, nitrification, denitrification and ammonification

Q4 Saprobionts are involved in breaking down the organic compounds when plants and animals die, releasing phosphate ions into the soil for assimilation by plants. They also release the phosphate ions from urine and faeces.

Q5 a) The waste produced by sea birds.

b) Because it returns a significant amount of phosphate ions to the soil from the oceans.

## 4. Fertilisers and Eutrophication

### Pages 65-66 — Application Questions

Q1 a) 100 m and 800 m, because these sites are where the nitrate concentration increases sharply.

b) i) 37 – 31 = 6 $mgl^{-1}$

(6 ÷ 31) × 100 = **19.4%**

ii) E.g. the second farm has more land on which crops are grown so more nitrate fertiliser is leached into the river. / The second farm uses a higher concentration of nitrate fertiliser on its land. / The second farm uses a chemical fertiliser whilst the first farm uses a natural/organic fertiliser. / The second farm applies more nitrate fertiliser than the crops can use. / The second farm applies fertiliser before heavy rain.

*There are lots of possible reasons why the water next to the second farm has a higher nitrogen concentration than the water next to the first farm — you just need to give a sensible answer.*

Q2 The nitrate concentration and algal content of the control river remain constant at 7 $mgl^{-1}$ and 10 thousand cells $cm^{-3}$. This indicates that the nitrate concentration and algal growth on rivers A and B were affected by the two farms and not due to any other environmental variable.

Q3 a) There is a correlation between the nitrate concentration of river A and its algal content. Shortly after the nitrate concentration increases in river A, the algal content increases too.

b) Nitrates leached from fertilised fields stimulate the growth of algae in rivers.

Q4 Large amounts of algae may block light from reaching the plants below. Eventually the plants might die because they're unable to photosynthesise enough. Bacteria would then feed on the dead plant matter. The increased numbers of bacteria would reduce the oxygen concentration in the water by carrying out aerobic respiration. This could reduce the number of fish and other aquatic organisms at these locations because there isn't enough dissolved oxygen in the water.

### Page 66 — Fact Recall Questions

Q1 Crops take in mineral ions from the soil as they grow. When crops are harvested, they're removed from the field where they're grown rather than being allowed to die and decompose there. This means the mineral ions that they contain (e.g. phosphates and nitrates) are not returned to the soil by decomposers in the nitrogen or phosphorus cycles.

Q2 E.g. manure / composted vegetables / crop residues / sewage sludge.

Q3 leaching

Q4 eutrophication

## Exam-style Questions — pages 68-69

1.1 The Sun ***(1 mark)***. Photosynthesis ***(1 mark)***.

1.2 $N = I - (F + R)$
$N = 2619 - (1571 + 785)$
$= \mathbf{263\ kJ\ m^{-2}\ yr^{-1}}$ ***(1 mark)***

1.3 percentage efficiency of energy transfer =
(net productivity of trophic level ÷ net productivity of previous trophic level) × 100
Between the producer and primary consumer 1 =
(2619 ÷ 38750) × 100 = 6.76%
Between the producer and primary consumer 2 =
(1265 ÷ 38750) × 100 = 3.26%
6.76 – 3.26 = **3.5%**
***(2 marks for the correct answer, or 1 mark for either 6.76% or 3.26%)***

1.4 The saprobionts feed on the remains of the dead organisms and on their waste products, breaking them down ***(1 mark)***. This allows important chemical elements in the remains and waste to be recycled ***(1 mark)***.

2.1 Mycorrhizae are symbiotic relationships that form between some fungi and plant roots ***(1 mark)***.

2.2 They should have controlled, any two from: e.g. the mineral content of the soil. / The mass of soil used. / The volume of water added to the soil. / The temperature that the two groups of seedlings were kept at. / The light intensity that the two groups of seedlings were exposed to.
***(Any two correct answers for 1 mark)***

2.3 Mean mass of seedlings on day 30 = 5 g.
Mean mass of seedlings on day 60 = 10 g.
(10 – 5) ÷ 30 = $\mathbf{0.2\ g\ day^{-1}}$ (1 s.f.) ***(1 mark)***

2.4 The fungi used to innoculate the mycorrhizal culture group increased the surface area of the seedlings' root systems compared to those in the control group ***(1 mark)***. This increased the mycorrhizal group seedlings' uptake of water/ important mineral ions compared to the seedlings in the control group ***(1 mark)***. This increased the growth of the seedlings in the mycorrhizal group ***(1 mark)***.

3.1 A field of potato crops with greenfly infestation that wasn't treated with any form of pest control ***(1 mark)***.

3.2 Field D is the negative control field because the consistently high numbers of greenfly reduce the amount of energy available to the crops for growth ***(1 mark)***, which means the crops are less efficient at converting energy so it will have the lowest net primary production ***(1 mark)***. Field A has been treated by an integrated system because at the end of the study it has the lowest numbers of greenfly ***(1 mark)***, which means the crops have lost the least energy and biomass, so net primary production will be the highest ***(1 mark)***.

3.3 E.g. take samples of the crop before and after the study period ***(1 mark)***. Dry the samples out in an oven, checking the weight each day until they become constant ***(1 mark)***. This gives the dry mass of each sample. Use the difference in mass between the two samples ***(1 mark)*** divided by the length of the study period, to determine the rate at which biomass has been added ***(1 mark)***.

# Topic 6

## Topic 6 — A: Stimuli and Responses

### 1. Survival and Response

#### Page 71 — Application Question

Q1 a) tactic/taxis
b) An environment higher in oxygen is a more favourable environment for them to be in.

#### Page 71 — Fact Recall Questions

Q1 To increase their chances of survival.
Q2 Directional movement in response to a stimulus.
Q3 Non-directional (random) movement in response to a stimulus.

### 2. Nervous Communication

#### Page 74 — Application Questions

Q1 a) Any one from, e.g. the response would be slower / the response would be voluntary.
b) Stimulus — light tap/touch.
Effector — quadriceps muscle.
c) i) The knee-jerk reflex doesn't involve a relay neurone in the spinal cord. / There are usually three neurones involved in a simple reflex.
ii) E.g. the quadriceps muscle may not contract/there may be no response. If the spinal cord is damaged then the sensory neurone may not be able to transmit nervous impulses to the motor neurone / the motor neurone may not be able to transmit nervous impulses to the leg muscle.

Q2 a) The nociceptors detect the stimulus and impulses are passed to a sensory neurone. This passes the electrical impulses to a relay neurone in the spinal cord/CNS which carries the impulse to a motor neurone. The motor neurone carries impulses to an effector (e.g. a biceps muscle).
b) Particular receptors are specific to a particular stimulus. This means that it's possible that while their pain receptors aren't functional (so pain isn't felt), their touch receptors are functional allowing light touches to be felt.
c) It helps to protect the body by reacting to situations/ environments that could cause the body harm.

## Page 74 — Fact Recall Questions

Q1 To detect stimuli.

Q2 Muscle cells / cells found in glands.

Q3 a) Transmits electrical impulses from receptors to the central nervous system (CNS).
b) Transmits electrical impulses from the CNS to effectors.
c) Transmits electrical impulses between sensory neurones and motor neurones.

Q4 a) Receptor cells detect a stimulus. Sensory neurones transmit electrical impulses from the receptors to the CNS. The CNS processes the information and sends impulses along motor neurones to effectors, which respond.
*This question asks about a voluntary response, so make sure that your answer includes the CNS processing the information.*
b) CNS

Q5 The response is localised because neurotransmitters are secreted directly onto cells. The response is short-lived because neurotransmitters are quickly removed once they have done their job.

Q6 The pathway of communication goes through the spinal cord but not through conscious parts of the brain, so the response is automatic.

Q7 Because they're so rapid.

# 3. Responses in Plants

## Page 77 — Application Question

Q1 a) positive
*The shoot is bending towards the stimulus.*
b) Y because this is where cell elongation is taking place, causing the shoot to bend towards the opposite side.

## Page 77 — Fact Recall Questions

Q1 phototropism

Q2 They grow in the opposite direction to the force of gravity.

Q3 The growing regions of the plant / shoot and root tips.

Q4 They stimulate growth by cell elongation.

Q5 IAA is an auxin that's produced in the tips of shoots and roots in flowering plants.

Q6 By diffusion and active transport over short distances, and via the phloem over long distances.

Q7 a) IAA concentration increases on the shaded side of the shoot. This means the cells on the shaded part of the shoot grow faster than the cells most exposed to light. This pattern of growth causes the shoot to bend towards the light.
b) IAA concentration increases on the underside of roots. This means the cells on the underside of the root don't grow as quickly as the cells on the upper-side. This pattern of growth causes the root to grow downwards in the same direction as gravity.

# 4. Receptors

## Page 79 — Application Questions

Q1 a) threshold level
b) B, because its generator potential reaches -60mV/the threshold level.
c) Approximately -87.5 mV (accept any value between -87 mV and -88 mV)
*Make sure you always read the axes carefully — especially on graphs to do with potential differences across cell membranes, because they nearly always involve negative numbers.*

Q2 E.g. pressure from touch would normally deform the stretch-mediated sodium ion channels in Pacinian corpuscles. However, by blocking sodium ion channels the drug would stop sodium ions from diffusing into the cell and generating an action potential. This would mean the person wouldn't be able to perceive that they were being touched.

## Page 81 — Fact Recall Questions

Q1 When a stimulus is detected, the cell membrane is excited and becomes more permeable, allowing more ions to move in and out of the cell. This alters the potential difference across the cell membrane and therefore produces a generator potential.

Q2 mechanical

Q3 A Pacinian corpuscle contains the end of a sensory neurone. The sensory nerve ending is wrapped in layers of connective tissue called lamellae.

Q4 When a Pacinian corpuscle is stimulated the lamellae are deformed and press on the sensory nerve ending. This causes deformation of stretch-mediated sodium ion channels in the sensory neurone's cell membrane. The sodium ion channels open and sodium ions diffuse into the cell, creating a generator potential. If the generator potential reaches the threshold, it triggers an action potential.

Q5 Cones are close together and each cone joins one bipolar neurone. So when light from two points that are close together hits two cones, an action potential from each cone goes to the brain. This means that the light can be distinguished as coming from two separate points. This doesn't happen in rods because many rods join the same bipolar neurone, which means light from two points close together can't be told apart.

Q6 Any three from: e.g. rods are found mainly in the peripheral parts of the retina and cones are mainly found packed together in the fovea. / Rods only give information in black and white but cones give information in colour. / Rods are very sensitive to light but cones are less sensitive. / Many rods join one bipolar neurone, but only one cone joins one bipolar neurone.

## 5. Control of Heart Rate

### Page 84 — Application Question

Q1 The chemoreceptors in a person with anaemia will detect low oxygen levels in the blood. The chemoreceptors will send impulses along sensory neurones to the medulla, which will send impulses along sympathetic neurones. These neurones will secrete noradrenaline, which will bind to receptors on the sinoatrial node/SAN and cause the heart rate to increase in an attempt to increase oxygen levels in the blood.

### Page 84 — Fact Recall Questions

Q1 a) To control unconscious activities of the body.
b) The sympathetic nervous system and the parasympathetic nervous system.

Q2 That it can contract and relax without receiving signals from nerves.

Q3 To act as a pacemaker, setting the rhythm of the heartbeat by sending out waves of electrical activity to the atrial walls.

Q4 medulla (oblongata)

Q5 a) baroreceptor/pressure receptor
b) aorta and carotid arteries

## Exam-style Questions — pages 86-87

1.1 phototropism ***(1 mark)***

1.2 The seedling should have been from a Goosegrass plant and potted in soil from the same source ***(1 mark)***. There should have been no lamp/light from any direction present ***(1 mark)***.

1.3 E.g. to make sure that only the variable being tested (light intensity) was changing ***(1 mark)***. / To keep all variables other than light intensity the same ***(1 mark)***.

1.4 Seedling A will be bent to the right because it will have grown towards the light ***(1 mark)***. Seedling B will have grown straight up because the rotation of the seedling means that the light is not continuously coming from one direction ***(1 mark)***. Seedling C will be bent towards the right but may have a kink in, so that it is not a smooth bend because it will have grown to the right for five days, then to the left for five days and to the right again for the last five days, as the position of the light source has been changed ***(1 mark)***.

1.5 IAA/auxins would become most concentrated in the shaded parts of the plant/shoots ***(1 mark)***. This would mean that the shaded parts of the shoot would grow faster/elongate more than the parts exposed to light ***(1 mark)***. This uneven growth would lead to the shoots bending towards the light ***(1 mark)***.

2.1 Light enters the eye, hits the photoreceptors/cones and is absorbed by light-sensitive optical pigments ***(1 mark)***. Light bleaches the pigments, causing a chemical change and altering the membrane permeability to sodium ions ***(1 mark)***. A generator potential is created and if it reaches the threshold an action potential is sent along a bipolar neurone ***(1 mark)***. These connect photoreceptors to the optic nerve, which takes impulses to the brain where the information is interpreted as colour ***(1 mark)***.

2.2 E.g. in low light conditions only rods are sufficiently light sensitive to trigger action potentials and send information to the brain ***(1 mark)***. This is because many rods join one bipolar neurone, so many weak generator potentials can combine to reach the threshold and trigger an action potential in low light ***(1 mark)***. However, bright light is required to trigger an action potential in a cone ***(1 mark)*** because each cone joins one neurone so it takes more light to reach the threshold and trigger an action potential ***(1 mark)***. In protanopia only the cones are affected so the ability to see in low light is not affected ***(1 mark)***.

2.3 E.g. bright light entering the eye could cause damage to it/ the photoreceptors/retina ***(1 mark)***. As the reflex to contract the pupil takes place quickly this reduces the risk of the eye being damaged ***(1 mark)***.

2.4 The photoreceptors detect the bright light and send an impulse down a sensory neurone to the CNS ***(1 mark)***. In the CNS a relay neurone carries the impulse to a motor neurone ***(1 mark)***, which carries the impulse to muscles in the eye causing them to contract and the pupil to narrow/ reduce in size ***(1 mark)***.

3.1 The delay gives time for the atria to fully contract and empty before the ventricles contract ***(1 mark)***.

3.2 It prevents the waves of electrical activity from being passed directly from the atria to the ventricles ***(1 mark)***.

3.3 The AVN passes the waves of electrical activity onto the bundle of His ***(1 mark)***. The bundle of His conducts the waves of electrical activity between the ventricles down to the apex/bottom of the heart to the Purkyne tissue ***(1 mark)***. The Purkyne tissue carries the waves of electrical activity into the muscular walls of the right and left ventricles causing them to contract simultaneously from the bottom up, which results in blood being pumped out of the heart ***(1 mark)***.

3.4 Noradrenaline is a neurotransmitter which binds to receptors on the sinoatrial node, causing the heart rate to speed up ***(1 mark)***. Beta-blockers therefore stop the heart rate being increased in response to low blood pressure or low blood oxygen levels ***(1 mark)***, so beta-blockers could be contributing to the slow heart rate/AV block symptoms seen in the patient ***(1 mark)***.

3.5 E.g. the delay in passage of electrical activity through the AVN caused by the second-degree AV block can result in a decreased heart rate ***(1 mark)***. This is because of the increased time taken for electrical activity to reach the ventricles and cause their contraction/the heart to beat ***(1 mark)***. This slow heart rate can result in low oxygen levels in the blood, which could cause dizziness and fainting ***(1 mark)***.

3.6 The aorta, carotid arteries and medulla ***(1 mark)***.

# Topic 6 — B: Nervous Coordination

## 1. Neurones

### Page 92 — Application Questions

Q1 A — The neurone is stimulated.
B — Depolarisation / Lots of sodium ion channels are open and lots of sodium ions are diffusing into the neurone.
C — The sodium ion channels are closed and the potassium ion channels are open.

Q2 –40 mV

Q3 –60 mV
*Remember to always include units in your answer when they're given on the graph.*

Q4 a) At a potential difference of +40 mV the sodium ion channels close and the potassium ion channels open. The membrane is more permeable to potassium so potassium ions diffuse out of the neurone down the potassium ion concentration gradient. This starts to get the membrane back to its resting potential. At the bottom of the curve the potassium ion channels are slow to close so there's a slight 'overshoot' where too many potassium ions diffuse out of the neurone. The potential difference (–70 mV) is more negative than the resting potential (–60 mV). The sodium-potassium pump then returns the membrane to its resting potential (–60 mV).
b) refractory period

Q5 The action potential would have the same potential difference values as the graph shown because once the threshold is reached, an action potential will always fire with the same change in voltage, no matter how big the stimulus is. However, there may be another action potential shown on the graph because a bigger stimulus will cause action potentials to fire more frequently.

### Page 92 — Fact Recall Questions

Q1 Sodium-potassium pumps and potassium ion channels.

Q2 Sodium ions diffuse into the neurone down the sodium ion electrochemical gradient. This makes the inside of the neurone less negative and so decreases the potential difference across the membrane.

Q3 More sodium ions diffuse into the neurone because more sodium ion channels open.

Q4 a) The ion channels are recovering and can't be made to open.
b) It makes action potentials discrete/separate impulses. It means there's a limit to the frequency at which the nerve impulses can be transmitted. It makes action potentials unidirectional.

Q5 During an action potential, some of the sodium ions that enter the neurone diffuse sideways. This causes sodium ion channels in the next region of the neurone to open and sodium ions diffuse into that part. This causes a wave of depolarisation.

Q6 A myelinated neurone has a myelin sheath. In the peripheral nervous system the myelin sheath is made of a type of cell called a Schwann cell. Between the Schwann cells are tiny patches of bare membrane called the nodes of Ranvier. Sodium ion channels are concentrated at the nodes of Ranvier.

Q7 In a myelinated neurone depolarisation/action potentials only happen at the nodes of Ranvier. However in a non-myelinated neurone, depolarisation/action potentials occur as a wave along the whole length of the axon membrane. Conduction along a myelinated neurone is faster than along a non-myelinated neurone.

Q8 Axon diameter and temperature.

## 2. Synaptic Transmission

### Page 97 — Application Questions

Q1 The main symptom will be muscle weakness. Calcium ions are unable to enter the synaptic knob. This means the synaptic vesicles won't fuse with the presynaptic membrane so ACh will not be released. Without the release of ACh there will be no action potential triggered in the muscle cell and therefore no response in the muscle.
*If you understand what happens when $Ca^{2+}$ ions do enter the synaptic knob then it should be pretty logical that when they can't enter, the opposite happens.*

Q2 a) They will reduce the sensation of pain. They function as inhibitory neurotransmitters so when they bind to receptors on the postsynaptic membrane it will be hyperpolarised. This means no action potential will be fired and therefore pain signals will not be transmitted.
b) It will reduce the sensation of pain / it will have the same effect as endorphins. This is because it is very similar in structure to an endorphin molecule so will bind to endorphin receptors and is likely to cause the same effect.

Q3 Carbachol mimics the action of ACh so the presence of carbachol will activate even more cholinergic receptors. This will make more action potentials fire in the postsynaptic neurone, so more saliva will be produced.

### Page 98 — Fact Recall Questions

Q1 A — synaptic knob, B — vesicle, C — Acetylcholine/ACh, D — presynaptic membrane, E — ACh receptor, F — postsynaptic membrane, G — synaptic cleft.

Q2 neurone, muscle, gland

Q3 Receptors are only on postsynaptic membranes. This means the neurotransmitter can't activate an action potential back along the presynaptic neurone.

Q4 a) The action potential stimulates voltage-gated calcium ion channels in the presynaptic neurone to open, so calcium ions diffuse into the synaptic knob.
b) The influx of calcium ions into the synaptic knob causes the synaptic vesicles to fuse with the presynaptic membrane. The vesicles release ACh into the synaptic cleft. ACh diffuses across the synaptic cleft and binds to specific cholinergic receptors on the postsynaptic membrane. This causes sodium ion channels in the postsynaptic neurone to open. If the threshold is reached, the influx of sodium ions into the postsynaptic membrane causes an action potential on the postsynaptic membrane.

Q5 So the response doesn't keep happening.

Q6 An inhibitory neurotransmitter hyperpolarises the postsynaptic membrane, preventing it from firing an action potential.

Q7 a) Where two or more presynaptic neurones release their neurotransmitters at the same time onto the same postsynaptic neurone, the small amount of neurotransmitter released from each of these neurones can be enough altogether to reach the threshold in the postsynaptic neurone. This makes an action potential more likely.

b) Where two or more nerve impulses arrive in quick succession from the same presynaptic neurone, more neurotransmitter is released into the synaptic cleft. This makes an action potential more likely.

Q8 A cholinergic synapse between a motor neurone and a muscle cell.

Q9 E.g. they both release ACh from vesicles in the presynaptic membrane. In both, ACh diffuses across the synaptic cleft and binds to cholinergic receptors on the postsynaptic membrane (which triggers an action potential if the threshold is reached). They both use acetylcholinesterase (AChE) to break down ACh in the synaptic cleft.

## 3. Muscle Structure

### Page 102 — Application Questions

Q1 The quadriceps because it relaxes when the leg is bent.
*Remember, the antagonist is the relaxing muscle and the agonist is the contracting muscle. In this case the agonist is the hamstrings — it is contracting, which pulls the lower leg backwards making it bend at the knee.*

Q2 a) B
b) C
c) A and C
d) B

Q3 Option 1. The A-band has stayed the same length, the I-band is shorter and the H-zone is shorter.
*Remember, the A-band is the length of the myosin filament and this doesn't get shorter during contraction. During contraction more of the actin filament slides over the myosin filament so the sections with only actin (the I-bands) get shorter and the sections with only myosin (the H-zones) get shorter too.*

### Page 102 — Fact Recall Questions

Q1 A pair of muscles that work together to move a bone. One muscle in the pair relaxes as the other contracts.

Q2 The T-tubules are parts of the sarcolemma that fold inwards across the muscle fibre and stick to the sarcoplasm. They help to spread electrical impulses throughout the sarcoplasm so they reach all parts of the muscle fibre.

Q3 To provide the ATP that's needed for muscle contraction.

Q4 An A-band contains myosin filaments and some overlapping actin filaments. Under an electron microscope it appears as a dark band.

Q5 Myosin and actin filaments slide over one another to make the sarcomeres contract (the myofilaments themselves don't contract).

## 4. Muscle Contraction

### Page 105 — Application Questions

Q1 a) i) X. The $Ca^{2+}$ concentration is low, suggesting that the muscle is at rest. Muscle fibres are longest when they are relaxed.

ii) Y. There is an influx of $Ca^{2+}$ ions into the sarcoplasm following an action potential, and the $Ca^{2+}$ ions bind to the protein attached to tropomyosin.

iii) Y. The $Ca^{2+}$ ion concentration is high and $Ca^{2+}$ ions activate ATP hydrolase.

b) The $Ca^{2+}$ ions are moved by active transport from the sarcoplasm back into the sarcoplasmic reticulum, where they're stored.

c) An action potential from a motor neurone stimulates a muscle cell and depolarises the sarcolemma. Depolarisation spreads down the T-tubules to the sarcoplasmic reticulum, causing the sarcoplasmic reticulum to release stored $Ca^{2+}$ ions into the sarcoplasm.

Q2 The influx of calcium ions triggers muscle contraction, so more calcium ions in the sarcoplasm would increase the strength of contraction of cardiac/heart muscle, which would help to pump more blood around the body of patients with heart failure.

### Page 107 — Application Question

Q1 a) For the first 26 miles, ATP is likely to be generated via aerobic respiration because the body is being supplied with oxygen. As she sprints the last 385 yards ATP is likely to be generated via anaerobic respiration because the body won't be taking in enough oxygen.

b) Slow twitch. E.g. because they can contract slowly and can work for a long time without getting tired, which makes them good for endurance activities like long-distance running.

### Page 107 — Fact Recall Questions

Q1 E.g. tropomyosin.

Q2 Calcium ions bind to a protein attached to tropomyosin, causing the protein to change shape. This pulls the attached tropomyosin out of the actin-myosin binding site on the actin filament. This exposes the binding site, which allows the myosin head to bind and form an actin-myosin cross bridge.

Q3 ATP is broken down by ATP hydrolase to provide the energy needed to move the myosin head from side to side, which pulls the actin filament along in a rowing action. ATP also provides the energy needed to break the myosin-actin cross bridge, so the myosin head detaches from the actin filament after it's moved.

Q4 a) ATP is made by phosphorylating ADP with a phosphate group taken from PCr.

b) Advantage: e.g. the ATP-PCr system generates ATP very quickly / it can be used during short bursts of vigorous exercise / it's anaerobic/doesn't need oxygen / it's alactic/doesn't form any lactate.
Disadvantage: e.g. PCr runs out after only a few seconds.

c) Aerobic respiration and anaerobic respiration.

Q5 E.g. they have lots of mitochondria and blood vessels to supply the muscles with oxygen, as they use aerobic respiration. They are rich in myoglobin, a red-coloured protein that stores oxygen.

## Exam-style Questions — pages 109-111

1.1 Low-intensity exercise uses aerobic respiration, which is how energy is released in slow twitch muscle fibres ***(1 mark)***.

1.2 Function — e.g. to contract very quickly / to contract powerfully ***(1 mark)***.
Adaptations — e.g. energy is released quickly through anaerobic respiration using glycogen in fast twitch muscle fibres ***(1 mark)***. They have stores of PCr so that energy can be generated very quickly when needed ***(1 mark)***.

1.3 ATP is needed for muscle contraction, so muscle cells need to generate more ATP when they contract ***(1 mark)***. ATP is generated through respiration, so the rate of respiration in the muscle cell increases ***(1 mark)***. An increased rate of respiration requires an increased amount of glucose, so more GLUT4 molecules are needed in the cell membrane to transport glucose into the muscle cells ***(1 mark)***.

1.4 Myosin filaments have globular heads that are hinged ***(1 mark)***. Each myosin head has a binding site for actin and a binding site for ATP ***(1 mark)***.

2.1 Action potentials have a refractory period ***(1 mark)***. During this period the ion channels are recovering and can't be made to open ***(1 mark)***. This means that no more sodium ions can diffuse into the neurone to trigger another action potential ***(1 mark)***.

2.2 0.5 s = 500 ms
There are 5 action potentials in 20 ms.
500 ms ÷ 20 ms = 25. So 5 × 25 = 125 action potentials.
***(2 marks for correct answer, otherwise 1 mark for correct working)***.

2.3 Axon Y has the biggest diameter as it conducts action potentials faster than axon X ***(1 mark)***. Action potentials are conducted quicker along axons with bigger diameters because there's less resistance to the flow of ions than in the cytoplasm of a smaller axon ***(1 mark)***. With less resistance, depolarisation reaches other parts of the neurone cell membrane quicker ***(1 mark)***.
***Still award marks for a correct explanation, even if an incorrect calculation in part 2.2 means that axon X is chosen.***

3.1 Schwann cell ***(1 mark)***

3.2 B — node of Ranvier ***(1 mark)***
C — dendrites ***(1 mark)***

3.3 Myelin is an electrical insulator ***(1 mark)***. It allows nervous impulses to travel very fast by saltatory conduction ***(1 mark)***.

3.4 Conduction of nervous impulses in non-myelinated neurones is slower than in myelinated neurones ***(1 mark)***. If the myelin is damaged then the nerve impulse may happen much more slowly or not at all, resulting in muscle weakness or paralysis ***(1 mark)***.

4.1 The biceps and triceps work antagonistically/are an antagonistic pair of muscles ***(1 mark)***. When the biceps contracts, the triceps relaxes ***(1 mark)***. This pulls the bone so the arm bends at the elbow ***(1 mark)***.

4.2 Acetylcholine is released from (the presynaptic membrane of) a motor neurone ***(1 mark)*** at a neuromuscular junction ***(1 mark)***. It then diffuses across the synaptic cleft ***(1 mark)*** and binds to nicotinic cholinergic receptors ***(1 mark)*** on the motor end plate/postsynaptic membrane, causing the postsynaptic/muscle cell to depolarise ***(1 mark)***.

4.3 A — H-zone ***(1 mark)***, B — I-band ***(1 mark)***,
C — A-band ***(1 mark)***

4.4 A/the H-zone and B/the I-band will appear longer ***(1 mark)*** and C/the A-band will stay the same length ***(1 mark)***.

4.5 ATP is made by phosphorylating ADP ***(1 mark)*** with a phosphate group taken from phosphocreatine/PCr ***(1 mark)***.
*Remember, the ATP-phosphocreatine (PCr) system is used during short bursts of vigorous exercise.*

4.6 E.g. ATP is generated very quickly ***(1 mark)***. / No oxygen is needed / the process is anaerobic ***(1 mark)***. / The process is alactic / no lactate is formed ***(1 mark)***.

5.1 Time 1 shows repolarisation ***(1 mark)*** because the sodium ion channels are closed and the potassium ion channels are open ***(1 mark)***. The membrane is more permeable to potassium so potassium ions diffuse out of the neurone down their concentration gradient ***(1 mark)***. Time 2 shows hyperpolarisation/the refractory period ***(1 mark)*** because both the sodium and potassium ion channels are closed ***(1 mark)***. There is no movement of sodium or potassium through their ion channels (by facilitated diffusion) ***(1 mark)***.
*If a question tells you to 'use evidence' from a source (like a diagram, graph, table, etc.) this means you need to include figures or descriptions using the source. So in this case, you need to say which ion channels are open and closed in Figure 4.*

5.2 Sodium-potassium pumps use active transport to move three sodium ions out of the cell ***(1 mark)*** for every two potassium ions moved in ***(1 mark)***.

5.3 The potassium ion channel is slow to close so too many potassium ions diffuse out of the neurone ***(1 mark)***. The potential difference is more negative than the neurone cell membrane's resting potential, so the pump returns the membrane to its resting potential ***(1 mark)***.

5.4 It would be faster at 30 °C than at 20 °C ***(1 mark)*** because the ions would diffuse faster across the membrane so depolarisation would reach other parts of the neurone cell membrane more quickly ***(1 mark)***.

5.5 temporal summation ***(1 mark)***

5.6 More acetylcholine/ACh will be released into the synaptic cleft, which means more acetylcholine/ACh will bind to receptors on the postsynaptic membrane ***(1 mark)***. This causes more sodium ion channels to open and a greater influx of sodium ions ***(1 mark)***, which makes the postsynaptic neurone more likely to reach threshold and fire an action potential ***(1 mark)***.
*The question asks specifically about a cholinergic synapse so you should be specific in your answer and write acetylcholine (or ACh) rather than just putting 'neurotransmitter'.*

5.7 When a stimulus excites the neurone, sodium ions won't be able to diffuse into the neurone through sodium ion channels ***(1 mark)***. This means that the threshold level won't be reached ***(1 mark)*** so there will be no action potentials/no nervous impulses ***(1 mark)***.

# Topic 6 — C: Homeostasis

## 1. Homeostasis Basics

### Page 116 — Application Questions

Q1 a) pH = $-\log_{10}(5.50 \times 10^{-8})$ = **7.26**
Yes, the patient could be suffering from metabolic acidosis (as the patient's blood pH is below 7.35).
*The value given (5.50) is written to three significant figures, so your answer should also be given to three significant figures.*
b) Enzymes in the blood work best within the normal blood pH range. If the blood pH becomes too high or too low, the ionic bonds and hydrogen bonds supporting the shape of the enzymes' active sites will be broken and the enzymes will become denatured. This means that they won't be able to catalyse metabolic reactions.

Q2 A is an example of negative feedback because increasing respiration rate will increase the rate at which carbon dioxide is removed from the body. This will increase the pH of the blood back to the normal level. B is an example of positive feedback because more oestrogen being released will increase the levels of LH further and amplify the change.

### Page 116 — Fact Recall Questions

Q1 The maintenance of a stable internal environment.

Q2 So that metabolic reactions can occur at an optimum rate. Low temperatures make metabolic reactions slower, but if the temperature gets too high the reaction essentially stops.

Q3 If blood glucose concentration is too high the water potential of blood is reduced to a point where water molecules diffuse out of cells into the blood by osmosis. This can cause the cells to shrivel up and die. If blood glucose concentration is too low, cells are unable to carry out normal activities because there isn't enough glucose for respiration to provide energy.

Q4 A positive feedback mechanism amplifies a change from the normal level, whereas a negative feedback mechanism restores the level to normal.

## 2. Control of Blood Glucose Concentration

### Page 120 — Application Questions

Q1 Carbohydrates in the pasta are broken down into glucose, so their blood glucose concentration will increase. When the pancreas detects the blood glucose concentration is too high, the β cells will secrete insulin and the α cells will stop secreting glucagon. Insulin will then bind to receptors on liver and muscle cells (the effectors). These cells will respond by taking up more glucose, activating glycogenesis and by respiring more glucose. Blood glucose concentration will then return to normal.

Q2 Glycogenolysis and gluconeogenesis both increase blood glucose concentration. If these processes don't work properly then when blood glucose concentration falls (i.e. if the person doesn't eat regularly) the body will be unable to raise the blood glucose concentration back to normal, so the person will suffer from hypoglycaemia.

### Page 120 — Fact Recall Questions

Q1 Insulin is secreted from the β cells and glucagon from the α cells of the islets of Langerhans in the pancreas.

Q2 It increases the permeability of muscle cell membranes to glucose by making glucose transporters available, activates enzymes in liver and muscle cells that convert glucose into glycogen/activates glycogenesis and increases the rate of respiration of glucose in those cells.

Q3 glycogenesis

Q4 Gluconeogenesis — glycerol and amino acids are converted to glucose. Glycogenolysis — glycogen is converted to glucose.

Q5 The pancreas detects blood glucose is too low. α cells secrete glucagon and β cells stop secreting insulin. Glucagon binds to receptors on liver cells. The liver cells respond to increase the blood glucose concentration (e.g. glycogenolysis is activated), so blood glucose concentration returns to normal.

Q6 When insulin binds to receptors on the muscle cell membrane, it triggers the movement of GLUT4/glucose transport proteins (channel proteins) from vesicles in the cytoplasm of the cell to the cell membrane. Glucose can then be transported into the cell through these channel proteins by facilitated diffusion.

Q7 Adrenaline binds to its specific receptors on the cell surface membrane (of liver cells), which causes an enzyme called adenylate cyclase to be activated inside the cell. Activated adenylate cyclase converts ATP into a second messenger called cAMP. cAMP activates an enzyme called protein kinase A, which activates a cascade (chain of reactions) that breaks down glycogen into glucose.

## 3. Diabetes and Blood Glucose Concentration

### Pages 124-125 — Application Questions

Q1 a) Day 1 because blood glucose concentration increased more after lunch on day 1 (by 4.5 mM) than it did after lunch on day 2 (by 3.8 mM).
b) E.g. the same dose of insulin was injected on both days. / Insulin was injected at the same time on both days.

Q2 a)

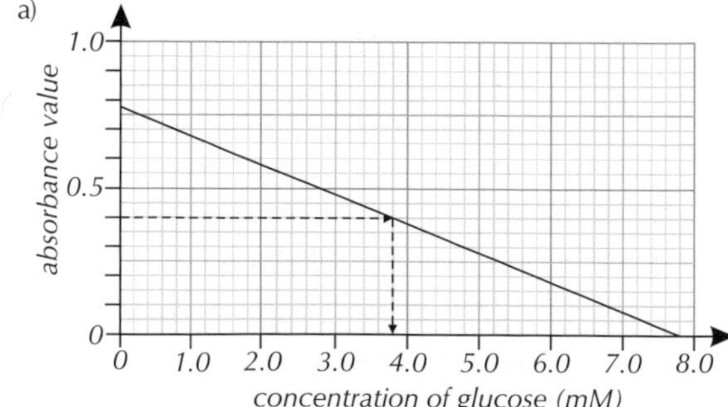


The glucose concentration is **3.8 mM**.

b)

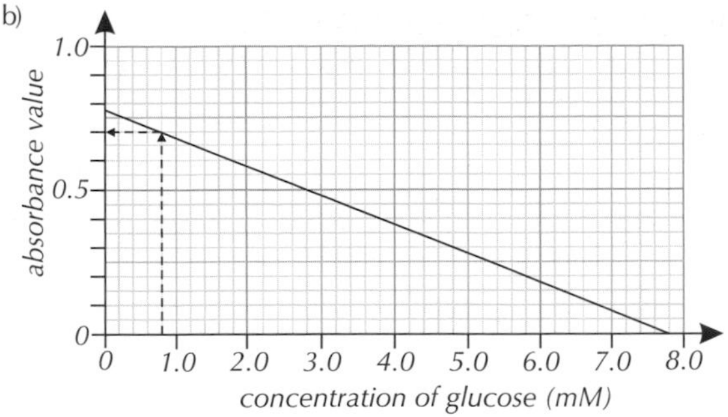


E.g. between **0.7** and **0.775**

*The highest 'normal' glucose concentration (0.8 mM) would be expected to have an absorbance value of 0.7, according to the graph. To find the absorbance of the lowest 'normal' glucose concentration (0 mM), just look at where the calibration curve meets the y-axis.*

## Page 125 — Fact Recall Questions

Q1 The immune system attacking the β cells in the islets of Langerhans so they can't produce any insulin.

Q2 Any two from: e.g. obesity / family history / lack of exercise / more advanced age / poor diet.

Q3 By eating a healthy, balanced diet, losing weight if necessary, exercising regularly or taking glucose-lowering medication if these don't work. Insulin injections may be needed eventually.

Q4 E.g. reduce the advertising of junk food, improve the nutritional value of their products, and use clearer labelling on products.

Q5 E.g. do the Benedict's test on each solution using quantitative Benedict's reagent, then measure the absorbance of each solution using a colorimeter (with a red filter). Next plot the absorbance of each solution against the glucose concentration and draw a calibration curve. Then do the Benedict's test on the urine sample using quantitative Benedict's reagent (under the same conditions as used for the serial dilutions, e.g. the same volume of solution and Benedict's reagent, the same temperature, the same amount of time) and measure its absorbance. Finally, use the calibration curve to find the concentration of glucose in the urine sample.

# 4. The Kidneys

## Page 128 — Application Questions

Q1 A — Bowman's capsule
B — loop of Henle
C — distal convoluted tubule/DCT
D — ureter

Q2 a) X — basement membrane
Y — epithelium of Bowman's capsule / podocyte

b) E.g. the structure of the barrier normally prevents larger molecules such as proteins from entering the tubules. If its structure is affected, large molecules such as proteins may be able to pass into the tubules and eventually end up in the urine, producing proteinuria.

## Page 128 — Fact Recall Questions

Q1 a) afferent arteriole

b) Bowman's capsule

c) Because vessel A/the afferent arteriole is larger in diameter than vessel B/the efferent arteriole, the blood in the glomerulus is under high pressure. The high pressure forces liquid and small molecules in the blood out of the capillary and into the Bowman's capsule (ultrafiltration).

*If you're struggling to remember the difference between the afferent and efferent arterioles, think afferent comes first, because it's first alphabetically.*

Q2 e.g. water and glucose

# 5. Controlling Blood Water Potential

## Page 131 — Application Questions

Q1 a) The runner is dehydrated because he has sweated a lot and not replaced any of the fluids he has lost. This has caused his blood water content to drop.

b) The low water content of the runner's blood is detected by osmoreceptors in his hypothalamus.

c) ADH molecules bind to receptors on the plasma membranes of cells of the runner's distal convoluted tubule/DCT and collecting duct. When this happens, protein channels called aquaporins are inserted into the plasma membrane. These channels allow water to pass through via osmosis, so make the walls of the DCT and collecting duct more permeable to water. This allows water to be reabsorbed from these tubules into the medulla and into the blood by osmosis, therefore conserving water in the runner's body.

d) The presence of sodium ($Na^+$) ions in the sports drink increases the concentration of $Na^+$ in the runner's glomerular filtrate. These ions are used to lower the water potential of the medulla in the loop of Henle in order to create a water potential gradient to drive the reabsorption of water back into the blood by osmosis.

*Make sure you understand water potential. If you don't, it makes understanding the regulation of water content by the kidneys pretty tricky. Remember, high water potential means a high concentration of water molecules and low water potential means a low concentration of water molecules. Water moves from a region of higher water potential to a region of lower water potential — from where there are more water molecules to where there are fewer.*

Q2 a) Normally if a person has consumed too much fluid, the osmoreceptors in the hypothalamus detect that the water content of the blood, and so its water potential, has risen. This causes the posterior pituitary gland to release less ADH into the blood. Less ADH means that the DCT and collecting duct are less permeable, so less water is reabsorbed into the blood by osmosis. This causes a large amount of dilute urine to be produced and so more water is lost.

b) If the body can't suppress ADH production, the DCT and collecting duct will continue to be made permeable, so water is reabsorbed into the blood by osmosis. This means that the excess water is not excreted and therefore accumulates, potentially affecting the balance of fluid in cells.

Q3 a) E.g. a longer loop of Henle means that more water can be reabsorbed from the glomerular filtrate, so the fennec fox can conserve as much water as possible.

b) E.g. frogs and toads live in wet environments, so they don't need to conserve water by reabsorbing it from the glomerular filtrate.

## Page 131 — Fact Recall Questions

Q1 The control of the water potential of the blood.
Q2 the medulla
Q3 the ascending limb
Q4 the hypothalamus

## Exam-style Questions — pages 133-135

1.1 At point A low concentrations of calcium in the blood are detected, which stimulates the secretion of PTH ***(1 mark)***. At point B effectors are responding by increasing the concentration of calcium in the blood ***(1 mark)***. At point C high concentrations of calcium in the blood are detected, which stimulates the secretion of calcitonin ***(1 mark)***. At point D effectors are responding by decreasing the concentration of calcium in the blood ***(1 mark)***.

1.2 Having more than one negative feedback mechanism means there is more control over changes in the blood calcium concentration ***(1 mark)***. It means that the blood calcium concentration can be actively increased or decreased to return it to normal rather than just changing it in one direction ***(1 mark)***.

1.3 The concentration of calcium in the blood may fall very low ***(1 mark)***. This is because less PTH will be released to bring the levels back up to normal ***(1 mark)***.

2.1 Useful substances are reabsorbed back into the blood from the tubules / selective reabsorption takes place ***(1 mark)***.

2.2 Microvilli ***(1 mark)***. The epithelium of the wall of the PCT has microvilli to provide a large surface area for the reabsorption of useful materials from the glomerular filtrate into the blood ***(1 mark)***.

2.3 glomerulus ***(1 mark)***

2.4 E and F ***(1 mark)***

2.5 Loop of Henle ***(1 mark)***. It controls the movement of sodium ions so that water can be reabsorbed by the blood. ***(1 mark)***.

3.1 $\alpha$ cells in the pancreas are secreting glucagon into the blood ***(1 mark)***. $\beta$ cells stop secreting insulin ***(1 mark)***.

3.2 The Type II diabetic doesn't produce as much insulin as the non-diabetic. / The body's cells don't respond properly to the insulin that's produced ***(1 mark)***. Insulin lowers blood glucose concentration when it's too high, so if there's not enough insulin / the body can't respond to insulin properly, this process will be much slower ***(1 mark)***.

3.3 More quickly, because more glucose is respired during exercise to provide energy ***(1 mark)***.

3.4 A Type I diabetic wouldn't produce any insulin ***(1 mark)***. This means that blood glucose concentration would remain high for much longer than for this Type II diabetic ***(1 mark)***.

3.5 22.5 minutes ***(1 mark)***. This is because this is the time when the blood glucose concentration is at its upper limit / 110 mg/100 $cm^3$ ***(1 mark)***.

You're told the normal range for blood glucose concentration in the introduction to the question — make sure you always read questions thoroughly in the exam.

3.6 Insulin is a hormone, so it takes time to travel in the blood to receptor cells ***(1 mark)***.

3.7 When insulin binds to receptors on a target cell, it triggers the movement of channel proteins/the glucose transporter GLUT4 from vesicles in the cytoplasm to the cell membrane ***(1 mark)***. Glucose can then be transported into the cell by facilitated diffusion ***(1 mark)***.

3.8 The hormones glucagon and adrenaline bind to specific receptors on liver cells ***(1 mark)***. This activates the enzyme adenylate cyclase ***(1 mark)***, which converts ATP into the second messenger, cyclic AMP (cAMP) ***(1 mark)***. Cyclic AMP then activates an enzyme called protein kinase A ***(1 mark)***, which activates a cascade that initiates glycogenolysis in the cell ***(1 mark)***.

4.1

| ***Substance*** | ***TF/P ratio of 1.0*** |
|---|---|
| *urea* | ✓ |
| *serum albumin (protein)* | X |
| *sodium ions ($Na^+$)* | ✓ |
| *glucose* | ✓ |
| *red blood cells* | X |

***(2 marks for all three correct, 1 mark for 2 correct.)***

Don't let the numbers throw you in this question. All you're really being asked is which substances can cross the filtration barrier and which can't.

4.2 Normally proteins like serum albumin can't pass through the filtration barrier into the tubular fluid because they are too large, so it stays in the blood ***(1 mark)***.

4.3 The reabsorption of $Na^+$ from the kidney tubule back into the capillaries lowers the water potential of the medulla ***(1 mark)***. This drives the reabsorption of water from the kidney tubule via osmosis ***(1 mark)***. If the amount of sodium reabsorbed is decreased then the amount of water reabsorbed will also decrease ***(1 mark)***. This means more water will be removed from the body in the urine, lowering the water content and therefore the volume of the blood ***(1 mark)***.

## Topic 7

# Topic 7 — A: Genetics

## 1. Genetic Terms

### Page 137 — Application Questions

Q1 A = tufted tail, B = tufted tail, C = non-tufted tail

Q2 a) yellow
b) YY
c) yy

You need to understand all the terms on pages 136 and 137 really well so that when you come across exam questions using any of the words, you'll understand what's being described and what you're being asked.

## 2. Genetic Diagrams — Simple Monohybrid Crosses

### Page 140 — Application Questions

Q1 The only possible genotype of offspring is heterozygous, e.g. Tt. Worked example:

*T — tall dominant allele*
*t — dwarf recessive allele*

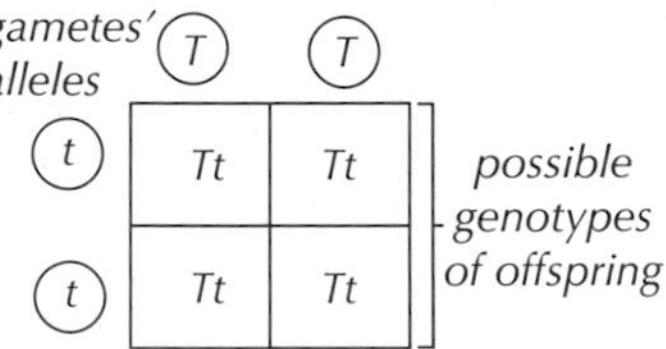


The question asked you to show your working. So even though you know that a monohybrid cross with two homozygous parents always produces all heterozygous offspring, you must draw a genetic diagram of some kind to show how you would work that out.

Q2 ½ / 0.5 / 50%. Worked example:

*D — polydactyly dominant allele*
*d — normal recessive allele*

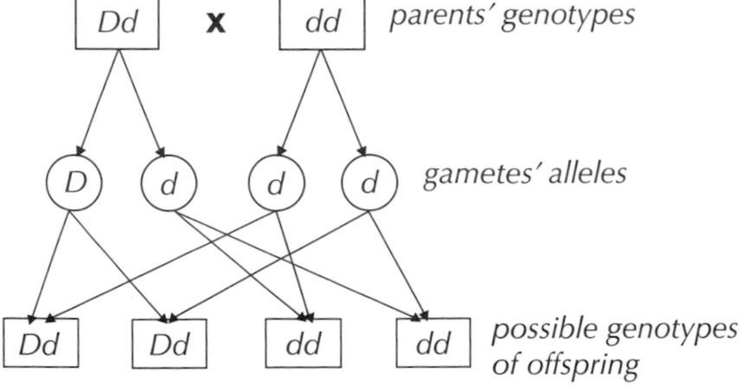


Q3 1 : 0 : 1 ratio of blue : yellow : striped organisms / 1 : 1 ratio of blue : striped organisms. Worked example:

*$C^Y$ — yellow allele*
*$C^B$ — blue allele*

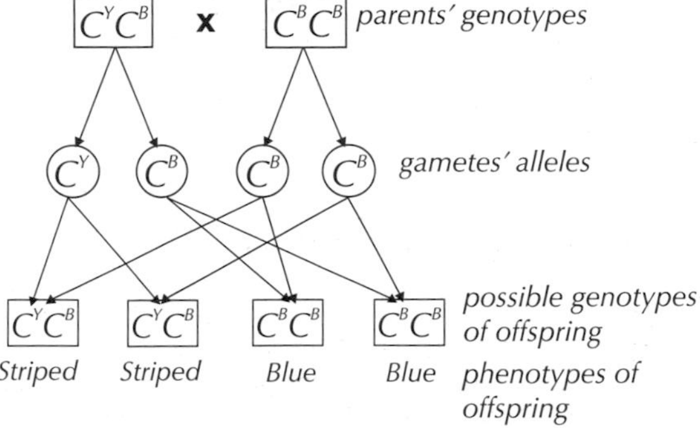


## 3. Genetic Diagrams — Multiple Allele and Dihybrid Crosses

### Page 143 — Application Questions

Q1 a) Melanic (M) is dominant to both of the other alleles, insularia is dominant to typical only and typical is recessive to all. / The dominance of the alleles is M > M' > m.

b) All heterozygous melanic (Mm). Worked example:

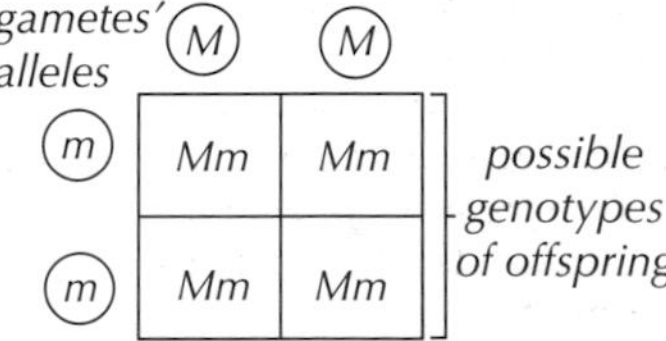


Q2 The possible striping patterns are Abyssinian (50%) and Mackerel (50%). Worked example:

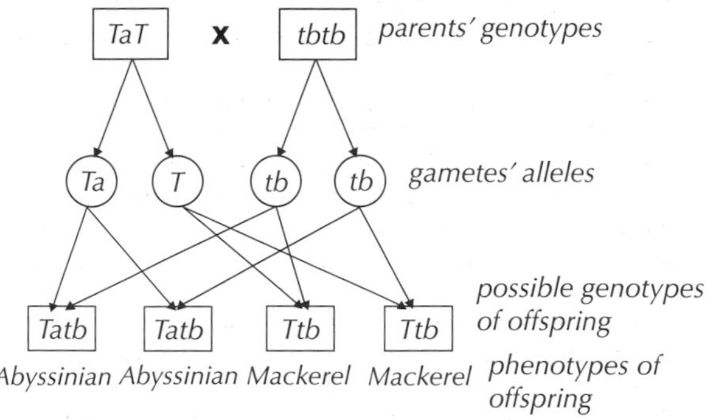

Q3 a)

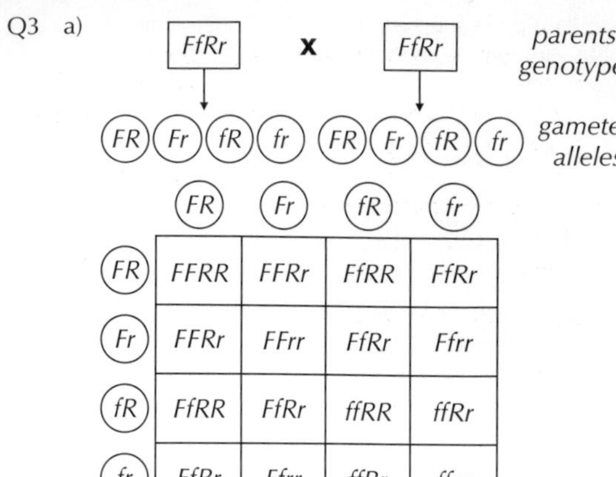


b) 9 : 1 ratio of round, red tomatoes to pear-shaped, yellow tomatoes.

Round, red tomatoes = FFRR, FFRr, FfRR, FfRr

Pear-shaped, yellow tomatoes = ffrr

Q4 a) The offspring would all be heterozygous (BbPp).

The red cow with horns must have a homozygous recessive phenotype (bbpp). Dihybrid crosses between homozygous dominant and homozygous recessive parents will always produce heterozygous offspring in the $F_1$ generation.

b)

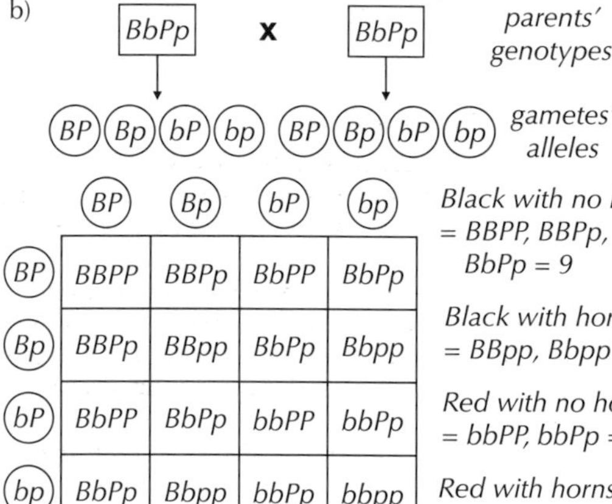


*Black with no horns = BBPP, BBPp, BbPP, BbPp = 9*

*Black with horns = BBpp, Bbpp = 3*

*Red with no horns = bbPP, bbPp = 3*

*Red with horns = bbpp = 1*

Phenotypic ratio: 9 : 3 : 3: 1

## 4. Linkage

## Page 147 — Application Questions

Q1 $X^FX^F$ (affected female), $X^FY$ (affected male), $X^FX^f$ (affected female), $X^fY$ (unaffected male). Worked example:

*$X^FY$ — affected male*
*$X^FX^f$— affected heterozygous female*

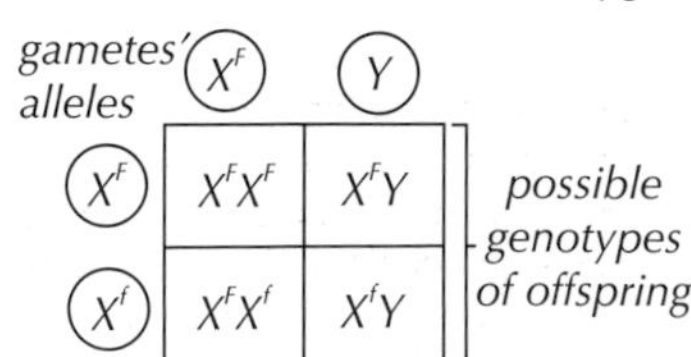

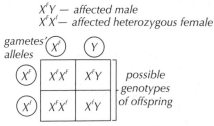

This question doesn't ask you to show your working, but it's best to always do so. Then if you write an answer down wrong for any reason, you could still pick up marks in your exam for your working.

Q2 Y-linked characteristics can only be passed on down the male (XY) line. So for a child to have a Y-linked disorder, its father must also have the disorder. So if a child has hairy ears but its dad doesn't, the dad might question if he was the father.

This is fairly tricky, but drawing a quick diagram would help you out:

*$XY^N$ — unaffected male*
*XX — female*

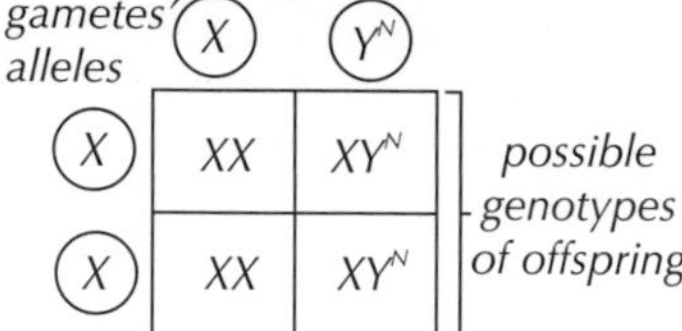


An unaffected male can't have a child with the disorder.

Q3 a) E.g.

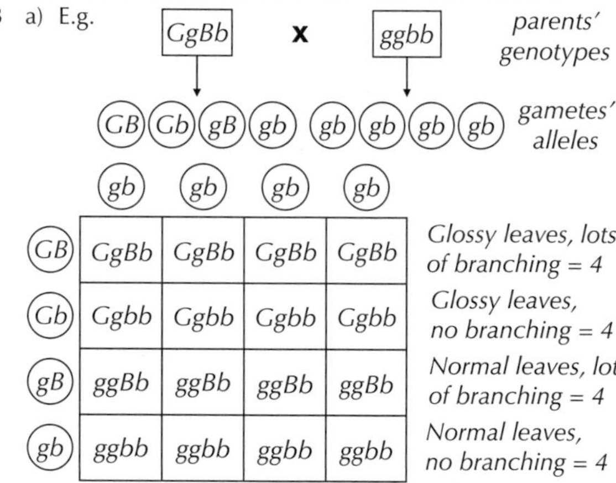


Expected phenotypic ratio = 1 : 1 : 1 : 1

b) Observed phenotypic ratio = 1.7 : 1.1 : 1 : 1.8

c) The GB alleles and the gb alleles in the GgBb parent may have been linked. This would mean that the GgBb parent produced mostly GB and gb gametes and make the GgBb and ggbb genotypes more common in the offspring. As a result, a higher proportion of the offspring would have their parents' phenotypes, instead of the even split of phenotypes predicted.

## Page 147 — Fact Recall Questions

Q1 ½ / 0.5 / 50%

Q2 If a characteristic is sex-linked it means that the allele that codes for it is located on a sex chromosome (X or Y).

Q3 Males are more likely than females to have X-linked disorders because males only have one X chromosome. Because they only have one copy of any alleles on the X chromosome, they express the characteristic of those alleles even if they're recessive, whereas women would need to inherit two copies to express the same characteristics.

Q4 An autosome is any chromosome that isn't a sex chromosome.

Q5 Genes on the same autosome are said to be linked because being on the same autosome usually means they'll stay together during the independent segregation of chromosomes in meiosis I. This means that their alleles will be passed on to the offspring together (unless crossing over splits them up first).

## 5. Epistasis

### Page 150 — Application Questions

Q1 a) i) EEBB, EeBB, EEBb, EeBb

For the dog to be black it must be able to express the dark pigment, so it much have at least one dominant E allele. Also, it must have at least one copy of the dominant B allele for the black pigment to be shown in the phenotype.

ii) Eebb, EEbb

For the dog to be chocolate it must be able to express the dark pigment, so it much have at least one dominant E allele. Also, it must have two copies of the recessive b allele for the chocolate pigment to be shown in the phenotype.

iii) eeBB, eeBb, eebb

For the dog to be yellow it must have two copies of the recessive e allele, so that it can't express the dark pigment. Gene 1 is epistatic over gene 2, so it doesn't matter what B or b alleles the dog has — it will still be yellow.

b) A cross between EEBB and eebb parents will give a 9 : 3 : 4 phenotypic ratio in the $F_2$ generation of black : chocolate : yellow. This is because gene 1 has a recessive epistatic allele (e) and two copies of the recessive epistatic allele (ee) will mask the expression of gene 2. Here's the cross to prove it:
B = black pigment, b = chocolate pigment, E = can express dark pigment, e = can't express dark pigment

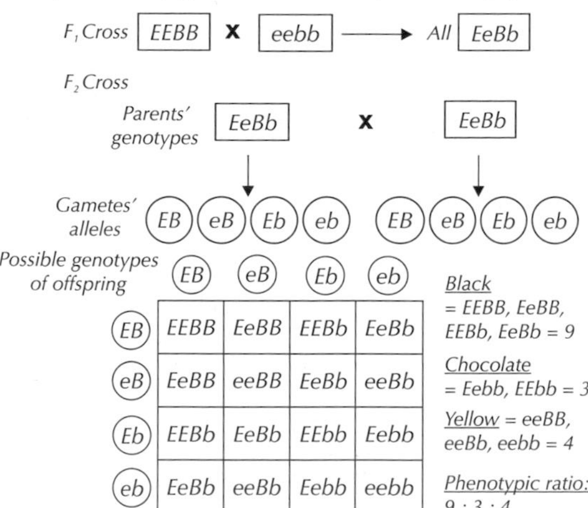


In the exam, you wouldn't need to draw out the genetic cross unless the question specifically asked you to. We've just included it here to help you out.

Q2 a) dominant epistasis

b) A cross between WWPP and wwpp produces a 48 : 12 : 4 or 12 : 3 : 1 phenotypic ratio in the $F_2$ generation of white : purple : red. This is because gene 1 has a dominant epistatic allele (W) and one or more copies of the dominant epistatic allele (Ww or WW) will mask the expression of gene 2.

c) W = white pigment, w = red pigment, P = purple pigment, p = no purple pigment

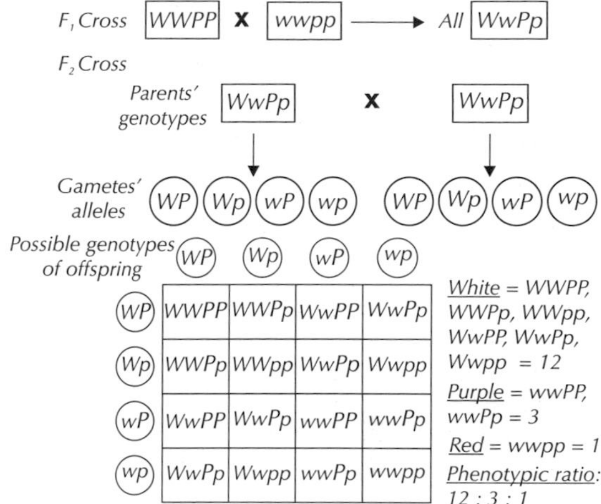


## 6. The Chi-Squared Test

### Pages 154 — Application Questions

Q1 a) Yes, the difference would be significant because the chi-squared value is greater than the critical value (6.20 > 5.99).

If the difference is significant it means the difference is unlikely to be due to chance and that the null hypothesis is rejected.

b) No, the difference would not be significant because the chi-squared value is smaller than the critical value (4.85 < 5.99).

If the difference is not significant it means the difference is likely to be due to chance — we're unable to reject the null hypothesis.

Q2 a)

| Phenotype | Ratio | Expected result (E) | Observed result (O) | O – E | $(O – E)^2$ | $\frac{(O – E)^2}{E}$ |
|---|---|---|---|---|---|---|
| Round, green | 9 | 72 | 74 | 2 | 4 | 0.06 |
| Round, yellow | 3 | 24 | 21 | –3 | 9 | 0.38 |
| Wrinkled, green | 3 | 24 | 26 | 2 | 4 | 0.17 |
| Wrinkled, yellow | 1 | 8 | 7 | –1 | 1 | 0.13 |
| | | | | | $\chi^2$ = | **0.74** |

b) There are 4 phenotypes which means there are 4 – 1 = 3 degrees of freedom. From the table, the critical value for a test with 3 degrees of freedom and a 0.05 probability level is 7.82. The chi-squared value is smaller than the critical value (0.74 < 7.82) so the difference between the observed and expected results is not significant.
This means we're unable to reject the null hypothesis.

Q3 a) There is no significant difference between the observed and the expected results.

b) This is unlikely to be an example of codominance. There are 3 phenotypes which means there are 3 – 1 = 2 degrees of freedom. From the table, the critical value for a test with 2 degrees of freedom and a 0.05 probability level is 5.99. The chi-squared value is greater than the critical value (8.6 > 5.99) so the difference between the observed and expected results is significant. This means that the null hypothesis can be rejected.

## Exam-style Questions — page 156-157

1.1 Number of agouti offspring = (256 ÷ 4) × 3 = **192** ***(1 mark)***

*A normal case of monohybrid inheritance would give a phenotypic ratio of 3 : 1 of agouti : solid coloured. So three quarters of the offspring would have agouti coat colour.*

1.2 ppAA, ppAa, ppaa ***(1 mark)***

1.3 A cross between PPAA and ppaa parents will give a 9 : 3 : 4 phenotypic ratio in the $F_2$ generation of agouti : solid coloured : albino ***(1 mark)***. This is because the P gene has a recessive epistatic allele (p) and two copies of the recessive epistatic allele (pp) will mask the expression of the pigmentation gene ***(1 mark)***. A dihybrid cross will only give a phenotypic ratio of 9 : 3 : 3 : 1 in the $F_2$ generation if the two genes do not interact and are not linked ***(1 mark)***.

2.1

| Genotype | Growth on substance 1 |
|---|---|
| AaBb | ✓ |
| aaBb | ✗ |
| AAbb | ✗ |
| AABb | ✓ |

***(1 mark for all 3 correct)***

2.2 They must have the genotype aaBb (or aaBB) ***(1 mark)***. They can't produce enzyme A but can produce enzyme B ***(1 mark)***, so if they're given substance 2 they can convert it to substance 3 ***(1 mark)***.

3.1 *$X^hY$ — haemophiliac male*
*$X^HX^h$ — female carrier*

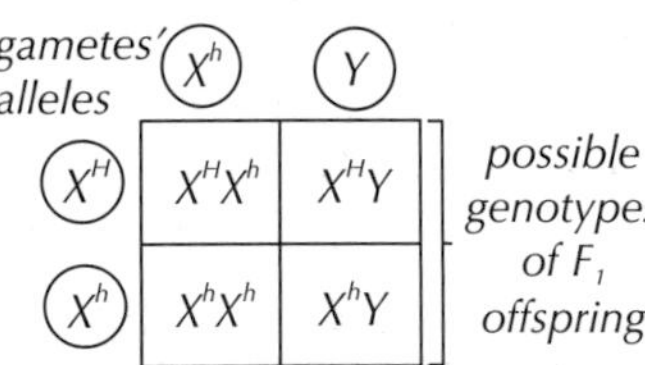


Possible phenotypes of $F_1$ offspring: carrier female ($X^HX^h$), normal male ($X^HY$), haemophiliac female ($X^hX^h$) and haemophiliac male ($X^hY$).

***(1 mark for correct gametes, 1 mark for correct $F_1$ genotypes, 1 mark for $F_1$ phenotypes matched to correct $F_1$ genotypes.)***

3.2 The difference between the observed and expected results is not significant because the critical value for this test at P = 0.05 is 7.82 ***(1 mark)*** and the chi-squared value (1.04) is less than this ***(1 mark)***.

# Topic 7 — B: Populations and Evolution

## 1. The Hardy-Weinberg Principle

### Page 162 — Application Questions

Q1 a) From the bar chart, $p = 0.10$

$p + q = 1$

$q = 1 - p$

$q = 1 - 0.10 = \mathbf{0.90}$

*You're given one allele frequency in the bar chart and are asked to find the other, so it's the simple equation.*

b) $p = 0.1$, $q = 0.9$, so $2pq = 2 \times 0.1 \times 0.9 = \mathbf{0.18}$

c) No, it does not apply. The frequency of the allele changes between the generations, and the Hardy-Weinberg principle is only true in cases where the allele frequency stays the same.

Q2 Say $p$ = frequency of $H^S$, $q$ = frequency of $H^N$.

frequency of genotype $H^SH^S = p^2 = 1 \div 500 = 0.002$

so $p = \sqrt{0.002} = 0.044...$

$q = 1 - p$

$q = 1 - 0.044... = 0.955...$

Heterozygotes have sickle cell trait, so the frequency of sickle cell trait is:

$2pq = 2 \times 0.044... \times 0.955... = \mathbf{0.09}$ (2 d.p.)

*$H^S$ and $H^N$ are codominant, so it doesn't matter which letter (p or q) you pick to represent the frequency of which allele ($H^S$ or $H^N$). Just write down which letter you've assigned to which allele so you don't get confused.*

Q3 $q = 0.16$ and $p + q = 1$, so $p = 1 - q$

$p = 1 - 0.16 = 0.84$

homozygous dominant genotype frequency = $p^2$

$p^2 = 0.84^2 = \mathbf{0.71}$ (2 d.p.)

Q4 recessive wrinkled allele = $q^2$ = 31% ÷ 100 = 0.31

$q = \sqrt{0.31} = 0.556...$

$p + q = 1$, so $p = 1 - q$

$p = 1 - 0.556... = 0.443...$

Heterozygous genotype = $2pq$

$2pq = 2 \times 0.443... \times 0.556... = 0.49$ (2 d.p.)

0.49 × 100 = 49, so **49%** of the population have a heterozygous genotype.

### Page 162 — Fact Recall Questions

Q1 A group of organisms of the same species living in a particular area.

Q2 The complete range of alleles present in a population.

Q3 How often an allele occurs in a population.

Q4 The Hardy-Weinberg principle is a mathematical model that predicts that the frequencies of alleles in a population won't change from one generation to the next as long as the population is large, there's no immigration, emigration, mutations or natural selection, and mating is totally random.

Q5 $p + q = 1$ and $p^2 + 2pq + q^2 = 1$, where $p$ = the frequency of the dominant allele, $q$ = the frequency of the recessive allele, $p^2$ = the frequency of the homozygous dominant genotype, $q^2$ = the frequency of the homozygous recessive genotype and $2pq$ = the frequency of the heterozygous genotype.

## 2. Variation and Selection

### Page 165 — Application Question

Q1 a) 3.5 cm – 1 cm = **2.5 cm**

b) Directional selection. In 1850 the average fur length was about 3.5 cm. In 1950, the average had moved to about 2.2 cm. The average has moved towards the 'extreme' shorter end, which shows directional selection.

c) Caribou with shorter fur length would have been better adapted to the warmer climate further south and so had a selective advantage. These caribou would have been more likely to survive, reproduce and pass on their alleles for shorter fur. So the average fur length has reduced and moved towards the 'extreme' shorter end.

### Page 165 — Fact Recall Questions

Q1 Genetic variation can be caused by mutation (which leads to the production of new alleles), during meiosis, and through random fertilisation of gametes during sexual reproduction.

*Remember, the main source of genetic variation is mutation.*

Q2 Competition, predation and disease are selection pressures which create a struggle for survival. Members of a species show variation in their alleles, which makes some individuals better adapted to these selection pressures than others. These individuals are more likely to survive, reproduce, and pass on their beneficial alleles to the next generation compared to individuals that are not as well-adapted. In this way allele frequencies in the gene pool change as the frequency of the beneficial alleles increases over time.

Q3 Stabilising selection is when individuals with alleles for a characteristic towards the middle of the range are more likely to survive, reproduce and pass on their alleles, whereas disruptive selection is when individuals with alleles for characteristics at either of the extreme ends of a range are more likely to survive and reproduce than individuals with alleles for characteristics in the middle of the range. This means that stabilising selection causes the range of values of a phenotype to narrow around the existing mean, whereas disruptive selection causes phenotypes at the extreme ends of a range to increase in frequency, and phenotypes in the middle of the range to decrease in frequency.

## 3. Speciation and Genetic Drift

### Pages 169-170 — Application Questions

Q1 Different populations were geographically isolated on the different islands. The different food sources caused different selection pressures, so on each island finches with different alleles for beak size and shape were more likely to survive, reproduce and pass on their alleles. Over time this caused changes in allele frequencies and gene pools, which eventually resulted in reproductive isolation and allopatric speciation.

Q2 Genetic drift could have a large effect in the Mauritian pink pigeon population because it is very small. This could lead to a loss of genetic diversity, which could make the species less able to adapt to changes in the environment. This may put the species at an even greater risk of extinction.

Q3 a) The frequency of pink eyes in the island population falls across the study period (eventually reaching zero), whereas the frequency of pink eyes in the mainland population remains roughly constant. The change in the pink eye frequency on the island is likely to be due to genetic drift. This can occur more easily on the island than on the mainland as the population on the island is smaller.

*You're told in the question that the colour of the rodents' eyes are not thought to affect the chances of survival or breeding, so this indicates that natural selection is not likely to be responsible for any changes in the frequency of eye-colour phenotypes.*

b) Male rodents on the island are likely to have become larger over time via natural selection. This is because a larger size means the rodents are more likely win territorial fights, so they're more likely to survive, reproduce and pass on their beneficial alleles for a larger size to the next generation. This may not have happened in the mainland population because a larger size also makes the rodents more visible in the undergrowth, which makes them more susceptible to predation. So on the mainland (where there are mammalian predators), having a larger size may not make an individual more likely to survive, so this trait may not have become more common via natural selection.

c) E.g. they could investigate whether rodents from the island can breed successfully with rodents from the mainland and produce fertile offspring.

### Page 170 — Fact Recall Questions

Q1 Speciation is the development of a new species from an existing species.

Q2 Allopatric speciation — this occurs when populations of the same species become geographically isolated and eventually become reproductively isolated. Sympatric speciation — this occurs when a population becomes reproductively isolated even though there is no geographical isolation.

Q3 E.g. behavioural changes to courtship rituals could make a group of individuals unattractive to the main population, preventing them from mating together, even if they could breed successfully.

Q4 Initially, there was one population of organisms. This population was divided, and the two populations evolved into separate species. This process repeated itself many times over a long period of time, leading to the diversity of life on Earth we see today.

## Exam-style Questions — page 172

1.1 A population is a group of organisms of the same species living in a particular area at a particular time, that have the potential to breed with each other ***(1 mark)***.

1.2 The variation could be caused by genetic factors/individuals having different alleles ***(1 mark)***. Genetic variation is most likely to be caused by mutation, in which changes in an individual's DNA base sequence lead to the production of new alleles ***(1 mark)***. Genetic variation within a species may also be caused by meiosis ***(1 mark)*** and by the random fertilisation of gametes during sexual reproduction ***(1 mark)***.

1.3 This means that changes in allele frequency have caused changes in the phenotypes of the two species of fish ***(1 mark)***, which means they cannot interbreed to produce fertile offspring ***(1 mark)***. These two species may be reproductively isolated because of e.g. differences in their behaviour / differences in the time of year when they breed / differences in their genes that make offspring infertile/ inviable ***(1 mark)***.

1.4 Sympatric speciation ***(1 mark)*** because the new species/*A. zaliosus* arose whist still living in the same geographic area as the original species/*A. citrinellus* ***(1 mark)***.

1.5 In disruptive selection two phenotypes are favoured by the environment, so individuals that show either of these two phenotypes can survive and reproduce ***(1 mark)***. In Lake Apoyo, it could have been that individuals with phenotypes that made them specialised to live in the open water column or on the lake bed were most likely to survive and reproduce ***(1 mark)***, so the alleles for these two phenotypes increased in frequency ***(1 mark)***. This could have resulted in two separate populations of *A. citrinellus* which were likely to only breed with other fish from their own population ***(1 mark)***. Eventually, changes in allele frequency between the two populations may have led to the fish becoming reproductively isolated and a new species/*A. zaliosus* developing ***(1 mark)***.

2.1 $q^2 = 5 \div 1000 = 0.005$
$q = \sqrt{0.005} = 0.070...$
$p = 1 - 0.070... = 0.929...$
$2pq = 2 \times 0.929... \times 0.070... = 0.1314...$
$0.1314... \times 100 =$ **13.14%** (2 d.p.)
***(2 marks for the correct answer, otherwise 1 mark for identifying 2pq as the frequency of heterozygotes in the population.)***

2.2 Genetic drift ***(1 mark)***. The syndrome does not increase a person's chance of surviving, so the allele must have become more common in the population by chance ***(1 mark)***.

# Topic 7 — C: Populations in Ecosystems

## 1. Ecosystems

### Pages 174-175 — Application Questions

Q1 a) abiotic conditions
*The kangaroo rat is adapted to a lack of water in its habitat — which is a non-living feature, and so an abiotic condition.*
b) By producing concentrated urine the kangaroo rat is able to conserve water. This helps it to survive in deserts where there isn't much water available.

Q2 a) The length of their probosci.
b) The new bee species would compete with the current species with a long proboscis. One species would compete more successfully until only it is left / until it has out-competed the other species.

Q3 a) Species A has a small beak length, with most individuals having a beak length of around 5 mm. Species B has a longer beak, with most individuals having a beak length of around 15 mm (a difference of 10 mm).
b) The two bird species occupy different niches. Their beaks are different sizes, which could mean that they eat different sized seeds, so they wouldn't be in competition with each other.

### Page 175 — Fact Recall Questions

Q1 All the organisms living in a community and all the non-living/abiotic conditions found there.

Q2 The place where an organism lives within an ecosystem.

Q3 The role of a species within its habitat.

Q4 a) E.g. the organisms a species eats, the organisms a species is eaten by.
b) E.g. the temperature range an organism can live in, the time of day when an organism is active.

Q5 A feature that increases an organism's chance of survival and reproduction.

Q6 a) Organisms with better adaptations are more likely to survive, reproduce and pass on the advantageous alleles for their adaptations, so the adaptations become more common in the population.
b) natural selection

## 2. Variation in Population Size

### Page 180 — Application Questions

Q1 The number of mice.
*Remember, biotic factors are the living things in an ecosystem.*

Q2 As the temperature fell, the size of the mouse population decreased. This could have been because the cold weather caused the temperature of the surroundings to fall below the body temperature of the mice. If that had happened the mice might have used up more energy maintaining their body temperature. This would have meant less energy was available for growth and reproduction, causing their population size to fall.

Q3 As the mouse population size increased, there was more food for the owls and so the owl population grew. As the owl population increased, more mice were eaten and so the mice population began to fall. This meant there was less food for the owls, so their population decreased — and so this cycle continued.

## Page 180 — Fact Recall Questions

Q1 a) All organisms of one species in a habitat.
b) All the populations of different species in a habitat.

Q2 Carrying capacity is the maximum stable population of a species that an ecosystem can support.

Q3 Interspecific competition is when organisms of different species compete with each other for the same resources. Intraspecific competition is when organisms of the same species compete with each other for the same resources.

# 3. Investigating Populations

## Page 183 — Application Questions

Q1 a) She could place the quadrat on the ground at random locations across the field and count how much of the quadrat is covered by daisies. A square in the quadrat should be counted if it's more than half-covered by a particular species.
b) E.g. the student could divide the field into a grid and use a random number generator to select coordinates. The quadrat could then be placed at these coordinates and the number of daisies in each quadrat counted.

Q2 The scientist could place a tape measure in a straight line from the sea to the top of the shore, to form a transect line. He could then place a quadrat at regular intervals along the transect, and count the number of limpets present in the quadrat, or the number of squares of the quadrat that contained limpets.

## Page 185 — Application Question

Q1 a) i) $\frac{19 \times 14}{3} = 88.67 = 89$ beetles

ii) $\frac{17 \times 21}{6} = 59.5 = 60$ beetles

b) No. E.g. the two samples were only taken a day apart, which may not be long enough for the marked beetles to mix back in with the population. Also, the beetles were marked with white paint which might have affected their chances of survival.

## Page 187 — Application Questions

Q1 The kite diagram shows that species A is present between 20 and 45 m from the road with a low percentage cover. It's also present between 80-140 m, and is most abundant between 130-140 m. Species B is present between 55-130 m from the road, and is most abundant between 60-85 m. Species C is present between 0-50 m from the road and is most abundant between 0-35 m.
The graph shows that soil salinity is high between 0-30 m from the road, falls sharply between 30-40 m, continues to fall until around 50 m and then remains low.

Q2 Salinity is high in coastal areas, so plants that grow there must be able to tolerate/be adapted for these conditions. Species C is present between 0-50 m from the road boundary and this overlaps with where salinity is the highest (0-30 m). This suggests that species C is adapted to high salinity conditions and therefore is suited to growing in coastal areas.

Q3 The data shows that at a high soil salinity there is an absence of species B, but this doesn't prove that salt spray from the road (and the resulting high salinity) is the cause. Species B might be absent for other reasons, e.g. because it is out-competed by species C.

## Page 187 — Fact Recall Questions

Q1 a) The number of individuals of one species in a particular area.
b) Where a particular species is within the area you're investigating.

Q2 Frequency, which is the number of samples a species is recorded in. Percentage cover, which is how much of the area you're investigating is covered by a species.

Q3 a) A square frame divided into a grid of 100 smaller squares by strings attached across the frame.
b) When quadrats are placed next to each other along transect to work out species frequency and percentage cover across an area/along the transect.

Q4
$$\text{Total population size} = \frac{\text{Number caught in 1st sample} \times \text{Number caught in 2nd sample}}{\text{Number marked in 2nd sample}}$$

# 4. Succession

## Page 191 — Application Questions

Q1 Primary succession, because there is no soil present in 1800.
*Remember, the key difference between primary and secondary succession is soil — it's present in secondary succession, but not in primary succession. If you have a good look at the graph you'll see that there's no soil moisture in 1800. That's a pretty good sign that there's no soil either.*

Q2 The dominant plant species would have been adapted to survive without much water/in a soil with low moisture content and fluctuating ground temperatures. They would have had seeds that could remain viable for long periods of time. They would have been species of small plants / they would not have been tree species.
*There's a lot going on in the graph with all the different lines — and you could get something like this in the exam. Don't let the graph's complexity put you off though. Take your time and make sure you really understand what the graph is showing, and read the questions carefully so you pick out the right bits from the graph for your answers.*

Q3 E.g. the average length of time dominant plant seeds remained viable for was relatively high between 1800 and 1860. This might have been because seeds that remained viable for a long time could lie dormant until conditions were favourable enough to germinate. Between about 1860 and 1880 the average length of time fell sharply, and then continued to fall more slowly until levelling off at around 1960. This may have been because the plants that were dominant between 1800 and 1860 were succeeded by other plant species which were better adapted to the changed conditions, e.g. a higher soil moisture content, so they no longer needed to be viable for long periods of time.

Q4 Between 1800 and 1920 because there were no tree species present during this time, so there would have been more light / less shade cast by the trees.

Q5 The soil moisture content is 0 between 1800 and 1820 because there is no soil. The soil moisture content increased gradually from 1820 until 1940 as the soil developed, then it increased more rapidly between 1940 and 2000 because the addition of decomposed organic material (plant material) helped to increase soil moisture content and the deeper soil was able to retain more water.

## Page 191 — Fact Recall Questions

Q1 Because ecosystems are constantly changing.
Q2 The process by which an ecosystem changes over time.
Q3 primary succession
Q4 E.g. marram grass, lichens, shrubs of the *Calligonum* genus.
Q5 The largest and most complex community of plants and animals that an ecosystem can support.

### 5. Conservation

## Page 194 — Application Questions

Q1 a) The areas of steppe in which succession was controlled by grazing and fire had the highest percentage cover of grasses compared to the control. The area of steppe controlled by fire also had the lowest percentage cover of trees. This would suggest that fire was the most effective method of controlling succession. Mowing was the least successful method. The area of steppe in which succession was controlled by mowing had the lowest percentage cover of grasses and the highest percentage cover of trees after the control.

*If you're asked to compare the effectiveness of something like different conservation methods, always make sure you know what the aim of the method is. In this case, the nature reserve want to stop the forest developing (so they want a low percentage of trees) and to keep the grassland (so they want a high percentage cover of grass).*

b) E.g. Grazing is less dangerous than fire. / Grazing could cause less harm to other species than fire.

Q2 There is a conflict between the needs of local people (for food and income) and the conservation aim of protecting the saiga. By educating local people about the importance of not hunting the saiga at unsustainable levels, and providing alternative sources of income (and food), this can contribute towards fewer saiga being killed and therefore the conservation of the species.

*Although there is a conflict between conservation and local people here, overhunting the saiga is in no-one's interest — if the saiga is hunted to extinction, the local people exploiting it will lose the saiga as a form of food and income completely.*

## Page 194 — Fact Recall Questions

Q1 The protection and management of species and habitats.
Q2 E.g. because there's often a conflict between human needs and conservation.
Q3 A managed fire is lit. After the fire, secondary succession will occur — the plant species that grow back first (pioneer species) are the species that are being conserved. Larger plant species will take longer to grow back and will be removed again the next time the area is burnt.
Q4 E.g. seed banks, captive breeding, fishing quotas, protected areas.

### 6. Conservation Evidence and Data

## Page 197 — Application Questions

Q1 The average percentage cover of non-native species was greatest on the control grasslands and lowest on the grazed fields. The average percentage cover of native species was greatest on the grazed fields and lowest on the harrowed and seeded fields. Overall, non-native species make up a greater proportion of plants than native species on average across all field types.

Q2 a) Grazing was the most successful method because it produced a larger proportion of native plants than harrowing and seeding, and the control, and a smaller proportion of non-native plants than harrowing and seeding, and the control.

b) Grazing worked because, e.g. the sheep prefer eating non-native to native plant species. / The non-native plants may have been less likely to grow back after grazing than the native plants. Seeding may not have worked because, e.g. the native plant seeds that were seeded on harrowed grassland were unable to compete with non-native seeds.

*For questions asking you to suggest an answer, you need to use your common sense — you won't have been taught the answer.*

Q3 a) E.g. the first study used a much larger sample size (14 fields per method) than the second study (1 field per method). The larger sample size of the first investigation would reduce the likelihood that the results seen were due to chance, so the results are more likely to be valid in the first investigation compared to the second investigation.

b) A negative control was used. The control field had no method applied so therefore it was used to check that the independent variable (method applied) was the only thing affecting the dependent variable (average percentage cover) — this is the aim of a negative control.

### Exam-style Questions — pages 199-200

1.1 E.g. they could set up a belt transect / place quadrats next to each other along a transect ***(1 mark)***. The transect could extend across the width of the field and the abundance of marsh marigolds recorded in each quadrat ***(1 mark)***.

1.2 They could count how many squares of each quadrat are covered by marsh marigolds by counting a square if it's more than half-covered ***(1 mark)***. The number of squares covered can be converted into a percentage ***(1 mark)***. Measuring percentage cover is a quick way to investigate the abundance of marsh marigolds as they wouldn't have to count all the individual marsh marigolds ***(1 mark)***.

1.3 The non-living features of an ecosystem ***(1 mark)***.

1.4 The graphs show that there is a positive correlation between the moisture of the soil and the abundance of marsh marigolds ***(1 mark)***. There is also a positive correlation between the soil pH and the abundance of marsh marigolds ***(1 mark)***. But you can't conclude from this data that all marsh marigolds will grow better in waterlogged ground, because the results are only taken from an investigation looking at one field ***(1 mark)***. The results don't show a causal relationship because it's not clear whether soil moisture or soil pH has the bigger effect on marsh marigold growth ***(1 mark)***. Also, there may be other factors involved that increase marsh marigold growth, e.g. fewer herbivores/ organisms that consume plants near the stream ***(1 mark)***.

1.5 E.g. There is risk of flooding, so they should check the weather forecast before doing fieldwork to check for heavy rain which could cause the field to flood and result in conditions being unsuitable for fieldwork ***(1 mark)***. There is a risk of falling on the boggy ground, so they should wear suitable footwear such as wellies with good grip ***(1 mark)***.

*There are two marks available for this question — but it's not enough to just describe two risks, you've also got to come up with suggestions about how they can minimise each risk to get full marks.*

2.1 He could use an appropriate method (e.g. pitfall trap) to capture and count a sample of centipedes ***(1 mark)***. The species Z centipedes caught should be marked in a harmless way and released back into their habitat ***(1 mark)***. After a week, the same method should be used to collect a second sample of centipedes from the same population ***(1 mark)***. The number of species Z centipedes in the second sample, and the number in the second sample that are marked, should be counted ***(1 mark)***. The population size can be estimated using the equation:

$$\text{Total population size} = \frac{\text{Number caught in 2nd sample} \times \text{Number caught in 1st sample}}{\text{Number marked in 2nd sample}}$$ ***(1 mark)***

*Try to use the correct ecological terms in your answers, for example talk about centipede habitats (not 'places where centipedes live').*

2.2 $\frac{10 \times 15}{8} = 18.75 =$ **19 centipedes *(1 mark)***

3.1 E.g. over 50 years, succession might lead to plants growing tall enough to decrease light intensity to a level too low for the endangered species to grow ***(1 mark)***. The process of burning the heathland might also alter soil pH so it's less suitable for the endangered species ***(1 mark)***.

3.2 Between 1991 and mid-1992, the population size of heather and shrubs falls dramatically because they were burnt by the fire ***(1 mark)***, and the population size of insects falls because the loss of heather and shrubs causes them to lose their habitat/source of food ***(1 mark)***. From mid-1992 until 2000 the population size of heather and shrubs starts to rise as (secondary) succession occurs, and the growth of shrubs and heather provides a habitat/source of food for insects so their population also gradually increases ***(1 mark)***.

3.3 The first species to colonise an area during succession ***(1 mark)***.

3.4 E.g. herb species X was not present before 1992, before the fire, perhaps because the abiotic conditions weren't favourable ***(1 mark)***. Between 1992 and 1994 the population size of herb species X increased dramatically, so it must be better adapted than other species to the changed abiotic conditions created by the fire ***(1 mark)***. The increase in population size of herb species X slowed down and then levelled off between 1994 and 2003. It then decreased dramatically after 2003, perhaps because it was out-competed by another species or because it wasn't adapted to the changed abiotic conditions created by the increasing population size of other plant species ***(1 mark)***.

3.5 E.g. the graph only shows data over a nineteen year period after a fire and it might take longer than this for the insect population to recover / the population size of insects shows an upward trend, and this may continue after 2010 ***(1 mark)***. The graph only shows data for one year before the fire, and the insect population size was decreasing — so the data in 1990 might not be representative of the normal population size of insects ***(1 mark)***.

3.6 E.g. animals could be allowed to graze the land and eat the growing points of the shrubs and heather, stopping them from establishing themselves ***(1 mark)***. This would help to keep vegetation low and so increase the amount of light / reduce the amount of shade for the endangered plant species ***(1 mark)***. Controlling the soil pH would help to keep the soil acidic for the plant ***(1 mark)***.

*Think about the conditions the plant needs to grow successfully in (which is given in the introduction to the question), and how these conditions can be brought about by different conservation methods.*

# Topic 8

## Topic 8 — A: Mutations and Gene Expression

### 1. Mutations

#### Page 203 — Application Questions

Q1 a) Mutation A = a substitution mutation
*The third base along is now C, not T.*
Mutation B = a substitution mutation
*The seventh base along is now C, not G.*
Mutation C = a deletion mutation
*The fourth base, C, has been deleted.*
Mutation D = a duplication mutation
*The first triplet, CTT, has been repeated.*

b) Mutation A: Leu-His-Asp-Thr
Mutation B: Leu-His-His-Thr
Mutation C: Leu-Met-Ile
Mutation D: Leu-Leu-His-Asp-Thr

Q2 a) Mutation A is likely to have the least serious effect on the protein's structure. CTC still codes for Leu so the amino acid sequence/primary structure of the protein won't change.
*This is an example of a silent mutation.*

b) Mutation C is likely to have the most serious effect on the protein's structure as it is a frameshift mutation, which means all the amino acids coded for after/downstream of the mutation will be different.

#### Page 203 — Fact Recall Questions

Q1 A change to the base (nucleotide) sequence of DNA.

Q2 In a translocation mutation a sequence of bases is moved from one location in the genome to another.

Q3 The mutation may result in a change to the shape of the enzyme's active site. This may stop substrates from being able to bind to the active site, leaving the enzyme unable to catalyse the reaction.

Q4 A mutation that is passed on to an individual's offspring as a result of a mutation in their gametes.

Q5 No. The genetic code is degenerate/some amino acids are coded for by more than one triplet. This means that not all mutations will result in a change to the amino acid sequence of a protein.

### 2. Mutagenic Agents

#### Page 204 — Application Questions

Q1 2-aminopurine can pair with both thymine and cytosine, which could cause a substitution mutation in the new DNA during DNA replication.

Q2 Alkylating agents such as mustard gas can add an alkyl group to guanine, changing the structure so that it pairs with thymine (instead of cytosine), which may result in a change in the amino acid sequence of a polypeptide.

#### Page 204 — Fact Recall Questions

Q1 E.g. during DNA replication.

Q2 Something that causes an increase in the rate of mutations.

Q3 E.g. ultraviolet radiation / ionising radiation / base analogs / alkylating agents / some chemicals / some viruses.

## 3. Cancer

### Page 208 — Application Questions

Q1 B. E.g. because the nuclei are larger and darker in B than in A, the cells are more irregularly shaped in B than A and the cells are denser in B than A (suggesting that they don't respond to growth regulating processes, and so divide more frequently than normal cells).

Q2 a) It slows cell division by producing a protein that stops cells dividing or causes them to self-destruct.

b) A mutation in p53 could inactivate the gene. The protein it codes for won't be produced. This will cause cells to start dividing uncontrollably, eventually leading to cancer.

*Don't worry if you've never heard of the p53 gene — you can still answer the question. You just need to apply your knowledge of tumour suppressor genes to the p53 example. You're likely to get a lot of questions like this in the exam.*

Q3 a) She has a malignant tumour as it has spread to other parts of her body.

b) E.g. HRT increases oestrogen levels in the body. Increased exposure to oestrogen over an extended period of time is thought to increase the risk of developing breast cancer.

Q4 Dichloroacetic acid causes hypomethylation of c-*myc*. Hypomethylation of proto-oncogenes like c-*myc* causes them to act as oncogenes, therefore increasing the production of proteins that encourage cell division. This stimulates cells to divide uncontrollably, which causes the formation of tumours.

### Page 208 — Fact Recall Questions

Q1 A mutation that occurs in individual cells after fertilisation.

Q2 a tumour

Q3 Proto-oncogenes stimulate cell division by producing proteins that make cells divide.

Q4 A mutated proto-oncogene.

Q5 Any one from: e.g. a malignant tumour is cancerous, whereas a benign tumour is non-cancerous. / Malignant tumours grow rapidly, whereas benign tumours grow more slowly.

Q6 When tumour suppressor genes are hypermethylated, the genes are not transcribed, so the proteins they produce to slow cell division aren't made. This means that cells are able to divide uncontrollably by mitosis and tumours can develop.

Q7 Any one from: e.g. oestrogen can stimulate certain breast cells to divide and replicate. The more cell divisions that are taking place, the greater the chance of mutations occurring, and so the chance of cells becoming cancerous is increased. / If breast cells do become cancerous, oestrogen's ability to stimulate division could also help tumours to form quickly. / Exposure to oestrogen could introduce mutations directly into the DNA of certain breast cells, again increasing the chance of these cells becoming cancerous.

## 4. Interpreting Data on Cancer

### Page 210 — Application Question

Q1 a) The results show that the relative risk of breast cancer for women in California is higher for women who previously smoked or still smoke compared to those who have never smoked.

b) No. E.g. just because there is a positive correlation between smoking and breast cancer, it doesn't mean that smoking causes breast cancer. The correlation may be due to chance, or there could be other risk factors involved that aren't considered here, such as genetic factors. Also, the study just looked at women in California so these results can't be applied to women in general.

### Page 212 — Application Questions

Q1 a) If a mutation only occurs in one of the RB1 alleles, the other one will still be able to produce a normal pRB tumour suppressor protein. This means that cell division can still be controlled. If a mutation occurs in both RB1 alleles, a normal pRB protein won't be produced and cells will start dividing uncontrollably. This could eventually lead to cancer.

b) E.g. it means that children who have inherited an RB1 mutation can be regularly screened, so that if further tumours do develop they can be diagnosed and treated earlier.

Q2 a) If CD117 is present, then it may be possible to treat the cancer with Imatinib. If it is not present, then Imantinib will be ineffective and another course of treatment will be necessary.

b) E.g. mutated tumour suppressor genes are inactivated. The protein they produce doesn't function. A drug which targets a mutated tumour suppressor gene would have to restore the function of the tumour suppressor protein, which could be difficult.

*This is one of those 'suggest' questions where you're not expected to know the exact answer, but you should be able to come up with a suggestion using what you already know. A sensible answer, like the one above, will get you the marks in the exam.*

## 5. Stem Cells

### Page 215 — Application Questions

Q1 unipotent

Q2 a) pluripotent

b) In an embryo.

c) totipotent

### Page 215 — Fact Recall Questions

Q1 Unspecialised cells that can develop into other types of cell.

Q2 In embryos and in some adult tissues.

Q3 Totipotent stem cells can mature/develop into any type of body cell in an organism, multipotent stem cells can only differentiate into a few different types of cell and unipotent stem cells can only differentiate into one type of cell.

Q4 Stem cells become specialised by only expressing certain genes and switching off others. Genes that are expressed get transcribed into mRNA, which is then translated into proteins. These proteins modify the cell. Changes to the cell produced by the proteins cause the cell to become specialised.

Q5 a) a heart muscle cell

b) unipotent stem cells

## 6. Stem Cells in Medicine

### Page 218 — Application Questions

Q1 The bone marrow comes from a healthy donor who does not carry the mutation for sickle cell anaemia. As a result, the multipotent stem cells in the donor marrow will divide and differentiate to produce new, healthy red blood cells. These red blood cells won't sickle and so will function normally, curing the patient.

Q2 a) Because the stem cells can be used to form new, specialised corneal cells to replace the damaged ones.

b) E.g. any two from: there's a reduced risk of rejection as the donated cells are from the same patient. / There's no need to use embryonic stem cells, so avoids the ethical issues surrounding their use. / There's no need to wait for a donor cornea to become available.

Q3 The plasmids could have the genes coding for transcription factors that are normally associated with pluripotent stem cells within their DNA. They could then be inserted into adult cells. The genes may then be passed into the adult cell's DNA, meaning that the cell is able to produce the transcription factors, and become pluripotent.

Q4 Answer should include a discussion of the pros and cons of using embryonic stem cells in this particular investigation. E.g. pros: the embryonic stem cells are taken from donated embryos, which would otherwise be discarded. The treatment could improve the quality of the patients lives/ reduce the amount of medical care they require by giving them more movement.
E.g. cons: the embryonic stem cells come from embryos which could have become a fetus if placed in the womb. There are other treatments also being developed, that use induced pluripotent stem cells, which means the patients could potentially be treated without needing embryonic stem cells to be used.
*If you're asked to discuss an issue such as this one, make sure you give both sides of the argument.*

## 7. Regulation of Transcription and Translation

### Page 221 — Application Questions

Q1 Less of the transcription factor coded for by the MECP2 gene is produced, so it is unable to repress the transcription of other genes. These genes remain active which affects the normal functioning of nerve cells, leading to Rett syndrome.
*You don't need to know anything about Rett syndrome to answer this question because it's testing your knowledge of transcription. But you still need to make sure that you apply your knowledge to the disease in the question.*

Q2 siRNA could be produced that is complementary to the genes causing AMD. The siRNA and associated proteins would bind to the target mRNA and the proteins would cut up the mRNA into sections so it would no longer be translated.

### Page 223 — Application Questions

Q1 Any three from, e.g. temperature / the presence of other amino acids / the length of time the bacteria are left for / volume of culture / number of bacteria / amount of tryptophan added.

Q2 a) In normal bacteria in the presence of tryptophan, the amount of target mRNA is reduced by about 70-fold. This is because when tryptophan is present it binds to the repressor, allowing it to bind to the target gene and reduce transcription. A reduction in transcription means much less mRNA is produced, and therefore much less tryptophan is produced.

b) Bacteria do not need to produce more tryptophan if it's already present, so transcription stops to prevent the bacteria from wasting energy on producing something they don't need.

Q3 The mutant bacteria produce a similar amount of tryptophan in both the presence and absence of tryptophan. This could be because, e.g. the mutation affected the DNA base sequence of the tryptophan repressor, so it can no longer bind to DNA even in the presence of tryptophan. This means it can't prevent transcription and so tryptophan is always produced.

### Page 223 — Fact Recall Questions

Q1 Protein molecules that control the transcription of genes.

Q2 a) A transcription factor that increases the rate of transcription.

b) A transcription factor that decreases the rate of transcription.

Q3 Because not all cell types have oestrogen receptors.

Q4 Oestrogen binds to the oestrogen receptor (a transcription factor) to form an oestrogen-oestrogen receptor complex. The complex then moves from the cytoplasm to the nucleus and binds to the DNA near the start of the target gene.

Q5 RNAi is where small, double-stranded RNA molecules stop mRNA from target genes being translated into proteins. The double-stranded siRNA molecule associates with several proteins in the cytoplasm and unwinds — one strand is selected and the other is degraded. The single strand of siRNA is fully complementary to the target mRNA and so binds to it. Its associated proteins cut the mRNA into fragments. The fragments are then moved to a processing body where they are degraded, and so the protein is not transcribed.

Q6 A mammalian miRNA molecule is not fully complementary to the target mRNA base sequence, so it is less specific than siRNA (which is fully complementary to its target mRNA).

## 8. Epigenetic Control of Gene Expression

### Page 226 — Application Questions

Q1 The DNA structure at the methylated sites would be altered so that the transcriptional machinery cannot bind to the genes and so they would not be transcribed.

Q2 E.g. different genotypes may have different responses to nutrient deprivation/environmental stress.

Q3 Most epigenetic marks are removed between generations. It is possible that the methyl groups added in the parental plant during stress were removed during reproduction.

### Page 226 — Fact Recall Questions

Q1 E.g. methyl groups (on DNA) and acetyl groups (on histones).

Q2 When acetyl groups are added to histones, the chromatin becomes less condensed, so transcriptional machinery can access the DNA and transcribe those genes.

## 9. Evaluating Data on Phenotypes

### Page 228 — Application Question

Q1 a) The mean difference in head circumference is approximately 0.5 cm for identical twins, 3 cm for non-identical siblings and 8.5 cm for unrelated individuals. So the mean difference in head circumference is much larger for unrelated individuals than for either identical twins or non-identical siblings.

b) The data suggests that genetic factors have a larger effect on head circumference, because the mean difference in head circumference is much larger for unrelated individuals than for either identical twins or non-identical siblings. However, the mean difference for identical twins wasn't zero, so environmental factors appear to play some role.

c) The mean difference in the number of steps taken is between 800 and 900 for all three sample groups. Identical twins and non-identical siblings show the lowest difference and unrelated individuals the highest but the margins are very small. This suggests that environmental factors play a more important role than genetic factors in determining activity level when measured by the number of steps taken per day.

### Page 228 — Fact Recall Question

Q1 They are genetically identical, so any differences in phenotype must be due to environmental factors.

## Exam-style Questions — pages 230-231

1.1 deletion ***(1 mark)***

1.2 mRNA codons: ACG GUU GUU GUG AGC ***(1 mark)***
amino acids: Threonine, Valine, Valine, Valine, Serine ***(1 mark)***

*It's always a good idea to show your working for questions like this, even if it doesn't say to in the question, as you might pick up a mark even if you get the amino acids wrong.*

1.3 It is an activator. The results show that both the normal and the mutant bacteria produce the transcription factor (7.9 and 7.7 arbitrary units) ***(1 mark)***. But the mutant bacteria produce much less antibiotic mRNA (0.9 arbitrary units compared to 8.2) and much less of the antibiotic itself (the blue-colour of the antibiotic can't be seen around the mutant bacteria) ***(1 mark)***. This means that the mutation must affect the transcription of mRNA ***(1 mark)***. This suggests the mutant bacteria have a faulty transcription factor protein which can't bind to the start of the target gene and so can't activate transcription ***(1 mark)***.

*The introduction to question 1 says that the bacteria produce a blue-coloured antibiotic. Figure 2 shows that mutant bacteria don't produce the blue colour, which suggests they don't produce the antibiotic.*

2.1 The APC gene must be the tumour suppressor gene. It slows cell division by preventing β-catenin from carrying out its function ***(1 mark)***. β-catenin activates genes needed for cell division, so the β-catenin gene must be the proto-oncogene ***(1 mark)***.

2.2 E.g. a mutation in the β-catenin gene could cause it to become overactive and stimulate the cell to divide uncontrollably, causing cancer ***(1 mark)***. A mutation in the APC gene could prevent the protein from carrying out its function of destroying β-catenin, so the cell would be stimulated to divide uncontrollably ***(1 mark)***.

2.3 A deletion of one or more bases will affect the number of bases present, causing a shift in all the base triplets that follow ***(1 mark)*** and this could cause a change in the amino acid sequence/primary structure of the protein ***(1 mark)***. This could change the tertiary structure of the protein and prevent it from functioning ***(1 mark)***.

2.4 Any one from: e.g. it could allow you to have regular screening/tests to help doctors diagnose colon cancer in its early stages. / It may affect the treatment you are given if and when you develop colon cancer. ***(1 mark for any sensible answer.)***

3.1 As the plant cells become more specialised, the relative concentration of alkaloid in the cells increases ***(1 mark)***.

3.2 $\frac{1.85 - 0.45}{0.45} \times 100 =$ **311%** (accept 300 to 322%) ***(1 mark)***

3.3 E.g. the auxins are needed to quickly produce a large number of cells early on in the tissue culture ***(1 mark)***, but alkaloid production is much higher in specialised cells, so auxins are later removed because they reduce cell specialisation ***(1 mark)***.

3.4 E.g. cells become specialised by expressing certain genes and switching off others ***(1 mark)***. Genes that are expressed get transcribed into mRNA and then translated into proteins ***(1 mark)***. The proteins then modify the cell, causing it to become specialised ***(1 mark)***. If auxins alter the genes that get expressed, the cell will transcribe and translate different proteins ***(1 mark)***. These proteins could then modify the cell in a different way, changing the type of cell it specialises into ***(1 mark)***.

# Topic 8 — B: Genome Projects and Gene Technologies

## 1. Genome Projects

### Page 233 — Fact Recall Questions

Q1 To determine the complete set of genetic material in an organism.

Q2 a) The proteome is all the proteins that can be made by an organism.

b) E.g. you can use it to identify the protein antigens on the surface of disease-causing bacteria and viruses, which can help in the development of vaccines to prevent the disease.

Q3 More complex organisms contain large sections of non-coding DNA and also complex regulatory genes, which determine when the genes that code for particular proteins should be switched on and off. This makes it more difficult to translate their genome into their proteome, because it's hard to find the bits that code for proteins among the non-coding and regulatory DNA.

Q4 In the past, many sequencing methods were labour-intensive, expensive and could only be done on a small scale. Now these techniques are often automated, more cost-effective and can be done on a large scale.

## 2. Making DNA Fragments

### Page 236 — Application Questions

Q1 reverse transcriptase

Q2 There is a *Bam*HI site on the left hand side of the fragment and an *Eco*RI site towards the right hand side. The DNA sample could be incubated with *Bam*HI and *Eco*RI, which would cut the DNA via a hydrolysis reaction at these sites. This is because the shape of each recognition sequence is complementary to each enzyme's active site.

### Page 236 — Fact Recall Questions

Q1 Recombinant DNA technology involves transferring a fragment of DNA from one organism to another.

Q2 It is possible to transfer DNA to a recipient organism of a different species because the genetic code and transcription and translation mechanisms are universal.

Q3 a) complementary DNA / a DNA copy of an mRNA molecule

b) mRNA is isolated from cells, then mixed with free DNA nucleotides and reverse transcriptase. The reverse transcriptase uses the mRNA as a template to synthesise new strands of cDNA.

c) E.g. mRNA is often easier to obtain than a DNA fragment containing the target gene. / There are generally more mRNA versions of a gene than DNA versions of a gene in a cell. / Only the exons are present in mRNA.

Q4 A sequence of DNA that consists of antiparallel base pairs/ base pairs that read the same in opposite directions.

Q5 Small tails of unpaired bases at the end of a DNA fragment. They can be used to bind/anneal the DNA fragment to another piece of DNA that has sticky ends with complementary sequences.

Q6 The sequence that is required is designed. The first nucleotide in the sequence is then fixed to some sort of support. Nucleotides are added step by step in the correct order, in a cycle of processes that includes adding protecting groups. Short sections of DNA called oligonucleotides, roughly 20 nucleotides long, are produced. Once these are complete, they are broken off from the support and all the protecting groups are removed. The oligonucleotides can then be joined together to make longer DNA fragments.

## 3. Amplifying DNA Fragments

### Pages 240-241 — Application Questions

Q1 a) Vector DNA was cut with the same restriction endonucleases as the DNA fragment, so complementary sticky ends were produced. The DNA fragment and cut vector were mixed with ligase and the pieces were joined together to form the recombinant DNA. A marker gene must also be present in the recombinant DNA, so may have been inserted at the same time as the DNA fragment or existed in the vector DNA already.

*In the exam, put down as much information as you can. Here there are a few details on how the DNA fragment was made and how the marker gene got in there, as they all form part of the recombinant DNA.*

b) It's likely he put a marker gene for resistance to penicillin in as part of the recombinant DNA. He grew the plates on agar containing penicillin so he could identify which colonies contained transformed cells (cells with the target gene in).

Q2 a) top strand = CGTA, bottom strand = GGTA

b) $2 \times 2 \times 2 \times 2 \times 2 \times 2 \times 2 =$ **128**

*Remember, you start with two single stands of DNA. The amount of DNA then doubles with each PCR cycle.*

Q3 a) The plasmids are vectors — they're used to transfer the target gene into the host cells/*E.coli*.

b) The ampicillin resistance gene is a marker gene. It means that only *E. coli* containing the plasmid will grow on the agar (which contains ampicillin).

c) *E.coli* that have taken up plasmids containing the target gene will be white/colourless because the target gene has disrupted the LacZα gene in the bacterial plasmids. This means the LacZα gene won't have produced the correct protein, so the *E.coli* won't have been able to produce β-galactosidase and therefore won't have been able to break down X-gal into a blue pigment. *E.coli* containing plasmids without the target gene will be blue because they will contain both the LacZα and LacZΩ genes — this will enable them to produce functional β-galactosidase and therefore breakdown X-gal into a blue pigment.

## Page 241 — Fact Recall Questions

Q1 In *in vivo* cloning, gene copies are made inside a living organism. In *in vitro* cloning, gene copies are made outside of a living organism (using PCR).

Q2 A vector is something that's used to transfer DNA into a cell.

Q3 E.g. a plasmid / bacteriophage

Q4 DNA ligase is used to join the sticky ends of the DNA fragment containing the target gene to the sticky ends of the vector DNA.

Q5 A cell into which the target gene/recombinant DNA is transferred.

Q6 That it has taken up the vector containing the target gene.

Q7 Not all cells will take up the vector — the ones that do need to be identified so they can be allowed to grow and produce lots of copies of the cloned gene.

Q8 Identifying transformed cells.

Q9 Promoter and terminator regions

Q10 The polymerase chain reaction (PCR).

Q11 a) The DNA sample, free nucleotides, primers and DNA polymerase.

b) The DNA mixture is heated to 95 °C to break the hydrogen bonds between the two strands of DNA. The mixture is then cooled to between 50 and 65 °C so that the primers can bind (anneal) to the strands. The reaction mixture is then heated to 72 °C, so DNA polymerase can work. The DNA polymerase lines up free DNA nucleotides alongside each template strand. Specific base pairing means new complementary strands are formed. Two new copies of the fragment of DNA are formed and one cycle of PCR is complete. The cycle then starts again.

# 4. Recombinant DNA Technology

## Page 244 — Application Questions

Q1 A DNA fragment containing the resistance gene could be made using reverse transcriptase, PCR or cut out using restriction endonucleases. The DNA fragment could be inserted into a plasmid vector which could then be added to a bacterium. The bacterium could then be used as a vector to get the gene into the soybean plant cells.

Q2 Fields of the soybean crop could be sprayed with the herbicide, killing the weeds but not the crop. This could increase the yield from the field.

Q3 E.g. if the transformed soybean crop interbreed with wild plants it could possibly result in 'superweeds' — weeds that are resistant to a herbicide. / Farmers might plant only this soybean crop, which could make the whole crop vulnerable to the same disease because the plants are genetically identical/biodiversity in the area is reduced. / This one large agricultural company could end up controlling soybean production, forcing smaller companies out of business.

*These are all good answers, but as the question specifically talks about herbicide resistance, the superweed concern is probably the best answer to give as it's the most specific to the context you're given.*

# 5. Gene Therapy

## Page 245 — Fact Recall Questions

Q1 Gene therapy involves altering the defective genes (mutated alleles) inside cells by inserting a DNA fragment into the original DNA.

Q2 Somatic therapy involves altering the alleles in body cells, particularly the cells that are most affected by the disorder, whereas germ line therapy involves altering the alleles in the sex cells.

# 6. Gene Probes and Medical Diagnosis

## Page 248 — Application Questions

Q1 A DNA microarray should be used — microscopic spots of DNA probes for different genetic mutations (different genetic disorders) are attached to a glass slide in rows. A fluorescently labelled sample of the child's DNA is washed over the array. The array is washed and visualised under UV light. Any labelled DNA attached to a probe will fluoresce, identifying any mutations in the child's DNA and so which genetic disorder they have.

Q2 They may undergo genetic counselling to help provide them with information on the treatment available for their child. They might also have counselling to help them understand the chances of them having another child with the recessive disorder. Genetic counselling will provide them with unbiased advice on the possibility of having IVF and screening their embryos for the alleles.

# 7. Genetic Fingerprinting

## Page 252 — Application Questions

Q1 Some parts of an organism's genome consist of variable number tandem repeats (VNTRs). These repeated sequences occur in lots of places in the genome and the number of times these sequences are repeated differs from organism to organism. Genetic fingerprinting looks at the number of times some of these sequences are repeated at different loci in an individual's genome.

Q2 a) To make many copies of the areas of DNA that contain the repeated sequences. / To add fluorescent tags to the DNA so it can be seen under UV light.

b) To separate the fragments of DNA by length, producing a genetic fingerprint.

*These techniques can be used for lots of different reasons in gene technology. So make sure you clearly understand what each one does, then you should be able to work out why it's been used in any situation you're given.*

Q3 No, the woman does not appear to be the diplomat's daughter. Only one band is found in the same position for both the woman and the diplomat. You would expect more than this if he was her father.

## Exam-style Questions — pages 254-255

1.1 Any two from, e.g. they may have been concerned that the crop would encourage farmers to plant monocultures, reducing biodiversity ***(1 mark)***. / They may have been concerned about the possibility of 'superweeds' — weeds that are resistant to herbicides because they've bred with genetically engineered herbicide-resistant crops ***(1 mark)***. / They may have been concerned that organic farmers nearby will have their crops contaminated by wind-blown seeds from the genetically modified crops ***(1 mark)***.

1.2 A DNA probe is a short strand of DNA with a base sequence that is complementary to a target sequence ***(1 mark)***.

1.3 A sample of DNA containing the resistance gene is digested using restriction enzymes and the digested fragments are separated by electrophoresis ***(1 mark)***. The separated fragments are then transferred to a nylon membrane and incubated with a fluorescently labelled DNA probe ***(1 mark)***. The probe will hybridise to any DNA fragment that contains a complementary DNA sequence ***(1 mark)***. The membrane is then exposed to UV light / X-ray film, so that the band the probe has attached to can be visualised ***(1 mark)***.

1.4 Colonies were added to the plate containing penicillin to identify the transformed cells (those that have taken up the recombinant DNA containing the target allele) ***(1 mark)***. A marker gene/genetic marker for penicillin resistance was added to the recombinant DNA so that only transformed cells will grow on plates containing penicillin, allowing them to be identified ***(1 mark)***. Colonies of bacteria were also added to a standard agar plate as a control to show that all the colonies grew in the absence of penicillin ***(1 mark)***.

1.5 Bacteria A is a control to make sure nothing in the host cells on their own makes them resistant to penicillin/ to make sure the penicillin is working ***(1 mark)***.

1.6 Any one of 1, 3, 5 or 7. These grew on the penicillin plate, and so must be transformed cells/contain the recombinant DNA with the allele of interest and the marker gene/genetic marker for penicillin-resistance ***(1 mark)***.

2.1 PCR is used to make many copies of the areas of the DNA that contain the VNTRs in each DNA sample ***(1 mark)***. A fluorescent tag is added to all the DNA (to allow it to be seen under UV light) ***(1 mark)***. The PCR mix from each sample is separated using gel electrophoresis ***(1 mark)***. Shorter DNA fragments move faster and travel further through the gel, so the DNA fragments separate according to length with longer pieces nearer the negative end ***(1 mark)***. The gel is placed under UV light to see the bands produced for each sample — these are the genetic fingerprints ***(1 mark)***.

2.2 Genetic fingerprint technology involves comparing the number of times repetitive, non-coding base sequences ***(1 mark)*** are repeated at a number of different, specific places (loci) in a genome ***(1 mark)***. The probability of two individuals having the same genetic fingerprint is very low because the chance of two individuals having the same number of sequence repeats at each locus tested is very low ***(1 mark)***.

2.3 Yes. The genetic fingerprint of the stolen horse and genetic fingerprint of horse 3 have exactly the same band pattern, so the DNA that produced both genetic fingerprints must have come from the same horse ***(1 mark)***.

2.4 Horse 4 and the stolen horse have 6 matching bands ***(1 mark)***, which suggests they must be closely related in some way ***(1 mark)***. The stolen horse had previously been sent to the farm for breeding purposes, so it seems likely that horse 4 is a child of the stolen horse ***(1 mark)***.
*Offspring get 50% of their DNA from each parent, so roughly 50% of bands will match between a parent and child in a genetic fingerprint.*

2.5 E.g. determining genetic relationships / determining genetic variability within a population / medical diagnosis / animal and plant breeding ***(1 mark)***.

3.1 E.g. they could use restriction endonuclease enzymes ***(1 mark)*** to cut the DNA at specific palindromic recognition sequences ***(1 mark)*** / They could use a gene machine ***(1 mark)*** to create fragments of the required sequence from scratch without the need for a pre-existing DNA template ***(1 mark)***.

3.2 They are important in *in vivo* cloning as complementary sticky ends are required to anneal (bind) the target DNA fragment and vector DNA together ***(1 mark)***.

3.3 Any six from: the vector DNA is cut using the same restriction enzyme to produce complementary sticky ends ***(1 mark)***. The DNA fragment containing the target gene and vector DNA are mixed together with DNA ligase ***(1 mark)***, which joins the sticky ends together creating recombinant DNA ***(1 mark)***. Marker genes are inserted into the vector at the same time as the DNA fragment ***(1 mark)***. The vector with the recombinant DNA and the fluorescent marker gene is then used to transfer the gene into host cells ***(1 mark)***. The host cells are grown on agar plates to produce colonies of cloned cells ***(1 mark)***. If the agar plate is placed under UV light, only colonies of transformed cells will fluoresce because only these cells will contain the marker gene ***(1 mark)***. Identified transformed cells are allowed to grow more producing lots of copies of the cloned gene ***(1 mark)***.

# Exam Help

## Page 258 — Exam-style Question

Q1 ***21-25 marks:***

The answer includes material from a variety of different topic areas and clearly shows its link to the question title. No irrelevant material is included. The answer includes a range of detailed and accurate biological facts that are all of A-level standard. No incorrect material is included. Appropriate scientific terminology is used. Explanations are clear and the overall essay is very well written. (To get top marks, evidence of wider reading beyond the specification must be shown.)

***16-20 marks:***

The answer includes material from several relevant topic areas and links these to the question title. An irrelevant topic may be included. The answer includes a range of biological facts that are accurate and of A-level standard but may sometimes be lacking in detail. There may be one significant error in the scientific content. Appropriate scientific terminology is used. Explanations are clear.

***11-15 marks:***

The answer includes material from several relevant topic areas but doesn't link them to the question title. More than one irrelevant topic may be included. The biological facts included in the answer are mostly correct and of A-level standard but material is lacking in detail. There may be a few significant errors in the scientific content. Appropriate scientific terminology is usually used. Explanations are usually clear.

***6-10 marks:***

The answer includes material from one or two relevant topic areas but doesn't link them to the question title. Several irrelevant topic areas may be included. Some A-level content may be included but it will be lacking in detail and may contain several significant scientific errors. There may be limited use of scientific terminology. Explanations lack clarity.

***1-5 marks:***

The answer includes material that is only vaguely linked to the question title. Material is presented as a series of facts. Most of the material is irrelevant. The content is below A-level standard and contains a large number of scientific errors. Scientific terminology is not used or is below A-level standard. Explanations are poor or absent.

***0 marks:***

Nothing relevant is included in the answer or nothing has been written.

**Here are some topic areas you might write about:**

- the importance of hydrogen ions in the redox reactions of photosynthesis and respiration;
- how the concentration of hydrogen ions determines the pH of solutions and how maintaining the pH of the blood is important for many enzyme-controlled metabolic reactions;
- the use of iron ions in haemoglobin to transport oxygen around the body;
- how the movement of sodium and potassium ions creates action potentials, allowing nervous communication;
- how calcium ions are involved in the transmission of action potentials across synapses;
- the use of sodium ions in the co-transport of glucose and amino acids into cells;
- the use of phosphate ions in the production of ATP, and the importance of ATP in storing and releasing energy for the cell;
- the use of phosphate ions in producing DNA and RNA nucleotides and the importance of these molecules as the carriers of genetic information.

This is not a full list of all the topic areas you could write about — it's just to give you an idea. Remember, you should aim to write about at least five of these topic areas. Whatever topic areas you include, you must relate them to the essay title — so in this case, don't just write about inorganic ions, make it really clear how inorganic ions are important to living organisms.

# Glossary

## A

**Abiotic condition**
A non-living feature of an ecosystem.

**Abundance**
The number of individuals of one species in a particular area (i.e. population size).

**Accurate result**
A result that is really close to the true answer.

**Acetylation**
Attachment of an acetyl group to something (e.g. histones).

**Acetylcholine (ACh)**
A type of neurotransmitter that binds to cholinergic receptors.

**Acetyl coenzyme A (AcetylCoA)**
A type of coenzyme involved in respiration. It transfers acetate from one molecule to another.

**Acquired mutation**
A mutation you develop during your lifetime.

**Actin**
The thin myofilament protein in muscle fibres.

**Actin-myosin cross bridge**
The bond formed when a myosin head binds to an actin filament.

**Activator**
A transcription factor that increases the rate of transcription.

**Active transport**
Movement of molecules and ions across plasma membranes, usually against a concentration gradient. Requires energy.

**Adaptation**
A feature that increases an individual's chance of survival and reproduction.

**ADP (adenosine diphosphate)**
A molecule made up of adenine, a ribose sugar and two phosphate groups. ATP is synthesised from ADP and a phosphate group.

**Adrenaline**
A hormone secreted from the adrenal glands that has many effects, including increasing the blood glucose concentration.

**Allele**
One or more alternative versions of the same gene.

**Allele frequency**
How often an allele occurs in a population.

**Allopatric speciation**
Where speciation occurs as a result of geographic isolation.

**Ammonification**
The process in which nitrogen compounds from dead organisms or waste material are turned into ammonium compounds by saprobionts.

**Anomalous result**
A measurement that falls outside the range of values you'd expect or any pattern you already have.

**Antidiuretic hormone (ADH)**
A hormone that regulates the water potential of the blood by controlling the permeability of the cells of the distal convoluted tubule and the collecting duct in the kidney.

**ATP (adenosine triphosphate)**
A molecule made up of adenine, a ribose sugar and three phosphate groups. It is the immediate source of energy in a cell.

**ATP hydrolase**
An enzyme that catalyses the hydrolysis of ATP into ADP and $P_i$.

**ATP-phosphocreatine (PCr) system**
A system that generates ATP very quickly by phosphorylating ADP using a phosphate group from phosphocreatine.

**ATP synthase**
An enzyme that catalyses the synthesis of ATP from ADP and $P_i$.

**Atrioventricular node (AVN)**
A group of cells in the heart wall that is responsible for passing waves of electrical activity from the SAN on to the bundle of His.

**Autonomic nervous system**
A division of the peripheral nervous system that controls unconscious activities, e.g. heart rate.

**Autosomal linkage**
When two genes are located on the same autosome and are inherited by the offspring together.

**Autosome**
A chromosome that isn't a sex chromosome.

## B

**Benign tumour**
A non-cancerous tumour.

**Bias**
When someone intentionally, or unintentionally, favours a particular result.

**Biomass**
The mass of living material in an organism.

**Biotic condition**
A living feature of an ecosystem.

**Bundle of His**
A group of muscle fibres in the heart, responsible for conducting waves of electrical activity from the AVN to the Purkyne fibres.

## C

**Cardiomyocyte**
A heart muscle cell.

**Carrier**
A person carrying an allele that is not expressed in their phenotype, but that can be passed on to their offspring.

**Carrying capacity**
The maximum stable population size of a species that an ecosystem can support.

**Causal relationship**
Where a change in one variable causes a change in the other.

**cDNA (complementary DNA)**
A DNA copy of mRNA made using reverse transcriptase.

**Chemical mediator**
A chemical messenger that acts locally (i.e. on nearby cells).

**Chemiosmosis**
The process of electrons flowing down the electron transport chain and creating a proton gradient across a membrane to drive ATP synthesis.

**Chlorophyll**
A photosynthetic pigment found in chloroplasts. There are different types of this pigment, e.g. chlorophyll a.

**Choice chamber**
A container with different compartments that can be used to investigate how animals respond to different environmental conditions.

**Cholinergic synapse**
A synapse that uses the neurotransmitter acetylcholine.

**Climax community**
The largest and most complex community of plants and animals an ecosystem can support.

**Codominant allele**
An allele whose characteristic appears together with another allele in the phenotype because neither allele is recessive.

**Codon**
A base triplet (three nucleotides) in DNA or mRNA that codes for an amino acid.

**Coenzyme**
A molecule that aids the function of an enzyme. They work by transferring a chemical group from one molecule to another.

**Community**
All the populations of different species in a habitat.

**Compensation point**
The point at which the rate of photosynthesis in a plant exactly matches its rate of respiration.

**Cone (eye)**
A photoreceptor cell found in the eye that gives information in colour.

**Conservation**
The protection and management of species and habitats (ecosystems) in a sustainable way.

**Continuous data**
Data that can take any value within a range.

**Control group**
A group in a study that is treated in exactly the same way as the experimental group, apart from the factor you're investigating.

**Control variable**
A variable you keep constant throughout an experiment.

**Coordinator**
Part of the nervous system (e.g. the CNS) which formulates an appropriate response to a stimulus before sending impulses to an effector.

**Correlation**
A relationship between two variables.

## D

**Dehydrogenase**
An enzyme that transfers hydrogen and electrons from one molecule to another.

**Denitrification**
The process in which nitrates in the soil are converted into nitrogen gas by denitrifying bacteria.

**Dependent variable**
The variable you measure in an experiment.

**Depolarisation**
A decrease in the potential difference across a cell's membrane, making it less negative (i.e. more positive) than the resting potential.

**Diabetes mellitus (Type I)**
A condition in which blood glucose concentration can't be controlled properly because the body doesn't produce any insulin.

**Diabetes mellitus (Type II)**
A condition in which blood glucose concentration can't be controlled properly because the body doesn't produce enough insulin or the body's cells don't respond properly to insulin.

**Dihybrid inheritance**
The inheritance of two characteristics, which are controlled by different genes.

**Directional selection**
Where individuals with alleles for a single extreme phenotype are more likely to survive, reproduce and pass on their alleles.

**Discrete data**
Numerical data that can only take certain values in a range.

**Disruptive selection**
Where individuals with alleles for phenotypes at the extreme ends of a range are more likely to survive, reproduce and pass on their alleles.

**Distribution**
Where a particular species is within an area being investigated.

**DNA polymerase**
An enzyme that joins together the nucleotides on a new strand of DNA during DNA replication.

**DNA probe**
A short single strand of DNA that has a complementary base sequence to part of a target gene.

**DNA sequencing**
A technique used to determine the order of bases in a section of DNA.

**Dominant allele**
An allele whose characteristic appears in the phenotype even when there's only one copy.

**Ecosystem**
All the organisms living in a community plus all the non-living (abiotic) conditions in the area in which they live.

**Effector**
A cell that brings about a response to a stimulus, to produce an effect.

**Electrochemical gradient**
A concentration gradient of ions.

**Electron transport chain**
A chain of proteins down which excited electrons flow.

**Epigenetic control (of gene expression)**
The attachment or removal of chemical groups to or from DNA or histone proteins, which determines whether a gene is switched on or off.

**Epistasis**
When an allele of one gene masks (blocks) the expression of the alleles of other genes.

**Eutrophication**
The process whereby nutrients build up in water, leading to the growth of large quantities of algae. This results in the death of plants, and the decomposition of dead plant matter causes the oxygen content of the water to fall, killing aquatic organisms.

**Evolution**
The change in allele frequency in a population over time.

**Exocytosis**
The process by which a cell secretes substances using vesicles.

**Exon**
A section of DNA that codes for amino acids.

**Extracellular digestion**
When food is broken down (digested) outside a cell. Saprobionts feed using extracellular digestion.

## F

**Facilitated diffusion**
The diffusion of particles through carrier proteins or channel proteins in the plasma membrane.

**FAD**
A type of coenzyme involved in respiration. It transfers hydrogen from one molecule to another.

**Fast twitch muscle fibre**
A muscle fibre that contracts very quickly but also gets tired quickly.

**Frameshift mutation**
A mutation that changes the number of bases in the DNA code, causing a shift in the base triplets that follow, so that the triplet code is read in a different way.

## G

**Gel electrophoresis**
A technique that allows DNA fragments to be separated on a gel according to size.

**Gene**
A section of DNA that codes for a protein (polypeptide) which results in a characteristic.

**Gene expression**
The transcription of a gene into mRNA and translation of the mRNA into a protein.

**Gene pool**
The complete range of alleles present in a population.

**Generator potential**
The change in potential difference across a cell membrane due to the presence of a stimulus.

**Gene technology**
Techniques that allow the study and alteration of genes and their functions.

**Gene therapy**
Possible treatment option for genetic disorders and some cancers that involves altering defective genes inside cells.

**Genetic code**
The sequence of base triplets (codons) in mRNA which code for specific amino acids.

**Genetic disorder**
An inherited disorder caused by an abnormal gene or chromosome.

**Genetic drift**
The process whereby an allele becomes more common in a population due to chance.

**Genetic engineering**
See Recombinant DNA technology.

**Genetic fingerprint**
A DNA gel that shows the number of times repetitive, non-coding base sequences are repeated at different loci in an individual.

**Genetic pedigree diagram**
A diagram that shows how an inherited trait (characteristic) runs in a group of related individuals.

**Genome**
All the genetic material in an organism.

**Genotype**
The genetic constitution of an organism (the different alleles an organism has).

**Geographical isolation**
When a physical barrier, e.g. a flood, divides a population of a species, causing some individuals to become separated from the main population.

**Germ line therapy**
Gene therapy that involves altering the alleles in sex cells.

**Glomerular filtrate**
The fluid present in the nephrons of the kidney, following ultrafiltration of the blood at the Bowman's capsule.

**Glomerulus**
A bundle of capillaries looped inside the Bowman's capsule of a nephron. Where ultrafiltration takes place.

**Glucagon**
A hormone secreted by the pancreas that has an important role in raising blood glucose concentration.

**Gluconeogenesis**
The conversion of glycerol or amino acids to glucose, activated by glucagon.

**Glycogenesis**
The conversion of glucose to glycogen, activated by insulin.

**Glycogenolysis**
The conversion of glycogen to glucose, activated by glucagon.

**Glycolysis**
The first stage of aerobic respiration — here glucose is converted into pyruvate.

**Gravitropism (geotropism)**
The growth of a plant in response to gravity.

**Gross primary production (GPP)**
The total amount of chemical energy converted from light energy by plants in a given area.

## H

**Habitat**
The place where an organism lives within an ecosystem.

**Hardy-Weinberg principle**
A mathematical model that predicts that the frequency of alleles in a population won't change from one generation to the next provided that certain conditions are met.

**Hereditary mutation**
A mutation that's inherited from your parents.

**Heterozygous**
When an organism carries two different alleles at the same locus.

**Histone**
A protein that DNA wraps around to form chromatin, which makes up chromosomes.

**Homeostasis**
The maintenance of a stable internal environment.

**Homozygous**
When an organism carries two copies of the same allele at the same locus.

**Host cell**
A cell that is used to carry recombinant DNA.

**Hyperpolarisation**
An increase in the potential difference across a cell's membrane, making it more negative than the resting potential.

**Hypothalamus**
A part of the brain that controls body temperature and monitors the water potential of the blood.

**Hypothesis**
A specific testable statement, based on a theory, about what will happen in a test situation.

## I

**Independent variable**
The variable you change in an experiment.

**Indoleacetic acid (IAA)**
An auxin produced in the tips of shoots and roots in flowering plants.

**Insulin**
A hormone secreted by the pancreas that has an important role in lowering blood glucose concentration.

**Interspecific competition**
Competition between organisms of different species for the same resources.

**Intraspecific competition**
Competition between organisms of the same species for the same resources.

**Intron**
A section of DNA that doesn't code for amino acids.

***In vitro* cloning**
When gene copies are made outside of a living organism using PCR.

***In vivo* cloning**
When gene copies are made within a living organism as it grows and divides.

**iPS (induced pluripotent stem) cell**
A type of pluripotent stem cell made in the lab by reprogramming a specialised adult body cell to express certain transcription factors.

## K

**Kinesis (kinetic response)**
Non-directional (random) movement in response to a stimulus.

**Krebs cycle**
The third stage of aerobic respiration. It is a series of oxidation-reduction reactions that produces reduced coenzymes and ATP.

## L

**Leaching**
The process in which water-soluble compounds in the soil are washed away, e.g. by rain.

**Ligase**
An enzyme that joins together the sticky ends of DNA fragments.

**Light-dependent reaction**
The first stage of photosynthesis. Light energy is absorbed by photosynthetic pigments and converted to ATP and reduced NADP.

**Light-independent reaction (Calvin cycle)**
The second stage of photosynthesis. Here ATP and reduced NADP (from the light-dependent reaction) are used to make glucose from carbon dioxide.

**Limiting factor**
A variable that can slow down the rate of a reaction.

**Link reaction**
The second stage of aerobic respiration where pyruvate is converted into acetyl coenzyme A.

**Locus**
The position on a chromosome where a particular allele is found.

**Loop of Henle**
Part of the kidney nephron responsible for establishing the water potential gradient, which allows water to be reabsorbed by the kidney.

## M

**Malignant tumour (cancer)**
A tumour that invades and destroys surrounding tissues.

**Margin of error**
The range in which the true value of a measurement lies.

**Marker gene**
A gene that can be inserted into transformed cells in order to identify them.

**Mark-release-recapture**
A method used to estimate the population size of motile organisms.

**Mean**
The average of the values collected in a sample, obtained by adding all the values together and dividing by the total number of values in the sample.

**Medulla (oblongata)**
A part of the brain that controls heart rate.

**Meristem**
A growing region of a plant, e.g. the roots and shoots, which contains totipotent stem cells.

**Methylation**
Attachment of a methyl group to something (e.g. DNA).

**Microarray**
A glass slide with microscopic spots of different DNA probes attached to it in rows.

**miRNA**
Small, single-stranded RNA molecules that can interfere with the translation of genes.

**Monohybrid inheritance**
The inheritance of a single characteristic (gene) controlled by different alleles.

**mRNA (messenger RNA)**
A type of RNA that is the template for protein synthesis. It carries the genetic code from the DNA in the nucleus into the cytoplasm.

**Multipotent stem cell**
A stem cell only able to develop into a few types of cell.

**Mutagenic agent**
Something that increases the rate of DNA mutations.

**Mutation**
Any change in the DNA base sequence.

**Mycorrhiza**
A symbiotic relationship between a fungus and the roots of a plant.

**Myelin sheath**
A layer of Schwann cells around a neurone that acts as an electrical insulator and speeds up conduction of nervous impulses.

**Myofibril**
A long, cylindrical organelle within a muscle fibre that's highly specialised for contraction.

**Myogenic contraction**
When muscle cells are able to contract and relax without receiving signals from nerves, e.g. heart cells.

**Myosin**
The protein that makes up the thick myofilaments in myofibrils.

**NAD**
A type of coenzyme involved in respiration. It transfers hydrogen from one molecule to another.

**NADP**
A coenzyme involved in photosynthesis. It transfers hydrogen from one molecule to another.

**Natural selection**
The process whereby an allele becomes common in a population because it codes for a characteristic that makes an organism more likely to survive, reproduce and pass on its genes to its offspring.

**Negative control**
An extra experiment set up to check that only the independent variable is affecting the dependent variable. It is not expected to have any effect.

**Negative feedback mechanism**
A mechanism that restores a level back to normal in a system.

**Nephron**
One of the filtering units of the kidney, responsible for removing waste products from the blood and involved in controlling the water potential of the blood.

**Net primary production (NPP)**
The energy available to plants for growth and reproduction (after respiratory loss has been deducted from GPP) and the energy available to the next trophic level in a food chain.

**Net production**
The energy in consumers that is available to the next trophic level in a food chain.

**Neuromuscular junction**
A specialised cholinergic synapse between a motor neurone and a muscle cell.

**Neurotransmitter**
A chemical that transmits a nerve impulse across a synapse.

**Niche**
The role of a species within its habitat, e.g. what it eats, and where and when it feeds.

**Nitrification**
The process in which ammonia and ammonium ions in the soil are changed into nitrogen compounds by nitrifying bacteria.

**Nitrogen fixation**
The process in which nitrogen gas in the atmosphere is turned into nitrogen-containing compounds, such as ammonia.

**Node of Ranvier**
A tiny area of bare cell membrane on the surface of a myelinated neurone, where depolarisation can take place.

**Null hypothesis**
A hypothesis that states there's no difference or correlation between the factors being investigated.

**Oestrogen**
A steroid hormone released by the ovaries that stimulates the uterus lining to thicken in the menstrual cycle.

**Oncogene**
A mutated proto-oncogene that stimulates cells to divide uncontrollably.

**Osmoreceptor**
A cell in the hypothalamus which monitors the water potential of the blood.

**Osmoregulation**
The regulation of the water potential of the blood.

**Oxidation**
A chemical reaction where a molecule loses electrons, and may have lost hydrogen or gained oxygen.

**Oxidative phosphorylation**
The final stage in aerobic respiration. Energy carried by electrons, from reduced coenzymes, is used to make ATP.

**Pacinian corpuscle**
A type of receptor found in your skin which detects mechanical stimuli.

**Palindromic sequence**
A sequence of DNA bases that consists of antiparallel base pairs (base pairs that read the same in opposite directions).

**PCR (polymerase chain reaction)**
A technique used to make millions of identical copies of a DNA fragment in a few hours.

**Phenotype**
The expression of the genetic constitution of an organism and its interaction with the environment (what characteristics an organism has as a result of its genes and the effect the environment has on them).

**Phenotypic ratio**
The ratio of different phenotypes (characteristics) in the offspring of a genetic cross.

**Phosphorylation**
The process of adding a phosphate group to a molecule.

**Photoionisation**
The process of turning an atom or a molecule into an ion using light energy.

**Photolysis**
The splitting (lysis) of a molecule using light (photo) energy.

**Photophosphorylation**
The process of adding phosphate to a molecule using light energy.

**Photoreceptor**
A receptor in the eye that detects light.

**Phototropism**
The growth of a plant in response to light.

**Pioneer species**
The first species to colonise an area during succession.

**Plagioclimax**
The climax community produced when succession is artificially stopped by human activities.

**Plasmid**
A small, circular molecule of DNA in bacteria, which is not part of the chromosomal DNA.

**Pluripotent stem cell**
A stem cell that can develop into any type of cell, apart from cells that make up the placenta.

**Polynucleotide**
A molecule made up of lots of nucleotides joined together in a long chain.

**Population**
All the organisms of one species in a habitat.

**Population growth curve**
A graph showing the change in the size of a population over time.

**Population growth rate**
How much the size of a population increases or decreases in a year.

**Positive control**
An extra experiment set up to check what a positive result looks like.

**Positive feedback mechanism**
A mechanism that amplifies a change away from the normal level in a system.

**Posterior pituitary gland**
Part of the pituitary gland (a gland located at the base of the brain), which secretes hormones such as antidiuretic hormone (ADH).

**Potential difference**
The voltage across a cell membrane.

**Precise result**
A result that is close to the mean.

**Predation**
Where an organism (the predator) kills and eats another organism (the prey).

**Prediction**
See Hypothesis.

**Primary succession**
Succession that happens on newly formed or exposed land with no soil.

**Primer**
A short piece of single stranded DNA that is complementary to the bases at the start of the DNA fragment you want to copy.

**Promoter region**
A DNA sequence that tells the enzyme RNA polymerase where to start producing mRNA.

**Proteome**
All the proteins that are made by an organism.

**Proto-oncogene**
A gene that produces proteins that make cells divide.

**Purkynje fibres**
Fine muscle fibres in the heart that carry waves of electrical activity into the muscular walls of the right and left ventricles.

**Quadrat**
A square frame, usually divided into 100 smaller squares, used for investigating populations of non-motile or slow-moving species.

**Random error**
A difference in a measurement caused by an unpredictable factor, e.g. human error.

**Receptor**
A cell, or protein on a cell surface membrane, that detects a stimulus.

**Recessive allele**
An allele whose characteristic only appears in the phenotype if there are two copies present.

**Recognition sequence**
A specific palindromic sequence in DNA recognised by a restriction endonuclease.

**Recombinant DNA**
The name for DNA formed by joining together DNA from different organisms.

**Recombinant DNA technology**
When DNA from different organisms is joined together by isolating a fragment from a donor organism and inserting it into the DNA of a host organism. Also known as genetic engineering.

**Reduction**
A chemical reaction where a molecule gains electrons, and may have gained hydrogen or lost oxygen.

**Reflex**
A rapid, involuntary response to a stimulus.

**Refractory period**
The period following an action potential in which a neurone cell membrane can't be excited.

**Repeatable result**
A result that can be repeated by the same person using the same method and equipment.

**Repolarisation**
The return of a cell membrane to its resting potential.

**Repressor**
A transcription factor that inhibits or decreases the rate of transcription.

**Reproducible result**
A result that can be consistently reproduced in an independent experiment.

**Reproductive isolation**
When changes in allele frequency mean that some individuals of the same species can no longer interbreed to produce fertile offspring.

**Respiratory loss**
The amount of energy lost to the environment as heat when organisms respire.

**Resting potential**
The potential difference across a cell membrane when the cell is at rest.

**Restriction endonuclease enzyme**
An enzyme that recognises specific recognition sequences and cuts DNA at these places.

**Restriction map**
A diagram of a piece of DNA showing where different recognition sites of restriction enzymes are found.

**Retina**
The part of the eye containing photoreceptor cells, which light is focussed onto.

**Reverse transcriptase**
An enzyme that makes a DNA copy of RNA.

**Ribosome**
An organelle found in the cell cytoplasm that assembles proteins.

**Ribulose bisphosphate carboxylase (rubisco)**
An enzyme which catalyses the formation of glycerate 3-phosphate from carbon dioxide and ribulose bisphosphate (RuBP) in the light-independent reaction of photosynthesis.

**RNA (ribonucleic acid)**
A type of nucleic acid, similar to DNA but containing ribose instead of deoxyribose sugar and uracil instead of thymine.

**RNA interference**
The mechanism by which siRNA or miRNA affects translation.

**RNA polymerase**
An enzyme that synthesises RNA from DNA.

**Rod (eye)**
A photoreceptor cell found in the eye that gives information in black and white.

## S

**Saltatory conduction**
The process in myelinated neurones by which a nervous impulse travels between nodes of Ranvier.

**Sample size**
The number of samples in the investigation, e.g. the number of people in a drug trial.

**Saprobiont**
A microorganism that feeds on the remains of dead plants and animals, using extracellular digestion to break down the remains.

**Saprobiotic nutrition**
Obtaining nutrients from dead organic matter using extracellular digestion.

**Sarcomere**
A short contractile unit that's part of a myofibril, made up of overlapping myosin and actin filaments.

**Sarcoplasmic reticulum**
A network of internal membranes that runs through the sarcoplasm. It stores and releases calcium ions that are needed for muscle contraction.

**Schwann cell**
The type of cell that makes up the myelin sheath around neurones.

**Secondary succession**
Succession that happens on land cleared of all plants but where the soil remains, e.g. after a forest fire.

**Second messenger**
A chemical that's produced inside a cell in response to a signal outside the cell. The chemical relays the signal to the inside of the cell.

**Selective reabsorption (kidneys)**
The reabsorption of useful substances along the kidney nephron back into the blood.

**Serial dilution**
The creation of a set of solutions that decrease in concentration by the same factor each time.

**Sex-linked characteristic**
When the allele that codes for the characteristic is located on a sex chromosome (X or Y).

**Sino-atrial node (SAN)**
A group of cells in the wall of the right atrium that set the rhythm of the heartbeat by sending out regular waves of electrical activity to the atrial walls.

**siRNA (small interfering RNA)**
A double-stranded RNA molecule that can interfere with the transcription and translation of genes.

**Sliding filament theory**
The theory that myosin and actin filaments slide over one another to make sarcomeres contract.

**Slow twitch muscle fibre**
A muscle fibre that contracts slowly and can work for a long time without getting tired.

**Somatic gene therapy**
Gene therapy that involves altering the alleles in body cells.

**Speciation**
The development of a new species from an existing species.

**Species**
A group of similar organisms that can reproduce to give fertile offspring.

**Splicing**
The process by which introns are removed from pre-mRNA strands and exons are joined to form mRNA.

**Stabilising selection**
Where individuals with alleles for characteristics towards the middle of the range are more likely to survive, reproduce and pass on their alleles.

**Standard deviation**
A measure of the spread of values about the mean.

**Stem cell**
An unspecialised cell that can develop into other types of cell. It's also able to divide to form new cells.

**Stem cell therapy**
Using stem cells to treat or cure medical disorders.

**Sticky end**
A small tail of unpaired DNA bases at the end of a DNA fragment.

**Stimulus**
A change in an organism's internal or external environment.

**Succession**
The process by which an ecosystem changes over time.

**Summation**
The process in which the effect of a neurotransmitter released from many neurones (or one neurone that's stimulated a lot in a short period of time) is added together.

**Survival curve**
A graph which shows the percentage of all the individuals that were born in a population that are still alive at any given age.

**Sympatric speciation**
Where speciation occurs without populations of a species being geographically isolated.

**Synapse**
A junction between a neurone and another neurone, or between a neurone and an effector cell.

## T

**Target cell**
A cell that has specific receptors for a particular type of chemical, such as a hormone or a neurotransmitter.

**Taxis (tactic response)**
Directional movement in response to a stimulus.

**Terminator region**
A DNA sequence that tells the enzyme RNA polymerase where to stop producing mRNA.

**Theory**
A possible explanation for something

**Totipotent stem cell**
A stem cell able to develop into any type of body cell.

**Transcription factor**
A protein molecule that controls the transcription of a gene.

**Transect**
A line used to help find out how non-motile or slow-moving organisms are distributed across an area, e.g. how species change from a hedge towards the middle of a field.

**Transformed cell**
A host cell that has taken up recombinant DNA.

**Transformed organism**
A plant, animal or microorganism that has had its genes altered by recombinant DNA technology.

**tRNA (transfer RNA)**
A type of RNA involved in translation. It carries the amino acids used to make proteins at ribosomes.

**Trophic level**
A stage in a food chain.

**Tropism**
The response of a plant to a directional stimulus.

**Tropomyosin**
A protein found between actin filaments attached to another protein. Together the two proteins help myofilaments move past each other.

**Tumour**
A mass of abnormal cells.

**Tumour suppressor gene**
A gene that slows the rate of cell division by producing proteins that stop cells dividing or cause them to self-destruct.

**Ultrafiltration (kidneys)**
The filtering of the blood that takes place under high pressure, as blood passes from the glomerulus into the Bowman's capsule.

**Uncertainty (in data)**
The amount of error measurements might have.

**Unipotent stem cell**
A stem cell that can only differentiate into one type of cell.

**Valid result**
A result that answers the original question and for which all the variables that could have affected it were controlled.

**Variable**
A quantity that has the potential to change, e.g. weight, temperature, concentration.

**Variation**
The differences that exist between individuals.

**Vector (in gene technology)**
Something used to transfer DNA into a cell, e.g. plasmids or bacteriophages.

**Visual acuity**
The ability to tell apart points that are close together.

**Water potential**
The likelihood of water molecules to diffuse into or out of a solution.

# Acknowledgements

*AQA specification material is reproduced by permission of AQA.*

**Data acknowledgements**

Data on pages 62 & 63 from Springer, Biogeochemistry, Nitrogen Cycles: Past, Present, and Future, volume 70, 2004, pages 153-226, Galloway et al. Figures 1a & 1b © 2004 Kluwer Academic Publishers. With kind permission from Springer Science and Business Media.

Data for graphs showing glucose concentration vs absorbance on pages 124 and 125 was obtained using a Mystrica colorimeter © Mystrica Ltd. www.mystrica.com

Graph of breast cancer and family history on page 209 reprinted from The Lancet, Volume 358, Issue No 9291. Familial Breast Cancer: collaborative reanalysis of individual data from 52 epidemiological studies including 58 209 women with breast cancer and 101 986 women without the disease, pages 1389-1399 (c) Oct 2001. With permission from Elsevier.

Graph of breast cancer and alcohol consumption on page 210 from 'Alcohol, Tobacco & breast cancer - collaborative reanalysis of individual data from 53 epidemiological studies, including 58 515 women with breast cancer and 95 067 women without the disease'. Reprinted by permission from Macmillan Publishers Ltd on behalf of Cancer Research UK: British Journal of Cancer (c) Nov 2002.

Data used to construct the smoking and breast cancer graph on page 210 reproduced with kind permission from Oxford University Press. P. Reynolds, et al. Active Smoking, Household Passive Smoking, and Breast Cancer: Evidence From the California Teachers Study. JNCI 2004; 96(1):29-37

**Photograph acknowledgements**

Cover photo **Steve Gschmeissner**/Science Photo Library, p 3 (top) **Andrew Lambert Photography**/Science Photo Library, p 3 (bottom) **Rafe Swan/Cultura**/Science Photo Library, p 23 **Dr Kari Lounatmaa**/Science Photo Library, p 29 **Biophoto Associates**/Science Photo Library, p 32 © **Arie J. Jager**/iStockphoto.com, p 34 **Sinclair Stammers**/Science Photo Library, p 38 **Dr David Furness, Keele University**/Science Photo Library, p 48 **Martin Shields**/Science Photo Library, p 58 **Scott Camazine**/Science Photo Library, p 60 **Dr Jeremy Burgess**/ Science Photo Library, p 61 (top) **Dr Jeremy Burgess**/Science Photo Library, p 61 (middle) **Alfred Pasieka**/ Science Photo Library, p 61 (bottom) **Steve Gschmeissner**/Science Photo Library, p 62 **B. G. Thomson**/Science Photo Library, p 64 (top) **Ian Gowland**/Science Photo Library, p 64 (bottom) © **Fotokostic**/iStockphoto.com, p 65 **Robert Brook**/Science Photo Library, p 74 **PH. Gerbier**/Science Photo Library, p 75 (top) **Martin Shields**/ Science Photo Library, p 75 (bottom) **Martin Shields**/Science Photo Library, p 79 **Ray Simons**/Science Photo Library, p 80 **Eye of Science**/Science Photo Library, p 81 **Eye of Science**/Science Photo Library, p 91 (top) **Dr David Furness, Keele University**/Science Photo Library, p 91 (bottom) **CMEABG-UCBL1, ISM**/Science Photo Library, p 93 **Don Fawcett**/Science Photo Library, p 96 **Kent Wood**/Science Photo Library, p 100 (top) **Steve Gschmeissner**/Science Photo Library, p 100 (bottom) **Eric Grave**/Science Photo Library, p 101 **Thomas Deerinck, NCMIR**/Science Photo Library, p 106 **Dr Gladden Willis, Visuals Unlimited/**Science Photo Library, p 116 Science Photo Library, p 118 **Conge, ISM**/Science Photo Library, p 122 © **Rachael Rogers**, p 126 **Dr Keith Wheeler**/Science Photo Library, p 127 **Steve Gschmeissner**/Science Photo Library, p 128 Science Photo Library, p 133 **Steve Gschmeissner**/Science Photo Library, p 137 © **Anakondasp**/iStockphoto.com, p 138 (top) **Wim Van Egmond, Visuals Unlimited/**Science Photo Library, p 138 (bottom) **J. C. Revy, ISM**/Science Photo Library, p 140 **Eye of Science**/Science Photo Library, p 142 **Wally Eberhart, Visuals Unlimited/**Science Photo Library, p 149 **Ed Young/AgStockUSA**/Science Photo Library, p 151 Science Photo Library, p 167 **Paul D Stewart**/Science Photo Library, p 169 **Peter Scoones**/Science Photo Library, p 173 (top) **Steve Gschmeissner**/ Science Photo Library, p 173 (bottom) © **imageBROKER/Alamy**, p 174 (top) **mtomline**/iStockphoto.com, p 174 (bottom) **Mary Beth Angelo**/Science Photo Library, p 178 **Jeff Lepore**/Science Photo Library, p 182 **Martyn F. Chillmaid**/Science Photo Library, p 183 **Nigel Cattlin**/Science Photo Library, p 184 (top) **Alexis Rosenfeld**/Science Photo Library, p 184 (bottom) **Photostock-Israel**/Science Photo Library, p 187 **Duncan Shaw**/Science Photo Library, p 189 **Simon Fraser**/Science Photo Library, p 193 (top) **David Aubrey**/Science

# Acknowledgements

Photo Library, p 193 (bottom) **Duncan Shaw**/Science Photo Library, p 195 (top) **Colin Varndell**/Science Photo Library, p 195 (bottom) **Adrian Bicker**/Science Photo Library, p 204 **Pascal Goetgheluck**/Science Photo Library, p 206 (top) **Zephyr**/Science Photo Library, p 206 (centre, left) **Pascal Goetgheluck**/Science Photo Library, p 206 (centre, right) **Pascal Goetgheluck**/Science Photo Library, p 207 **Steve Gschmeissner**/Science Photo Library, p 208 **Biophoto Associates**/Science Photo Library, p 211 (top) **G-I Associates/Custom Medical Stock Photo**/Science Photo Library, p 211 (bottom) **Alfred Pasieka**/Science Photo Library, p 213 **Professor Miodrag Stojkovic**/Science Photo Library, p 214 (top) **Dr Tony Brain**/Science Photo Library, p 214 (middle) **CNRI**/Science Photo Library, p 214 (bottom) **Biophoto Associates**/Science Photo Library, p 215 **Steve Gschmeissner**/Science Photo Library, p 216 **Steve Gschmeissner**/Science Photo Library, p 217 **Chassenet/BSIP**/Science Photo Library, p 222 **Mitchell Lewis, University of Pennsylvania Medical Center**/Science Photo Library, p 227 **National Cancer Institute**/Science Photo Library, p 230 © **Jane Ellingham**, p 233 **David Parker**/Science Photo Library, p 237 **J. C. Revy, ISM**/Science Photo Library, p 238 (top) **Biozentrum**, **University of Basel**/Science Photo Library, p 238 (bottom) **Martin Shields**/Science Photo Library, p 240 **Robert Longuehaye, NIBSC**/Science Photo Library, p 242 **Makoto Iwafuji/Eurelios**/Science Photo Library, p 243 **International Rice Research Institute**, p 246 **Peter Menzel**/Science Photo Library, p 247 **Patrick Dumas/Eurelios**/Science Photo Library, p 250 (top) **Tek Image**/Science Photo Library, p 250 (bottom) **Larry Mulvehill**/Science Photo Library

Every effort has been made to locate copyright holders and obtain permission to reproduce sources. For those sources where it has been difficult to trace the originator of the work, we would be grateful for information. If any copyright holder would like us to make an amendment to the acknowledgements, please notify us and we will gladly update the book at the next reprint. Thank you.

# Index

## N



## O



## P



## Q



## R

## S



## T



## U



## V



## W



BATB62